FIELD GUIDE *to the* BIRDS *of* AUSTRALIA

INDIAN OCEAN
TIMOR SEA
DARWIN
Melville I
Croker
Bathurst I
Mary R
Daly R
Katherine Gorge
Joseph Bonaparte Gulf
Bigge I
Augustus I
Collier Bay
King Sound
Kimberley
Drysdale R
Chamberlain R
King Leopold Ra
Ord R
L. Argyle
Victoria R
Mt Ord 937
Fitzroy R
Broome
Eighty Mile Beach
Great Sandy Desert
Tanami Desert
Dampier Archipelago
Barrow I
De Grey R
Yule R
Fortesque R
Pilbara
North West Cape
Mt Meharry 1251
Ashburton R
L. Dora
L. White
L. Mackay
Gibson Desert
Macdonnell Ranges
L. Macdonald
Mt Zeil 1531
L. Neale
L. Amadeus
L. Disappointment
Tropic of Capricorn
WESTERN AUSTRALIA
L. Macleod
Lyons R
Shark Bay
Gasgoyne R
Wooramel R
Murchison R
Dirk Hartog I
L. Carnegie
Rawlinson Ra
Mt Olga
Uluru 867
Musgrave Ra
Great Victoria Desert
L. Austin
L. Barlee
L. Carey
L. Moore
Kalgoorlie-Boulder
L. Lefroy
L. Cowan
L. Dundas
Nullarbor Plain
Darling Ra
Swan R
PERTH
Blackwood R
C. Naturaliste
C. Leeuwin
Stirling Ra
Archipelago of the Recherche
Twilight Cove
Streaky
GREAT AUSTRALIAN BIGH
SOUTHERN OCEAN
0 200 400 600
Scale (kilometres)
0 200 500 metres
Shallow water
Above 500 m
0 200 500 metres
CAPITAL CITIES and Other Towns
Economic Exclusion Zone
1237 Spot elevation
Rivers
State boundary
Lake, perennial
Reef
Lake, intermittent
105°
110°
115°
120°
125°
130°
10°
15°
20°
25°
30°
35°
40°
45°

TORRES STRAIT
C. York
CORAL SEA
GULF OF CARPENTARIA
Groote Eylandt
Wenlock R
Archer R
Great Barrier Reef
SOUTH PACIFIC OCEAN
C. Melville
Cape York Peninsula
Normanby R
Vanderlin I
Mornington I
Staaten R
Mitchell R
Calvert R
Cairns
Gilbert R
Nicholson R
Mt Bartle Frere 1622
Gregory R
Leichhardt R
Hinchinbrook I
Norman R
Flinders R
Burdekin R
Mount Isa
Clark Ra
Great Dividing Range
Selwyn Ra
Mt Dalrymple 1259
Georgina R
Belyando R
Broad Sound
Isaacs R
QUEENSLAND
Rockhampton
Thomson R
Curtis I
Capricorn Group
Diamantina R
Nogoa R
Dawson R
Channel Country
Consuelo Peak 1174
Fraser I
Warburton Ck
Warrego R
Darling Downs
Condamine R
Cooper Ck
Grey Ra
Bulloo R
Moreton I
N Stradbroke I
BRISBANE
Moonie R
L. Frome
Barrier Ra
Paroo R
Gwydir R
Clarence R
C. Byron
Barwon R
Pilliga Scrub
Flinders Ra
Darling R
Macquarie Marshes
Castlereagh R
Namoi R
Round Mtn 1583
St Mary Peak 1180
Bogan R
Macquarie R
Broken Hill
NEW SOUTH WALES
Great Dividing Range
Mt Lofty Ra
Lachlan R
Port Stephens
Spencer Gulf
Lord Howe I
SYDNEY
ADELAIDE
Murrumbidgee R
Sunset Country
L. Alexandrina
Murray R
ACT
CANBERRA
Kangaroo I
Loddon R
Goulburn R
Mt Bogong 1986
Mt Kosciuszko 2228
The Grampians
TASMAN SEA
MELBOURNE
La Trobe R
Otway Ra
VICTORIA
SOUTH PACIFIC OCEAN
King I
BASS STRAIT
Flinders I
Cape Barren I
Launceston
Mt Ossa 1617
L. Pedder
HOBART
TASMANIA
140°
145°
150°
155°
160°
165°
10°
15°
20°
25°
30°
35°
40°
45°

Quick Index

Ken Simpson & Nicolas Day

WITH PETER TRUSLER

FIELD GUIDE *to the* BIRDS *of* AUSTRALIA

VIKING
an imprint of
PENGUIN BOOKS

Dedication
To the memory of four excellent naturalists, field ornithologists, and colleagues:
Peter Alexander DISHER, Marcus D. GOTTSCH, Jack HYETT and Graham Martin PIZZEY

Viking

Penguin Group (Australia)
250 Camberwell Road, Camberwell, Victoria 3124, Australia
Penguin Books Ltd
80 Strand, London WC2R 0RL, England
Penguin Group (USA) Inc.
375 Hudson Street, New York, New York 10014, USA
Penguin Books, a division of Pearson Canada
10 Alcorn Avenue, Toronto, Ontario, Canada M4V 3B2
Penguin Books (NZ) Ltd
Cnr Rosedale and Airborne Roads, Albany, Auckland, New Zealand
Penguin Books (South Africa) (Pty) Ltd
24 Sturdee Avenue, Rosebank, Johannesburg 2196, South Africa
Penguin Books India (P) Ltd
11, Community Centre, Panchsheel Park, New Delhi 110 017, India

First published by Lloyd O'Neil Pty Ltd, 1984
as *The Birds of Australia: A Book of Identification*
Second edition 1986
First published in this format in 1989 (third edition) by
Penguin Books Australia Ltd as *Field Guide to the Birds of Australia*
Fourth edition 1993; Fifth edition 1996; Sixth edition 1999
This seventh edition published by Penguin Group (Australia),
a division of Pearson Australia Group Pty Ltd, 2004

10 9 8 7 6 5 4 3 2

Jacket design by Cathy Larsen © Penguin Group (Australia)
Jacket illustrations by Nicolas Day
Internal design and typesetting by DiZign, Lane Cove, New South Wales
Original design by Zoë Gent-Murphy
Printed and bound in China through Bookbuilders

National Library of Australia
Cataloguing-in-Publication data:

Field guide to the birds of Australia.

7th ed.
Bibliography.
Includes index.
ISBN 0 670 04180 7.
1. Birds – Australia – Identification. I. Simpson, Ken,
1938– . II. Day, Nicolas, 1955–

598.0994

Birds on front cover, clockwise from top right: Swift Parrot; Rainbow Lorikeet; Laughing Kookaburras; Gouldian Finches; Red-footed Booby. Spine: Lesser Sooty Owl. Birds on back cover, from left: Flame Robin; Rufous Treecreeper.

www.penguin.com.au

Acknowledgements

We very sincerely thank all of our colleagues who contributed in varying ways to the previous six editions, and also the following people, who have assisted with this seventh edition of the field guide: Peter Allen, Bob Anderson, Arthur Batho, Peter Bennett, Jeremy Boot, Adrian Boyle, Marilyn Bradley, Mike Carter, Les Christidis, Barry Clarris, Mark Clayton, Tonia Cochran, Clare Coney, Alistair Coutts, Margot Craddock, Chris Dahlberg, Gail and Alan Curl, Jeff Davies, Betty and Harry Day, Stephen Debus, Richard Donaghey, Chris Doughty, David Eades, John Eames, Janet Flinn, Bob Forsyth, Glenn L. Gillies, Denise Goodfellow, Ken Harris, Chris Hassell, Ian Hutton, Tania Ireton, Andrew Isles, Rod Kavanagh, Louis Kennedy, Tess Kloot, André Konter, Wayne Longmore, Richard Loyn, Ellen and Peter McCulloch, Keith McDougall, S. M. McLean, Leah Maarse, Ian Mason, Jamie Mathews, Lisa Mills, Ralph and Caroline O'Brien, Rory O'Brien, Tony Palliser, Tony Palmer, Robert Parsons, Enid Pascoe, Howard and Jill Plowright, David and Shirley Purchase, Stephen Reynolds, Del Richards, Alan and Sue Robertson, Len Robinson, Peter and Jennifer Rogers, Tony Russell, Bernard Ryan, Denis Saunders, Richard Schodde, Sally Simpson, Fred T. H. Smith, Eric Sticklen, Bob Swindley, Trish Teesdale, Gael Trusler, Bessie Tyers, Philip Veerman, Andrew Wegener, Zoë Wilson, John Wombey and Linda Worden.

Allen's Rule, Bergman's Rule and Gloger's Rule, from *A Dictionary of Birds* (1985) by Bruce Campbell and Elizabeth Lack, reproduced by kind permission of the British Ornithologists' Union.

For this seventh edition, we are particularly grateful for the general assistance of the staff and librarians, CEOs and Curators, for permission to access the books and bird skin collections in the Bird Observers Club of Australia, and Ornithology Department, Museum Victoria.

Editor
Ken Simpson

Illustrator
Nicolas Day

Art director
Peter Trusler

Field consultants
Mike Carter
Jeff Davies
Stephen Debus
Fred T. H. Smith
Robert Swindley

Contents illustrator
Peter Trusler

Note to seventh edition: We have received, as ever, some wonderful advice and assistance and utterly appreciate it all. As a result, there are substantial changes in this edition. Your further ideas for text or artwork, confirmed range extensions for our maps, and any constructive criticisms to improve this book, are welcome. We cannot always quickly include, alter or remove all that is suggested, but we do consider everything received, or written in reviews, and we try to acknowledge everybody who helps us.

In any discussion on matters pertinent to content, including taxonomy, arrangement, illustrations, maps, or concept, only this seventh edition is relevant. All prior editions are out of date.

Contents

Preface

Ornithology is a very dynamic part of the general science of zoology. Entering a new century, we see some old ornithological concepts being swept away, and new ones taking their place. Australia's ecosystems and the birds within them, are continually under threat from long-term drought, and beyond that, land clearance, erosion, salination, pollution and other forms of environmental damage. These are the inevitable result of an increasing human population and our sometimes inappropriate requirements.

The recent severe drought has led to some spectacular movements of birds away from central Australia, often far outside of their 'normal' distribution, and is reflected in new 'spots' on many of the maps.

Our philosophy, together with Penguin Australia, remains, in that we prepare new editions as often as we reasonably can. We intend to remain close to the cutting edge in presentation of new information. Books such as ours must be read with an open mind, and the will to follow up your new information from many current sources.

Space is crucial. We pack as much as possible into the smallest mass. Our interpretation of what a field guide should be may not suit everybody. A lot of white space was never our aim. All four major Australian guides vary in the manner of presenting the birds. Each book has great merit. Each has a different way of looking at and interpreting the avalanche of new information about our birds. Each book has a fascinating but very different history. We advocate using all four in conjunction! Enjoy the luxury of four high-quality works.

This book is for furthering the enjoyable and fascinating pastime of birdwatching in all its varied intensities and facets. Our primary aim is to enhance our readers' capabilities in identifying the birds they may encounter.

It is for everybody, of all ages.

Introduction

Welcome to our seventh edition. Following our sixth edition, we received, as ever, some wonderful advice and assistance. As a result, we have made substantial changes to this edition.

The numbering system for birds has been dropped. All texts have been revised, with some additional attention to songs and calls. In this edition we are working within the framework of a more traditional, slightly lighter, field guide. Part of our Handbook (widely praised for its content, but at the expense of extra weight) has been removed, but our breeding section now contains more detail of nests, eggs, incubation and fledging.

Distribution maps Our maps continue to set the standard for Australian field guides. Every map has been enhanced by including all currently accepted races (subspecies).

These additions to the maps will add appreciably to your understanding of the reasons for variation in plumage and of song differences (dialects) within species, and also of summer and winter dispersal of many species or races across the nation as migrants, nomads or vagrants.

Major breeding areas, and breeding islands, are shown as dark green areas or darts. Open darts show non-breeding records on islands, and are also used for offshore sightings, i.e. from ships or boats. Other areas where a species is likely to be seen are plain pale green, with pale green hatching where records are usually sparse. Thus, many maps now clearly show wintering and non-breeding areas.

For the symbols in colour, see **Distribution maps**, under **Codes used in this book** (p. x).

Mainland islands Darts on the maps refer (apart from some oceanic islets where seabirds breed, such as Ashmore Reef) to the following principal islands (listed in clockwise order from Darwin): Melville and Bathurst Islands, Groote Eylandt, Sir Edward Pellew Group, Mornington Island Group, South-west Torres Strait Island Group, Northern Torres Strait Island Group (Boigu, Dauan, Saibai, etc.), Hinchinbrook Island, Fraser Island, Furneaux (Flinders Island) Group, Maria Island, Bruny Island, King Island, Kangaroo Island, Rottnest Island, Houtman Abrolhos Group, Dirk Hartog Island, Dorre/Bernier Island Group, Barrow Island, and assorted non-specified islands of the Bonaparte Archipelago. **Note**: At this stage the darts should not be the basis for making comprehensive bird lists for any of the islands concerned. They indicate selected species only. We would welcome receipt of current bird lists dealing with offshore islands.

Mapping changes within the songbirds (passerines) were greatly facilitated by our 1998 access to a manuscript copy of Richard Schodde and Ian Mason's *The Directory of Australian Birds: A taxonomic and zoogeographic atlas of the biodiversity of birds in Australia and its territories*, Vol. **2**, *Perching Birds (Passerines)*, CSIRO Publishing, Victoria.

We sincerely thank them and also Dr Denis Saunders (Assistant Chief, Wildlife & Ecology, CSIRO) for permitting us to use their important information. Any errors in interpretation are entirely ours. It should be noted here that although we had been given a copy of the manuscript, we held off publishing any of the Schodde & Mason new species and races in the sixth edition, because the chance of our publishing first was far too high. That would have been an unethical scientific crime of the first order! Consequently, we have played 'catch-up football', with both species and race names, and with the respective maps, but all are now complete.

Vagrant bird bulletin Here we discuss the vagrants, the waifs, strays and overshoots which reach our shores and adjacent islands from overseas. New birds continue to arrive in Australia as vagrants or occasional visitors. From time to time we expect to alter this section, now increased to 20 pages, to include more new records. We may later remove species proved to visit regularly, restoring them to the main plates. Remember that to reliably identify vagrants and rarities, you first need to know all the common birds intimately.

Australian island territories checklists These have been updated, with assistance from Mike Carter and his colleagues, to give the best possible picture of what birds may be seen on a visit to any of these major islands. Several new birds for Australia are included in the various checklists.

Ken Simpson, Nicolas Day and Peter Trusler
June 2004

Changes to the 7th edition

Waterproof endpapers Some additional seabird bills have been drawn. Remember that the surface on which the beaks are printed is waterproof – you can wipe off any undesirable fluids after testing your latest beach-washed seabird.

Map of Australia This has been slightly modified, establishing the area the Field Guide concentrates on.

Introduction Pages have been rearranged and the section **'Believing your eyes'**, with three new colour illustrations, added to it.

Key to Families All artwork on these ten pages has now been standardised.

Field Information and Plates All consecutive numbering of species has been removed in line with modern practice. The names of all species and many races are now on the colour plates. Eight new plates are presented; twelve others have been modified.

Texts Have all been considered, revised, rewritten and rearranged to offer better sequencing and standardisation. Description of the breeding male is first, followed by that for the adult female, and plumages for any others required, including many races. 'Size', given for birds in each text entry, reflects the accepted measurements in five of the six volumes – from Ostrich to Chats – of *HANZAB* published to date.

Distribution maps All have been reconsidered. Hundreds have been fully redrawn, or modified. Every single race (subspecies) presently nominated for mainland Australia is shown and named.

Line drawings More than 80 new or redrawn images are scattered through the book.

Vagrant Bird Bulletin This has been renamed and extended radically. 'Rare bird bulletin' was not the best title for it. Nine recently accepted vagrant species for Australia have been added, and for purposes of standardisation, twenty-three species have been transferred to it from the Field Information text pages.

Australian Island Territories Checklists All have been revised and updated by Mike Carter and colleagues. A new composite list is added for Boigu, Dauan and Saibai Islands, which are Queensland islands in far northern Torres Strait, very close to the New Guinea coastline.

Glossary, Core Library, Indices All have been considerably expanded and the references and indices, as always, updated.

The 80-page Family summaries in our old **Handbook** have been removed, so that this book is a little lighter and therefore a slightly more portable field guide. Only the Breeding bars, but with expanded Breeding information text, have been retained.

How to use this book

Step 1 Key to Families (pages 8–17)
By using the illustrations and text in the **Key to Families**, try to work out which family your bird belongs to. For example, does it look like a gull, an owl, a kingfisher, a fairy-wren or a honeyeater? The illustrations show a typical or common member of each family. They are not drawn to precise scale one to the other, but do give a guide to size relationships.

Step 2 Field Information (pages 18–281)
When you think you know which family your bird belongs to, turn to the **Field Information** section. The appropriate pages are indicated in bold type in the **Key to Families**. Look for your bird on the colour plate(s). The name beside the illustration refers you to the text for that species on the opposite page, where all the field information for the species appears. Distribution maps are given for each species as well.

Read the text carefully, then check the map (see **Codes used in this book**, p. x) to make sure the bird you have seen is likely to be found in the area you have seen it. Remember, the maps are only a general guide to distribution. If all the information provided corresponds with what you have seen, then you have probably identified your bird correctly. You may wish to record it in the ticking boxes beside the map. If not sure of your identification, recheck the illustrations and text, or refer back to the **Key to Families** again. The indexes of Latin and common names, or Quick Index, may be used if you know the name of the bird you wish to look up.

Step 3 Breeding Information (pages 310–31)
If you want to read more about a bird's breeding season or its nest, eggs and chicks, the second page reference in the **Key to Families** will refer you to this information. So too will the running heads on each Field Information page.

Number of Australian species

The total number of Australian species is based on the list published by Christidis & Boles (1994), with the addition of some passerine species nominated by Schodde & Mason (1999). Total number of bird species in the world is now based on Sibley & Monroe (1990). The numbers are included in the **Key to Families** to give a broad idea of the ratio of Australian to world species, on a family by family basis. So, where it says of the Family Pedionomidae, the Plains-wanderer, 'Species: World 1; Australia 1', it means that there is only one species in the world and it is endemic to Australia. By contrast for (say) the Family Hirundinidae, Swallows and Martins, 'Species: World 78; Australia 6', means that Australia has just six of the world's 78 species. In essence, the total for a few Australian families has been adjusted because of Schodde & Mason's taxonomic changes.

Codes used in this book

Within the heading to text of each bird species in the **Field Information** section, you will find two codes, representing the 'abundance of the species' (letters) and its 'general movement pattern' (diagram). These codes apply only to the area shown on the distribution map for that species. 'Mainland Australia' includes Tasmania and all islands on the continental shelf, but excluding Boigu and the other Torres Strait islands.

Intro. = a bird species deliberately introduced in Australia.

E = an endemic species recorded only in Australia.

Br. E = a breeding endemic species recorded beyond Australia in certain seasons, e.g. Short-tailed Shearwater.

Abundance codes

Two codes may be shown to indicate disparity within a species' abundance or range; e.g. LMC–C. A question mark indicates uncertainty in our own knowledge or that of other sources.

A	Abundant
LA	Locally Abundant
C	Common
MC	Moderately Common
LC	Locally Common
LMC	Locally Moderately Common
UC	Uncommon
LUC	Locally Uncommon
V	Vagrant
R	Rare

Movement codes

- Annual migrant
- Partial migrant
- Nomadic
- Sedentary

Darts

Small open black darts on the colour plates indicate key identification features of that particular bird.

Distribution maps

Capital letters = position of races named in legend below map

- Breeding
- Non-breeding (includes wintering range)
- Vagrants on mainland
- Larger mainland islands where birds have been recorded breeding
- Larger mainland islands where non-breeding birds have been recorded; also birds reliably identified at sea
- Migration trends
- Known boundary between races
- Uncertain boundary between races
- **?** An area of distribution or hybrid uncertainty
- **I** A bird species deliberately introduced to an island or small area of Australia

E = an endemic race recorded only in Australia, e.g. Black-faced Cuckoo-shrike, race *subpallida*.

Br. E = a breeding endemic race recorded beyond Australia in certain seasons, e.g. Black-faced Cuckoo-shrike, races *novaehollandiae* and *melanops*.

The words 'No races' indicate that only one name is used (a binomial) and the bird is considered monotypic; that is, there has been no need to 'divide it up' into races (= subspecies). Where practicable, the nominate name of the species is presented first; all other race names follow.

Breeding information bars

Breeding season is taken as the whole period from the beginning of nest construction to fledging of the young.

Seasonal breeding periods are coded as small bars, one square to a month.

- Main breeding season
- Casual breeding and breeding in response to unseasonable rainfall

Sources: maps and taxonomy

Ostrich to Shrike-thrushes – *Handbook of Australian, New Zealand and Antarctic Birds (HANZAB)*, OUP, Melbourne, Vols 1–6

Pigeons to Dollarbird – *HANZAB*, Vol. 4, plus Schodde & Mason (1997).

Red-bellied Pitta to Common Myna – Schodde & Mason *The Directory of Australian Birds, Passerines* (1999).

Western Australian Birds, Vol. 1, *Non-passerines*, Johnstone & Storr (1999).

How to Observe a Bird

'**What bird is that?**' The question is common, the cliché obvious. But it is the business of this book!

First impressions Try to see your bird clearly. Remain quiet and watch it for as long as possible. Build up a little mind portrait of the bird and then improve on this mental image as quickly as you can. Make written notes or a labelled sketch at the first opportunity. Then reach for your field guide.

Size and shape Look at the whole bird first. How big is it – tiny, small, medium, big, very big, huge? What shape is it – thin, plump, tall? Compare its size and shape to a bird you already know. Have you seen that sort of shape before? If so, look in our **Key to Families** immediately.

More detail Now scan the whole bird again. Look at its major body parts in turn – head, back and upper body, underside of the body, the wings, legs and feet, and finally the tail. Look for any distinguishing features, the things that first take your eye. Bill and wing shapes, tail and leg lengths, are good starting points.

Plumage Now look directly at its feathering. Zero in on the two or three really noticeable feather groups or most obvious colour features of the bird. Memorise them; write them down. Look at the diagrams below. Feather group names are displayed. Learn them and use these correct names when possible.

Listen! Did you hear that? What does your bird sound like? What calls does it give? Learn a few common bird calls. Most birds have more than one. Some people find call identification easier than identification by sight.

Behaviour How does your bird walk, run, swim or fly? Where does it perch? Is it alone or in a group? How does it feed? Where does it drink? Where does it live, in what kind of countryside? Consideration of all these facets of a bird's behaviour will fire your interest and help to 'fine tune' your knowledge. Soon you will confidently and accurately identify a bird every time.

Practise and enjoy! Use these basic observational skills on all the common birds about you. The better you know your 'local identities', the easier you will find the others. It is a wonderfully satisfying feeling to identify a previously unknown bird from your own observations, using only your field guide. There are more handy hints on pages 342–5.

Rainbow Bee-eater ♂
Size in the field guide text refers to an average measurement taken from bill tip to tail tip.

Parts of a bird's body

Profile

Crest
Crown
Eyebrow (superciliary)
Ear coverts
Neck
Nape
Lesser coverts
Mantle
Scapulars
Median coverts
Back
Greater coverts
Tertials
Rump
Secondaries
Primaries
Uppertail coverts
Undertail coverts
Outer tail
Central (pair) tail feathers
Eye-ring
Lores
Forehead (frons)
Bill (mandible)
Chin
Gape
Throat
Cheek
Bend of wing
Breast
Alula
Greater coverts
Flank
Belly (abdomen)
Thigh (tibia)
Leg (tarsus)
Front toes
Hind toe

Underwing

Bend of wing
Axillaries
Underwing coverts
Secondaries
Primaries

Upperwing

Lesser coverts
Bend of wing
Alula
Greater coverts
Median coverts
Scapulars
Greater coverts
Tertials
Secondaries
Primaries

For other terms see the Glossary on pages 346–9.

Believing your eyes

No amount of written description or illustration is going to completely prepare you for the range of 'views' you are likely to gain of any given bird. A field guide is just that: a guide, one that will help steer you to the correct identification of the bird you have observed. As you gain experience and knowledge, the task becomes very much easier. Soon you will be able to identify some of the more difficult species, and to quickly recognise many common species from the most fleeting glimpses. Many birds have an uncanny habit of alighting behind obstacles and vegetation, out of your line of sight. An extra effort by the observer is then required to complete the identification. Quite often you will make identifications with some certainty by recognising calls and song without having first sighted the bird.

'Jizz' (or GISS)

The 'general impression of size and shape' is the overall mix of characters that can narrow down the possibilities for identification. Originally a term coined to identify aircraft during World War II, it has grown to become an all-embracing term, the entire 'character', the 'essence', of the bird in the field.

It can lead you to place the bird quickly in its family and in many instances enable you to immediately identify the genus and even its species. Let's look at this more closely, as it will help to be aware of factors met in the field that are likely to confuse the issue. These can be things that distort your observations, and also various exceptions to 'the norm', both natural and man-made.

Size

The overall impression of a bird's size is important. With experience you can gain considerable confidence in judging it. Familiarising yourself with the sizes of a range of common species is useful for such comparisons. 'It appeared to be slightly smaller than a magpie', or, 'It was about sparrow-sized with a much longer tail and bill!' or, 'Perhaps Silver Gull-sized, with longer wings and bulkier body'.

Note the relative sizes of these three common passerines: Little Raven, House Sparrow and Mistletoebird.

Size and distance Keep in mind that size is always relative to the distance from which you observe the bird. This is particularly difficult to ascertain when observing flying or soaring solitary birds, or when such birds are viewed over expanses of water. Here you have little or no chance to relate the bird to familiar objects or other individuals, and thus to improve the accuracy of your impression. Be aware that the binoculars you use also produce optical 'distortions' of size as a result of their magnifying power and the extent of the distortion varies slightly depending on the distance to which you need to focus; e.g. when viewing birds in a flock the ones at the back may appear bigger than those at the front as you focus toward the foreground. Practice overcomes this. Note that large telephoto lenses and telescopes produce the same distortion.

Size impressions These also vary with surrounding environment. When one species is observed with another you can gain a better impression of comparative size but this too can be misleading. House Sparrows will look large when observed with Red-browed Finches at a feeding table but the same sparrows will look small among Silver Gulls and Torresian Crows at the local waste disposal centre.

The foliage in which a bird is perched will likewise alter your impression of its size. Large leaves will tend to diminish your estimations and fine foliage will enhance the apparent size of the bird.

Size measurements Those given in our book are an average measurement taken from specimens of each species, from the bill tip along the back to the tail tip [see Rainbow Bee-eater diagram, p. 1]. Note that this is not 'body size'. Obviously those birds with long bills, necks or tails will give greater length measurements. This measure does not indicate how a tall bird may stand or how large a bird trailing long legs will appear in flight. To help we have qualified these measurements for species that exhibit marked sexual disparity (Plains-wanderer, Masked Owl) and occasionally for great size, e.g. height of an Emu, and for wingspan (albatrosses, Wedge-tailed Eagle). For these birds, wingspan measure is from wing tip to wing tip across the back, with the wings fully outstretched.

Upper: The Brown Cuckoo-Dove viewed from below. A typical glimpse of a bird perched high in the canopy of a rainforest.

Lower: The Brown Cuckoo-Dove in profile. Note how markedly different the impression of shape appears with a different angle of view.

Shape

The body form is often distinctive, even in silhouette. It is a most useful tool to narrow down the identity of a bird. Body shape, together with the length and shape of the tail, wings, bill and the form of the head, allow many groups and species to be instantly recognisable. Leg length is also important. However, the posture and behaviour of birds, while often characteristic, can also confuse your impression of shape. Plumage can be sleeked down, erected or ruffled to change a bird's shape. Flight behaviour and mannerisms greatly alter impressions of shape. Experience is most helpful, especially with seabirds, waders and raptors. As far as possible the shapes and postures most typical for a species have been illustrated in this book. Many of the line drawings show typical flight silhouettes and displays which can also aid identification.

A less than perfect view The angle from which you glimpsed your bird also needs to be considered. So often you can only make your observation from a back view of the bird or by craning your neck skyward, thus seeing the underside of its body. This is where some of birdwatching's challenges really begin.

Colour and light

Pied birds, and boldly coloured and patterned species, present few identification difficulties. Birds plumaged in subtle variations of browns and greys, and those with complex markings (cryptically patterned) are not only more difficult to describe and compare with sibling species, but also may individually vary in colour and pattern. General colours and markings may also change geographically or from one habitat to the next. We shall discuss such variation shortly.

How light affects plumage colour: Two views of a Short-tailed Shearwater show (left) how 'coloured' such a dark species may look in direct sunlight against an intensely colourful background, and (right) the blackening effect of heavily overcast conditions.

Field guides and colour Colour is a personal and subjective sensation, greatly affected by surroundings and the light conditions. The representation of colour is consequently a difficult issue. Also, the reproduction process for field guides, whilst constantly improving with technological developments and despite the artists' every care to strive for accuracy, still has limitations, both technical and perceptual. Consequently, systems devised to standardise the depiction of colour simply do not provide a consistent field solution. Shadows and dappled light effects in illustrations, and the colours used to model shape, present problems of interpretation, as these effects do in life. Making notes of light conditions with your field records will assist evaluation.

The male Red-capped Robin in back view (left) gives little indication of his colourful pattern. The frontal display (centre) fully accentuates the extent of his brilliant red cap and breast. The profile view (right) shows the Robin's overall colour scheme, but not its dual functional purpose, as in the other two views.

Plumage patterns, markings and behaviour Bird feathering serves a variety of functions, from insulation, body temperature control, and waterproofing, to the aerodynamics of flight and locomotion. The differentiation of feathers into a variety of functional types is indicative of this. The variation of plumage colours serves a variety of functions too. In some instances it is to protect the bird from predation by blending it right into the background (Australasian Bittern, p. 79), or breaking up its form against its habitat (gull hatchlings, p. 106).

Signal markings Most typically, discrete areas of plumage are coloured or contrasted to serve as visual signalling mechanisms. These may denote a bird's social status within its group or species, its sex, breeding condition or age, or simply allow them to distinguish others of their kind. Knowing this allows us to identify their species, as well. Markings are often used to signal danger. Typically the location of markings and plumage patterns is accentuated by displays and frequently such diagnostic features are only visible from certain positions or when the bird adopts a particular posture. Markings can be concealed and changed as skin or feathers are moved (Willie Wagtail, p. 236) or raised (Great Bowerbird, p. 248) or when the wings and/or tail are spread (Victoria's Riflebird, p. 246).

Display plumes Birds often have spectacular displays and a great many species have specialised, extended plumes for this purpose. Much display pertains to the breeding cycle. Strong visual advertising is contrary to the need for concealment and birds have solved this in a variety of ways.

Changing plumages through life A single species may have several entirely different plumages in a lifetime. These differentiate young birds from adults or distinguish males from females. Sexual differences may become apparent in successive plumage stages from young to adult, or perhaps only become evident when the birds become adults. Furthermore, males in some species are only obvious by distinctive markings when in breeding condition. They enter an undistinguished, non-breeding plumage after breeding (male fairy-wrens, pp. 172–5); this is called 'eclipse plumage' for some species, e.g. male ducks. Despite the overall need of birds for protective coloration, breeding display is essential and this dictates the changing purpose of distinctive markings in each species.

Bare skin and 'soft parts' To add to the complexity of plumages, some birds also have – and display – areas of unfeathered skin. These may contrast with the plumage and are coloured either by pigmentation or blood flow. Bare skin is most typically about the head, neck and eyes and may differ in colour and expanse with age, sex, breeding condition and emotional state. You are probably familiar with domestic fowl: these have a wide variety of combs and wattles. 'Soft part colour' is the name given to include the colour of legs, feet, bill and all areas of bare skin that normally form part of a species' coloration. This includes the eyes. Iris colour may also vary and allows us to identify some species or discern the age or sex of others. If you examine a dead bird, record its soft parts' colours, but remember that these colours are likely to have rapidly changed from life.

Structural colour and reflective plumage Many species have reflective or iridescent plumage and markings that change colour dramatically with the light or the position of view. The wing speculum of the Pacific Black Duck is a simple example. It may appear black in poor light; normally it is a bright green in good sunlight but when seen from acute angles it becomes a beautiful violet colour (see illustration). Structural colour, as the name implies, is derived from the interference or scattering of light waves by the structure of the feather barbules. Blue, non-iridescent plumage is also a structural colour and not the result of a biochemical pigment (for further explanation, see 'Plumage Pigments', opposite). Glossy black ravens and crows may occasionally glisten 'white', as illustrated.

The highly reflective speculum of the Pacific Black Duck in two lights and at three angles.

Even Ravens may occasionally look 'white', as above, in a glistening trick of backlighting in the early morning.

Structural colours together with pigmented and unpigmented feathers combine to form the multitude of colours and patterns seen in the plumages of birds.

Plumage pigments

Feathers of birds may contain one or a series of basic pigments, made from simple to complex biochemicals. Melanin is the best known, and is widely distributed, occurring in micro-granular form. It can either be black (eumelanin) or brown, red or yellowish (phaeomelanin). Carotenoids are yellow, orange or red pigments which birds obtain by eating plant materials, or secondarily by feeding on lower animals that eat plants. Both melanin and carotenoids are represented in skin, bill and leg colours; the yellow carotenoids, xanthophylls, only enter feathers. Haemoglobin in blood near the skin surface may also cause pink to red coloration in a few birds – certainly the Common Turkey and chicken; possibly the Southern Cassowary, but in this species the colour could also be caused by, or enhanced by, eating fruits.

Plumage pigment anomalies

Although this subject is too complex to pursue in detail here, it may help you to be aware of rare but regularly reported natural anomalies encountered in the field.

Albinism Total absence of pigment, resulting in white birds; e.g. a totally white Laughing Kookaburra or Australian Magpie. A bird must also have pink eyes to qualify fully as an albino. There are many examples in bird literature.

Partial albinism Typically, a few pure white feathers or variably positioned, pure white patches of plumage; this is a condition frequently encountered in introduced species where populations have grown from an initial small number of individuals, e.g. Common Blackbird.

Melanism An over-abundance of melanin pigment gives rise to blacker or darker-feathered birds than usual.

Dilution Partial loss of all pigments in the feathers results in pale birds, but this is rare and 'paleness' is often the consequence of other factors. Sometimes abnormalities in pigmentation give rise to birds with stronger than normal colours. When yellow pigment is missing from green parrot plumage, the birds will appear blue (blue domestic Budgerigar). In other instances, where areas of melanin are missing, some parrots may show yellow patches (some wild Australian King-Parrots). An excess of carotenoid pigments may produce excessively yellowish parrots (yellow domestic Budgerigar). Dietary deficiencies or excesses, diseases and parasites, can all affect plumage colour.

Other factors affecting plumage

It is vital that birds maintain the condition of their plumage. They constantly preen, clean, bathe, dust and repair split feather vanes. As feathers age and wear they often become paler from sunlight bleaching (especially because the black melanin pigment slowly becomes brown). Abrasion of the feather structure visibly reduces the amount of coloured surface. Where feathers should have contrasting tips and edges, these may be completely worn away. The spotted and striated effect of plumages may thus be reduced or absent. In some species this factor alone produces the seasonal changes in a species' coloration. The Common Starling (p. 280–1) is a simple case where the new, post-moult feathers have pale tips. This constitutes the birds' non-breeding plumage. These tips wear easily, so by breeding time the spots are absent. The birds are then darker and appear more iridescent; more of the basal colour of the feathers is visible.

One feather at a time

A bird's plumage is a mosaic of individual feathers, varying in size, shape, colour and pattern. Feathers may be white or coloured but usually their base is not strongly pigmented.

Feathers may be *banded* (hawk), *vermiculated* (Australian Wood Duck), *spotted* or *blotched* (Grass Owl), may have *contrasting shafts* (Stubble Quail) or *edges* (Crimson and Eastern Rosellas), or be variously *tipped* (Spotted Bowerbird).

The extent and sequence of markings and colours typically vary slightly from one feather to the next to create an overall pattern, or may change abruptly to form a stronger marking. Examples are shearwater underwing patterns; gerygone tail patterns; overall patterns of Hooded and Mangrove Robins.

Descriptive words used for a few of these patterns are *scalloping* (Bassian Thrush), *crescents* (Australasian Shoveler; Crescent Honeyeater), *chevrons* (Powerful Owl), *striations* (Rufous Whistler), *panels* (Australian Shelduck), *hoods* (Hooded Plover), *mottling* (juvenile Dusky Robin), *spots* (Helmeted Guineafowl; Painted Finch), *gorget* (Yellow-bellied Sunbird), *bull's eyes* or *roundels* (Black-breasted Buzzard), *barring* (Shining Bronze-Cuckoo; Barred Cuckoo-shrike), *banding* (Double-banded Plover; Banded Honeyeater), *tail tips* (Black Currawong), *subterminal tail banding* (Nankeen Kestrel), *trailing wing edges* (Little Penguin; Pacific Gull), *wing bars/bands* (European Goldfinch), *shoulder patches* (Red-winged Parrot).

Feather diseases

Diseases may also alter the colour, pattern or general appearance of birds. Ill-formed feathers may not lie correctly and so may disrupt patterns, or they may simply lack pigmentation. Dietary deficiencies during feather development may produce pale bands – particularly evident on larger flight feathers, which become weakened and are likely to break. Ectoparasites, especially feather lice *Mallophaga*, can damage feathers quite severely.

Missing and broken plumage is common: predatory birds will damage plumage in pursuit of prey, just as prey species will lose feathers in lucky escapes! Old injuries are sometimes noticeable because they affect pigmentation in scarred areas. Flight hazards are often evident in injuries and feather loss. These problems for birds are dramatically enhanced by man-made hazards.

Moulting The natural changeover of a bird's plumage, the replacement of old with 'fresh' feathers, can happen either by a complete moult over a short period, or in a gradual sequence, perhaps even being arrested for a time by some circumstance or another. Moulting birds may show some quite bizarre plumage, occasionally fooling even experienced observers. At the very least they can look rather tatty.

General impression of size and shape (yes – that's 'jizz' again) of a bird can be dramatically affected by moult. This typically is most evident when immature 'brown' birds gain adult plumage or when adult birds don distinctive breeding or display colours. Penguins gain weight prior to their moult to enable a period out of the sea, and so *are* in fact larger. Moulting highlights age changes. Once it has been worked out, the pattern of changes in moulting birds can reliably be used to age many species.

An Australian White Ibis with grubby plumage, a frequent occurrence. See also page 81.

Plumage staining Waterbirds and seabirds may become stained and once-white feathers can appear pink, orange, brown or green. White Ibis and Magpie Geese often look very grubby. Some seabirds may look 'rusty' from swimming in water containing iron-fixing bacteria. Oil pollution is a well-known hazard and in less severe cases seabirds often have dark flecks about head and underparts. Dyes or paints may stain birds frequenting rubbish tips.

A lightly-oiled Little Penguin. This bird would recover, as fouling is not severe.

Pollen on plumage Australia has an abundance of nectar-feeding bird species. Honeyeaters and lorikeets clambering through flowering shrubs in the bush, or in suburban gardens and parks, are a familiar sight. Sometimes you will be amazed to see these birds with unusual coloured patches on their heads. These odd dustings of colour – in some cases red, in others yellow, orange, brown, even blue or purple – are due to pollen on the plumage, especially on the frons (forehead), having been deposited as the birds repeatedly thrust their bills into blossoms. Their activity and mobility serves the vital pollination of plants in the Australian landscape.

A Little Pied Cormorant stained from swimming in water containing iron-fixing bacteria.

Variation

Individual variation Birds naturally vary individually and, with close observation, subtle changes in plumage pattern between some individuals can be detected. This can materially assist your bird studies, enhancing your knowledge of what goes on in the avian world around you. True individual variation is consistent throughout the life of the individual; other variations may only be temporary.

Detail of Red Wattlebird head to show an orange frons (forehead) due to pollen deposition following its foraging for nectar.

Marking birds for identification and study It is not always possible to identify an individual wild bird over and over again, so artificial means are used. You must be licensed to carry out any such work. During the course of bird study a wide variety of techniques can be employed to 'mark' individual birds for observation. Brightly coloured dyes are used, as are a variety of leg rings (either/or coloured plastic or numbered metal) or leg or wing tags (coloured and/or numbered). Transmitters are also employed to track bird movements.

Polymorphism This occurs when a bird species has two or more plumage colorations, or morphs, in the one breeding population. We feel that use of the older word 'phase' is outmoded and possibly not even correct. Polymorphism is not related to normal sexual dimorphism. The most obvious example is the Eastern Reef Egret (p. 77) with its white and dark grey ('blue') morphs. Two others are the Red-footed Booby (p. 51) and Grey Goshawk (p. 123). Proportions of each morph in the population may vary geographically. Historically, the extreme variations of the Grey Goshawk were initially considered as separate species – the Grey and the 'White' Goshawks.

A Pied Oystercatcher wearing a numbered metal band and colour-coded leg bands (rings). A commonly employed technique to allow identification of individuals for scientific study. Read the code for left and right legs separately, and from the *top* down! This bird is therefore 'black, red, green' (left); 'white, over metal' (right).

Geographic variation As you birdwatch about Australia, studying your ever-present field guide, you will encounter the natural variation of bird species from different areas of their distribution. In some cases this is gradual, almost imperceptible. In other instances the changes are quite noticeable or very abrupt. For some species these changes occur over a continuous range and for others as disjunct (fragmented), often isolated populations. Beyond natural events, an artificial population fragmentation has, of course, invariably been assisted by recent massive land clearance.

Hybridisation The situation can be further complicated when bird populations of the same species but of different races (subspecies) come in contact with each other – regularly, intermittently or over a narrow area. This may eventually produce further variations, or a hybrid zone with birds showing intermediate plumage characteristics.

One really well-known hybrid zone is that where the Australian Magpie races meet across the south-east section of the Great Dividing Range. Driving more or less due north from Melbourne you leave the coastal plains race of 'White-backed' Magpies behind, and enter a hilly hybrid zone. As you cross the Range just before Kilmore and on to about Seymour the birds are patchy-patterned variations of 'White-backed' and 'Black-backed' Magpies. After pressing due north, well beyond the Murray River, you are in purely 'Black-backed' Magpie country. But if, instead, you turn north-east from Seymour, and travel the Hume Highway toward Sydney, you will see those patchy-patterned variations (p. 254) of 'White-backed' and 'Black-backed' Magpies most of the way, because you are driving along the length of this massive hybrid zone.

Without running off the road (very important), keep the score: Grand Total of Magpies seen; plus totals of 'White-backed'; 'patchy-patterned (hybrid)'; 'Black-backed'. Somewhere, as you eventually begin to descend the ranges into Sydney, you will meet mainly 'Black-backed' Magpies again. We don't know precisely where all of the boundaries run, but that is the gist of it – give it a go. On your return journey, count again to check the totals!

Hybridisation between *totally different species* also occurs naturally, but offspring are usually sterile.

Finally, birdwatching in Australia is an occupation that becomes ever more fascinating. The longer it is practised the more fascinating things there are to watch for. Continuing study by amateurs and professionals, and debate over the nature of variations in bird species, is clarifying bird relationships and presenting a better understanding of the Australian avifauna. It is because of such advances that we can present an important new level of bird maps in this volume, and better describe the species and their races.

Three good rules

In biology, as in other branches of the sciences, long periods of observation have led to the recognition that certain factors are constants, and once recognised can be expected to occur, or be demonstrable, over and over again.

1 Bergman's Rule

Geographic variation in size: *That, among the forms of a polytypic species, body size tends to be larger in cooler parts of the total range and smaller in the warmer parts.*

A 'polytypic species' is one where more than one form (race or subspecies) of the species exists. What does this rule mean? It could be considered an ecogeographic function. It applies both latitudinally (body size larger toward the poles; smaller toward the equator) and possibly also vertically (smaller to larger with increasing altitude).

2 Allen's Rule

Geographic variation in body proportion: *That, among the forms of a polytypic species, extensions of the body (in birds, chiefly the bill) tend to be longer in the warmer parts of the species' total range and shorter in the cooler parts.*

Firstly, the 'total range' of a species is the area which it naturally occupies (inhabits) in its lifetime. Our maps show the total range of Australian endemic species, and part of the total range of international migratory species.

In the cooler southern or northern parts of the world, birds need to keep warmer, and so tend to be more heavily feathered, and to have slightly shorter legs and bills. In the tropics, keeping cool is a problem and birds of the same species, or a race of it, tend to have slightly longer legs and noticeably longer bills. Presumably the extra vascularisation of these helps reduce the bird's overall temperature.

3 Gloger's Rule

Geographic variation in plumage: *In a given species, its races (subspecies) in warmer and humid areas are apt to be more heavily pigmented than those in cooler, drier areas.*

Species in a bird population may vary locally or regionally, and sometimes even across the whole continent. Sometimes there are subtle and gradual changes in colour or pattern and in other instances, dramatically distinct colour differences. The latter is more likely to be the case where populations of a species are widely separated latitudinally, i.e. from north to south.

More simply, birds in the tropics are likely to be either darker, or more richly coloured, than those in more southerly areas. The Figbird is an example (p. 245). Figbirds of the southern race *vieilloti* have more green on their flanks, are grey-chested and necked. About Darwin, the most north-westerly birds, race *ashbyi*, have far richer yellow underparts.

(The italic quotes above are from *A Dictionary of Birds*, Bruce Campbell and Elizabeth Lack, eds, T. & A.D. Poyser, London, 1985.)

Key to Families

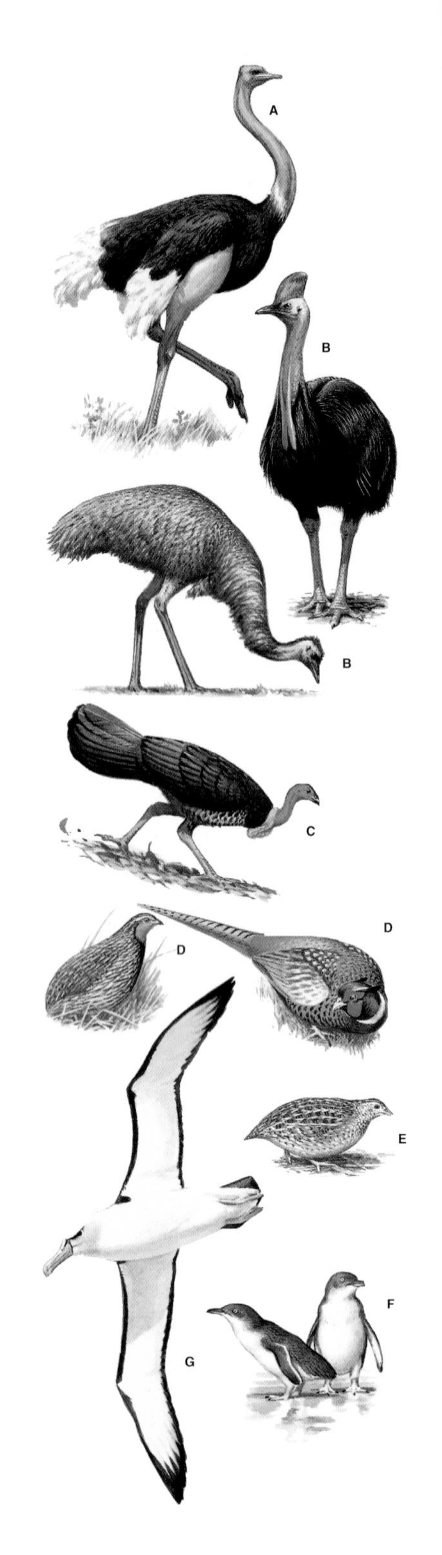

World species numbers based on Sibley & Monroe (1990). Australian species numbers based on Christidis & Boles (1994); Schodde & Mason (1999); these include vagrants. Page references are to text pages and plates; also breeding bars.

A Ostriches *Family Struthionidae* **18–19**

The world's largest living bird. Male Ostrich plumage is black and white; the female's is brown. The feet are two-toed – the only bird with less than three. Species: World 1; Australia 1.

B Cassowaries, Emu *Family Casuariidae* **18–19**, 312

Cassowary: Stocky, flightless, large jungle-dwelling ratite with black, hair-like plumage, a helmeted head, a bright face and distinctive neck wattles. Species: World 3; Australia 1.

Emu: Australia's national emblem and largest endemic bird. Flightless, fast-running, strong-legged, stands two metres high. Has loose, shaggy grey-brown plumage. Species: World 1; Australia 1.

C Mound-builders (Megapodes) **20–1**, 312
Family Megapodiidae

Large, strong-legged, dark or spotted, ground birds. Some have bare heads and bright wattles. Eggs incubated in large sand, soil or leaf-litter mounds. Species: World 12; Australia 3.

D Quails, Pheasants *Family Phasianidae* **20–1**, 312

Small, plump, short-tailed and striped, to very large, long-tailed, bright ground birds. Species: World approx. 211; Australia approx. 7.

California Quail *Family Odontophoridae* **22–3**, 312
Introduced patterned, striped quail. Male has prominent black crest, throat markings. Species: World approx. 1; Australia 1.

Helmeted Guineafowl *Family Numididae* **22–3**
Introduced; farmed; a few are feral. Species: World approx. 7; Australia 1.

E Button-quails *Family Turnicidae* **24–5**, 312

Like 'true' quails (Phasianidae) but lack a hind toe. Females larger and brighter, mating with several males in each breeding season. Grassland, scrub and woodland. Species: World 14; Australia 7.

F Penguins *Family Spheniscidae* **26–7**, 312

Plump, small to large seabirds with upright stance. Waddle when walking. Dense, waterproof plumage. Only one annual moult. Wings became flippers for swimming, diving. Fish and plankton-eaters. Species: World 18; Australia 11.

G Albatrosses *Family Diomedeidae* **28–33**, 312

Medium to very large, long-winged, gliding, oceanic seabirds. Small tubular nostrils at side of large, hook-tipped bills; webbed feet. Take live food; scavenge. Species: World 13; Australia 10.

A Petrels, Shearwaters, Diving-Petrels **34–47**, 313
Family Procellariidae

Petrels and shearwaters are small to very large, long-winged, gliding, oceanic seabirds. All have tubular nostrils on top of stout, hooked bills; webbed feet. Diving-Petrels are tiny, dumpy, short-winged; busy flight; dive and swim well. Giant-Petrels are almost albatross-sized. Species: World approx. 70; Australia 46.

B Storm-Petrels *Family Hydrobatidae* **46–7**, 313

Tiny blackish or grey, long-legged petrels. Rapid swooping flight. Feed on plankton. Flutter or patter over wave surfaces. Largely pelagic, migratory or nomadic. Species: World 20; Australia 9.

C Pelicans *Family Pelecanidae* **48–9**, 313

Australian Pelican has spectacular long bill, loose gular pouch. All four toes webbed. Swims; soars. Species: World 8; Australia 1.

D Gannets, Boobies *Family Sulidae* **48–51**, 313

Stout-billed seabirds which indulge in spectacular plunge-diving. Feet fully webbed. Gannets are in colder seas; boobies more tropical seas. Eat live food only. Species: World 9; Australia 5.

E Frigatebirds *Family Fregatidae* **52–3**, 313

Large, dark seabirds with long, hooked bills and long, deeply forked tails. Soar on long, pointed wings over tropical seas. Feed on the wing. Piratical behaviour. Species: World 5; Australia 3.

F Tropicbirds *Family Phaethontidae* **52–3**, 313

Stout, red-billed, white-plumaged seabirds with two long, central red or white tail streamers. Plunge-dive for food; strong direct flight; soar in updrafts. Species: World 3; Australia 2.

G Anhingas (Darters) *Family Anhingidae* **54–5**, 313

Darters lunge with snake-like necks, slender bills, to spear fish under water. Like cormorants but larger, slimmer, broader-winged, longer-tailed. All toes webbed. Species: World 4; Australia 1.

H Cormorants *Family Phalacrocoracidae* **54–5**, 313

Cormorants swim and dive for fish, perch with outstretched wings. Their feet are fully webbed. Species: World 38; Australia 5.

I Grebes *Family Podicipedidae* **56–7**, 314

Sharp-billed, chunky. Divers. Legs far back on body; lobed toes. Rarely walk on land. Floating nests.
Species: World 20; Australia 4.

J Magpie Goose *Family Anseranatidae* **58–67**, 314
Geese, Swans, Ducks *Family Anatidae*

Magpie Geese are large, knob-headed, black and white, flocking geese with partly webbed toes. Species: World 1; Australia 1. *Anatidae* are wetland birds with dense waterproof plumage, webbed feet, flattened bills. Dabble, filter-feed, or dive. Most fly strongly. Some are game birds. Species: World 145; Australia 24.

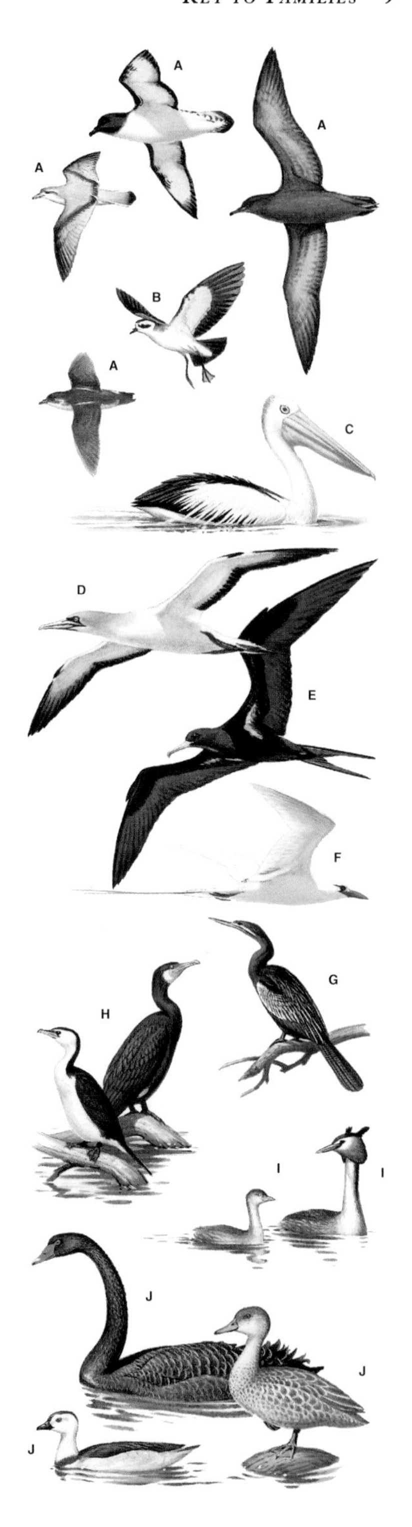

A Rails, Crakes, Swamphens, Coot — 68–73, 314
Family Rallidae

Small to large skulking aquatic birds. Some have coloured bill shields. All are stout-bodied, short-tailed and long-toed (lobed in coots). Plumage of some is plain and sombre; others are cryptically streaked. Very loud calls. Species: World 123; Australia 16.

B Herons, Egrets, Bitterns — 74–9, 315
Family Ardeidae

Tall, slender, long-legged, long-necked aquatic birds. Their dagger-like bills spear at prey. They may be grey, pied or cryptically coloured; others entirely white. Some feed, breed as pairs; others are gregarious feeders and nest in colonies. Normally, all the species eat live prey. Species: World 61; Australia 14.

C Ibises, Spoonbills — 80–1, 315
Family Threskiornithidae

Diagnostic bills distinguish these from the similar but spear-billed herons. They feed by touch, probing with long, down-curved bills (ibises), or by sweeping laterally through shallow water with spatulate bills (spoonbills). Species: World 32; Australia 5.

D Storks *Family Ciconiidae* — 80–1, 315

The only Australian species has pied plumage. Tall, large waterbirds with long, stout bills. When flying or soaring, their broad wings, extended neck and long red trailing legs are distinctive. Species: World 17; Australia 1.

E Cranes *Family Gruidae* — 82–3, 315

Tall, elegant, long-legged birds with long sharp bills. Elaborate dancing displays. Whooping calls. Slow wing-beat; soaring flight. The two Australian species have grey bodies and red on their heads. Species: World 16; Australia 2.

F Bustards *Family Otididae* — 82–3, 315

Large, stately, stout-bodied, grassland-dwelling birds with long legs, pointed bills and cryptic plumage. Species: World 24; Australia 1.

G Plains-wanderer *Family Pedionomidae* — 82–3, 316

Like button-quails but have a hind toe. Weak, fluttering flight. An endangered grassland species. Species: World 1; Australia 1.

H Curlews, Sandpipers, Snipes, Godwits, Phalaropes *Family Scolopacidae* — 84–95, 316

Large Family of usually long-billed, often long-legged, migratory waders. Most are cryptically plumaged. Smallest are the stints; largest the Eastern Curlew. No species breeds in Australia. All are from the N Hemisphere: are regular annual migrants, irregular visitors (possibly nomads) or rare individual vagrants. Species: World approx. 88; Australia approx. 48.

I Pratincoles *Family Glareolidae* — 94–5, 316

Long-winged, brownish 'tern-like' waders of inland and barren areas. One species breeds in Australia. Species: World 16; Australia 2.

A Painted Snipe *Family Rostratulidae* **96–7**, 316

Long-billed ('Woodcock-like'). Strikingly patterned waders. Female brighter. 'Freezes' if disturbed. Species: World 2; Australia 1.

B Jacanas (Lotusbirds) *Family Jacanidae* **96–7**, 316

Rail-like, jacanas are waders with extremely long thin toes and hind claws for running over floating freshwater plants. Adults carry juveniles under their wings. Species: World 8; Australia 2.

C Stone-curlews (Thick-knees) **96–7**, 316
Family Burhinidae

Tall, large-eyed, plover-like, bush- and beach-dwelling waders. Large bills. Cryptically plumaged. Both species widespread but (with exceptions) relatively uncommon. Species: World 9; Australia 2.

D Oystercatchers *Family Haematopodidae* **96–7**, 316

Black or pied, large red-billed, red-legged, coastal waders. Piping calls in flight. Species: World 7; Australia 3.

E Lapwings, Plovers, Dotterels **98–103**, 316
Family Charadriidae

Short-billed, round-headed, large-eyed, plump waders. Migrants or nomads. Lapwings vocal. Species: World 64; Australia 19.

F Stilts, Avocets *Family Recurvirostridae* **102–3**, 317

Medium-sized, distinctive waders with very long red or blue-grey legs. Bills slender: straight (stilts), upturned (avocets). Often in large flocks. Yapping calls. Species: World 13; Australia 3.

G Skuas, Jaegers, Gulls, Terns **104–15**, 317
Family Laridae

Piratical skuas, jaegers, have variable plumage with increasing age, long central tail feathers, white wing flashes, webbed feet, strong curved sharp claws. Gulls are scavengers with white, grey and dark to black plumage, heavy bills, webbed feet. Terns, noddies, are slender-bodied, thin-billed, and narrow-winged. Some crested. Stand 'horizontally'. Terns dive for live food or pick it from surface. Species: World approx. 94; Australia 35.

H Osprey (sometimes in own *Family Pandionidae*), **Kites, Goshawks, Eagles, Harriers** *Family Accipitridae* **116–25**, 317

Ospreys are fishing hawks with broad wings, strong legs and talons to seize slippery prey. Nests are large, conspicuous stick platforms. All birds of prey have short heads, broad wings, hooked bills, large talons. Females are normally larger than males. Most take live food; some are opportunist scavengers. Slow wing-beat in level flight. Angle that wings are held when gliding aids identification. Often seen circling, soaring. Species: World approx. 220; Australia 18.

I Falcons *Family Falconidae* **124–7**, 318

Swift-flying, predatory birds with 'toothed' upper bill, a dark cap or teardrop cheek mark, and long, pointed wings. Two species (Brown Falcon, Nankeen Kestrel) can hover. Species: World 61; Australia 6.

A Pigeons, Doves *Family Columbidae* **128–35**, 318

Plump, plain or colourful, fast-flying fruit- or seed-eaters. Some have crests. Minor sexual differences. Stout bill; some drink by sucking. Tails short or long. Some species are increasing their distribution. Species: World approx. 297; Australia 27.

B Cockatoos *Family Cacatuidae* **136–9**, 318

Medium to large parrots. Erectile crests, orbital ring; plumages vary: black to white. Often raucous voices. Feed on roots, seeds, blossom; some eat insects. Fly strongly. DNA work in W. Aust. solved corella, black-cockatoo, identification. Cockatiel is a true cockatoo. Species: World approx. 18; Australia 14.

Parrots *Family Psittacidae* 319

All parrots are 'true' parrots: stocky-bodied; stout, hooked bills; two toes forward and two back. In this book, all parrots are regarded as one Family, with well-defined Subfamilies and/or Tribes (see below). Species: World approx. 326; Australia 41.

C 'Old' Tropical Parrots *Tribe Psittaculini* **138–9**

Two species restricted to Cape York Penin: green male and scarlet female Eclectus Parrot; smaller Red-cheeked Parrot.

D Lorikeets *Subfamily Loriinae* **140–1**

Shrill-voiced, noisy, fast-flying, foliage-foraging green parrots. Red or black bills. Small, with short, pointed tails, or medium-sized, with long pointed tails. All eat nectar, pollen and fruit.

E Fig-Parrots *Tribe Cyclopsittacini* **140–1**

Smallest Australian parrot. Tail is short, rather rounded. Predominantly green. Facial markings, and the fact of three isolated populations (races), aids identification.

F 'Long-tailed' Parrots *Tribe Polytelini* **142–3**

Male, female, plumage differs. Bills are small. Tails long and graduated; each narrow tail feather with a fine tip. Wings are long, pointed. Fast-flying, with rocking, undulating flight.

G 'Broad-tailed' Parrots **144–51**
Subfamily Platycercinae

Parrots with slow undulating flight. Tails medium to long in proportion to body length; frequently fanned in display.

H Parasitic Cuckoos *Family Cuculidae* **152–5**, 319

Slender, small to large, plain or barred, long-tailed birds. Narrow wings, fast undulating flight and repetitive, ventriloquial calls. Nest-parasites on other birds. Species: World approx. 100; Australia 12.

I Coucals *Family Centropidae* **154–5**, 320

Large, dark, long-tailed birds with rounded wings, poor flight. Long, loud, cackling, hooting, calls. Not parasitic on other birds; build own nests. Species: World 27; Australia 1.

A Hawk Owls *Family Strigidae* **156–7**, 320

Small to large, dark-coloured predatory nocturnal birds, with large pale eyes set in an indistinct facial disc. Often give hooting territorial calls. Silent flight. Species: World 135; Australia 5.

B Barn Owls *Family Tytonidae* **158–9**, 320

Large, slender-legged, pale- or dark-coloured nocturnal birds. Dark eyes in wide facial disc. Female larger. Silent flight. Mostly silent but have screeching calls. Hunt by listening for rodents, reptiles, large insects. Species: World 12; Australia 5.

C Frogmouths *Family Podargidae* **160–1**, 320

Plump, dark, nocturnal birds. Long tails, rounded wings, broad bills. Silent flight. Cryptic plumage (streaks, spots). By day, perched, they resemble branch stubs. Species: World 13; Australia 3.

D Owlet-nightjars *Family Aegothelidae* **160–1**, 320

Very small, delicate, grey, nocturnal bird with 'possum-like' striped face. Small, broad bill edged by prominent bristles. Large, forward-facing eyes, weak feet, rounded wings and long, broad tail. Almost no reflective eye shine. Species: World 8; Australia 1.

E Nightjars *Family Caprimulgidae* **160–1**, 320

Small to medium nocturnal birds with long tails, small broad bills and long pointed wings. Very reflective eye shine. Roost by day on the ground. Nest amid leaf litter. Cryptic plumage gives marvellous protection. Species: World 75; Australia 3.

F Swiftlets, Swifts *Family Apodidae* **162–3**, 321

Fast-flying, aerial-feeding insectivores. Have long, swept wings, square or forked tails, large eyes, a small bill but wide gape. Larger swifts are migratory; feed about weather fronts. Aust. tropical swiftlets breed in caves. Species: World 84; Australia 6.

G River Kingfishers *Family Alcedinidae* **164–5**, 321

Tiny, brightly coloured, and stout-bodied, with large heads, long pointed black bills, short tails, tiny feet. Fast, direct flight. Feed only on live food from streams. Species: World 24; Australia 2.

H Tree Kingfishers *Family Halcyonidae* **164–7**, 321

Usually brightly coloured, tree kingfishers have stout bodies, large heads, long heavy bills and small feet. Fast, direct flight. Kookaburras are much larger, slower. Cackling calls. Nest holes in trees, banks, termite mounds. Species: World 70; Australia 8.

I Bee-eaters *Family Meropidae* **164–5**, 321

Vocal, gregarious, brightly coloured birds. Bill black, long, down-curved; legs small. Hawk aerial insects. Nest burrow in sandy sloping ground or bank. Migratory. Species: World 24; Australia 1.

J Rollers *Family Coraciidae* **164–5**, 321

Red-billed, dull green, plump. Perch on dead branches. 'Silver-dollar' wing spots visible in 'rolling' aerial display flights and when hawking insects. Migratory. Species: World 11; Australia 1.

A Pittas *Family Pittidae* **168–9**, 321

Plump, medium-sized, 'thrush-like', colourful tropical birds. Short tails; long legs; upright stance. White wing patches in flight. Secretive, ground-dwelling. Loud, distinctive calls often given while perched high. Species: World 26; Australia 4.

B Lyrebirds *Family Menuridae* **168–9**, 321

World's largest songbirds. Large, brown-grey birds of wet forests. Legs, toes, are strong for scratching and moving ground litter as birds forage. Fly only weakly. Breeding males have long decorative tails, and loud, rich, protracted song, with much mimicry included. It is given during spectacular displays on prepared dancing mounds. Females and young are plain-tailed. Species: World 2; Australia 2.

C Scrub-birds *Family Atrichornithidae* **168–9**, 322

Considered to have close affinities with lyrebirds (Menuridae). 'Soft-looking' plumages are dark rufous and dark brown, with fine vermiculated patterns. Sexes differ. Birds are retiring, remain near ground, rarely fly. Loud, ventriloquial voice, containing much mimicry. The Noisy Scrub-bird is an endangered species, hard to see. Species: World 2; Australia 2.

D Sittellas *Family Neosittidae* **170–1**, 322

These birds tend to forage spirally downward on upper tree-trunks and branches. They are small, social, grey-black and white, with orange to white wing bars, slightly upturned bills, yellow legs and feet. One very variable species. Usually in family parties, small flocks. Species: World 1; Australia 1.

E Treecreepers *Family Climacteridae* **170–1**, 322

These birds climb upward on tree-trunks and lower to mid-level branches; some also feed on the ground. They are small and brownish with pale fawn wing bars, slightly down-curved bills, strong legs, with long toes and claws. Sexes are different. Breed, roost, in tree hollows, cavities. Species: World 6; Australia 6.

F Fairy-wrens and allies *Family Maluridae* **172–9**, 322

Three genera of small, cocked-tailed, insectivorous 'wrens'. All species are normally seen in family parties. Breeding fairy-wren males are brilliantly coloured. Non-breeding and young males, and females, are brown. Both sexes generally similar in the streak-plumaged grasswrens, but emu-wrens have sexual differences; modified tail feathers. Species: World approx. 23; Australia 21.

G Pardalotes *Family Pardalotidae* **180–93**, 323
Bristlebirds, Scrubwrens, Gerygones and Thornbills *Family Acanthizidae*

Two Families of small to tiny birds. Pardalotes are tiny, spotted and colourful, with short tails, and short, broad bills. They breed in hollows or burrows, sometimes in loose colonies. Acanthizids are browner, duller, and active, with pleasant voices. Most are ground-dwelling or foliage-foraging insectivores. Most are sedentary; a few are nomadic. Nests are dome-shaped, sometimes pendant. The three larger-bodied Bristlebirds are all endangered species. Species: World 67; Australia 46.

A Honeyeaters and Australian Chats **194–215**, 324
Family Meliphagidae

Honeyeaters, mostly nomadic, have brush-tipped tongues and decurved bills (1–3 cm long). Most are dull olive, grey or brown, with brighter patches of identifying plumage or skin about the face, and are slim. Nomadic chats have bright males; duller females and juveniles. Chats, closely allied to the true honeyeaters, are often in flocks on inland plains, salt lakes, or coastal heath and salt marshes. Species: World 151; Australia 74.

B Logrunner, Chowchilla **216–17**, 325
Family Orthonychidae

Ground-dwelling medium-sized birds of wet forests. Sedentary, territorial, and in family groups. Very strong songs and calls. Species: World 2; Australia 2.

C Whipbirds, Wedgebills, Quail-thrushes *Family Cinclosomatidae (Eupetidae)* **216–19**, 325

Three genera of rather secretive, long-tailed songbirds which live on or close to the ground, although in diverse habitats. Most are camouflaged; some are crested; some are mimics. May be difficult to locate in bushland. Species: World 15; Australia 9.

D Australo-Papuan Babblers **220–1**, 325
Family Pomatostomidae

Noisy, gregarious, largely ground-feeding family parties. Plump brownish bodies; longish tails; pointed, down-curved bills. Territorial groups build large, domed stick nests for nesting, communal roosting. Species: World 5; Australia 4.

E Australasian Robins *Family Petroicidae* **222–9**, 326

Small insectivorous birds, some with brilliantly coloured males. May perch sideways on vertical stems. Hunt prey from low perches. Young heavily mottled. Species: World 46; Australia 21.

F Shrike-tits, Crested Bellbird, Shrike-thrushes, Whistlers *Family Pachycephalidae* **228–35**, 326

Plain or strongly coloured, medium-sized insectivores. Some are sexually dimorphic. Four species are crested. Most are excellent songsters. Forest birds. Species: World 47; Australia 16.

G Monarchs, Magpie-lark, Flycatchers, Fantails, Drongo *Family Dicruridae* **236–43**, 326

A varied group of small to medium-sized insectivorous birds. Utilise a wide variety of habitats. Swish tails from side to side to disturb prey. Often take prey on the wing. Usually excellent songsters. Many are sexually dimorphic. Some juveniles are spotted. Magpie-lark ('plover-like'), is long-legged, vocal, and a mud-nest builder. Pairs are often seen on roadsides or in winter flocks. Gleaming black, fish-tailed, red-eyed, the Spangled Drongo is distinctive. Species: World 140; Australia 21.

H Orioles, Figbirds *Family Oriolidae* **244–5**, 327

Olive-back Oriole is a migrant. Both sexes of Australian orioles (green) and females of Figbirds (brown) are heavily streaked. Male Figbirds are highly coloured. Species: World 25; Australia 3.

A Birds of Paradise *Family Paradisaeidae* **246–7**, 327

Adult sexes are different. Polygamous breeding males are spectacular in colour, feathering, and in display behaviour. Females and immature males are drab and camouflaged. Rainforest birds. Mainly fruit-eaters. Species: World 43; Australia 4.

B Bowerbirds *Family Ptilonorhynchidae* **246–9**, 327

Male bowerbirds are plain or brightly plumaged; females plainer. Catbirds are green. Polygamous male bowerbirds display on courts; at bowers. Species: World 18; Australia 9.

C Cuckoo-shrikes, Trillers **250–1**, 328
Family Campephagidae

Insectivorous, arboreal birds; slender bodies, long, pointed wings, graduated tails. Plumages are in black, grey, brown, or pied combinations; some are barred. Undulating flight; refold wings on alighting; have trilling voices. Species: World 72; Australia 7.

D Woodswallows, Butcherbirds, Currawongs *Family Artamidae* **252–7**, 328

Woodswallows are small, aerial feeders with bluish black-tipped bills. Mostly nomadic. Distinctive 'batwing' shape in flight. Rotate tails when perched; often huddle together. Butcherbirds, incl. Australian Magpie, and currawongs, are solid, arboreal and ground-foraging, strong-flying birds. Black, or black, grey and white. They have large, robust, hooked bills and strong voices, harsh or melodious. Species: World 20; Australia 15.

E Ravens, Crows *Family Corvidae* **258–9**, 329

Uniform, glossy black birds with minor physical differences, and strong black bills. Plumage in sunlight often reflective. Calls harsh, wailing, cawing. Flocks. Species: World 112; Australia 6.

F Australian Mud-nesters **260–1**, 329
Family Corcoracidae

Large black White-winged Chough and smaller grey Apostlebird live in sociable groups, build solid mud nests. Family members all help breeding adults. Species: World 2; Australia 2.

G Swallows, Martins *Family Hirundinidae* **262–3**, 329

Small songbirds that hawk aerial insects with a fast, jinking flight. Long, straight, pointed wings, and either forked or square tails. Most migratory or nomadic. Species: World 78; Australia 6.

H Old World Pipits, Wagtails **264–5**, 329
Family Motacillidae

Slender ground feeders; often wag their long tails up and down. Pipits resemble larks (Alaudidae) but have pink legs, no crest. The mostly vagrant N Hemisphere wagtails have pied, yellow, green or grey plumages. Species: World 54; Australia 8.

I Old World Larks *Family Alaudidae* **266–7**, 329

Small, streaked, grassland songbirds. Hind toe long, sharply clawed. Erectile head feathers form a short crest. Endemic Bush-lark, introduced Skylark, have aerial displays. Identify from Australian (Richard's) Pipit. Species: World 82; Australia 2.

A Old World Warblers *Family Sylviidae* **268–9**, 330

A Family whose membership has been unclear. Currently includes small, plain brownish, or cryptically plumaged, grass- and reed-dwelling, strong-voiced songbirds. Some have spectacular aerial display flights. Species: World approx. 400; Australia 10.

B Old World Sparrows *Family Passeridae* **270–1**, 330

Small, brown and grey finch-like seed-eaters. Thick, conical bills. Scavengers about city, suburban, country dwellings. May roost in reedbeds. Introduced. Species: World 37; Australia 2.

C True Finches *Family Fringillidae* **270–1**, 330

Small grassland seed-eaters with stout conical bills. Often about industrial wasteland, orchards. Plumage is plain (Greenfinch) to more brightly coloured (Goldfinch). The nest is cup-shaped. Introduced into Australia. Species: World 440; Australia 2.

D Waxbills, Grass-Finches, Mannikins **272–7**, 330
Family Estrildidae

Small, colourful seed-eaters. Often in flocks. In grassland, woodland; a few in denser cover. Grass-finches are the longest tailed; mannikins more chunky. Species: World 120; Australia 20.

E Sunbirds *Family Nectariniidae* **278–9**, 330

Small, brightly coloured, slender-billed, quick-flying, nectar and insect feeders. Resemble honeyeaters and humming-birds in behaviour and flight mannerisms. Build pendulous nests with side entrances. Species: World 117; Australia 1.

F Flowerpeckers *Family Dicaeidae* **278–9**, 331

Tiny, short-billed and short-tailed, Mistletoebirds spread the parasitic mistletoe on which they largely depend for food. Species: World 58; Australia 1.

G White-eyes *Family Zosteropidae* **278–9**, 331

Small green-yellow insectivorous birds with extensible brush-tipped tongues for nectar and pollen. Most have white eye-ring. Most migratory or nomadic. Fast-flying. Species: World 84; Australia 3.

H Bulbuls *Family Pycnonotidae* **280–1**, 331

Small Old World birds. Brown, black-headed and crested, with a decurved notched bill, distinctive face marks. Two species introduced; one species (Red-whiskered) survives in SE Australia. Species: World 118; Australia 1.

I Old World Thrushes *Family Muscicapidae* **280–1**, 331

Small to medium-sized, brown or black birds. Feed on ground in E. Aust. Indigenous Bassian, Russet-tailed Thrushes have crescentic marks. Introduced Common Blackbird and Song Thrush use mud in the nest. Species: World 496; Australia 7.

J Starlings, Mynas *Family Sturnidae* **280–1**, 331

Solid, sharp-beaked, dark-plumaged (iridescent in two species), strong-legged birds. They are vocal, aggressive, nomadic or migratory colonists. Species: World 108; Australia 3.

Field Information

Ostrich *Struthio camelus* Intro.

Flightless. The world's largest living bird species. Runs with vestigial wings held out, at up to 55 km/h. Plumage black, long, soft, loosely webbed. Bill broad, flat. Head, neck, upper legs, grey. White plumes in wings and tail. Lower legs and feet grey-brown. Two toes – only bird in the world with fewer than three. **M br.** Develops reddish colour on gape, edge of upper mandible, on feet. A red, protrusible hemi-penis may be apparent at times. **F** Lighter brown body plumage with off-white plumes. **Size** Up to 240 cm. **Hatchl.** Downy, dark, stripes on neck. **Juv.** Brownish; black stripes on head, neck. **Imm.** Mottled brown and grey plumage, darkening with age. **Hab.** Wherever birds escape in Australia.

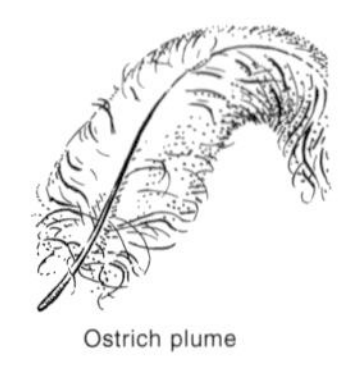

Ostrich plume

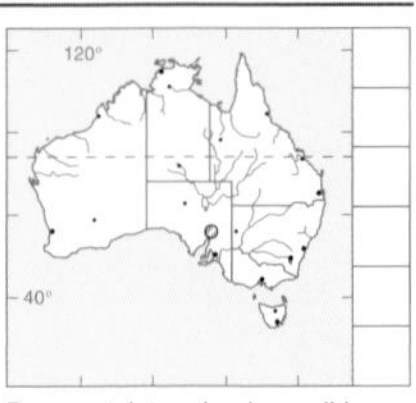

Race not determined; possibly hybrids. Feral population no longer survives. Many new farms established; escapes are likely.

Southern Cassowary *Casuarius casuarius* **UC** ◎ Endangered

Flightless. Adults aggressive; kick (approach with care). Bill black. Tall, brown casque (helmet). Skin on head pale blue, becoming darker down neck; some red lateral skin on neck. Two long red-to-crimson free-swinging fleshy wattles originate at front of neck. Wattle colour changes with mood. Body plumage black; feathers coarse, hair-like, with shaft and aftershaft. Legs, feet, short, stout, green-grey or brown-grey; three toes. Inner toe-nail an elongated spike up to 120 mm. **F** Taller casque, brighter head and neck, larger feet. **Size** 170–175 cm. **Hatchl.** Downy; striped yellow, black, to about 3 months. **Juv.** Brown-bodied head as adult but duller; smaller wattles; no casque. **Imm.** Similar, but casque developing; body plumage is blacker with increasing age. Adult plumage 2–3 yrs. Males may breed in imm. plumage. **Voice** Coughs, hissing; foot stamping, booming. **Hab.** Tropical rainforest, preferring stream banks, clearings.

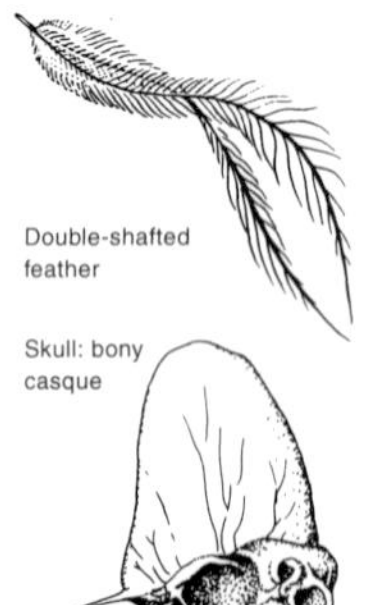

Double-shafted feather

Skull: bony casque

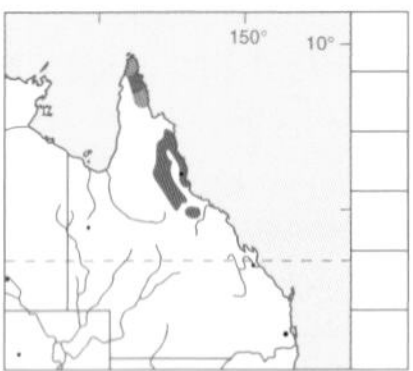

Race *johnsonii* **E Endangered** Queensland population: in late 1999, estimated only 1100–1500 birds left.

Emu *Dromaius novaehollandiae* **LA** ◌–◎ E

Flightless. Runs with bouncy, swaying motion. May be solitary, in family groups or in large flocks. Squat to drink. Males brood eggs, rear chicks. Short black bill. 'Hairy' crown. Skin of head, throat, blue. Whitish ruff. Plumage dark brown to grey-brown. Feathers have shaft, aftershaft; plumage long, thick, drooping, soft, appears shaggy. Freshly moulted birds of both sexes have black feathering on head and neck; this abrades and thins with wear. Long legs and feet dark grey-brown; three toes. **F** Larger in mated pairs. Body plumage darker before breeding; black feathers cover head and neck. Race *rothschildi* (B) SW Aust. Darker, no ruff in breeding plumage. Race *?woodwardi* (C) N Aust. Slender and paler. **Size** 150–190 cm. **Hatchl.** Crown spotted; body downy with dark brown to black body stripes. **Juv.** Smaller. Dark head, neck; plumage finely barred. **Imm.** Darker face; mixed barred and black-tipped plumes. **Voice** Booming; grunting. Only female drums. **Hab.** Varies widely; arid inland plains, tropical woodland, heathland, coastal dunes; not rainforest. Farmed in some areas.

♀ ♂

Breeding

Tracks

Hard surface

Soft surface

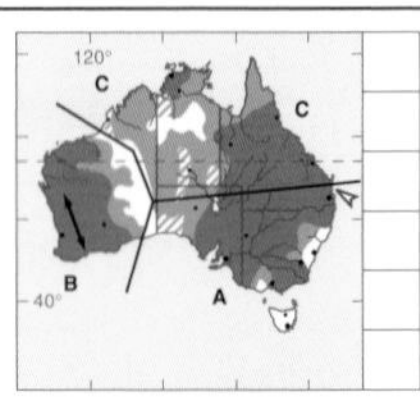

A = Race *novaehollandiae* **E**
B = Race *rothschildi* **E**
C = Race ? *woodwardi* **E**
North–south annual migrant in W Australia.

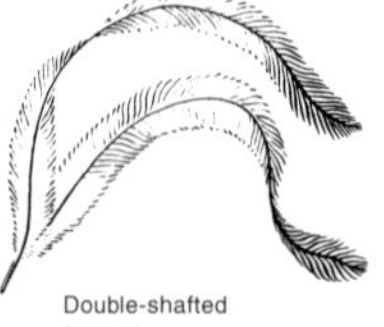

Double-shafted feather

Emu
Ostrich ♂
Ostrich ♀
Ostrich
Hatchling
Emu Imm.
Emu ♀
Emu ♂
Emu Hatchling
Southern Cassowary
Juv.
Southern
Cassowary
♀
Southern
Cassowary
Hatchling
N.DAY

Orange-footed Scrubfowl *Megapodius reinwardt* **C–LC** ◎

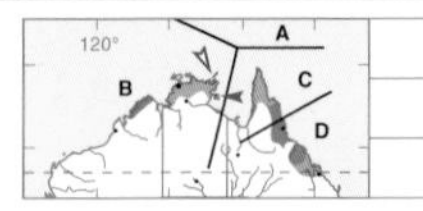

A = Race *duperyii*
B = Race *tumulus* **E**
C = Race *yorki* **E**
D = Race *castanotus* **E**

Pairs often on ground near large nest mound. Bill reddish-brown. Dark chestnut-brown above with short, pointed, brown nuchal crest; prominent orange legs, feet. Neck, underparts, slate-grey. **Size** 42–47 cm. **Voice** Loud cackling, gurgles, thuds; often many at once. **Hab.** Rainforest, monsoon forest, vegetation near water.

Malleefowl *Leipoa ocellata* **UC** ◎ E Vulnerable

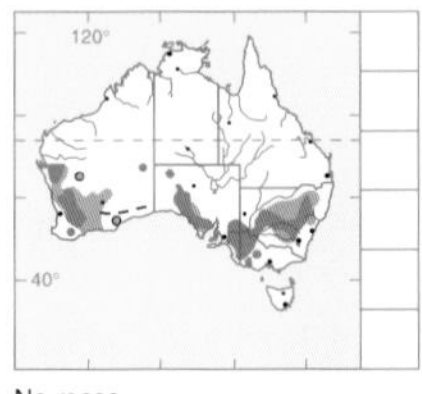

No races

Cryptic plumage. Pairs often at large sand nest mound, tended by male. Bill, lores, grey. Brown iris; white line below; large ear hole. Head, neck, breast, grey. Black stripe over crown to nape. Upperparts barred white; blotched, brown, black and grey. Throat rich cream. Black central streak down to breast. Underparts light fawn. Legs dark grey; large feet. **Size** 60 cm. **Juv.** Dull brown, barred. **Imm.** Dark iris; blue eye-line. **Voice** Boom (territorial); grunt (alarm); soft contact calls. **Hab.** Dry inland scrub, mallee.

Australian Brush-turkey *Alectura lathami* **LC** ◎ E

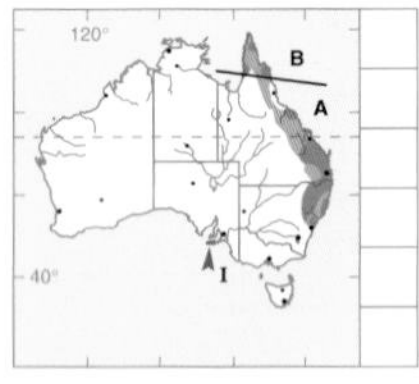

A = Race *lathami* **E**
B = Race *purpureicollis* **E**

Pairs often at large nest mound, tended by male. Strong black bill. Bright red skin on head, neck; sparse black bristles, denser on crown. Large yellow collar/pouch. Body dull black; lightly scalloped below. Black, fowl-like, fan-shaped tail. Legs brown. **M non-br.** Bare parts paler, no pouch. **F/Imm.** Small collar; 'hairy' head and neck. Race *purpureicollis* (B) Purplish-white collar. **Size** 60–70 cm. **Voice** Male booms at mound. Grunts. **Hab.** Closed forest; dense woodland. Gardens, picnic grounds.

Stubble Quail *Coturnix pectoralis* **C** E

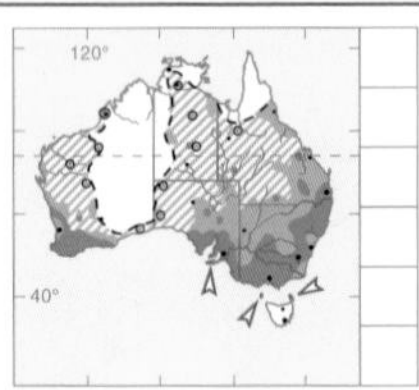

No races

In flight, large brown quail with white streaks. When alighting, wings back, small white patch (alula) appears in 'carpal region'. Bill grey. Eye red. Grey-brown above, with obvious cream streaks; dark brown, buff and grey vermiculations. Throat orange. Black patch on breast. Cream below; strong black streaks on breast, flanks. Legs pale. **F** Throat white. Finely streaked breast. **Size** M 16–20; F 17–20 cm. **Imm.** Throat as adults. **Voice** High whistle 'titch-u-wip'. **Hab.** Grassland, crops, light shrubland.

Brown Quail *Coturnix ypsilophora* **C**

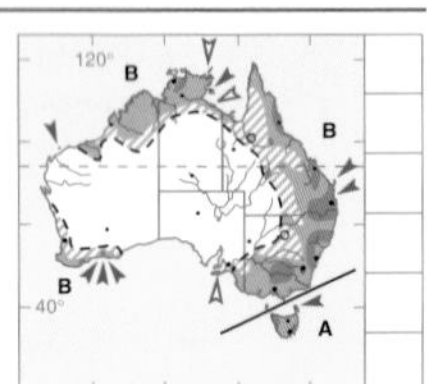

A = Race *ypsilophora* **E**
B = Race *australis* **E**

In flight, rich brown; plumage streaks faint. Race *ypsilophora* (A) 'Swamp Quail' Bill blue-grey. Eye pale yellow. Red-brown; black barring, grey-white streaks. Legs orange-yellow. No rufous birds. Race *australis* (B) Smaller. Eye red to yellow. Very variable chestnut to grey-brown with faint white streaks, black barring. **F** (both races) Heavier black-white pattern, less rufous. Duller brown in flight. **Size** 17–22 cm. **Voice** Rising 'be-quick, be-quick'. **Hab.** Dense grassland, near or at edge of open forest.

King Quail *Coturnix chinensis* **UC**

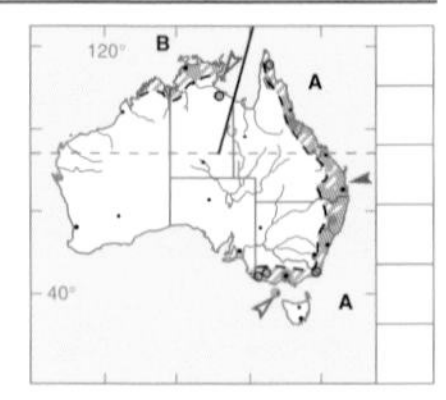

A = Race *victoriae* **E**
B = Race *colletti* **E**

In flight, all-dark, much smaller than Brown Quail. Bill dark. Eye red. Slate-blue sides of face, chest and flanks. Cap, wings, brown with faint white streaks, blackish bars. Black and white lores, chin; white crescent, bordered black, below. Chestnut belly to vent. Legs yellow. **F** Rufous face, white throat. Dark brown, faint streaks. Buff, barred black, below. Eye brown. **Size** 12–15 cm. **Juv.** Show faint adult face patterns. **Voice** 2–3 descending notes. **Hab.** Dense grass, often swampy.

Orange-footed Scrubfowl
Malleefowl
Australian Brush-turkey
King Quail ♀
King Quail ♂
King Quail ♀
Brown Quail ♂
Race *ypsilophora*
Brown Quail
Race *australis*
Brown Quail
Race *australis*
Stubble Quail ♂
Stubble Quail ♀
Stubble Quail ♂

Red Junglefowl (Feral Chicken) *Gallus gallus* Intro. **UC** ◎

Many colour variations. Large red comb, wattles, on head. Long, drooping green tail. **F** Smaller. Smaller comb; short tail. **Size** M 70; F 40–45 cm. **Voice** Male 'cock a doodle-do'. Clucking; soft churring. **Hab.** Introduced to thick scrub on some Great Barrier Reef islands; birds now allegedly removed.

Small, diminishing, feral populations on North West Is., Heron Is. in Capricorn island group, Great Barrier Reef.

Common Pheasant *Phasianus colchicus* Intro. **UC** ◎

Red facial skin, wattles. Blue-green head and neck. White collar. Body reddish-golden, spotted black below. Long barred tail. **F** Brown with buff and blackish mottles. No wattles. **Size** 55–100 cm. **Voice** 'korrk-koh'. Introduced on various islands. Some 'shooting parks' recently established Vic., Tas. **Hab.** Scrub, rank grassland.

Flight

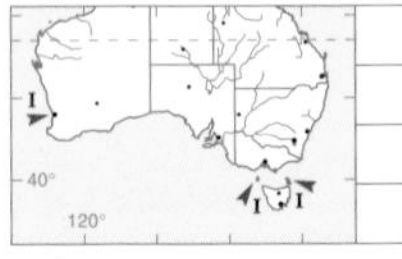

Only feral populations on Bass Strait islands; Rottnest Is. Other records are local escapes.

Indian Peafowl (Peacock) *Pavo cristatus* Intro. **UC** ◎

Blue with fan-shaped crest. Long uppertail coverts ('tail') have green spots with bronze reflections and blue spots surrounded by brown near tips. **F** Body chestnut brown, metallic green sheen. 'Tail' shorter than male. **Size** M 200–225 cm (of which 'tail' 80–160 cm); F Smaller, approx. 90 cm. **Voice** Strident 'kee-ow, kee-ow'. **Hab.** Ornamental gardens, parks, farms, light woodland. Introduced to Rottnest Island (WA).

Courtship display

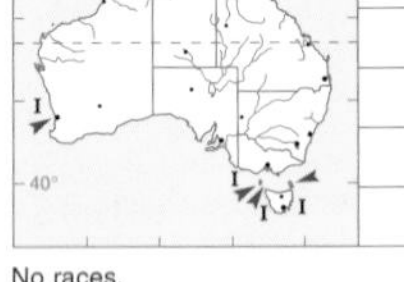

No races.
Feral on King Is., Three Hummock Is. off NW Tas. Minor scattered feral populations elsewhere.

Wild Turkey *Meleagris gallopavo* Intro. **LUC** ◎

Dark brown to blue-black, speckled, slightly iridescent 'bronze' plumage. Naked rear neck purple and white. Fleshy red wattle and throat. **F** Smaller, duller; little head decoration. **Size** M 120–125, F 90–95 cm. **Voice** Coarse 'gobbling'; clucks, yelps. **Hab.** Grassland, farms, pasture; light scrub.

Courtship display

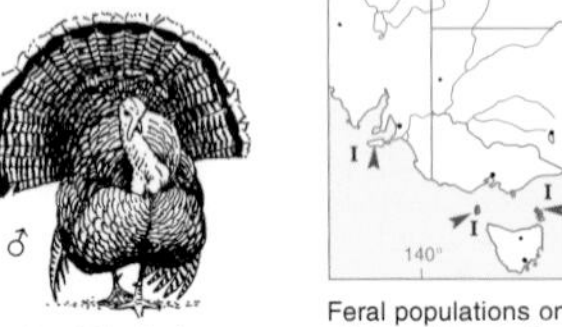

Feral populations on some offshore islands. Domestic escapes elsewhere.

California Quail *Callipepla californica* Intro. **LC** ?◎

Perches on posts. Long black, forward leaning, crest. Black and white striped head. Brown nape, grey upperparts. Blue-black collar finely spotted white. Grey chest. Blackish below, spotted and streaked white. **F** Smaller, no face pattern, duller. **Size** 25 cm. **Voice** 'wit-wit'; 'cu-a-cow'. **Hab.** Grassland; light scrub.

Male perching

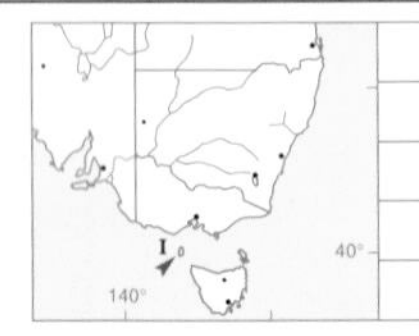

Ex-NZ birds intro. to King Is., Norfolk Is.

Chukar *Alectoris chukar* Intro. ?**R** ?◎

Plump partridge. Runs, flies noisily if pressed, then glides. Grey-white face, throat surrounded by black line. Bill, eye-ring, legs red. Brown-grey above and on chest. Flanks barred black, white, chestnut. **Size** 32–34 cm. **Voice** Loud wails, drummings. **Hab.** Allegedly released for sport in Gulgong district, NSW.

Flight

Unsuccessful attempts at intro. in Aust.; a few scattered records. Not on official Aust. list yet.

Helmeted Guineafowl *Numida meleagris* Intro. **UC** ◎

Plump, upright grey fowl. Small head. Bony red-brown helmet (casque). Grey-black body with fine, white spots. Bluish skin on sides of face, neck. **Size** Approx. 60 cm. **Voice** Often repeated, loud cackling. **Hab.** Feral populations on Heron and other Great Barrier Reef islands, Qld.

Calling

Race *meleagris*
Domestic escapes may persist here and there. Not on official Aust. list yet.

Red Junglefowl ♂
Common Pheasant ♂
Red Junglefowl ♀
Indian Peafowl ♂
Indian Peafowl ♀
Common Pheasant ♀
Helmeted Guineafowl
Wild Turkey ♂
Chukar
California Quail ♀
California Quail ♂
N.DAY

Red-backed Button-quail *Turnix maculosa* **LC** ◎

In flight, wing panel buff-yellow, black spots. Fine, pointed bill. Pale eye. Rufous collar, shoulder. Back grey; barred rufous, black. **F** Richer chestnut face, collar, shoulder. **Size** M 12–14, F 13–16 cm. **Juv.** Dark head. **Imm.** No wing panel, less rufous overall. **Voice** Low 'woop, woop', rising, getting louder. **Hab.** Moist grassland.

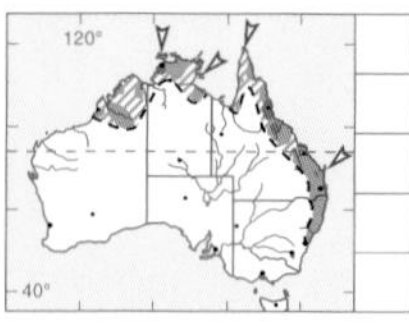

Race *melanota* **E**

Painted Button-quail *Turnix varia* **MC** ♧

Greyish inner wing in flight. Pale eyebrow, face; orange-red eye. Upperparts barred black, rufous, streaked white. Breast 'painted' with buff spots, edged black. **F** Brighter rufous in upperparts; plain chestnut shoulder. **Size** M 17–19, F 18–23 cm. **Juv.** As adult male. Eye pale orange. **Voice** Female, soft 'ooming', faster than call of Common Bronzewing. Slow single notes. **Hab.** Grassy forest, woodland.

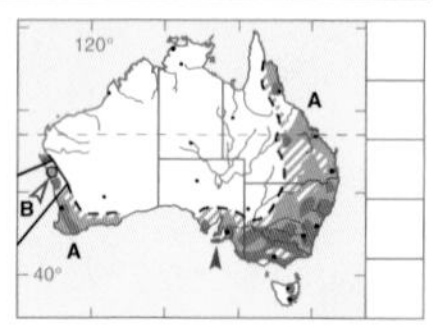

A = Race *varia* **E**
B = Race *scintillans* **E Vulnerable**

Chestnut-backed Button-quail *Turnix castanota* **MC** ◎ E

In flight, plain cinnamon rump, tail. Stout bill. Yellow eye. Back cinnamon, mottled black, streaked white. Breast grey, faintly spotted buff. **F** Brighter rufous, less black. **F non-br.** Head paler. **Size** M 14–16, F 17–20 cm. **Juv.** Face, neck, coarse white spots. **Voice** Soft 'oom'. **Hab.** Grassy woodland.

Most button-quail leave 'saucer-shaped' feeding patches in forest or grassland litter.

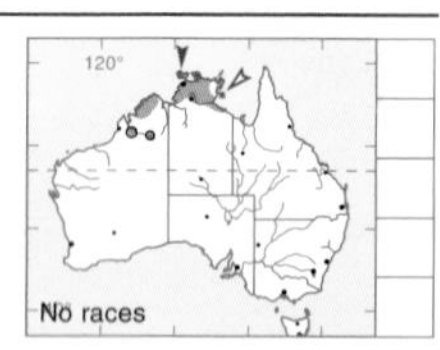

No races

Buff-breasted Button-quail *Turnix olivii* **UC** ◎ E Endangered

Plainer than Painted. In flight, lower back, rump, tail, rufous. Rufous shoulder; breast dull buff. **F** Darker face. Richer rufous; wing panel shows less contrast in flight. **Size** M 18, F 19–27 cm. **Voice** F Deep boom. **Hab.** Unburnt stony rises in grassy woodland.

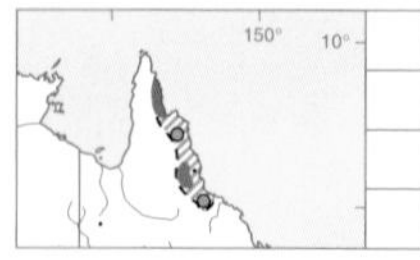

No races

Black-breasted Button-quail
Turnix melanogaster **UC** ◎ E Vulnerable

Feed throughout day. Shy; darkest button-quail. White eye. Back mottled grey-brown. Black breast scalloped bold white. **M** Pale face, belly. **F** Black head, darker body. **Size** M approx. 18, F 18–19.5 cm. **Juv.** Duller brown than male; more black. **Voice** Female drumming. **Hab.** Reduced by clearing. Prefer drier low closed forest, thick understorey, deep litter. Some plantations.

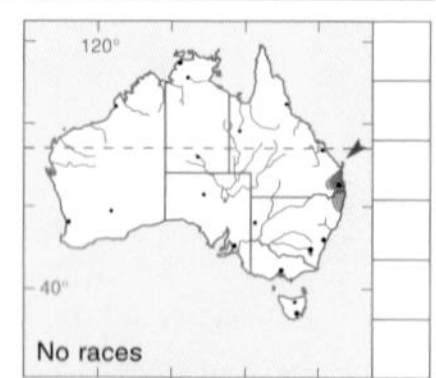

No races

Little Button-quail *Turnix velox* **C** ♧ E

Mainly nocturnal. In flight, rufous wing panel, rump, tail; contrasting white flanks. Pale eye. Bold scalloped 'shoulder'. Back brownish, faintly streaked white. Pink legs, feet. **F** Rufous head, neck, breast, not scalloped. **Size** M 12–14, F 14–16 cm. **Voice** 'woop, woop'. **Hab.** Dry, arid woodland, grassland.

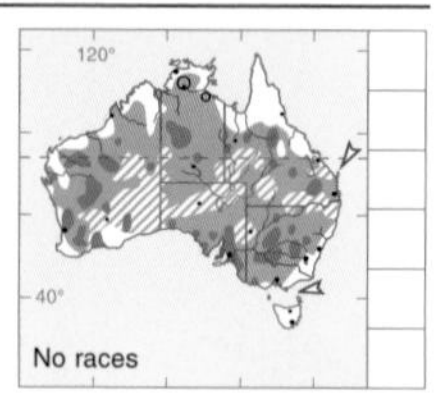

No races

Red-chested Button-quail *Turnix pyrrhothorax* **C** ♧ E

Often associate with Little Button-quails. Like Little Button-quail but darker above. Back grey-brown, black, with buff streaks. Black scallops on side of upper breast. Flanks, undertail coverts, dull orange-buff. **F** Head whiter; body markings finer. Brighter cinnamon throat, breast. No shoulder scallops. **Size** M 12–14, F 14–16 cm. **Juv.** Eyes blue; legs brown-tinged. Dark chest marks persist about one month. **Hab.** Grassland.

The Plains-wanderer, previously positioned on this page, is now known to be a wader, and not related to button-quails as originally thought. See p. 82.

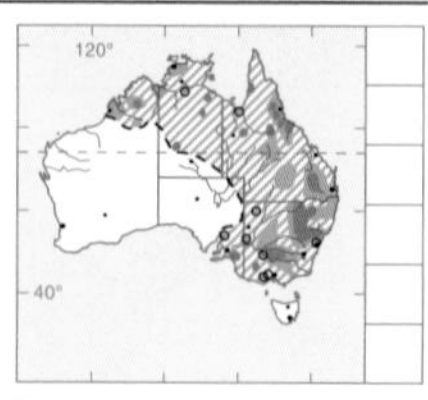

No races

Painted Button-quail ♀
Painted Button-quail ♂
Painted Button-quail ♀
Chestnut-backed Button-quail ♀
Chestnut-backed Button-quail ♀
Black-breasted Button-quail ♂
Buff-breasted Button-quail ♀
Black-breasted Button-quail ♀
Little Button-quail ♂
Little Button-quail ♀
Little Button-quail ♀
Red-chested Button-quail ♀
Red-chested Button-quail ♀
Red-chested Button-quail ♂
Red-backed Button-quail ♀
Red-backed Button-quail ♀
Red-backed Button-quail ♂
♀ Plains-wanderer

King Penguin *Aptenodytes patagonicus* R

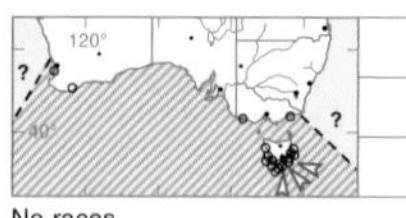
No races

World's second largest penguin. Swims, dives; 'porpoises' for speed. Stands 'tall', to 1 m. Long decurved dark bill; red sides to lower mandible. Black head has greenish gloss. Bright orange ear patch; thin black line joins it to throat and wider shoulder mark. Steel-blue back. Orange patch below black throat. White below. Large dark patch on underflipper tip. Legs, feet, black. **Juv./Imm.** Ear patch white to pale cream. Colour increases with age. **Size** 85–95 cm. **Voice** Braying trumpeting. **Hab.** Coastal sub-Antarctic seas. Some younger birds nomadic, pelagic. Over 25 Tas. and mainland records; tend to be juv./imm. penguins.

Macaroni (Royal) Penguin *Eudyptes chrysolophus* R–UC

Imm. 1–2 yrs: early development of frontal crest

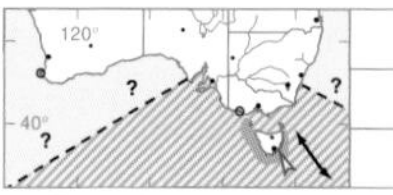
A = Race *chrysolophus* **Vulnerable**
B = Race *schlegeli* **Vulnerable**

Huge red-brown bill. Pink fleshy gape. Black above, white below. Head black to dark grey. Rich gold fibrous-textured frontal crest. Legs, feet, flesh. No Australian mainland records of this black-faced nominate race. Race *schlegeli* (B) 'Royal Penguin' Irregular visitor from Macquarie Island. Fibrous golden frontal crest; white to pale- or medium-grey face, often a yellow bloom around eyes, upper face. Black triangle at underflipper tip. **Size** 65–75 cm. **1st–4th yr** Crest shorter. **Hab.** Oceans, coasts.

Rockhopper Penguin *Eudyptes chrysocome* R–UC

Position: anterior tip of crest/stripe

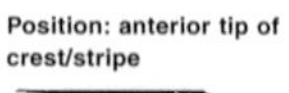

Rockhopper Penguin Ad.

Erect-crested Penguin Ad.

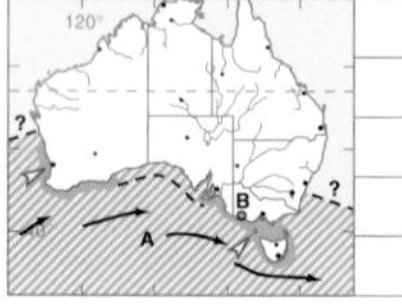
A = Race *moseleyi*
B = Race *filholi* **Vulnerable**

Race *moseleyi* (A) Visits Aust. regularly. Large red-brown bill; dark mandibular skin. Front of long straw-yellow fibrous lateral eye-stripe/crest exactly bisects line from gape angle to culmen base (diagnostic for all Rockhoppers). Dull black cheeks. Black above; white below. Heavy black marking on underflipper tip. **Size** 45–48 cm. **1st yr** Dark bill, horn-tipped. Undeveloped eye-stripe hidden above centre of eye. Chin whitish. Check Little Penguin. **Imm./Sub. ad.** Better developed crests. Some moult in WA; only one record SE Aust. No confirmed records of full adult *moseleyi* in Aust. Race *filholi* (B) White mandibular skin; tiny black underflipper tip mark. Breeds on Aust. sub-Antarctic islands; only one confirmed Aust. record (Portland, Vic., 1936).

Fiordland Penguin *Eudyptes pachyrhynchus* R–UC

Position: anterior tip of crest/stripe

Fiordland Penguin Ad.

Snares Penguin Ad.

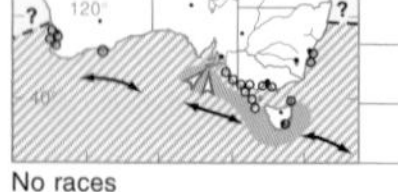
No races

Red-brown bill; brown mandibular skin. Crown, nape, back, bluish. Position of each end of silky lateral eye-stripe/crest is diagnostic. Tip is right into frons between culmen and latericorn. Behind crown, crest spreads toward centre without meeting in midline. White-streaked, dull blackish cheeks. **Size** 55 cm. **1st year–Imm.** Eye-stripe white; poorly defined; chin whitish. **Hab.** Oceans, coastal seas. Visitor from southern New Zealand.

Little Penguin *Eudyptula minor* LA–C

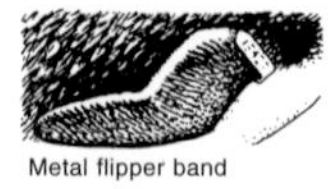
Metal flipper band

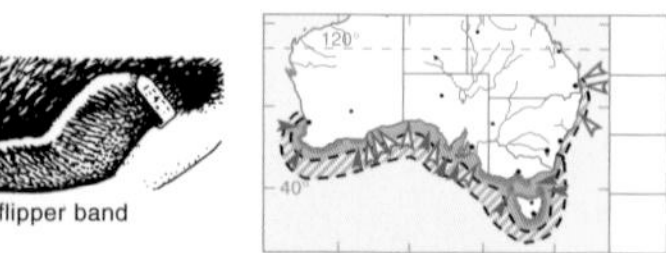
Race *novaehollandiae*

Smallest penguin. Swims on surface; 'porpoises'. Bill leaden-black. Greyish cheeks. Dark blue above; whitish about tail base. Tail bluish, black shafts. White trailing flipper edge. Underflipper white; tiny grey smudge at tip. Flesh legs, feet. **Size** 40–45 cm. **1st yr** Bill blackish. Chin, throat greyish. **Voice** Yapping contact calls. **Hab.** Feeds coastal seas, bays. Breeding: burrows on vegetated sand dunes; crevices in rocky cliff-bases, breakwaters.

Gentoo Penguin *Pygoscelis papua*, **Chinstrap Penguin** *Pygoscelis antarctica*, **Adelie Penguin** *Pygoscelis adeliae*, **Magellanic Penguin** *Spheniscus magellanicus*, **Erect-crested Penguin** *Eudyptes sclateri*, **Snares Penguin** *Eudyptes robustus* see **Vagrant Bird Bulletin**, pp. 282, 283.

Chinstrap Penguin
Magellanic Penguin
Snares Penguin
Gentoo Penguin
Adelie Penguin
Ad.
King Penguin
Imm.
Erect-crested Penguin
'Royal Penguin'
E. chrysolophus
Race schlegeli
Rockhopper Penguin
1st yr
Race moseleyi
Rockhopper Penguin
Race moseleyi
Fiordland Penguin
Moulting
Fiordland Penguin
Imm.
Little Penguin
Hatchling
Little Penguin

Wandering Albatross *Diomedea exulans* **LA–MC** ○ Endangered

Most common 'great albatross' in Australian seas. 'Domed' crown, 'humped' back, give 'angular' appearance in flight. Identify from Royal Albatross, Shy Albatross (similar underwing pattern); smaller Australasian Gannet. Races *exulans* (A), *chionoptera* (B), treated together in this account. Seven different plumage stages recognised over a lifetime – juv. to old mature adult (5 stages in diagram). Race *chionoptera* considered most common in Australian seas. Plumage varies widely; amount of white developed by an individual depends on its sex, age, and population characteristics at its breeding island. Whitens over very many years. Powerful pink bill, tipped yellow. White above and below, including crown. Breast has varying densities of fine black vermiculation. Dorsal wing white; outer wing, trailing edge, black. Tail white; some have remnant black tips. Underwing white, extreme tip always black; underwing pattern constant, little variation with sex or age. Legs, webbed feet, pale flesh. Race *gibsoni* (C) 'Gibson's Albatross' Less white in maturity; remaining always partly brownish. **F** Always has brown speckles or striations on crown. **Size** 110–135 cm; wingspan 250–350 cm. **Juv.** Completely chocolate-brown except for white face; underwing like adult. Brown slowly replaced by white. A dark to pale brown collar and wide breast band are carried into early imm. plumages. Tail black. **Imm.** Varies widely (see diagrams). Upperparts with varying black chequered back patterns. Upperwing increasingly white with age, spreading outward from body along centre of wings, typically beginning with white patches. Brown collar, breast bands, fade over several years. Tail white, black terminal band. **Voice** Croaking, guttural cackles; bill clappering. **Hab.** Oceanic, coastal seas; only rarely enters bays. Habitually follows ships, fishing boats.

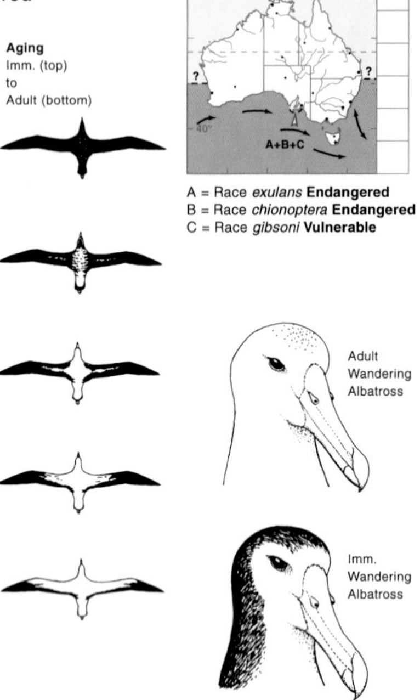

A = Race *exulans* **Endangered**
B = Race *chionoptera* **Endangered**
C = Race *gibsoni* **Vulnerable**

Royal Albatross *Diomedea epomophora* **UC** ○ Endangered

Attends fishing boats; less inclined to follow ships. More 'rounded', larger-billed, less 'angular' in flight than Wandering. Identify from Wandering and much smaller Australasian Gannet. Check underwing of White-capped Albatross, also backs of all mollymawks for race *sanfordi*. Five different plumage stages recognised (4 in diagram). Powerful bill flesh-coloured, less pink than Wandering, usually longer. Diagnostic black cutting edge along upper bill visible at close range. Crown less domed, forehead gently sloped. Race *epomophora* (A) 'Southern Royal Albatross' Wholly white above and below (no vermiculation). White develops along leading edge of upper wing only. Where white merges with black tips and along trailing edge, it appears as dusting or speckling, not chequered as in Wandering. Underwing like Wandering Albatross. Tail wholly white. Old adults resemble the whitest 'Wanderers'. Legs, feet, fleshy-white. Race *sanfordi* (B) 'Northern Royal Albatross' Smaller. Upperwing wholly black; 'pincer'-like extensions on to the back formed by black tips to long scapular feathers. Underwing has diagnostic broad black mark along leading outer wing edge to the carpal. **Size** 107–122 cm; wingspan 305–350 cm. **Juv.** Both races generally like adult *sanfordi* but few black flecks on crown, back, rump. Tail has narrow sub-terminal band or spots. **Imm.** Both races like *sanfordi* but *epomophora* has sprinkling of white along leading edge of inner upperwing. **Voice** Coarse croaking, guttural sound; bill clappering. **Hab.** Oceanic, more so than Wandering Albatross.

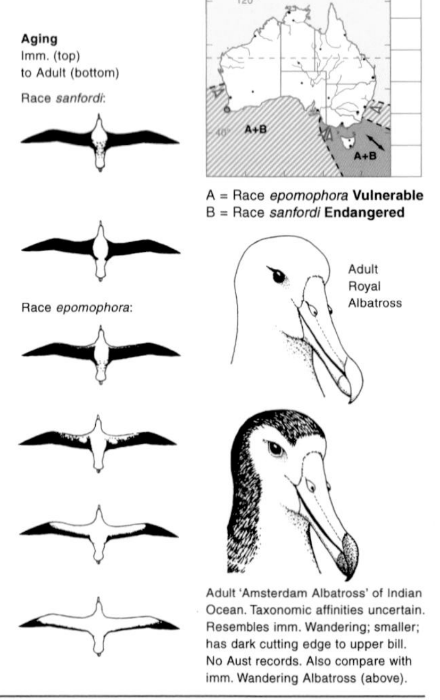

A = Race *epomophora* **Vulnerable**
B = Race *sanfordi* **Endangered**

Adult 'Amsterdam Albatross' of Indian Ocean. Taxonomic affinities uncertain. Resembles imm. Wandering; smaller; has dark cutting edge to upper bill. No Aust records. Also compare with imm. Wandering Albatross (above).

Royal Albatross Juv. Race epomophora
Royal Albatross Race sanfordi
Royal Albatross Race epomophora
Wandering Albatross
Wandering Albatross Imm.
Wandering Albatross Imm.
Wandering Albatross Juv.
Royal Albatross Ad. Race epomophora
Royal Albatross Ad. Race sanfordi
Wandering Albatross Juv.
Wandering Albatross Imm.
Wandering Albatross Ad.
Wandering Albatross Juv.
Royal Albatross Race epomophora
Wandering Albatross Imm.
Royal Albatross Juv. Race sanfordi
N. DAY.

Black-browed Albatross *Diomedea (Thalassarche) melanophris* LA–MC Endangered

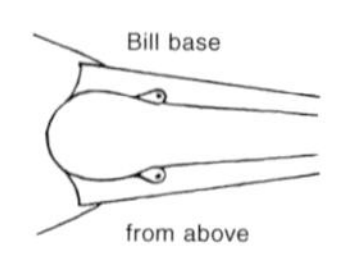

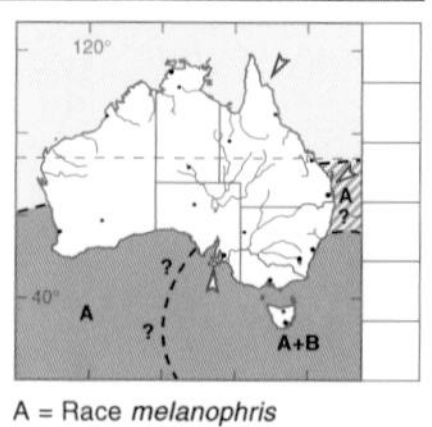

A = Race *melanophris* **Endangered**
B = Race *impavida* **Vulnerable**

Bill yellow-orange, pink tip. Head, neck, rump, underparts, white. Thin black eye-brow. Iris black. Mantle, upperwing, tail, black. Underwing white; broad black leading edge (one-third of wing breadth), wider at 'elbow' and past the carpal joint. Tip, trailing edge, black. Legs flesh-white. Race *impavida* (B) 'Campbell Albatross' As Black-browed adult; pale honey-coloured iris; eyebrow blacker. Black streaks on inner, outer, leading underwing edge. **Size** 80–95 cm; wingspan 210–250 cm. **Juv./Imm.** Bill black-brown, or base dull yellow, black tip. Grey collar, crown. Underwing all-dark, pale grey centre, white-centred with age. Race *impavida* As juv. *melanophris* but iris dark honey. **Sub-ad.** Bill browner, black tip (both races). Underwing blacker. **Hab.** Oceanic, coastal, wide bays; follows ships.

Buller's Albatross *Diomedea (Thalassarche) bulleri* UC Vulnerable

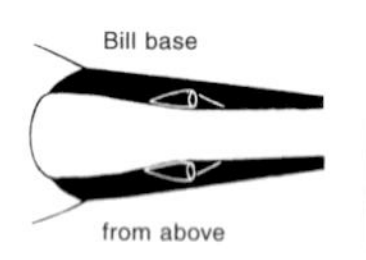

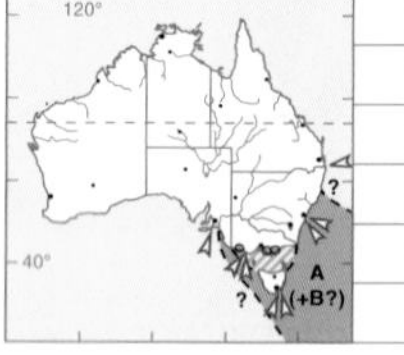

A = Race *bulleri* **Vulnerable**
B = Race *platei* **Vulnerable**

Black bill like Grey-headed Albatross, but yellow broader along top ridge of bill (culmen). Hood dark grey with silver-white cap. Black patch before, above, eye. Neck, chin, throat, grey. Tail grey-black. Underwing has wider black leading edge than Black-browed, Grey-headed; narrower trailing edge. Black primaries with white bases, secondaries black. Feet flesh-pink. Race *platei* (B) 'Pacific Albatross' Larger bill; cap silver-grey; hood, feet, darker. **Size** 76–81 cm; wingspan 205–213 cm. **Juv.** Bill dark horn-brown, darker on sides, tip. **Hab.** Oceanic, coastal. Follows shipping. Race *bulleri* visits Australian seas; *platei* less often.

Grey-headed Albatross *Diomedea (Thalassarche) chrysostoma* UC Vulnerable

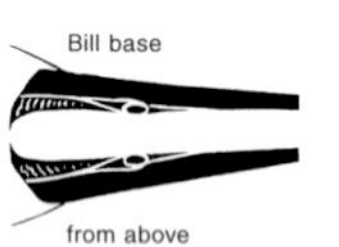

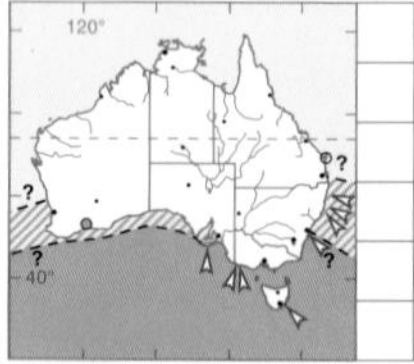

No races

At sea, identify from sub-ad. Black-browed by black (not pale) bill, wider white centre in black-edged underwing. Yellow along top ridge of black bill; small pink mark on bill tip. Yellow or pink also on basal edge of lower bill to halfway along its length. Even pearl-grey hood, slightly paler cap. Black eye-ring. Otherwise as Black-browed adult, almost similar underwing. Flesh legs, feet. **Size** 70–85 cm; wingspan 180–205 cm. **Juv.** Bill black, very faint colour areas; tip black. Head dark grey; may have white throat, cheeks. Underwing dark, pale grey in centre. **Imm./Sub-ad.** As adult; bill duller. Head varies from white with grey nape, to grey with white cheeks, front, crown. Underwing has broad black edges, grey on leading edge nearer body. **Hab.** Oceanic.

An interim taxonomy for all albatrosses except the 'Sooties' has been proposed, and partly introduced. Not adopted in this book yet.

Yellow-nosed Albatross *Diomedea (Thalassarche) chlororhynchos* MC Vulnerable

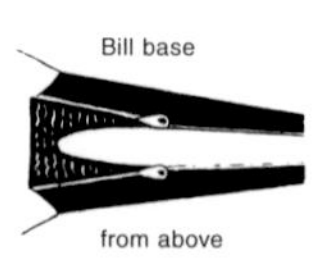

Race *bassi*

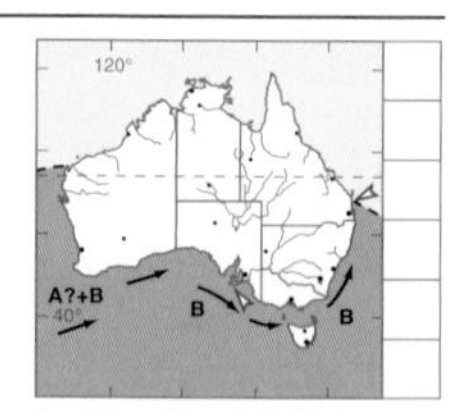

A = Race *chlororhynchos* **Vulnerable**
B = Race *bassi* **Vulnerable**

Small white mollymawk with warm black-brown upper wing. Race *chlororhynchos* (A) Originating in Atlantic Ocean, may occur off SW Australia but possibly only as vagrant. Bill long, slender, black, orange to pink-tipped. Thin orange skin vertically at base of bill; yellow only on culmen ridge. Round culmen base (from above). Grey hood, white forecrown; large blackish triangle before eye. Underwing as Buller's Albatross but primaries all black. Slightly narrower black along leading edge of underwing. Feet whitish blue-grey. Indian Ocean race *bassi* (B) Smallest mollymawk. As *chlororhynchos* but pointed culmen base (from above). Head white, may have grey cheeks. Soft pale grey about dark brown eye. **Size** 75 cm; wingspan 200 cm. **Juv.** Black bill, or a soft horn-colour on culmen. Head white. Less grey about eye. Pale grey nape. **Hab.** Oceanic. Race *bassi* usual in Aust. seas.

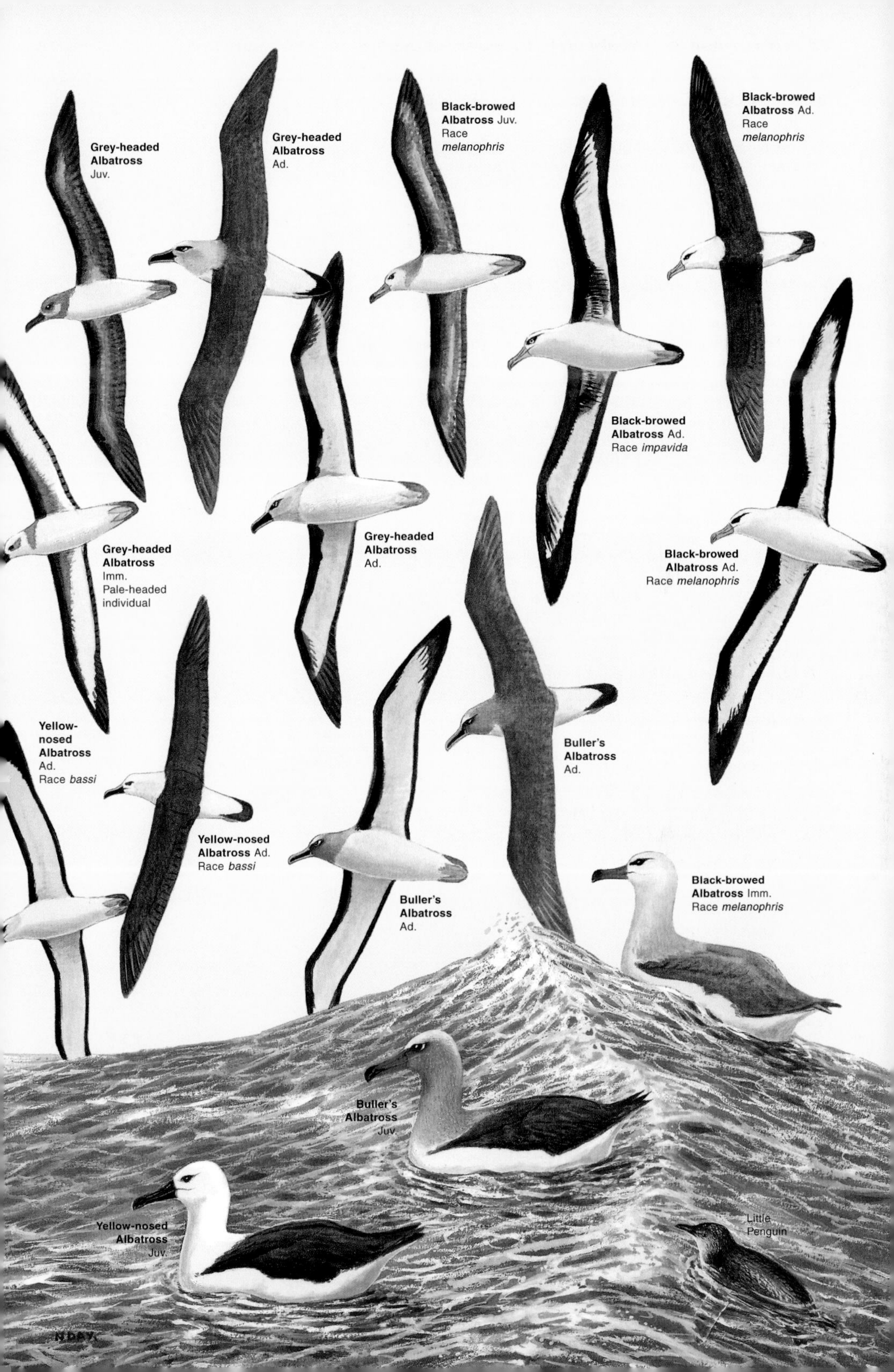
Grey-headed Albatross Juv.
Grey-headed Albatross Ad.
Black-browed Albatross Juv. Race melanophris
Black-browed Albatross Ad. Race melanophris
Black-browed Albatross Ad. Race impavida
Grey-headed Albatross Imm. Pale-headed individual
Grey-headed Albatross Ad.
Black-browed Albatross Ad. Race melanophris
Yellow-nosed Albatross Ad. Race bassi
Yellow-nosed Albatross Ad. Race bassi
Buller's Albatross Ad.
Buller's Albatross Ad.
Black-browed Albatross Imm. Race melanophris
Buller's Albatross Juv.
Yellow-nosed Albatross Juv.
Little Penguin
N DAY

Shy Albatross *Diomedea (Thalassarche) cauta* LA–C ○ Vulnerable

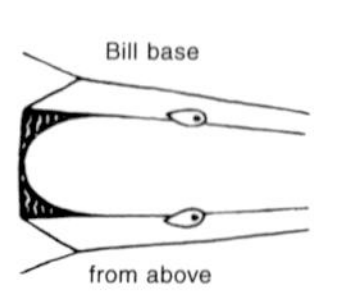

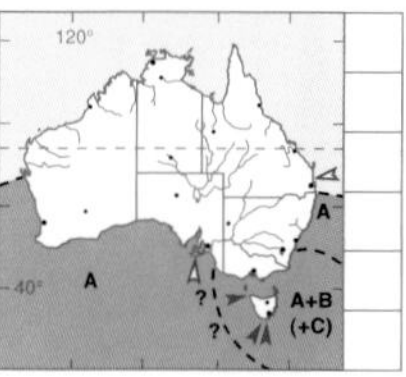

A = Race *cauta* **Vulnerable**
B = Race *salvini* **Vulnerable**
C = Race *eremita* **Endangered**
In Australian seas, race *cauta* is common, breeds; *salvini* uncommon; *eremita* a few records only.

Largest mollymawk. Three races.
Race *cauta* (A) Bill grey on sides, with yellow tinge and tips. Cap white. Thin black line from eye to bill. Head either white, grey-cheeked or grey-hooded, cut off by a white collar. Mantle grey. Wings, tail, grey-black. Rump, underparts, underwing, white except for thin black borders (check Wandering Albatross). Primaries white at base, black outer half. Small, black triangle at leading base of wing. Feet pale blue-grey.
Size 90–100 cm; wingspan 212–256 cm. **Juv.** *cauta* Head moults progressively from all-grey with white cheeks, frons and cap, to a collared appearance. Bill grey, whole tip black. Underwing with slightly broader borders than adult. Primaries about two-thirds black. **Imm.** *cauta* Bill greyer, small black spot at tip. Head white, pale grey, or with a strong grey collar. In distance, check juv. Black-browed, Grey-headed Albatrosses.
Race *salvini* (B) 'Salvin's Albatross' Like *cauta* but yellower bill; small black spot on lower tip. Head, neck, grey, forming a hood. Cap white. Underwing like *cauta* but primaries all black; only faint ghosting of white at their bases. **Size** Approx. 95 cm.
Juv. *salvini* Bill like juv. of *cauta*. Head similar to *cauta*, normally greyer. Sometimes only pale frons, lores and throat.
Imm. Collar like *cauta*; underwing like adult *salvini*.
Race *eremita* (C) 'Chatham Island Albatross' Smallest race. Bill bright yellow; small black spot on lower tip. Head all leaden-grey; cap slightly paler. Underwing like *salvini*. Feet bright orange-pink. **Size** Approx. 90 cm. **Juv.** *eremita* Bill olive-brown, with black tip. Plumage like its adult; grey sometimes extends over upper breast.
Hab. (all races) Oceanic, coastal. Attends trawlers.

Sooty Albatross *Phoebetria fusca* UC ○ Vulnerable

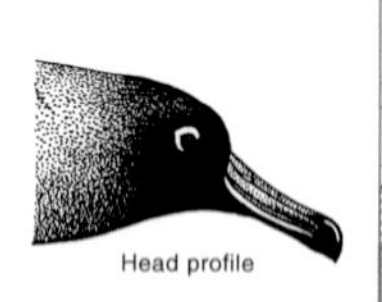

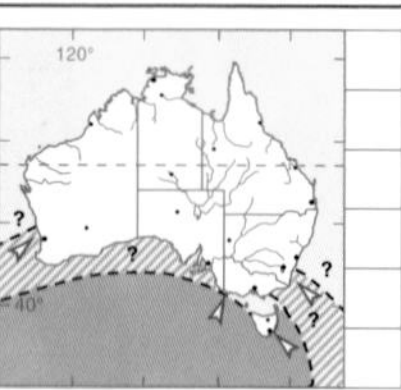

No races
More commonly recorded off SW Australia.

Graceful gliding flight on long wings, rises, falls, more than most other albatrosses. Identify from Light-mantled Sooty Albatross; giant-petrels; large dark procellariiform petrels (p. 40). Slightly smaller, more slender, than Light-mantled Sooty Albatross. Looks all-dark at sea. Warm chocolate brown; paler across wings, mantle (plate may show head and mask as too prominent). Incomplete eye-ring white, black at front. Long bill has straight upper surface; black with cream to orange sulcus (line along lower bill side). Pale primary shafts near wing tip. Tail long, wedge-shaped or pointed. Legs, feet, pale grey with flesh tones. **Size** 84–89 cm; wingspan 203 cm. **Juv.** Like adult but grey sulcus, grey eye-ring, buffy 'scales' may show across neck, collar, mantle, breast; primary shafts may be dark. **Hab.** Oceanic.

Light-mantled Sooty Albatross *Phoebetria palpebrata* UC ○ Vulnerable

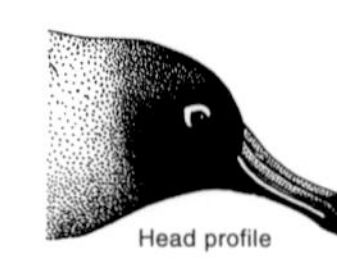

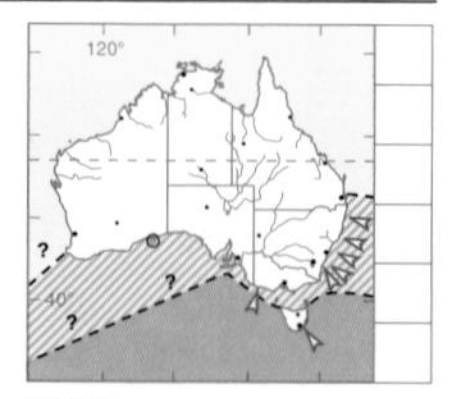

No races
More commonly recorded off SE Australia.

Flight like Sooty Albatross. Slightly larger, 'deeper-chested', than Sooty Albatross but has a frosty grey mantle, belly and rump contrasting with a black face and wings. Head shape is 'rounder' than Sooty. Bill is 'more shapely', with concave upper surface, and a blue line (sulcus). Tip of bill rounded, prominent. Incomplete eye-ring white, black at front. Legs, feet, pale grey with flesh tones. **Size** 80–90 cm; wingspan 180–220 cm.
Juv. Like adult but has buffy scales on back, neck and breast.
Voice Normally silent at sea. Wailing 'sky-calls' about nest sites e.g. Macquarie Island. **Hab.** Oceanic.

Laysan Albatross *Diomedea immutabilis* see **Vagrant Bird Bulletin** p. 286.

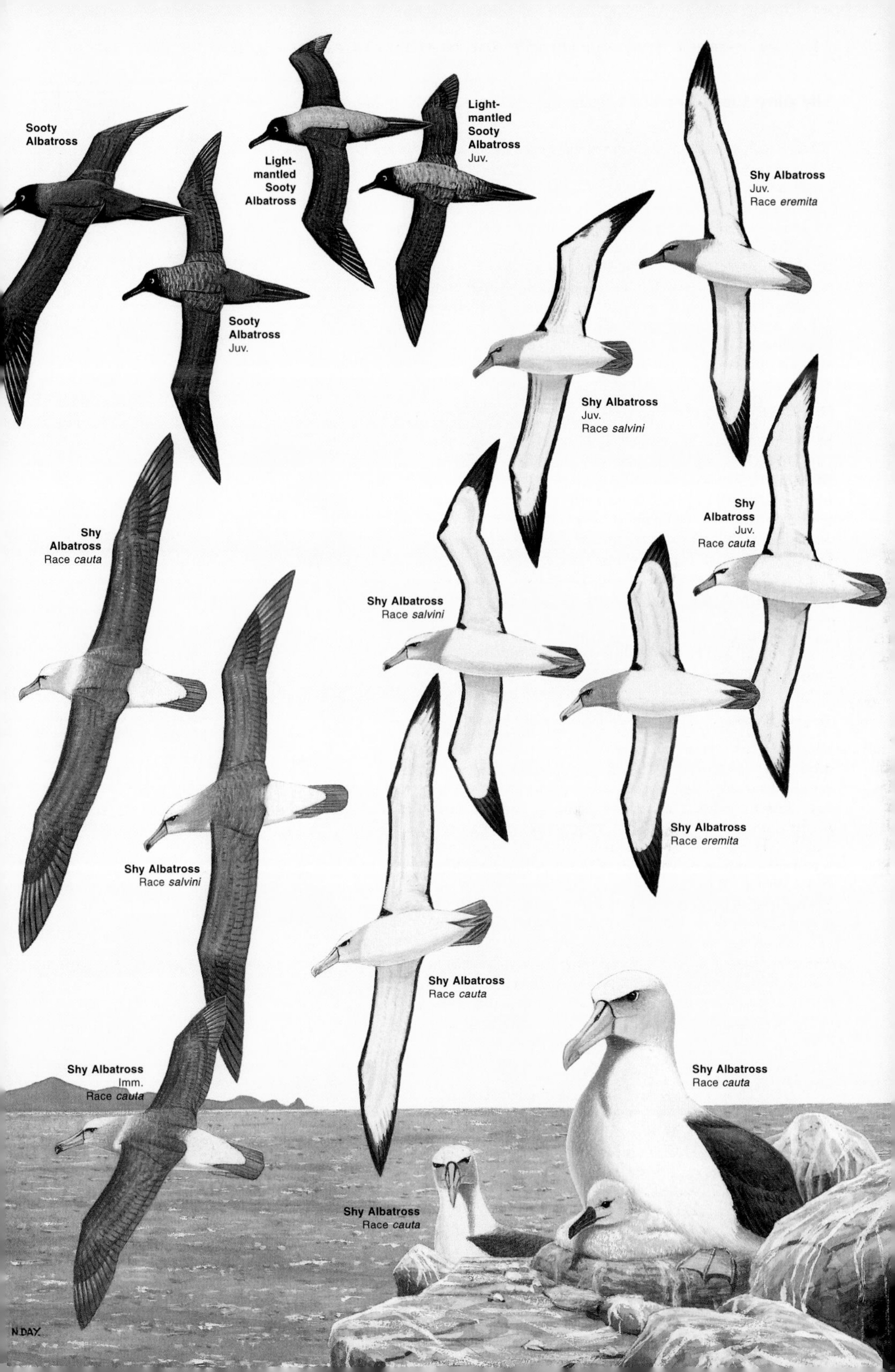

Sooty Albatross
Light-mantled Sooty Albatross
Light-mantled Sooty Albatross Juv.
Sooty Albatross Juv.
Shy Albatross Juv. Race *eremita*
Shy Albatross Juv. Race *salvini*
Shy Albatross Race *cauta*
Shy Albatross Juv. Race *cauta*
Shy Albatross Race *salvini*
Shy Albatross Race *eremita*
Shy Albatross Race *salvini*
Shy Albatross Race *cauta*
Shy Albatross Race *cauta*
Shy Albatross Imm. Race *cauta*
Shy Albatross Race *cauta*
N.DAY.

Southern Giant-Petrel *Macronectes giganteus* **MC** Vulnerable

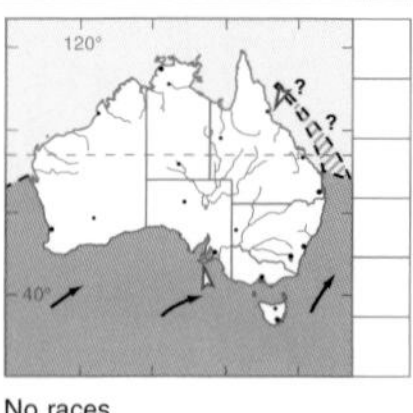

No races

'Hump-backed' appearance in flight. Identify from Sooty Albatross by short, less pointed tail, pale bill; Wandering Albatross juv. is larger, has white underwing. An Albatross-sized petrel with a bulbous bill. **Dark morph** (adults rare in Australian seas; juv. common) Bill horn, tipped pale green. Nostrils extend far along bill. Brown or grey eyes. Dark brown body. White head. White mottling down neck and leading edge of wing to carpal. Tail medium length with a shallow wedge. Feet fleshy-grey. **White morph** Bill similar. Plumage white, a few large black spots on body, wings. **Juv./Imm.** All dark; face whitens with age. Sometimes green tip on bill duller. **Size** 85–100 cm; wingspan 150–210 cm. **Hab.** Oceans, bays. Follows ships, scavenges.

Northern Giant-Petrel *Macronectes halli* **MC** Vulnerable

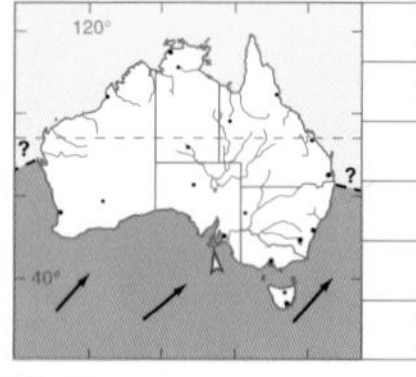

No races

'Hump-backed' appearance in flight. Identical to Southern Giant-Petrel except bill tipped reddish-brown. Iris grey or grey-brown. White about bill and face, mottled at borders. Eye, throat, rest of head dark. No white on leading edge of wing. No white morph. **Juv.** All dark. Bill often duller red tip than adult. **Size** 80–95 cm; wingspan 150–210 cm. **Hab.** Oceans, bays. Follows ships, scavenges.

Southern Fulmar *Fulmarus glacialoides* **UC**

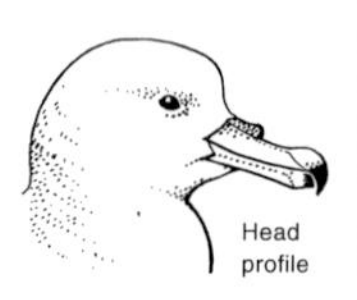

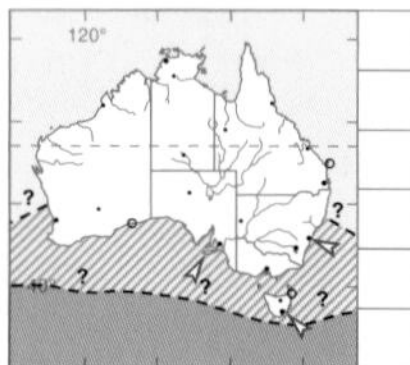

No races

Flight stiff-winged; manoeuvrable; quick flapping, then gliding. Pink bill with black tip and blue nostrils. Eye dark. Face, underparts, white. Silver-grey from behind eye to tail. Primaries and their coverts black; large white primary patch; covert bases grey. Secondaries black. Underwing white; edge of primaries to carpal black, thin grey trailing edge. Feet blue, webs pink. **Size** 45–50 cm. **Hab.** Oceans. Occasional storm 'wrecks'; varying numbers reach Australia. Visits ships, trawlers, whalers; rarely follows for long.

Cape Petrel *Daption capense* **C–UC**

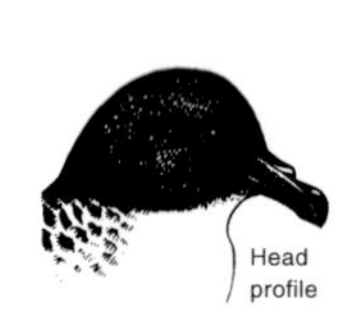

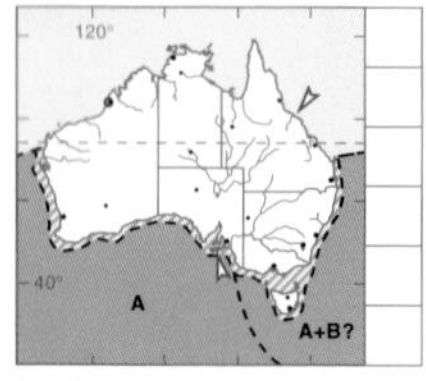

A = Race *capense*
B = Race *australe*

Flight stiff-winged; quick fluttering, flapping, and then gliding. Black and white petrel. Bill, legs, feet, black. Race *capense* Blackish head, hind neck, upper back. Lower back and rump white, spotted black. Upperwing black with two large separate white patches, one at primary bases, the other at secondary bases. Tail black. Throat white, mottled black. Underwing white, edged black. Underparts white. Race *australe* (B) (NZ) Black is more extensive on back, wings. White dorsal wing spots smaller. Races not easy to identify at sea; intermediates occur. **Size** 35–45 cm. **Hab.** Oceans, bays, follows shipping.

Snow Petrel *Pagodroma nivea*

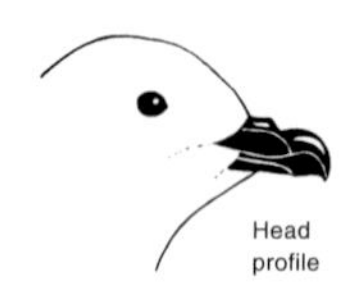

A = Race *nivea*
B = Race *confusa*

Flight erratic, gliding, fluttering. All white. Short stout black bill. Eye, legs, feet, black. **Size** 30–40 cm. **Hab.** Antarctic oceans. Despite early claims, no confirmed records in local Aust. seas.

Note May be removed from Field Guide in the future.

Antarctic Petrel *Thalassoica antarctica*, **Juan Fernandez Petrel** *Pterodroma externa*, **Barau's Petrel** *Pterodroma baraui*, **Bulwer's Petrel** *Bulweria bulwerii*, **Jouanin's Petrel** *Bulweria fallax* see **Vagrant Bird Bulletin** p. 284, 285.

Southern Fulmar
Antarctic Petrel
Southern Giant-Petrel
Juv.
Cape Petrel
Snow Petrel
Cape Petrel
Race *australe*
Cape Petrel
Race *capense*
Southern Giant-Petrel
White morph
Southern Giant-Petrel
Dark morph
Northern Giant-Petrel
Juv.
Northern Giant-Petrel
Southern Fulmar
Cape Petrel
N.K.T. Day

Great-winged Petrel *Pterodroma macroptera* **LA–C**

Attends trawlers. Wheeling flight, wings held forward. All dark brown. Race *macroptera* (A) Dark face. Race *gouldi* (B) Paler face. **Size** 38–43 cm; wingspan 97–102 cm. **Hab.** Oceanic.

A = Race *macroptera*
B = Race *gouldi*

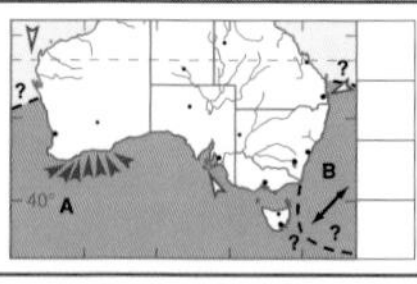

White-headed Petrel *Pterodroma lessonii* **UC**

Nears ships; stays briefly. Whitish head, black eye-line. Faint grey collar. Grey above; white below. Dark underwing; white basal leading edge. **Size** 43 cm. **Hab.** Pelagic; cold southern seas.

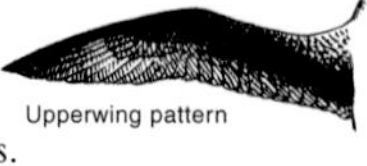
Upperwing pattern

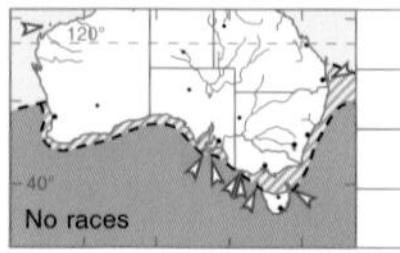

Providence Petrel *Pterodroma solandri* **LA** Vulnerable

Check other dark petrels; paler than Great-winged race *gouldi*. Black bill. Brown-grey head; pale about face; 'hooded'. Grey body. White primary bases separated from black-tipped white greater coverts. Tail a wedge. **Size** 40 cm. **Hab.** Tropical seas.

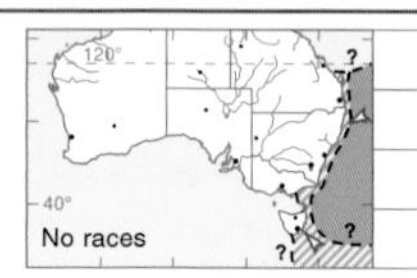

Kermadec Petrel *Pterodroma neglecta* **R** Vulnerable

Avoids ships. **Dark morph** All dark underwing like Providence, with white basal leading edge. **Light morph** White head and body. **Intermed. morph** Variable. **Size** 38 cm. **Hab.** Oceanic.

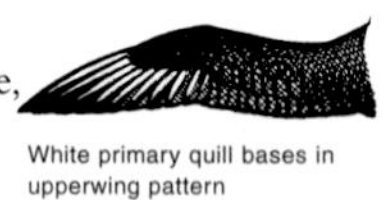
White primary quill bases in upperwing pattern

Herald Petrel *Pterodroma heraldica* **V–UC** Vulnerable

P. heraldica 'light morph' only. Upperwing dark. More white underwing stripe than Kermadec; smaller. 'Dark morph' now considered new species *P. atrata*. **Size** 34–39 cm. **Hab.** Oceanic.

Now full species. Prior race heraldica *of* P. arminjoniana.

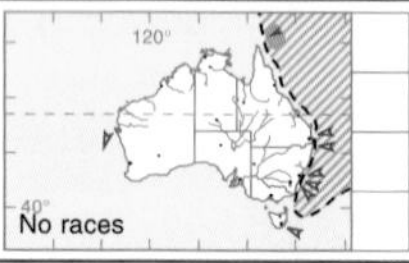

Tahiti Petrel *Pseudobulweria rostrata* **UC**

Flight low over sea, wingtips upturned, unlike other small *Pterodroma* petrels. 'Bulbous' black bill. Uniform brown. White breast, belly, undertail coverts. **Size** 38–40 cm. **Hab.** Oceanic.

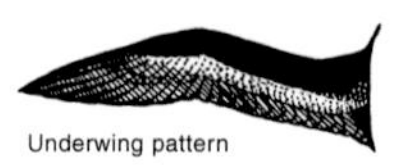
Underwing pattern

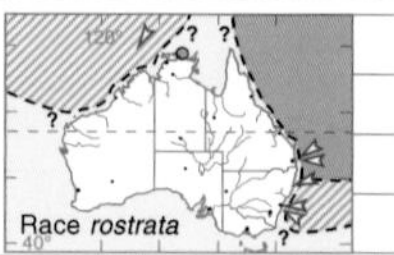

Kerguelen Petrel *Lugensa brevirostris* **UC**

Flight drifting, wing-flicking. 'Large' head. Dark grey. Dark 'M' on underwing; whitish inner edge. **Size** 33–36 cm. **Hab.** Oceanic.

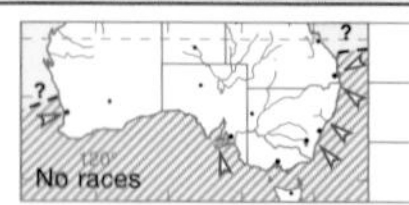

Soft-plumaged Petrel *Pterodroma mollis* **UC** Vulnerable

Flight typical of most *Pterodroma*. Like White-headed Petrel but much smaller; darker head, rump, tail. Black bill. Grey collar, breast band. Dark 'M' above. **Size** 32–37 cm. **Hab.** Oceanic.

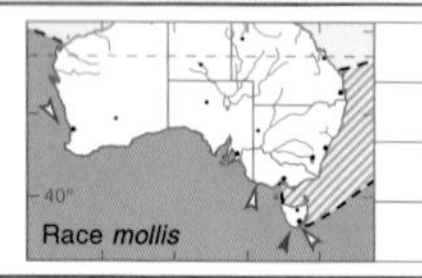

Mottled Petrel *Pterodroma inexpectata* **UC**

Underwing as Gould's, stronger central line; tips, black edges, narrower. White below; grey belly. Underwing white. **Size** 35 cm. **Hab.** Oceanic. Occasional beach-washed birds.

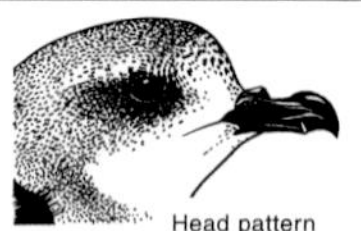
Head pattern

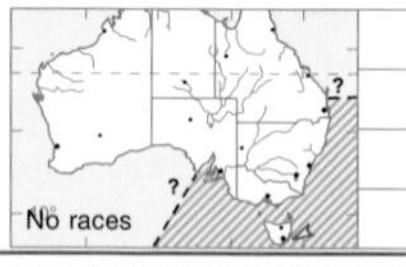

Gould's Petrel *Pterodroma leucoptera* **R** Br. E Vulnerable

Dark head, half collar. Pale below. Underwing white; tip, trailing edges, leading edge, black; thin black line into underwing centre (check Mottled, Black-winged). **Size** 30 cm. **Hab.** Oceanic.

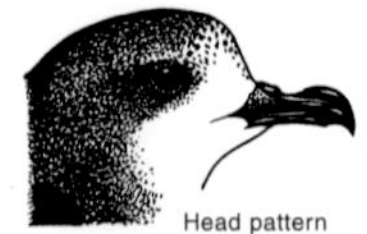
Head pattern

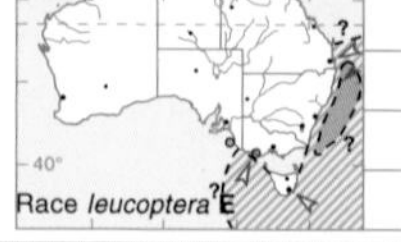

Black-winged Petrel *Pterodroma nigripennis* **LC**

Underwing as Gould's, all black edges, central line, broader. Head pale grey, black ear patch. Check Mottled, Cook's, White-necked. **Size** 28–30 cm. **Hab.** Oceanic.

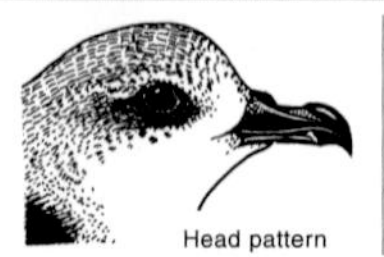
Head pattern

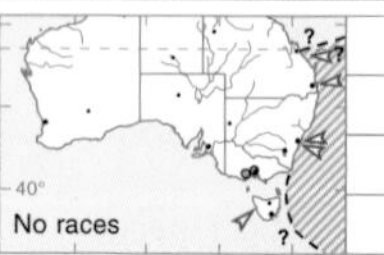

Providence Petrel
Great-winged Petrel
Race *macroptera*
Soft-plumaged Petrel
Kerguelen Petrel
Providence Petrel
Herald Petrel
Formerly 'Light morph'
Great-winged Petrel
Race *gouldi*
Soft-plumaged Petrel
White-necked Petrel
White-headed Petrel
P. atrata
Formerly Herald Petrel
'Dark morph'
Mottled Petrel
Black-winged Petrel
Black-winged Petrel
Mottled Petrel
Kermadec Petrel
Light morph
Kermadec Petrel
Light morph
Kermadec Petrel
Dark morph
Tahiti Petrel
Gould's Petrel
Gould's Petrel
N. Day

Cook's Petrel *Pterodroma cookii* **R**

Pale grey from cap to mantle. Dark upperwings. Underparts, underwing white; narrow black line along trailing edge to primary carpal region and into centre of secondary median coverts. **Size** 25–30 cm. **Hab.** Oceanic. Few Australian records.

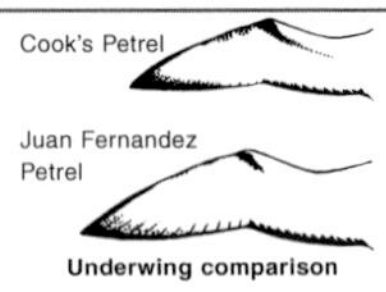

Underwing comparison

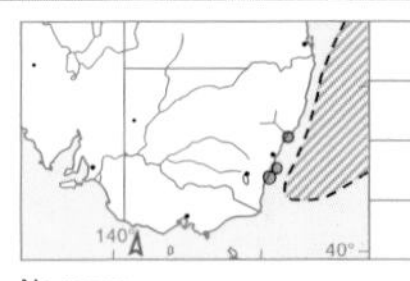

No races

White-necked Petrel
Pterodroma cervicalis **UC** ○ Vulnerable

Larger than Gould's, Black-winged. Black cap on white head. Broad white collar. Blue-grey above; broad black 'M' across wings. Underparts, underwings, as Cook's; black margins a little broader. **Size** 43 cm. **Hab.** Oceanic. Sightings increasing.

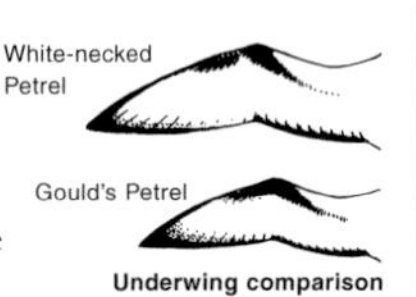

Underwing comparison

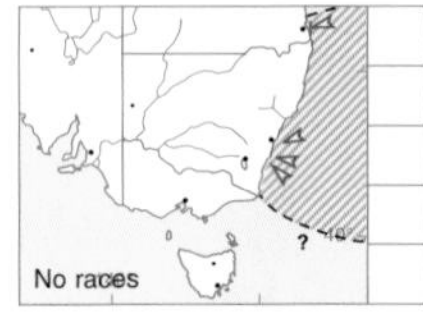

Blue Petrel *Halobaena caerulea* **UC** ○ Vulnerable

Long-winged graceful flight. Bill slender, black. Blue line on lower bill. Frons white. Cap black. Blue-grey above, faint 'M' across wings. Tail 'square'; dark sub-terminal band; only petrel with white tail tip. White below. **Size** 26–32 cm. **Hab.** Oceanic.

Head pattern

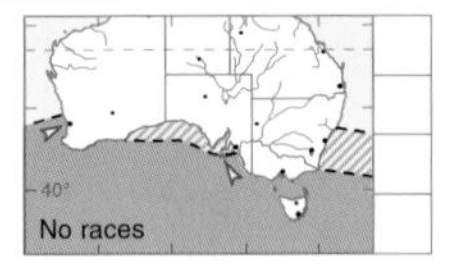

Broad-billed Prion *Pachyptila vittata* **UC–R** ○

Largest prion. Glides, banks; flutters on surface. Among prions, relatively huge, bowed (or boat-shaped) steel-grey bill; extensive exposed lamellae; small nail. Blue line on lower bill. Head, frons, dark grey. Thin white eyebrow. Large dark collar. Blue-grey above; strong 'M' marking. White below. Narrow black tail tip. Undertail barred grey, white; black centre. Feet blue; webs yellowish. **Size** 28 cm; folded wing 19–23 cm. **Hab.** Oceanic.

Head pattern

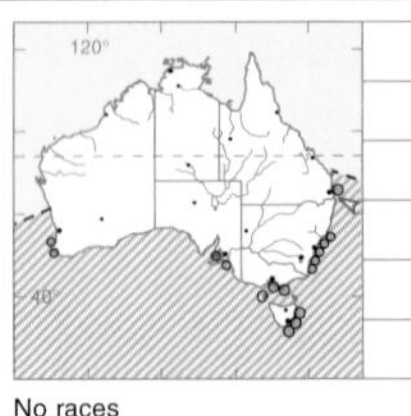

No races

Salvin's Prion *Pachyptila salvini* **UC** ○

As Broad-billed but bill generally smaller, narrower; distinctly bowed; sides bluish. Less, but still obvious, lamellae. Nail small. Head, frons, paler grey. As other prions, legs, feet typically blue; pale webs. **Size** 28 cm; folded wing 17–21 cm. **Hab.** Oceanic.

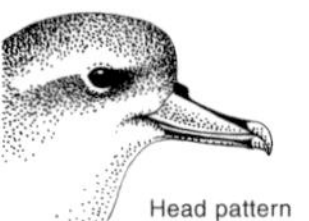
Head pattern

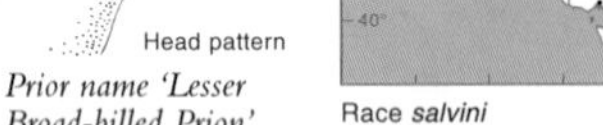
Prior name 'Lesser Broad-billed Prion'.

Race *salvini*

Antarctic (Dove) Prion
Pachyptila desolata **LA–UC** ○ Vulnerable

Note All prions have pale grey mark on outer central undertail; *Pterodroma* petrels do not.
All prions fly fast, jinking, banking; often turning back. Identical at sea to Salvin's Prion. In hand, bill generally narrower; sides straighter; little lamellae; larger nail. **Size** 26 cm. **Hab.** Oceanic.

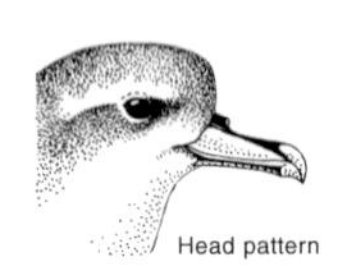
Head pattern

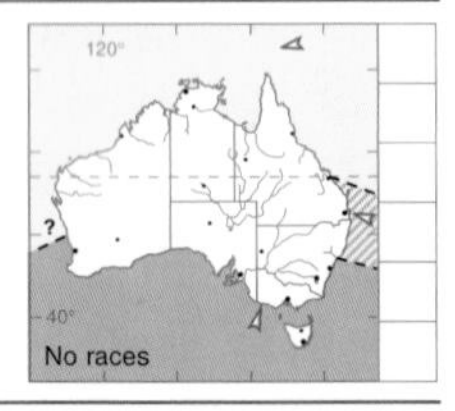

Slender-billed Prion *Pachyptila belcheri* **UC** ○

The prion with greyest back. Like Antarctic Prion (some indistinguishable at sea) but bill thinner (no lamellae seen if bill closed). Frons white; eyebrow broad. Fainter 'M' marking across upper surface than other prions. **Size** 26 cm. **Hab.** Oceanic.

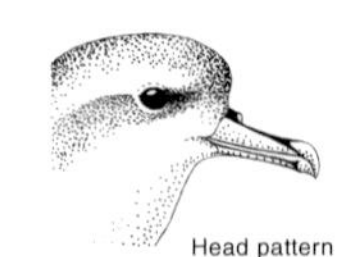
Head pattern

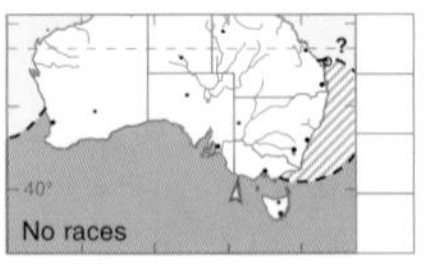

Fairy Prion *Pachyptila turtur* **C** ○ Vulnerable

'Bluest' prion (except Fulmar Prion). Bill short; nail large. Eyebrow faint. Bold black 'M' on wings. Tail band twice as broad as Antarctic Prion. Undertail broadly tipped black; thin central grey smudge. **Size** 25 cm. **Hab.** Oceans, coastal breeding islands.

Head pattern

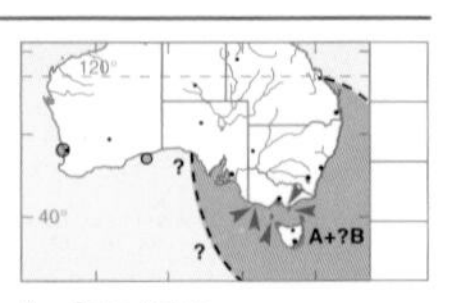

A = Race *turtur*
B = Race *subantarctica* **Vulnerable**

Fulmar Prion *Pachyptila crassirostris* see **Vagrant Bird Bulletin** p. 285.

Slender-billed Prion

Broad-billed Prion

Fairy Prion

Antarctic Prion

White-necked Petrel

Blue Petrel

Fairy Prion

Fulmar Prion

Antarctic Prion

Cook's Petrel

Salvin's Prion

Broad-billed Prion

Cook's Petrel

White-necked Petrel

Slender-billed Prion

Blue Petrel

Grey Petrel *Procellaria cinerea* **R–UC** Vulnerable

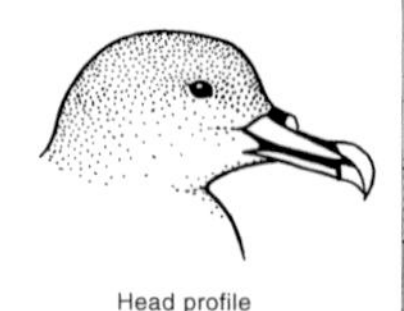
Head profile

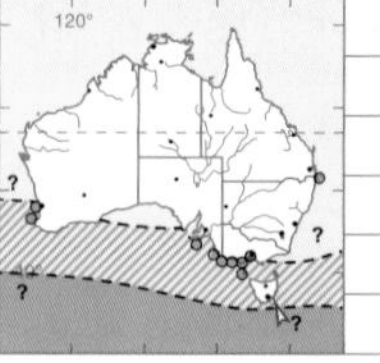

No races

Often described as 'duck-like' in flight, but high, wheeling flight, much gliding in strong wind; shearwater-like flight in calmer winds; also shallow dives, submerged swimming. Solitary or in small flocks; known to follow ships. Identify from Buller's, Streaked Shearwaters. Pale-tipped bill greenish or greyish-flesh coloured with black saddle on culmen. Dark crown extends to include eye. Plumage reflective. Grey upperparts; brown 'wash' on wings, crown and tail; often appears uniformly dark. Prominent wedge-shaped tail. Throat, breast, belly, white. Underwings, undertail coverts, dark. Legs as bill. **Size** 50 cm. **Juv.** Plainer grey, no dark brownish 'wash'. **Hab.** Oceanic.

Black Petrel *Procellaria parkinsoni* **V–R**

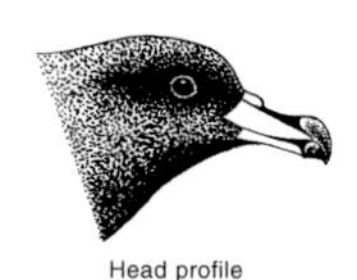
Head profile

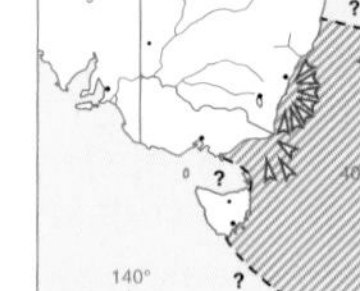

No races

Buoyant flight; dives. In practice, very difficult species to identify. Dark-tipped pale yellow bill very visible at sea. Body completely black, including feet. Distinguish from Flesh-footed Shearwater by heavier bill and black, rather than pale, feet; from Great-winged Petrel (both races) by relatively short, pale bill and lack of face colour; from White-chinned Petrel by dark bill tip and lack of chin colour. Most problems occur with closely related Westland Petrel from which it can only really be differentiated by its smaller size. **Size** 46 cm. **Juv.** Bill ivory-white; slowly changes over 5-year period. **Hab.** Oceanic. Only small numbers recorded.

Westland Petrel *Procellaria westlandica* **V–R**

Head profile

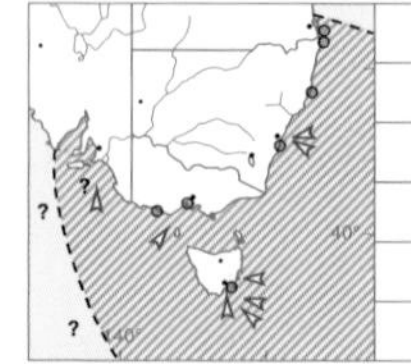

No races

Dark-tipped pale bill very visible at sea. Body completely black, including feet. In all respects a larger version of the Black Petrel from which it cannot be readily distinguished. Differentiate from similar species by using same criteria as for Black Petrel. Its greater size distinguishes it further from Great-winged Petrel but makes confusion with White-chinned Petrel race *aequinoctialis* more likely. **Size** 50–55 cm. **Juv.** Bill black; greyer about base. **Hab.** Oceanic.

White-chinned Petrel
Procellaria aequinoctialis **UC** ◌ Vulnerable

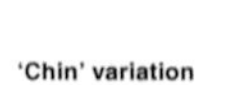
'Chin' variation

Race *aequinoctialis*

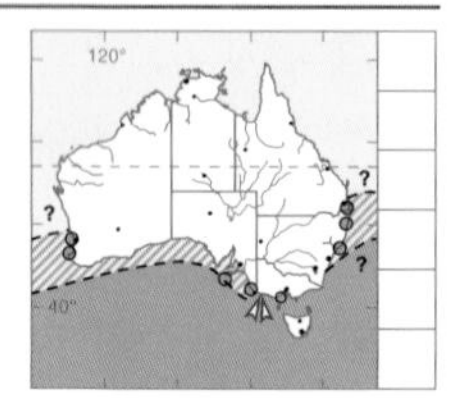

Race *aequinoctialis*

Local race *aequinoctialis* might be confused with juvenile giant-petrels, but much smaller size and complete absence of white in plumage, except on the chin, should differentiate it. Birds with worn plumage may appear paler or mottled rusty brown. Generally solitary or in small groups. Known to be aggressive when feeding and a regular ship follower. Flight like that of a small albatross with slow, deliberate wing beats and glides. Entirely dark except for a rather variable white chin patch. This feature is not always prominent; thus confusion with Black and Westland Petrels is possible. The conspicuously large, all-pale bill distinguishes it from these species. Distinguished from Flesh-footed Shearwater by black, not pale feet; from Great-winged Petrel (both races), by bill colour, body size. **Size** 51–58 cm. **Juv.** Very similar to adult. **Hab.** Oceanic.

Race *aequinoctialis* Race *conspicillata*

A South Atlantic race conspicillata *(illustrated) is relatively rare (only a small breeding population on Tristan da Cunha) and may be wholly sedentary. These birds have extensive white on face, chin, giving a dramatic spectacled appearance. There are no Aust. records of this race. Future revision in this species is likely; race* conspicillata *may become a full species. An early sailors' name 'Shoemaker' may have related to* conspicillata.

Black Petrel
Black Petrel
Grey Petrel
Grey Petrel
Flesh-footed Shearwater
Westland Petrel
Westland Petrel
Great-winged Petrel Race gouldi
Northern Giant-Petrel Imm.
White-chinned Petrel
White-chinned Petrel
N. DAY.

Flesh-footed Shearwater *Puffinus carneipes* **A** ○

Check Black, Westland, White-chinned Petrels. In flight holds wings straight; tail rounded. Large chocolate-brown or black-brown shearwater; entirely dark above. Bill horn, tipped black. Underwing dark; reflective coverts and primaries. Feet flesh-pink; do not trail beyond tail. **Size** 40–45 cm. **Voice** Wailing, and also soft cackling, at breeding colonies. **Hab.** Oceanic, coastal.

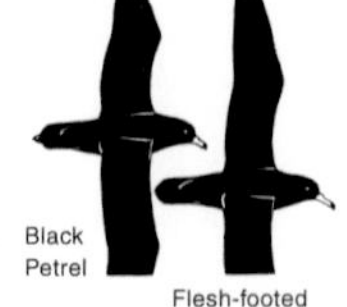

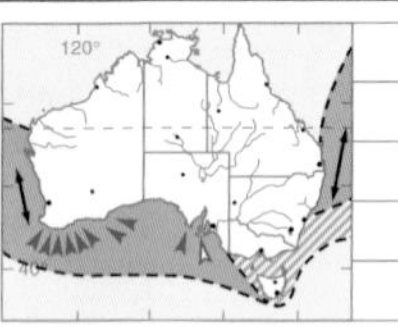

No races

Wedge-tailed Shearwater *Puffinus pacificus* **A** ○

Attends trawlers. Holds wings well forward, glides low over sea. Smaller than Flesh-footed. Bill leaden-grey, looks pale in distance; tip black. **Dark morph** All dark; paler non-reflective centres to underwings. Tail long, wedge-shaped to rounded. Legs flesh-white. **Light morph** Slightly greyer above; faint 'M' mark. 'Hooded' appearance. Throat to vent white. Underwing white, but black primaries, secondaries; grey blotching on axilla, leading edge. Check Flesh-footed. **Size** 38–46 cm. **Hab.** Oceanic, coastal.

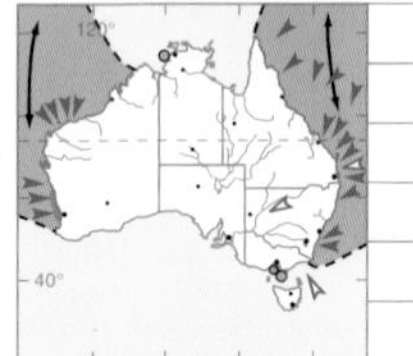

No races
Light morph more common in W Australia.

Buller's Shearwater *Puffinus bulleri* **UC** ○

Check White-necked Petrel, also Flesh-footed Shearwater, Pink-footed, and light morph of Wedge-tailed. Gliding, graceful flight. Slender. Bill blue-black. Cap black, contrasts with blue-grey upperparts and strong 'M' marking. Underparts, underwing white. Narrow black trailing edge to underwing. Tail slightly wedge-shaped. Feet pink. **Size** 46–47 cm. **Hab.** Oceanic, coastal.

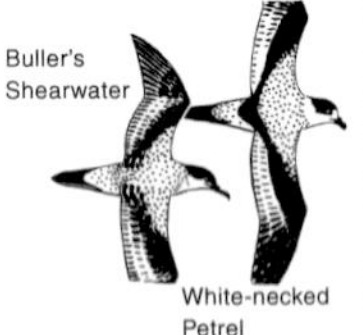

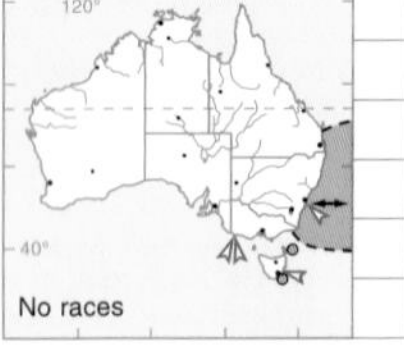

No races

Sooty Shearwater *Puffinus griseus* **MC** ○

Flies with rapid wing beat, gliding. In summer, southern birds are visibly in heavy wing moult; gaps appear in wings. All dark. Wedge-tailed Shearwater-sized; both are larger than Short-tailed. Dark grey, large, long bill. Underwing may vary: (a) greyish centre, streaked black; (b) white on primary coverts extends down wing through median coverts; some black streaking; (c) mostly white, faint streaks. Tail short, rounded. Feet trail. Outside of legs black; inside flesh-pink. **Size** 40–46 cm. **Hab.** Coastal, oceanic.

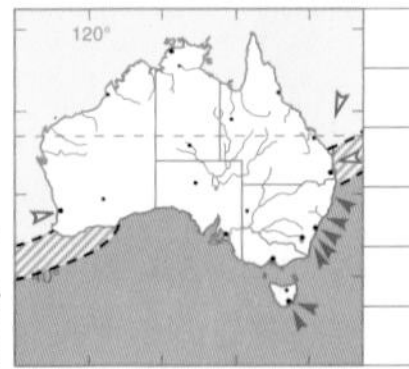

No races

Short-tailed Shearwater *Puffinus tenuirostris* **A** ○ Br. E

Flight like Sooty but more rapid. Huge flocks. From January to April birds do not moult on wings; no gaps appear. Like Sooty but much smaller; shorter-billed. Usually has darker underwing than Sooty; variable gradation: (a) all dark silvery-grey; (b) grey; white central streak, faint black streaks; not usually white on primary medians or greater coverts; (c) all white centre (rare). Short rounded tail. Blackish feet trail beyond tail tip; similar to Sooty Shearwater. **Size** 41–45 cm. **Hab.** Coastal, oceanic.

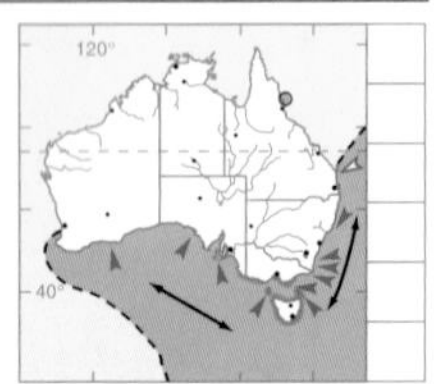

No races
See also map p. 44.

Streaked Shearwater *Calonectris leucomelas* **UC** ○

Bow-winged; albatross-like gliding. Largest shearwater to consistently visit Australia. Check Buller's Shearwater, vagrant shearwaters. Very large pale bill, dark tip. Head white. Black streaks on crown (variable). Black nape. Upperparts grey-brown with pale scalloping. Indistinct 'M' across back. White tips to upper tail coverts. Underparts white. Underwing white, black primaries, secondaries. Fine streaking on axilla, leading wing edge. Tail rounded. Feet pink. **Size** 48 cm. **Hab.** Coastal, oceanic.

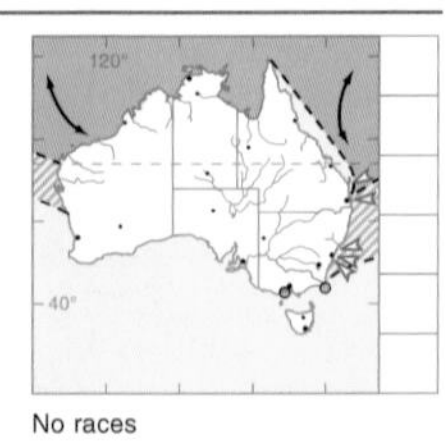

No races

Pink-footed Shearwater *Puffinus creatopus*, **Great Shearwater** *Puffinus gravis* see **Vagrant Bird Bulletin** p. 285.

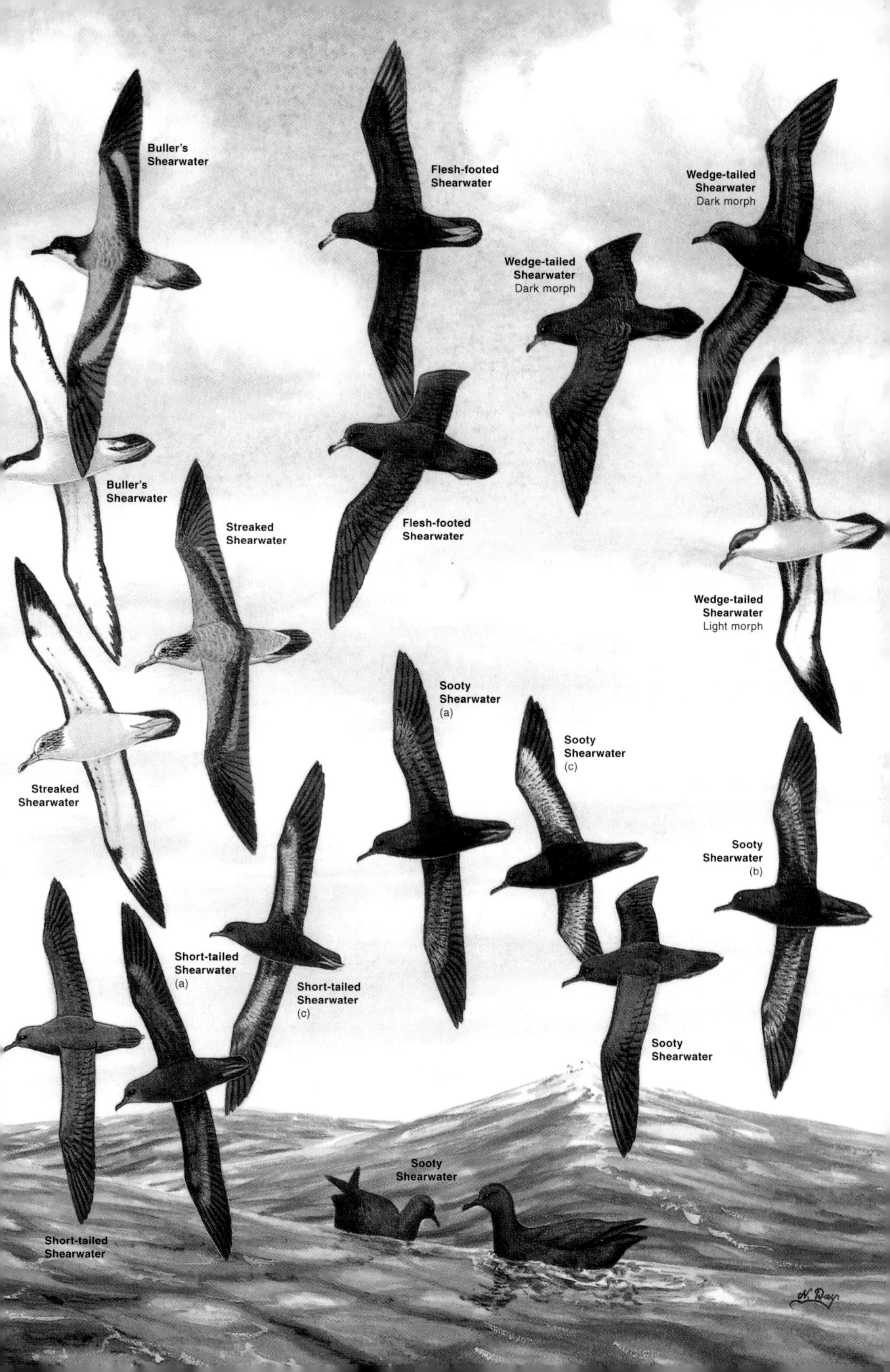
Buller's Shearwater
Flesh-footed Shearwater
Wedge-tailed Shearwater Dark morph
Wedge-tailed Shearwater Dark morph
Buller's Shearwater
Streaked Shearwater
Flesh-footed Shearwater
Wedge-tailed Shearwater Light morph
Sooty Shearwater (a)
Sooty Shearwater (c)
Streaked Shearwater
Sooty Shearwater (b)
Short-tailed Shearwater (a)
Short-tailed Shearwater (c)
Sooty Shearwater
Sooty Shearwater
Short-tailed Shearwater
N. Day

Fluttering Shearwater *Puffinus gavia* **LA**

Sometimes feeds around Australasian Gannets. Flies with rapid, whirring wing beats close to the sea, banks only in strong wind. Most birds are slightly smaller than Hutton's Shearwater, but some are so similar that they may not be distinguished at sea. Blackish above, including slight collar, ear coverts and below eye. Underwing white, but dark axillaries tipped white. Central feather shafts on leading edge of wing dark; appears streaked (a variable feature). Undertail coverts white. **Size** 32–37 cm. **Hab.** Usually coastal, occasionally oceanic.

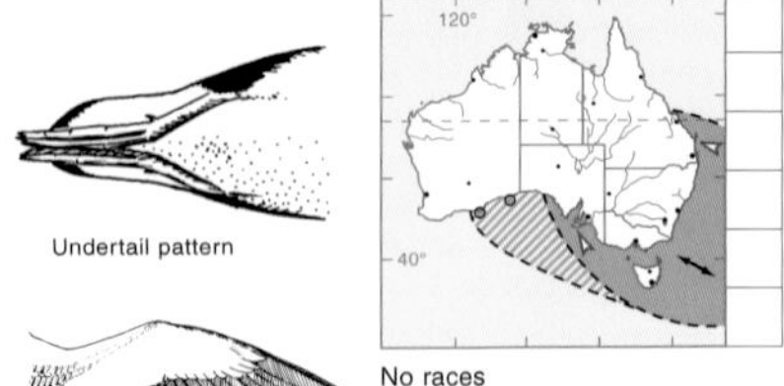

Undertail pattern
Underwing pattern
No races

Hutton's Shearwater *Puffinus huttoni* **UC**

In body size, bill length, most are larger than Fluttering Shearwater. Blacker above than Fluttering. Like Manx Shearwater, but smaller. Collar usually very prominent; at sea gives a hooded effect. Underwing varies: (a) grey with faint white centre and dark streaking, or (b) extensive white centre, strongly streaked; axillaries black. Undertail coverts vary, from heavily flecked black, to white. Sides of undertail usually flecked. **Size** 36–38 cm. **Hab.** Prefers coast, also oceanic. Flies like Fluttering.

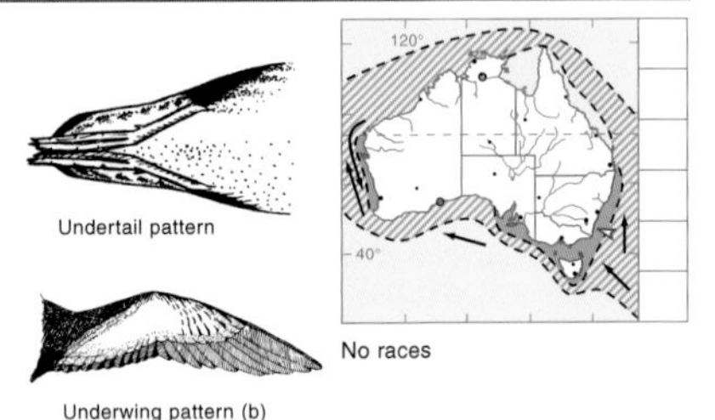

Undertail pattern
Underwing pattern (b)
No races

Little Shearwater *Puffinus assimilis* **LC**

Approaches ships; quickly leaves. Fastest wing beats of any shearwater. Smaller than Fluttering Shearwater. Bill very short. White above eye; eye-ring, ear coverts white. Dark above. Wing-tips 'rounded'. Underwing (incl. axillaries) white except for black outer half of primaries and thin leading edge. Legs, feet, blue-grey, a key feature. **Size** 25–30 cm. **Hab.** Coastal, oceanic. Best seen near breeding islands.

Head pattern

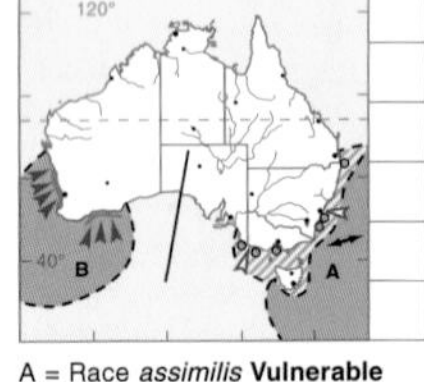

A = Race *assimilis* **Vulnerable**
B = Race *tunneyi* **E**

Manx Shearwater *Puffinus puffinus*, **Audubon's Shearwater** *Puffinus lherminieri* see **Vagrant Bird Bulletin** pp. 285, 286.

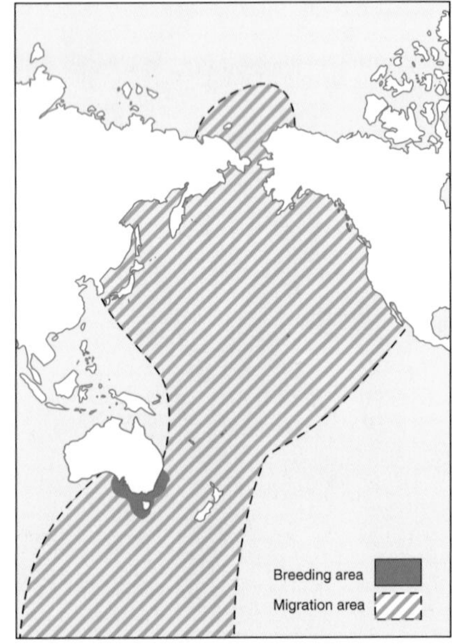

Short-tailed Shearwater; provisional map

Manx
Shearwater
Manx
Shearwater
Audubon's
Shearwater
Hutton's
Shearwater
(a)
Audubon's
Shearwater
Hutton's
Shearwater
(b)
Fluttering
Shearwater
Little
Shearwater
Hutton's
Shearwater
Fluttering
Shearwater
Little
Shearwater
N. DAY

Wilson's Storm-Petrel *Oceanites oceanicus* **MC**

Looks black and white at sea. In flight, long legs, yellow webbed feet project beyond square tail. Dangle in slow flight, feeding. Two races not identifiable at sea. Sooty-black; prominent white 'crescentic' rump. Wings rounded; pale greyish crescent on greater upperwing coverts. Tail often folded upward – a shallow dihedral. Dark brown-black below, except white flanks. Dark line from belly to undertail coverts. **Size** 15–19 cm. **Hab.** Oceanic.

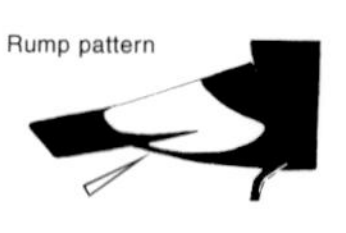

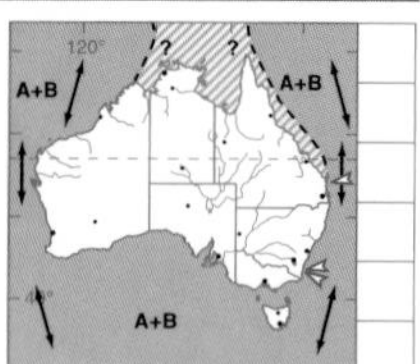

A = Race *oceanicus*
B = Race *exasperatus*

Grey-backed Storm-Petrel *Garrodia nereis* **UC**

'Hooded'. Head to chest brown-black; sharply cut off. Pale ash-grey back; paler grey rump, tail. Upperwings dark grey; pale grey upper coverts; black primaries. White underwing is dark bordered. Wide black band on grey square tail. White belly. **Size** 16–19 cm. **Hab.** Oceanic. Former name *Oceanites nereis*.

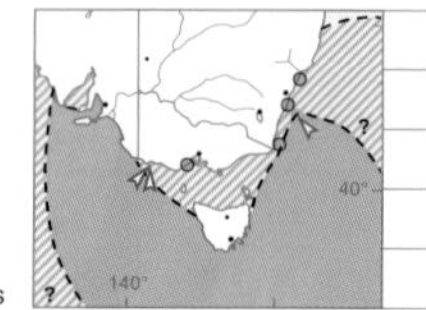

No races

White-faced Storm-Petrel *Pelagodroma marina* **LA**

Yellow webbed feet project in flight. Flutters, bounces over sea. Bill black. White frons, prominent eyebrow. Dark grey crown. Broad blackish eye-stripe. Grey shoulders, back; browner with wear. Black primaries. Rump pale grey. White below. Underwing white; few smudges on leading edge; dark bordered at rear. Square dark tail; blackish undertail. **Size** 18–21 cm. **Hab.** Oceanic.

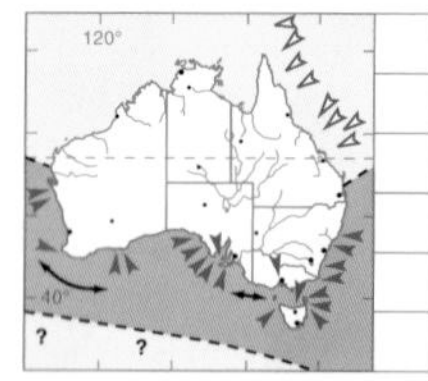

Race *dulciae* **E**

Black-bellied Storm-Petrel *Fregetta tropica* **UC**

Feet project beyond square tail. 'Hooded'. Bill black. Black above; head, primaries darkest. Grey on greater upperwing coverts. Chin pale. Throat black (in hand, tendency to have white feather bases, unlike White-bellied). Black 'V' on chest usually present; leads to narrow central stripe; some lack this (diagram). Underwing white, bordered black. Otherwise white below. White flanks onto rump forms 'crescent'. **Size** 20 cm. **Hab.** Oceanic.

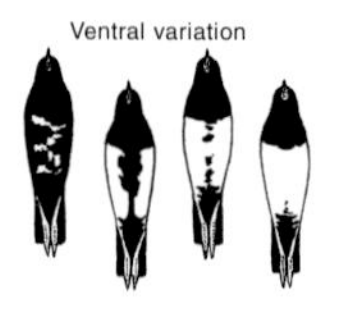

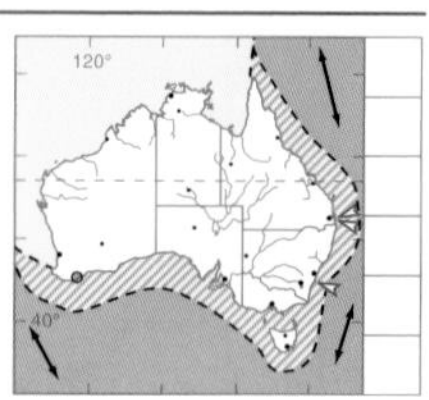

Race *tropica*

White-bellied Storm-Petrel *Fregetta grallaria* **UC**

Feet do not extend beyond square tail. **Light morph** As Black-bellied but black chest cuts straight off from white belly. Black throat. **Dark morph** Some have dark rump, or streaked, dusky, or dark underparts (diagram). **Size** 18–22 cm. **Hab.** Oceanic.

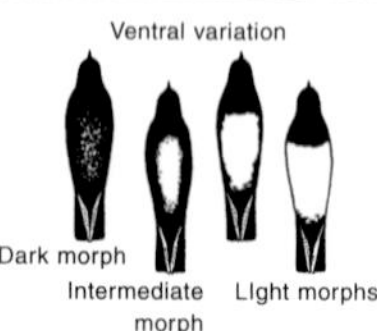

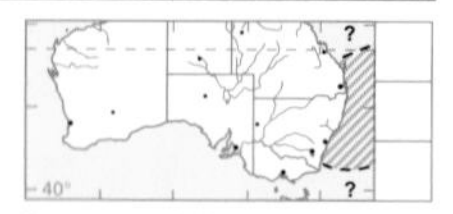

Race *grallaria* **Vulnerable**

Matsudaira's Storm-Petrel *Oceanodroma matsudairae* **UC**

Follows ships. Large sooty-brown storm-petrel. Bill black. Long wings; paler crescents on coverts; quill bases show as white patches. Deeply forked tail. Legs, feet black. **Size** 24–25 cm. **Hab.** Oceanic. Increasingly seen at sea off NW Shelf, WA.

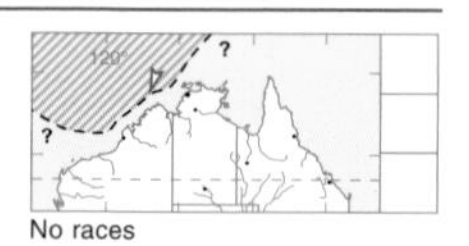

No races

Common Diving-Petrel *Pelecanoides urinatrix* **LA–C**

'Whirring', quail-like flight, neck out. Tiny, dumpy petrel. Bill black; sides parallel. Glossy blackish above; gloss lessens with wear. White below; silvery-grey underwing. Tail short. Legs, feet blue; webs black. **Size** 20–25 cm. **Hab.** Oceanic, coastal seas.

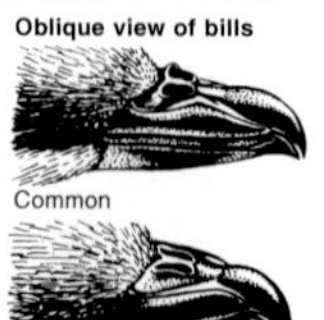

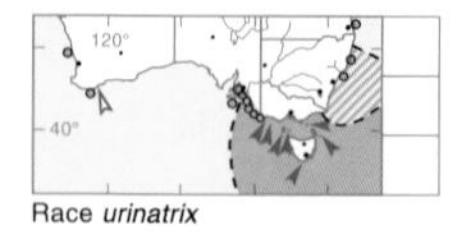

Race *urinatrix*

South Georgian Diving-Petrel *Pelecanoides georgicus*, **Leach's Storm-Petrel** *Oceanodroma leucorhoa*, **Swinhoe's Storm-Petrel** *Oceanodroma mornorhis*, **Tristram's Storm-Petrel** *Oceanodroma tristrami* see **Vagrant Bird Bulletin** pp. 284, 286.

VT 182
GYGIS
Cape Petrel
Common Diving-Petrel
Black-bellied Storm-Petrel
Matsudaira's Storm-Petrel
Black-bellied Storm-Petrel
White-bellied Storm-Petrel
Leach's Storm-Petrel
Wilson's Storm-Petrel
Grey-backed Storm-Petrel
White-faced Storm-Petrel
South Georgian Diving-Petrel
Common Diving-Petrel
Common Diving-Petrel
Nicolas Day

Australian Pelican *Pelecanus conspicillatus* **LA–C** Br. E

Flies in lines or 'V's; soars in graceful circles, often to great heights. Glides low over water surface; alights heels down. Swims in flocks. Often attended by Little Black Cormorants, Silver Gulls, when flocks feeding. Scavenges from people fishing. Very large black and white bird. Long pink bill. Distensible throat pouch. Primaries, shoulders, rump, tail, upperwing except centre, black; otherwise white. Head, nape, side of neck can be greyish. Legs, webbed feet grey. **Br.** Bill, facial skin, becomes red when courting. **Size** 160–180 cm. **Juv.** Smaller; grey-brown where adults are black. **Voice** Grunting. **Hab.** Open fresh and salt water. Breeding colonies widespread; some permanent, some ephemeral.

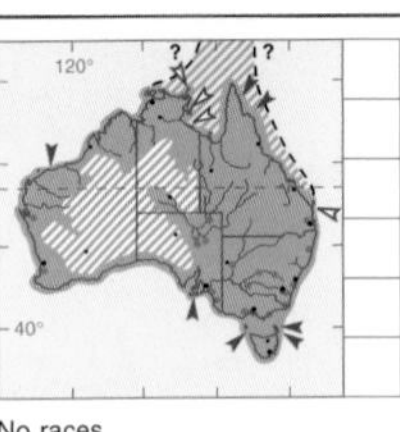

No races
Breeding colonies are widespread across Australia; some permanent; some ephemeral.

Australasian Gannet *Morus serrator* **LA–C**

Some flight similarity between juvenile Australasian Gannet and smaller Streaked Shearwater. Bill grey; edges of plates (sheaths) bordered black. Short black gular stripe in centre of throat. Black line through gape. Eye-ring dark blue; iris grey. Head buff-yellow. Rest of body white, with black primaries, secondaries. Black centre to tail (edges white). Black feet with narrow green lines on toes. **Size** 84–91 cm. **Juv.** Uniform grey-brown including hood. Spotted white upperparts; white underparts. **Imm.** Patchy brown; head, upperparts spotted white. Older birds have patchy black feathers on wings, mantle. Tail may be all black, especially during moulting period. **Hab.** Oceans, bays.

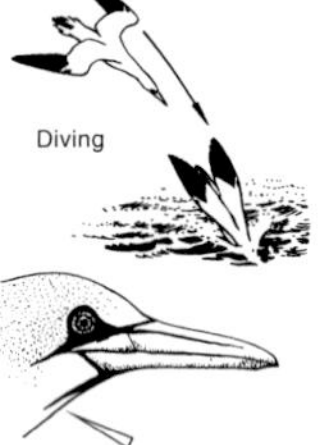

Adult: short gular stripe

Genus has reverted to Morus *from* Sula.

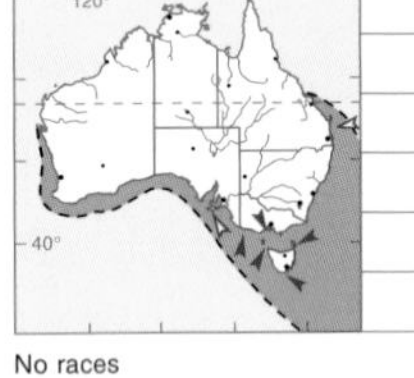

No races

Cape Gannet *Morus capensis* **V–R**

Like Australasian Gannet, but always has longer black gular stripe down throat. Broader black margins around plates of bill, face. White iris. Eye-ring larger, brighter blue, than Australasian. Wholly black tail. **Size** 84–94 cm. **Juv./Imm.** As equivalent ages of Australasian Gannet but has long black gular stripe. **Hab.** Oceans, bays. One bird resident on Wedge Light, Port Phillip (Vic.) from 1981; still present February 1998, now presumed dead. Hybrid fledglings of this Cape x Australasian Gannet mating (Wedge Light) also have long dark gular stripe. Three at Lawrence Rocks, off Portland (W Vic.), early 1992; seven in February 1995. A few other records off SW of WA.

Adult: long gular stripe

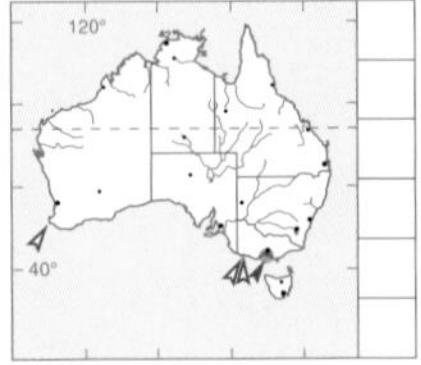

No races

Relative sizes of some common 'white' seabirds of Australia

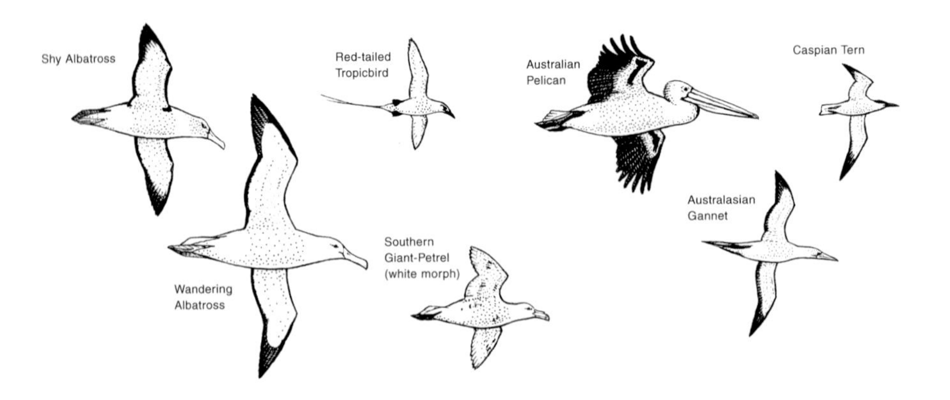

Australian Pelican
Non-breeding
Cape Gannet
Australasian Gannet
Australasian Gannet
Australasian Gannet
Imm.
Australasian Gannet
Juv.
Cape Gannet
Australasian Gannet
Juv.
Australasian Gannet
Australasian Gannet
Juv.
Australian Pelican
Australian Pelican
Non-breeding
Australian Pelican
Breeding
Australian Pelican
Juv.
N. DAY

Red-footed Booby *Sula sula* **LA**

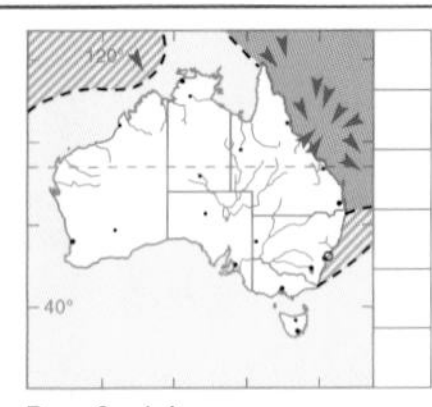

Race ? *rubripes*

Three colour morphs. All have bright red legs, feet that are visible in flight; white rump, tail, and abdomen. **White morph** Blue-grey bill, eye-ring. Pink skin about bill-base (mask). White body. Black primaries, secondaries. Dark area near carpal on underside of wing in white morph only. **Dark morph** Dark brown body, wings, white rump, tail, abdomen. **Intermediate morph** Brown areas lighter. **Size** 71–80 cm. **Juv./Imm.** Entirely brown, becoming mottled white with age. Bill black, may be tinted dull blue. Legs, feet dark grey. **Hab.** Oceans; the most pelagic booby.

Masked Booby *Sula dactylatra* **LA**

Largest booby. Race *personata* (A) Yellow bill. Black mask. Yellow or white eye. Body white with black primaries, secondaries. Tail black. Legs grey. **F** Green base to bill. Race *fullagari* (B) Dark eye, has smaller black mask (breeds Norfolk, Lord Howe, Kermadec islands). **Size** 75–85 cm. **Juv./Imm.** Head, neck brown; white collar. Upperparts grey-brown, tipped white. Narrow brownish rump speckled white. Underwing white with band running from carpal to axillaries; black trailing edge. Plumage whitens with age. Upperparts whiten from rump; upper wing becomes whiter; collar becomes more extensive. Identify from young gannets by more contrasting head pattern; darker mask; longer tail. Bird 'dumpier'. **Hab.** Oceans, reefs.

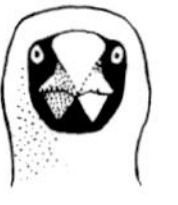

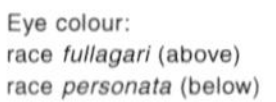

Eye colour:
race *fullagari* (above)
race *personata* (below)

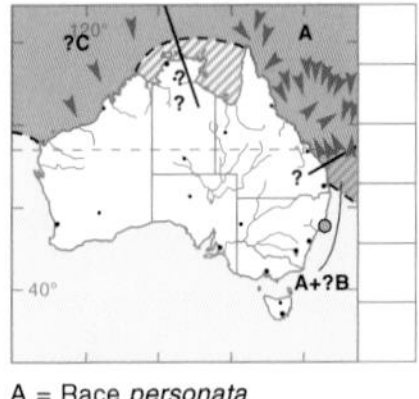

A = Race *personata*
B = Race *fullagari* **Vulnerable**
C = Race *bedouti* **Vulnerable**

Brown Booby *Sula leucogaster* **LA**

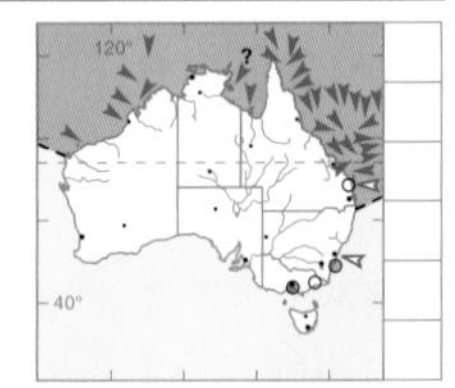

Race *plotus*

Yellow bill; bluish base. Iris varies – yellow to deep brown. Upperparts, breast, dark brown, sharply demarcated from white underparts. Underwing white, broadly bordered dark brown. Legs, feet, yellowish. **F** Slightly larger. Bill all yellow; feet may be brighter. **Size** 65–75 cm. **Juv.** Belly, underwing, dull brown, contrasts with otherwise dark brown pattern of adults. **Imm.** Bicoloured bill; blackish mask. Paler mantle; white feathers scattered on neck, throat. White underparts may be speckled with brown. **Hab.** Oceans, reefs, rocky islets, harbour structures.

Abbott's Booby *Papasula abbotti* see **Vagrant Bird Bulletin** p. 287.

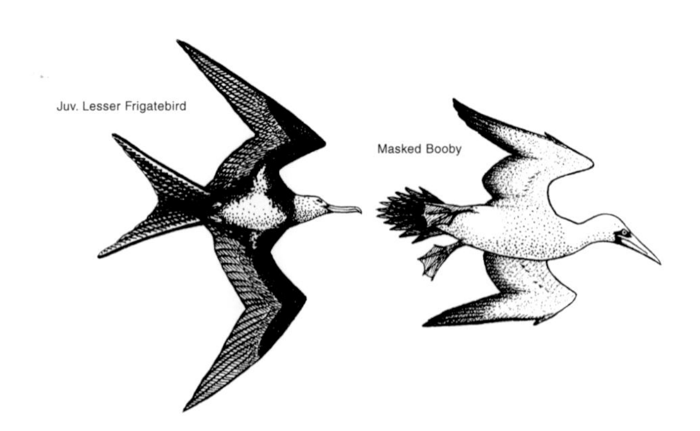

Boobies are frequently attacked and robbed of food by piratic Frigatebirds

Red-footed Booby Dark morph
Red-footed Booby Intermediate morph
Red-footed Booby Intermediate morph
Red-footed Booby Dark morph
Red-footed Booby White morph
Red-footed Booby White morph
Red-footed Booby Juv.
Brown Booby
Masked Booby Juv.
Masked Booby Race personata
Brown Booby Juv.
Masked Booby Race personata
Brown Booby
Masked Booby Juv.
Brown Booby ♀
Red-footed Booby White morph
Red-footed Booby Juv.
Brown Booby ♂
Red-footed Booby Intermediate morph
Brown Booby Juv.
Masked Booby Juv.
Masked Booby Race personata
N. DAY.

Great Frigatebird *Fregata minor* **LA**

Soars. Black. 'Albatross-like' long pale hooked bill. Eye-ring black-brown; iris dark brown. Red throat pouch; inflated in courtship. **F** Pink bill. Eye-ring pink; iris dark brown. Feet reddish. White chest; pale grey throat. Brown wing bars. **Size** 86–100 cm; wingspan 205–230 cm. **Juv./Imm.** Initially has a tawny-coloured head, throat; this gradually becomes darker all over (male) or develops black cap (female). Pale to bluish eye-ring. **Hab.** Tropical seas.

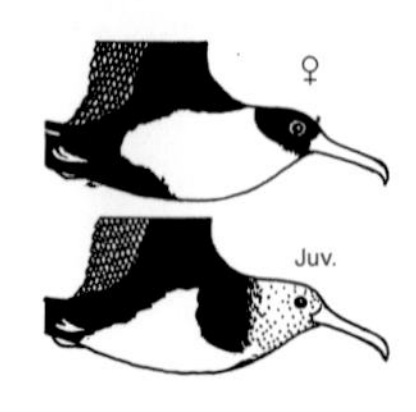

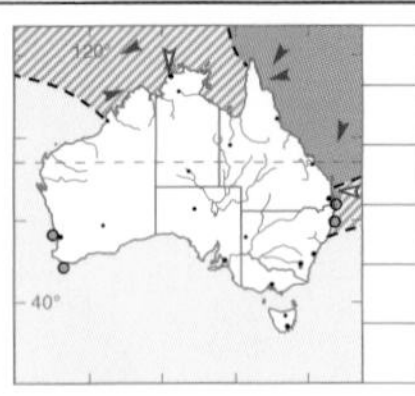

No races

Lesser (Least) Frigatebird *Fregata ariel* **LA**

Often seen soaring high during cyclonic weather. Black. Long pale hooked bill. Eye-ring, iris as Great. Red throat pouch; inflated in courtship. Thin white markings from flanks on to wings. **F** As Great Frigatebird, smaller. Pink bill. Eye-ring red. Black chin, throat. White collar, markings on underwings. **Size** 70–80 cm. **Juv./Imm.** Initially has a tawny-coloured head, throat. Pale eye-ring. Normally difficult to distinguish from other frigatebirds. **Hab.** Tropical seas.

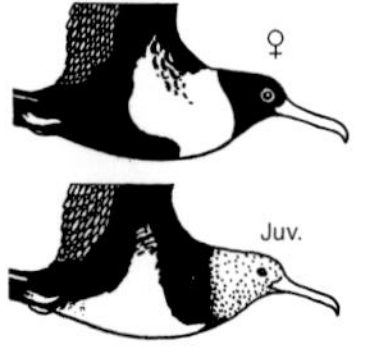

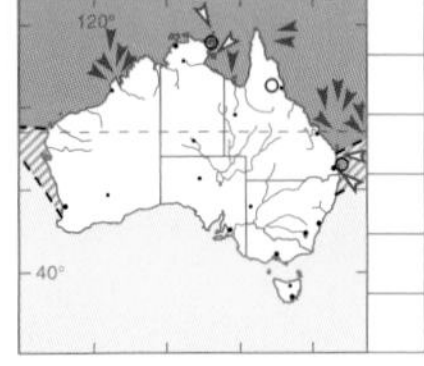

Race *ariel*

Red-tailed Tropicbird *Phaeton rubricauda* **LA**

Soars, glides, hovers, flies high and fast, dives into sea; swims with tail feathers cocked up. Pointed, stout, tern-like, scarlet to orange bill. Black crescent-shaped patch before and through eye. Body white, with variable amount of pink suffusion ('Pink morph'). White tail with two long (to 35 cm), red central tail streamers. Legs, feet black. Black primary shafts; broader black marks on tertiary feathers. **Size** 95–104 cm (incl. streamers). Birds vary in size across range; those off E Australia possibly larger. **Juv.** Bill black. Lacks tail streamers. White body with strongly black-barred area of dorsal surface – inner wings, mantle, back, rump, upper tail. **Imm.** Far fewer black marks on dorsum; red tail streamers appear. **Voice** Clamorous rattles, screams. **Hab.** Tropical, subtropical seas.

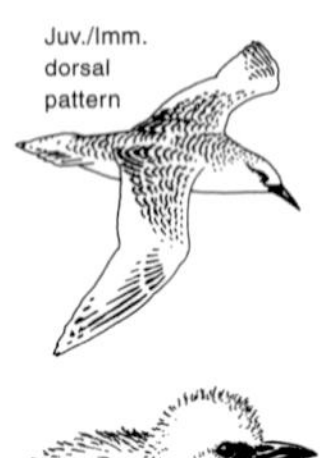

Hatchling

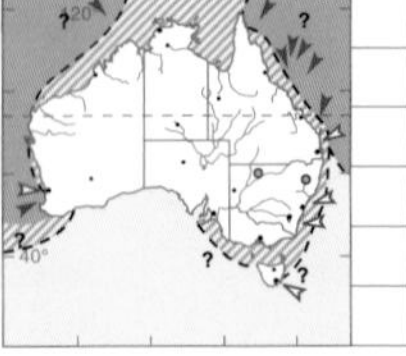

No races

White-tailed Tropicbird *Phaeton lepturus* **UC**

Flight like Red-tailed but quicker, more graceful, 'pigeon-like'. Two colour 'morphs', varying in size across range. Some birds of seas off NW WA tinted apricot-yellow (previously race *fulvus* 'Golden Bosunbird'). Birds in E Aust. seas smaller, no gold tint. Body brilliant white. Bill yellow to orange. Black crescent-shaped patch before and through eye. Black central wing bar; primary bases black. White central tail streamers long (to 45 cm) and black at base. Legs, feet blue-grey to off-white; webs black. **Size** 70–90 cm (incl. streamers). **Juv.** Numerous narrow, black, crescentic dorsal barrings from crown to rump, and on inner wings. Dark tail margins; no white tail streamers or golden tint. **Imm.** As Red-tailed Tropicbird, smaller. **Voice** Harsh rattles, screams, at nest site. **Hab.** Tropical, subtropical seas.

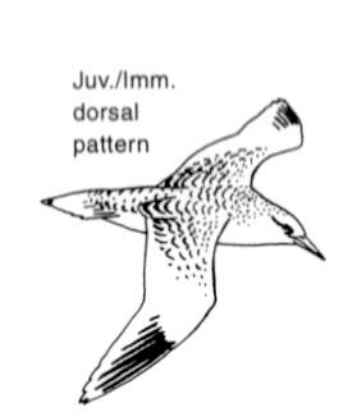

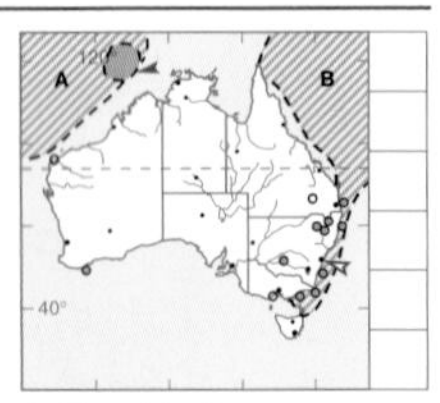

A= 'Race *fulvus*'
B= 'Race *dorotheae*'
Recent geographic variation study of White-tailed Tropicbird may see reinstatement of colour morphs '*fulvus*' and Pacific Ocean '*dorotheae*' as full races. Christmas Island breeding population, previously included in 'race *fulvus*', considered Critically Endangered.

Christmas Frigatebird *Fregata andrewsi* see **Vagrant Bird Bulletin** p. 287.

Christmas Frigatebird ♀
Lesser Frigatebird ♀
Great Frigatebird ♀
Christmas Frigatebird ♂
Lesser Frigatebird
Juv.
Great Frigatebird
Juv.
Lesser Frigatebird ♂
Lesser Frigatebird ♂
Great Frigatebird ♂
Red-tailed Tropicbird
'Pink morph'
White-tailed Tropicbird
Golden morph
'Golden Bosunbird'
White-tailed Tropicbird
White morph
Red-tailed Tropicbird
N. K. T. Day

Darter *Anhinga melanogaster* MC ♳

Spectacular large bird. In flight, cream upperwing streaks form a dorsal wing bar. Soars, often to great height. Holds wings out 'to dry' when perched. Often with cormorants. Often immerses in water up to neck. Long pointed bill. Snake-shaped neck. Dark grey to glossy black; a variable white stripe bordered by black and chestnut, from eye to first bend in neck. Wings iridescent with cream streaks. Long rounded tail. Legs, feet, flesh colour, unlike all cormorants. **F** Grey-brown above; pale grey below; also has white neck stripe. **Size** 86–94 cm. **Juv./Imm.** Like female, but stripe less distinct; body paler. **Voice** Clicks, rattles, clanging. **Hab.** Lakes, rivers, swamps, estuaries; rarely marine.

Swimming

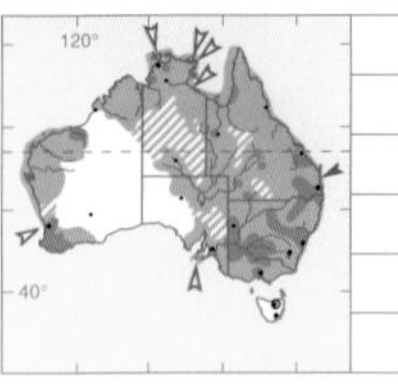

Race *novaehollandiae*

Black-faced Cormorant *Phalacrocorax fuscescens* **MC** ?◎ E

As Darter, cormorants normally spread wings when perched. Eye aqua-green. Black bill, facial skin, cap (no white over eyes), wings, tail and thigh stripe to legs. Black-edged feathers glossed green above, white below. Narrow black hind neck. Short white nuptial plumes on hind neck; few on rump, thighs. **Non-br.** Lacks white nuptial plumes. **Size** 61–69 cm. **Juv./Imm.** Browner above; face, neck, sooty; eye brown. **Voice** Grunts, hisses. **Hab.** Marine, offshore rock stacks, islets, outer harbour beacons.

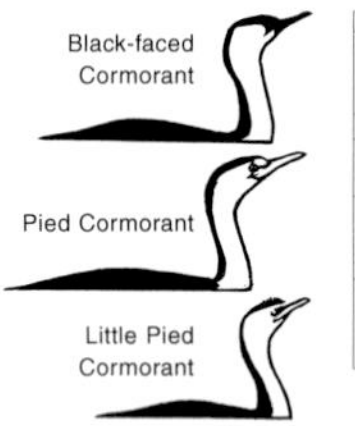

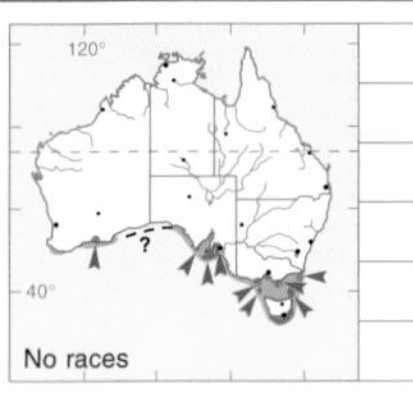

No races

Previously 'Black-faced Shag', genus Leucocarbo.

Pied Cormorant *Phalacrocorax varius* **A** ♳

Regularly flies in 'V's, lines. Like Black-faced Cormorant but larger. Longer, pale horn bill. Blue eye-ring. Orange facial and throat skin at brightest when breeding. Side of neck all white. Belly sometimes stained (rusty). Bold black thigh stripe. **Size** 65–85 cm. **Juv./Imm.** Browner; face duller. **Voice** Grunts. **Hab.** Prefers large areas of water, coastal or inland lakes, rivers, mangrove-lined estuaries.

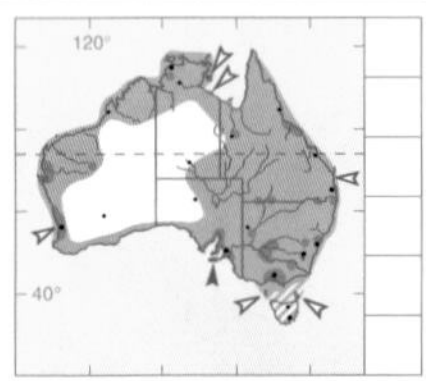

Race *hypoleucos* **E**

Little Pied Cormorant *Phalacrocorax melanoleucos* **A** ♳

Smallest Australian cormorant. Does not usually fly in formation. Appears to be only Australian cormorant that soars in thermals. Resembles Pied, but side of neck equally divided black and white. Short, yellow bill with black borders; no bare throat skin. Face blackish. White over eye to bill. Crest of short black feathers before bill. No black thigh stripe. White below (often stained rusty). **Size** 55–65 cm. **Juv./Imm.** Black extends below eye; black thigh stripe. **Voice** Mutters. **Hab.** Most aquatic.

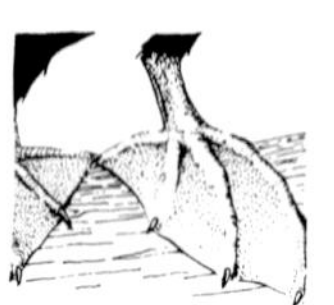
Typical cormorant foot with all toes webbed

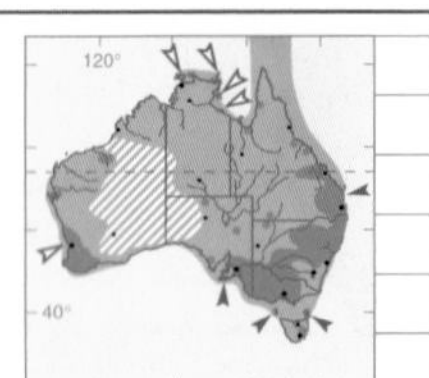

Race *melanoleucos*

Great Cormorant *Phalacrocorax carbo* **A** ♳

Largest Australian cormorant. Flies in long lines; also 'V's at times. All black with yellow facial skin and throat pouch. White nuptial plumes on neck. White chin; white thigh stripe. Worn plumage is browner. **Size** 80–85 cm. **Juv./Imm.** Dirty blackish-brown; facial skin duller; belly often pale brown. **Voice** Gargling, grunts, hisses. **Hab.** All coastal and inland aquatic habitats.

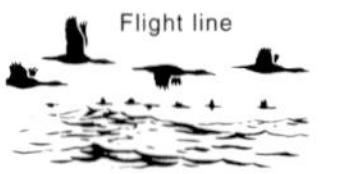

Previously called 'Black' or 'Large Black Cormorant'.

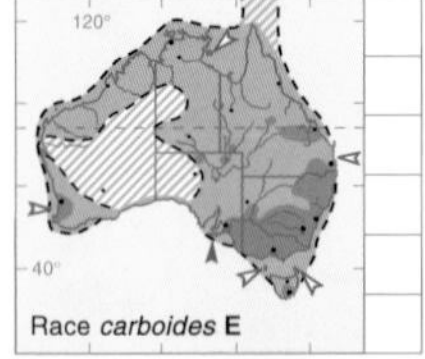

Race *carboides* **E**

Little Black Cormorant *Phalacrocorax sulcirostris* **A** ♳

Flies in 'V' formation. In flight, check Glossy Ibis. Congregates in larger flocks than other cormorants. Fishes co-operatively with Australian Pelicans. Second smallest cormorant; slender, dark, with glossy bronze-green back. Slender lead-grey bill. **Size** 55–65 cm. **Juv.** Browner. **Voice** Generally silent. **Hab.** Most estuarine and inland aquatic habitats.

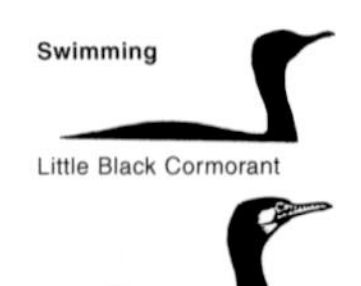

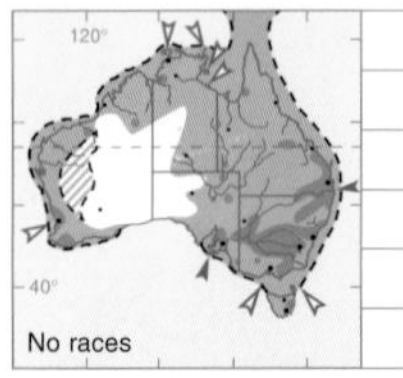

No races

Darter ♀
Ad.
Darter ♂
Ad.
Darter Juv.
Darter ♂
Darter ♀
Little
Black
Cormorant
Great Cormorant
Non-breeding
Little Pied Cormorant
Black-faced
Cormorant
Pied Cormorant
Little Pied
Cormorant
Juv.
Black-faced
Cormorant
Juv.
Black-faced
Cormorant
Breeding
Pied Cormorant
Breeding
Great
Cormorant
Juv.
Great
Cormorant
Breeding
Pied Cormorant
Juv.
Little Pied
Cormorant
Breeding
Little Black
Cormorant
Juv.
Little Black
Cormorant
Breeding
Little Pied
Cormorant
Juv.

Great Crested Grebe *Podiceps cristatus* **MC** ♧

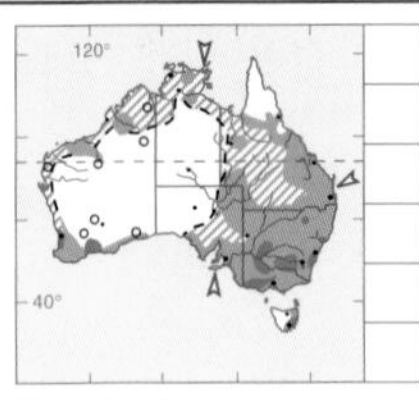

Race *australis*

Distinctive. Largest grebe. Has pointed black crests ('ear tufts') on dark brown head. In flight, conspicuous white margins on dark grey wings. Dives (without splashing) for food and to escape from danger; average duration less than 30 seconds. Identify at distance from Hardhead (large head, diving habits, 'square' white undertail patch). Dagger-like bill. Eye red. Lores narrow, black. Cheeks and throat white. Neck encircled with prominent rufous, black-tipped ruff. Dark back, buff flanks. Silky-white underparts gleam snow-white in sunlight. **Non-br.** Ruff and crest greatly reduced or absent in winter. Body then dull. **F** Slightly smaller. **Size** 48–61 cm. **Hatchling** Dark brown with white stripes on head and body. **1st yr** Retains some stripes on head. **Imm.** No ear tufts or ruff; many resemble wintering adult. **Voice** Associated with breeding/territory defence; barking, croaking, rattling; otherwise silent. **Hab.** Pairs in breeding season on freshwater lakes with emergent aquatic and marginal vegetation. Gregarious at other times, on fresh or saline waters – lakes, lagoons, reservoirs, estuaries, open water of bays. Winter flocks may appear unexpectedly.

Great Crested Grebe: courtship behaviour

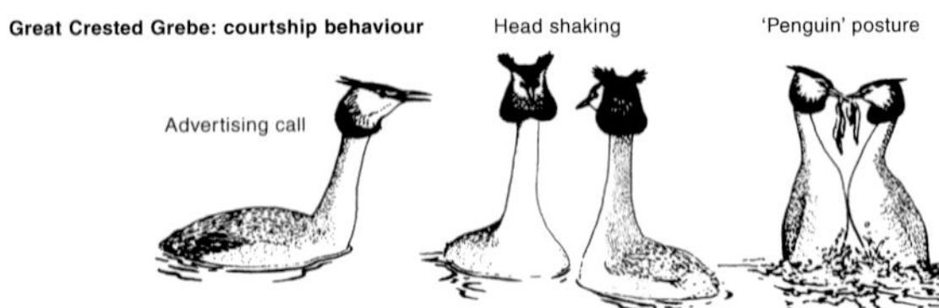

Hoary-headed Grebe *Poliocephalus poliocephalus* **LA** ♧ E

Small pale grey grebe. Appears 'thin-necked' at times. Frequently flies away from danger or observer. Has a long splashing take-off from water surface; quick wing beats in flight; white wing bar shows. Also dives to escape and for food. Identify from non-breeding Australasian Grebe (which still has pale skin at gape). Bill dark, tipped cream. Eye pale. Head black with white plumes. Back dark grey, occasionally brownish. Breast pale buff. Underparts silky white. **Non-br.** Pale grey body. Head without white facial plumes or with only a few. **Size** 29–30.5 cm. **Juv.** Head striped black and white. **Voice** Normally silent; soft churrings near nest. **Hab.** Lakes, swamps, settling ponds; frequently on brackish water or estuaries.

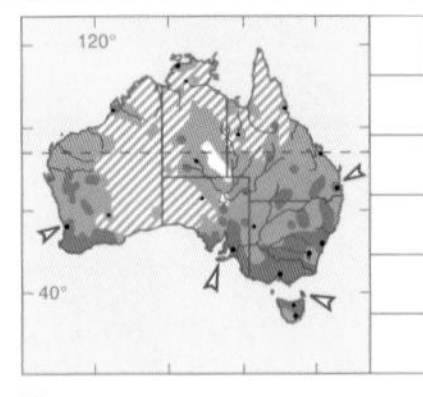

No races
Endemic, except for some late 1970s–early 1980s breeding in New Zealand. Not a successful colonisation yet.

Australasian Grebe *Tachybaptus novaehollandiae* **MC** ◎–?♧

Smallest grebe, usually in pairs. This species is more likely to dive than to flee danger (or observer) by flying. Bill dark, tipped cream. Bare skin forms a pale yellow face 'spot' at gape. Eye golden-yellow. Head and neck black. Richly coloured chestnut stripe extends from behind eye to side of neck. Back dark brown. Underparts silver-grey. **Non-br./Imm.** Duller; gape skin whitens; may be barely visible. Easily confused with Hoary-headed in non-breeding plumage. **Size** 23–25 cm; smaller than Hoary-headed Grebe. **Juv.** Face striped black and white. **Voice** More varied; different calls from Hoary-headed. Rapid trills; 'pit' of alarm. Carrying duet of 'chittering' territorial calls. **Hab.** Generally on fresh water; rarely on brackish or saline water. May join Hoary-headed Grebes in mixed flocks during winter but less gregarious.

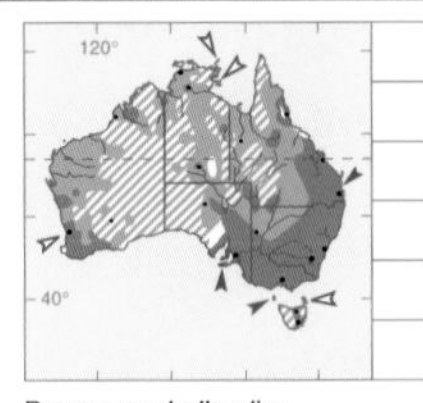

Race *novaehollandiae*

Little Grebe *Tachybaptus ruficollis* see **Vagrant Bird Bulletin** p. 287.

Great Crested Grebe
Australasian Grebe
Hoary-headed Grebe
Great Crested Grebe Non-breeding
Great Crested Grebe Breeding
Great Crested Grebe Late juv. plumage
Hoary-headed Grebe Breeding
Hoary-headed Grebe Non-breeding
Australasian Grebe Breeding
Australasian Grebe Non-breeding
Australasian Grebe Juv.
N. Day

Magpie Goose *Anseranas semipalmata* **LA–C**

Large pied goose. Swims, up-ends for food; white plumage often heavily stained. Congregates in huge flocks. Perches in trees. Head, neck, black, with distinct knob on crown of older birds. Hooked bill. Face, skin yellow to flesh. Neck to upper breast, black. Mantle, upperwing coverts, rump and belly, white. Upperwing black with white coverts. Underwing black with white wing linings. Tail black. Legs long, orange-yellow. Partly webbed toes. **Size** M 75–99; F 70–80 cm; wingspan 150–160 cm approx. **Gosling** Head, neck, rufous. **Imm.** As adult; white on mantle, black parts mottled grey or brown. **Voice** Very vocal, honking when feeding and in flight. **Hab.** Rush and sedge-dominated swamps, flood plains, rice crops.

Gosling

Head comparison (adults)

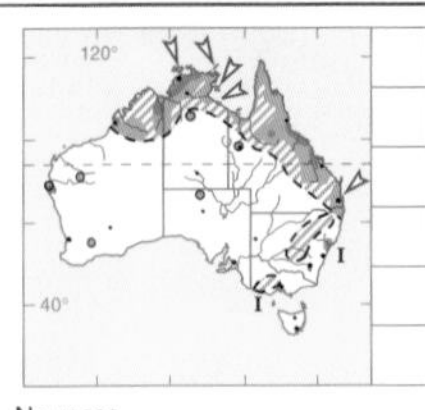

No races

Black Swan *Cygnus atratus* **A–C** E

Very large black waterbird with long slender neck, white-tipped wings. Often in very large flocks. Travelling birds fly in long lines with neck extended, white primaries, secondaries flashing. Flightless during moult. Bill red with white bar near tip, nail whitish. All black feathers faintly edged grey-brown. Black legs, feet. Carries head higher than female in mated pair. **F** Slightly smaller. Bill, iris, paler. **Size** 110–140 cm; head and neck half of this length; wingspan 160–200 cm approx. **Cygnet** Downy, pale grey. **Imm.** Grey-brown; paler feather edgings, white primaries tipped black (thin black trailing edge). **Voice** Musical fluting, trumpeting, often heard during nocturnal flight. Aggressive hissing. **Hab.** Large expanses of fresh to marine open water with abundant aquatic vegetation, exposed mudflats; pasture, crops.

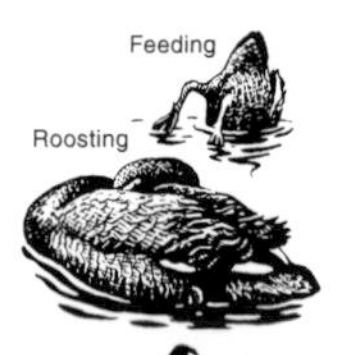

Relative size and posture of mated pair

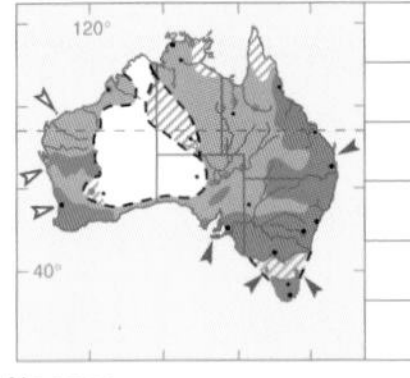

No races

Mute Swan *Cygnus olor* Intro. **R–UC** ◎

Huge, entirely white swan with loud musical wingbeat. Bill orange, black knob at base. Legs, feet, black. **Non-br./F** Knob smaller. **Size** 130–160 cm; wingspan 220–240 cm approx. **Imm.** Grey-brown (except for white 'Polish' morph) with grey knobless bill. Younger adults may retain some buff colour on neck. **Hab.** Rivers, ornamental lakes. Probably fewer than 40 birds feral in SW of WA. A few in private collections.

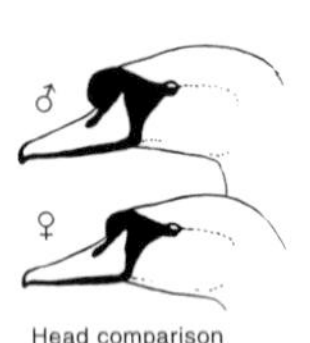

Head comparison (adults)

No races

Cape Barren Goose *Cereopsis novaehollandiae* **MC** O– E

In flight diagnostic black wing tips, undertail coverts, tail. Very large pale grey 'goose' with small head; short, black, triangular bill. Prominent lime-greenish cere. Large dark spots (variable) on scapulars, wing coverts. Legs pink to deep red; feet black. **Size** 75–91 cm. **Gosling** Pied. **Imm.** Paler cere; duller body. **Voice** Single or double honk; pig-like grunts. **Hab.** Mostly breeds on small offshore islands with tussocks, grassland, scrub. After breeding, disperses to improved pasture on breeding and other islands, and adjacent mainland.

Gosling

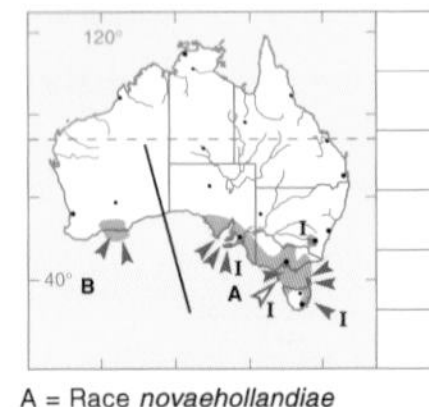

A = Race *novaehollandiae*
B = Race *grisea* **Vulnerable**

Domestic Greylag Goose varieties

Cape Barren
Goose
Magpie Goose
Magpie Goose
Mute Swan
Black Swan
Black Swan
Pied Heron
Magpie Goose ♀
Magpie Goose ♂
Mute Swan ♂
Mute Swan
Imm.
Black
Swan
Imm.
Black Swan
Cygnets
Cape Barren Goose
Black Swan ♂
Cape Barren
Goose
N.DAY.

Wandering Whistling-Duck *Dendrocygna arcuata* **LA**

Tall, 'goose-like'. Roosts on ground in very large camps. In flight has short rounded wings, trailing legs. Long flank plumes white, edged chestnut. Identify from Plumed Whistling-Duck by richer, darker, body plumage; shorter flank plumes. Black bill. Blackish crown and hind neck contrast with uniform buff face and foreneck. Upperparts brownish-black, feathers edged chestnut. Shoulders chestnut. Undertail white. Legs, feet, black. **Size** 55–60 cm. **Imm.** Similar to adults, duller. **Voice** Distinctive twittering whistle; squeaks. **Hab.** Deep, vegetated rivers, lagoons and swamps, flooded grassland; occasionally in estuarine areas.

Duckling

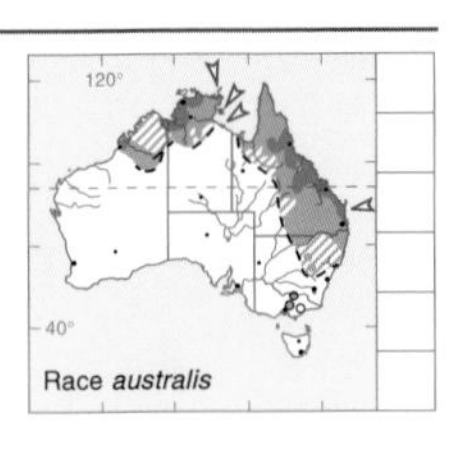

Race *australis*

Plumed Whistling-Duck *Dendrocygna eytoni* **LA** E

Tall, 'goose-like'. Large roosting camps on banks. Paler overall than Wandering Whistling-Duck. Long buff flank plumes, edged black, extend over back. Bill pink. Pale brown crown, hind neck. Face, foreneck, whitish-buff. Upperparts brown; upper back feathers edged buff. Wings brown above, paler below. Tail, rump, darker brown; upper tail coverts buff, spotted brown. Breast pale chestnut, finely barred black. Pale buff abdomen. Legs, feet, pink. **Size** 40–60 cm. **Imm.** Paler; indistinct breast markings. **Voice** Shrill whistling, high chatter. **Hab.** Wetlands of tropical to temperate grassland.

Duckling

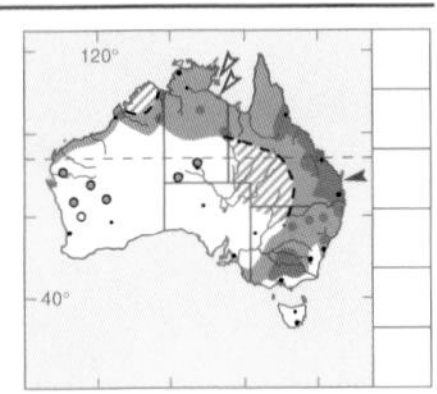

No races

Roosting camp

Australian Shelduck *Tadorna tadornoides* **LA** E

Often flies in long lines or 'V' formation, unlike other Australian ducks. In flight, large 'square' white panel on dark forewing. Briefly flightless during moult. Large-bodied, brightly coloured, with small head and black bill. Head, neck, black, glossed green. White ring at base of neck, occasionally around bill. Upperparts mainly black. Upperwing coverts white; primaries black; large green speculum. White underwing linings. Cinnamon breast. Underparts dark brown. Legs, feet, dark grey. **M eclipse** Not easily identified in field. Resembles female but yellowish-brown breast; less defined neck ring. **F** Eye-ring, base of bill, white; may be separate or merged. Chestnut breast. **Size** M 59–72, F 56–58 cm. **Imm.** Duller. Neck ring absent or partial. Both sexes have white flecking on front of head. **F imm.** White mark at base of upper bill. **Voice** Female strident; 'qua-quaarrk'. **Hab.** Large open brackish or fresh lakes, dams, pastures, tall forest margins, open woodland, coastal areas including tidal flats, saltmarsh.

Duckling

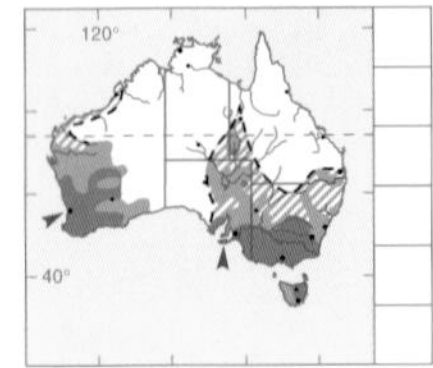

No races

Alert posture

Also called 'Mountain Duck', 'Chestnut-breasted Shelduck'.

Radjah Shelduck *Tadorna radjah* **MC**

Striking stocky white shelduck with chestnut breast band. White plumage often stained. Flesh-pink bill. White eye. Dark back, rump, tail, undertail; flanks black. White upperwing coverts; black primaries; chestnut tertials. White-edged green speculum visible in flight. Legs, feet, flesh pink. **F** Breast band narrower. **Size** 49–61 cm. **Imm.** Patchy dark crown. Incomplete breast band. White plumage may be flecked grey-brown. **Voice** Very vocal, often utters harsh rattles, whistles, while flying through thick timber. **Hab.** Tropical coastal wetlands, rivers, flooded areas; also mudflats, salt-marsh, mangroves, paperbark swamps.

Duckling

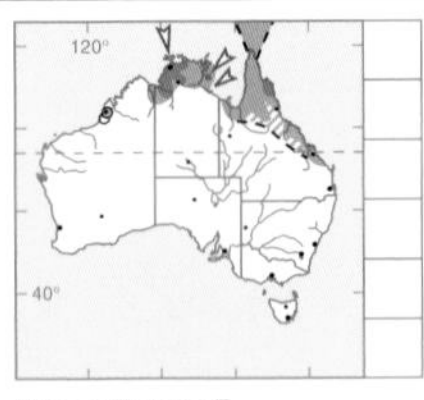

Race *rufitergum* **E**

Spotted Whistling-Duck *Dendrocygna guttata* see **Vagrant Bird Bulletin** p. 287.

Note Recently identified presence, and breeding attempts, of Spotted Whistling-Duck on Cape York Penin., N Qld, may lead to successful colonisation.

Wandering Whistling-Duck
Plumed Whistling-Duck
Radjah Shelduck
Australian Shelduck ♂
Wandering Whistling-Duck
Plumed Whistling-Duck
Radjah Shelduck
Australian Shelduck ♀
Plumed Whistling-Duck
Wandering Whistling-Duck
Wandering Whistling-Duck
Plumed Whistling-Duck
Radjah Shelduck
Imm.
Australian Shelduck ♂
Radjah Shelduck ♂
Australian Shelduck ♀
Australian Shelduck ♀
Faces vary
Radjah Shelduck ♀
N.DAY.

Pacific Black Duck *Anas superciliosa* **A** ◎–♧

Identify in flight from Freckled Duck (more 'hunched'); female Mallard, Chestnut Teal, Australasian Shoveler, by dark-striped pale face, dark brown body, white underwing linings. Bill leaden. Iris dark. Face white to buff with black crown, eye-line, malar stripe. Upperwing has purple to green speculum. Legs, feet, grey-yellow-green. **Size** 47–60 cm. **Voice** Harsh quacks; strong fading 'laughing' call; loud 'seep'. **Hab.** Usually rivers, creeks; deep, permanent, heavily vegetated swamps; open water and margins; wet paddocks, ornamental lakes. Rarer in saline, brackish, water.

Duckling

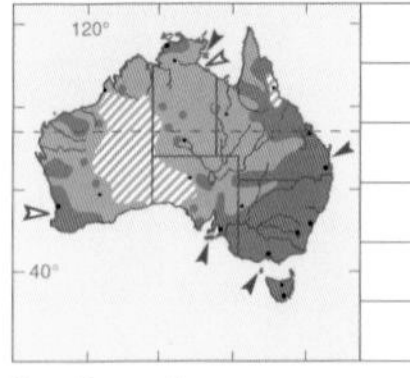

Race ?*rogersi*

Called 'Grey Duck' in NZ.

Mallard *Anas platyrhynchos* Intro. **MC** ◎

Identify in flight from Pacific Black Duck. Green head, white neck ring. Bill yellow-green. Iris dark. Pale grey-brown above. Curled central tail feathers. Purple-chestnut breast. White underparts. Legs, feet, orange. **Non-br. M** As female, but bill dull green. **F** Bill orange-grey. Single dull eye-line. Mottled, streaked, dusky brown. Straight central tail feathers. Many domestic forms. Hybridises with Pacific Black Duck. **Size** M 55–70; F 50–60 cm. **Voice** As Pacific Black Duck. **Hab.** Often about picnic grounds with lakes in urban parks; also farm dams, larger lakes.

Domestic varieties

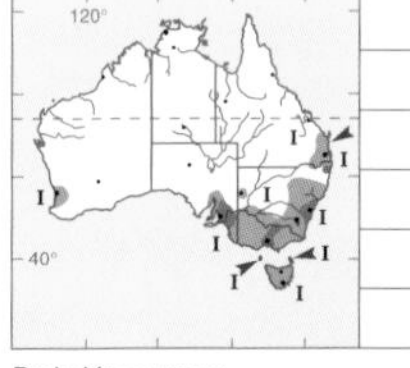

Probably no races

Grey Teal *Anas gracilis* **A** ♧

Highly nomadic. Mottled grey-brown duck. Short bill; red iris. In good light, white throat, paler face, distinguish from darker female Chestnut Teal. Narrow white upperwing stripe; small white triangle in centre of underwing. **Size** 42–44 cm. **Imm.** Paler. **Voice** Rising, falling 'laughing' call. Loud 'kwark, kwark'. **Hab.** Any available water: floods, lakes, tanks and dams. Coastal estuaries, tidal flats, during inland dry periods.

Duckling

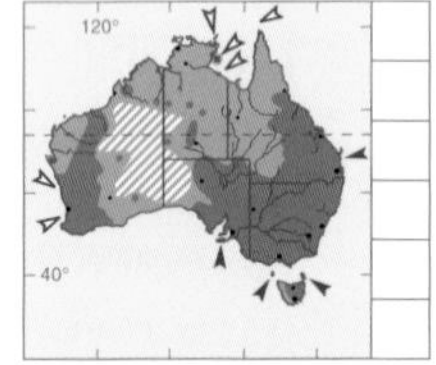

No races

Chestnut Teal *Anas castanea* **A–LC** ♧ E

When swimming, identify from male Australasian Shoveler (bluish face with white crescent, long dished bill). Short bill; red iris. Dark iridescent green head. Rich chestnut collar, underparts, prominent white flank patch. Brown back. **M eclipse** Very similar to imm. male. **F** Similar to Grey Teal but darker body plumage, and lacks pale throat. **Size** M 40–50; F 35–45 cm. **M imm.** Dark patchy head pattern, 'oily', blotchy body plumage. **Voice** Falling laugh. **Hab.** Breeds in brackish to fresh coastal swamps. Disperses to fresh water, tidal mudflats, inlets.

Duckling

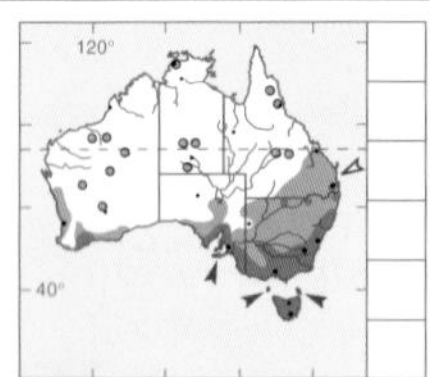

No races

Australasian Shoveler *Anas rhynchotis* **LA–MC** ♧

Only Australian duck with whirring, wing-whistling flight. Heavy spatulate black bill, low sloping forehead, diagnostic. 'Long-bodied'; body plumage similar to male Chestnut Teal, paler about breast. Head blue-grey, vertical white cheek crescent. Iris yellow. Prominent white flank patch. Upperwing coverts, pale blue-grey. Legs, feet, bright orange. **M eclipse** Loses colour, resembles imm. female. **F/Juv./Imm.** Bill dark. Iris brown. Body mottled brown, paler chestnut underparts; blue forewing duller; less white in wing. Slight sex differences. **Size** 45–55 cm. **Voice** Male soft double note. Female rapid, repeated, descending quacks, the first of each set loudest. **Hab.** Heavily vegetated swamps, floodwaters; ornamental lakes, farm dams; estuaries, tidal flats.

Duckling

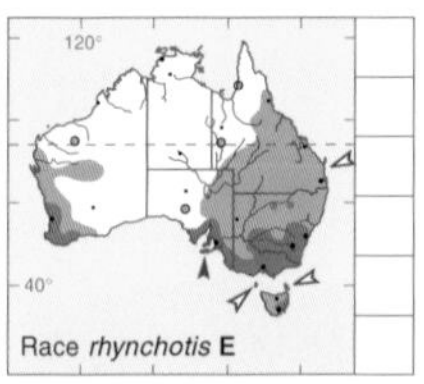

Head comparison of females

Australasian Shoveler

Northern Shoveler

Northern Pintail *Anas acuta*, **Northern Shoveler** *Anas clypeata* see **Vagrant Bird Bulletin** p. 288.

Chestnut Teal ♂
Grey Teal
Australasian Shoveler ♂
Pacific Black Duck
Australasian Shoveler ♂
Chestnut Teal ♀
Grey Teal
Australasian Shoveler ♀
Mallard
Pacific Black Duck
Mallard ♂
Pacific Black Duck
Northern Shoveler ♂
Mallard ♀
Australasian Shoveler ♂
Australasian Shoveler ♀
Chestnut Teal ♂
Pacific Black Duck
Pacific Black Duck/Mallard Hybrid
Chestnut Teal ♀
Grey Teal
N. Day

Garganey *Anas querquedula* **R–UC**

Teal-sized. Check Pacific Black Duck, female Grey Teal, Aust. Wood Duck. Striking white eye-stripe. Blue-grey forewing. Rich brown head, neck, breast. Black-brown above; long black and white scapulars. White below with fine black bars. **Eclipse** As female, forewing blue-grey. **F** Dark crown, eye-stripe; pale face. Broadly mottled grey-brown above. Forewing pale grey. White belly. **Size** 37–41 cm. **Voice** Male harsh rattle; perhaps not heard in Aust. **Hab.** Vegetated shallow swamps; sewage ponds.

Dotted line marks approx. edge of irregular migration from N Hemisphere; mostly stragglers to the south.

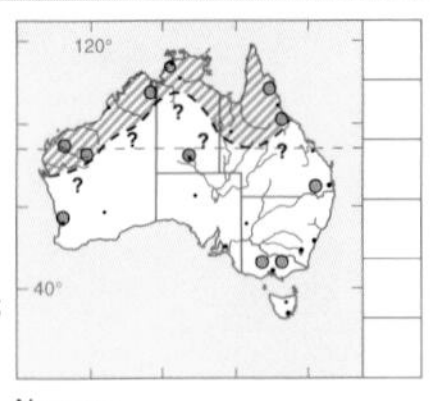

No races

Pink-eared Duck *Malacorhynchus membranaceus* **LA–UC** E

Striking 'zebra' plumage. Filter feeds, often in vast flocks. Long grey, square-ended, spatulate bill. Large brown eye patch in white, finely barred face. Small cerise ear patch. Upperparts brown. Upperwing brown, white trailing edge. Bold white rump crescent. Underwing linings white, finely barred brown. White underparts, barred dark brown. Undertail buff. Tail brown, white tip. **Size** 36–45 cm. **Imm.** Paler, less distinct pink ear patch. **Voice** Distinctive chirruping, chirring. Louder when frightened into flight. **Hab.** Breeds on inland floodwaters. Disperses to open water, coastal sewage farms.

Filter feeding

Duckling

Also called 'Zebra Duck'.

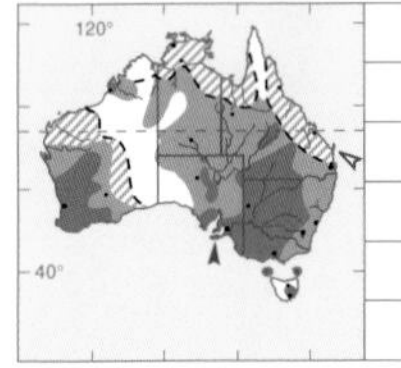

No races

Hardhead (White-eyed Duck) *Aythya australis* **LA–C**

White wing bar diagnostic in flight. Dives. Rests on open water in loose groups; check for Great Crested Grebe, male Blue-billed Duck. Bill black, blue bar at tip. Eye white. Large dark brown head. Body rich mottled brown. Upperwing brown, broad white bar across flight feathers. Underwing white, bordered dark brown. Undertail coverts white. **F** Iris brown. Paler body. **Size** 45–60 cm. **Juv./Imm.** Iris also dark. Uniform yellow-brown plumage. **Voice** 'brrk' in courtship. **Hab.** Deep, vegetated swamps, open water.

Duckling

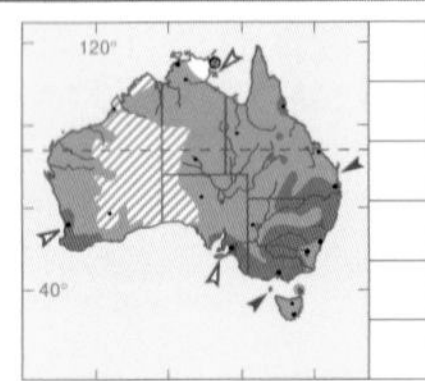

No races

Australian Wood (Maned) Duck *Chenonetta jubata* **LA** ◎– E

Walks in small flocks. Perches in trees. In flight, narrow green speculum; white rear edge of secondaries. At rest, folded black wing-tips contrast with grey forewing to form bold dorsal stripes. 'Goose-like' dark-headed, pale-bodied duck. Very short black bill. Head, neck, brown, short dark mane. Body grey with speckled brown breast. Edge of bright green speculum just visible (not in Plate). Black lower belly, undertail. **F** Paler head. Whitish line above and below eye. Grey-brown mottled body, white lower belly, undertail. **Size** 47–48 cm. **Imm.** As female, paler. **Voice** Nasal 'weh?'. Female lower 'waaah?'. Courting 'di-di-di-di-did' in trees. **Hab.** Short grassy woodland near water; around dams.

Duckling

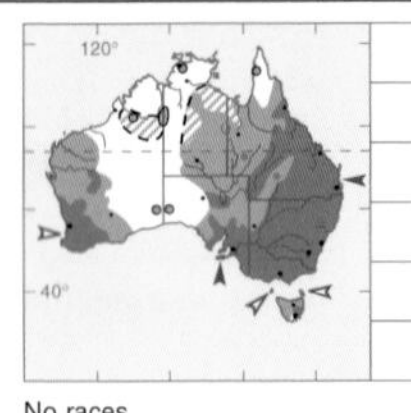

No races

Freckled Duck *Stictonetta naevosa* **R–LMC** ◎– E

Loafs by day in groups on fallen trees, sand spits. 'Black' in poor light. In flight, identify from Pacific Black Duck. 'Dished' bill slate-grey; red to orange base when breeding. Large dark 'peaked' head, fine white or buff freckles. Dark brown above with even freckling. Upperwing dark brown; coverts freckled. Underwing light brown; dull white wing linings mottled pale brown. Belly, undertail, paler. **F** Paler; bolder freckles. **Size** 51–56 cm. **Imm.** Pale brown, deep buff freckles. **Voice** Hoarse chatter. **Hab.** Breeds in densely vegetated permanent fresh swamps; moves to fresh or salty permanent open lakes, esp. in drought.

Duckling

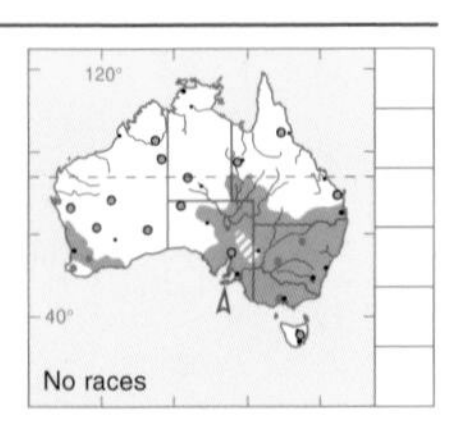

No races

Underwing patterns

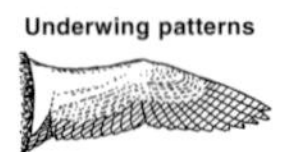
Freckled Duck

Pacific Black Duck

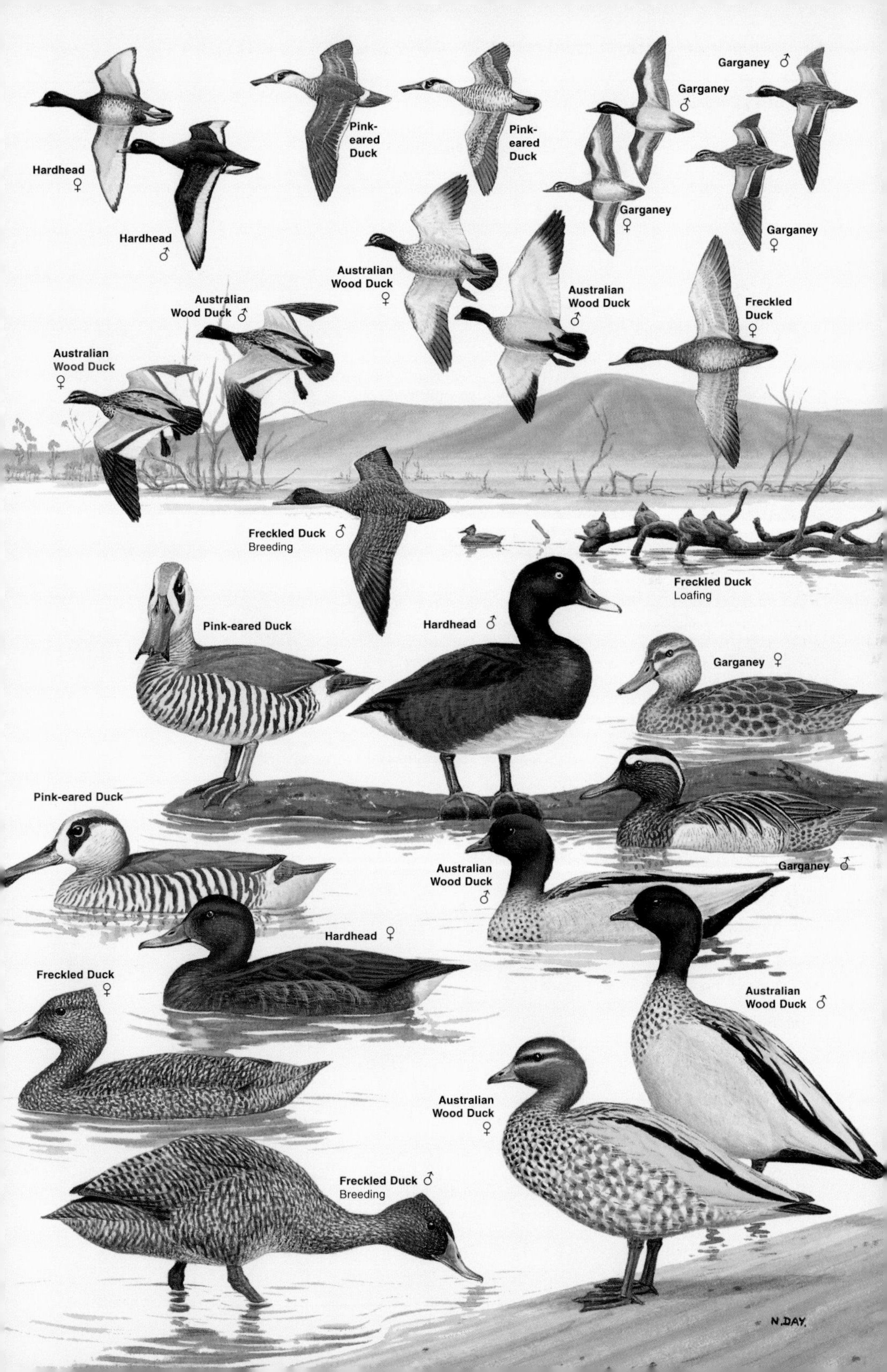
Hardhead ♀
Hardhead ♂
Pink-eared Duck
Pink-eared Duck
Garganey ♂
Garganey ♂
Garganey ♀
Garganey ♀
Australian Wood Duck ♀
Australian Wood Duck ♂
Australian Wood Duck ♂
Australian Wood Duck ♀
Freckled Duck ♀
Freckled Duck ♂
Breeding
Freckled Duck
Loafing
Pink-eared Duck
Hardhead ♂
Garganey ♀
Pink-eared Duck
Australian Wood Duck ♂
Garganey ♂
Hardhead ♀
Freckled Duck ♀
Australian Wood Duck ♂
Australian Wood Duck ♀
Freckled Duck ♂
Breeding
N. DAY

Cotton Pygmy-goose *Nettapus coromandelianus* UC ◎

A tiny duck. Surface feeder. In flight, distinguish from Green Pygmy-goose by white on primaries. Short black bill. Crown, upperparts, blackish glossed green. White face, neck, underparts. Narrow black breast band. Legs, feet, pale grey. **F** More dusky with bold white eyebrow and dark eye-line. Thin white trailing edge to wing (wider in Green Pygmy-goose). **Size** 34–38 cm. **Imm.** As female but no green gloss. **Voice** Staccato 'wek'; soft buzzing. **Hab.** Deep lagoons, swamps, dams, particularly with waterlilies and other floating vegetation.

Duckling

Aust. race albipennis *is slightly larger than nominate Asiatic race* coromandelianus.

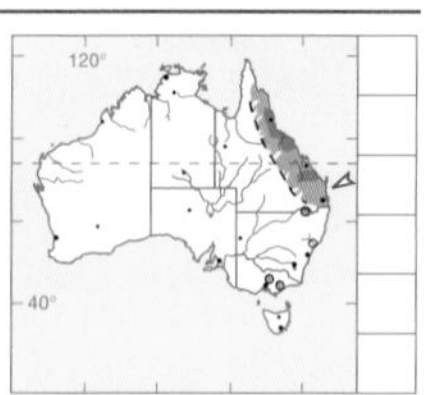

Race *albipennis* E

Green Pygmy-goose *Nettapus pulchellus* C ◎

Occasionally dives, unlike Cotton Pygmy-goose. In flight, distinguish from Cotton Pygmy-goose by large white panels on trailing edge of wing next to body. Bill bi-coloured pink and blackish. Head, neck, upperparts, blackish, glossed green; bright white face patch. Breast, flanks, rump, white, beautifully and coarsely vermiculated grey. Abdomen off-white. Legs, feet, pale grey. **F** Duller; flanks, neck, more mottling than Cotton, white eyebrow more obscure. **Size** 30–36 cm. **Imm.** As female. **Voice** Male distinctive shrill 'pee-whit'. **Hab.** As Cotton Pygmy-goose; also shallow, spike-rush dominated swamps in wet season.

Duckling

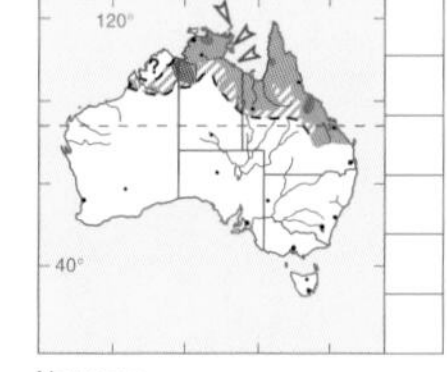

No races

Blue-billed Duck *Oxyura australis* LA–MC ⚪–⚘ E

Dark, compact diving duck with short 'dished' bill. Swims with tail erect at times. Flight rapid and low on short narrow wings. Floats higher than Musk Duck. Distinguished in all plumages from Musk Duck by 'dished', not triangular, bill, also more rounded head, smaller size; from Hardhead by lack of white undertail and broad white wing bar. Head black. Bright blue bill. Body deep chestnut. Tail black with stiff, pointed feathers, usually carried below the water surface but sometimes erected and fanned. **Eclipse** Plumage becomes duller, feathers broadly edged pale brown. Bill slate-grey. **F** Bill dark grey. Head dark brown; paler on throat, below eye. Body finely barred, freckled, buffish. Paler below. **Size** 40 cm. **Imm.** Paler, barring more distinct. **Voice** Low 'squark-wak'. **Hab.** Deep freshwater marshes with dense vegetation; more open waters in non-breeding season.

Duckling

♀ with duckling

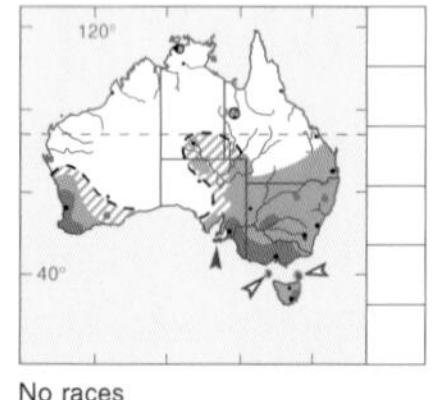

No races

Musk Duck *Biziura lobata* LC–UC ⚘ E

Large, powerful, bizarre-looking stiff-tailed duck, often swims partially submerged. Smooth, expert diver. Rarely seen to fly or come ashore. Swims with tail erect at times. When disturbed, thrashes across water in a cloud of spray. Looks black in poor light. Identify from smaller female Blue-billed Duck; swimming cormorants. Stout, dark-grey triangular bill with large black lobe of skin hanging below. Heavy thickset head. Very dark body with faint vermiculations when seen close-up. **F** Very small bill lobe. **Size** M 66; F 55 cm. **Juv./Imm.** As female, smaller; undeveloped bill lobe. **Voice** Spectacular splashing 'steamboat' displays by courting male includes 'plonk' and descending whistle. **Hab.** Permanent swamps with dense vegetation. s Large open lakes, tidal inlets, bays.

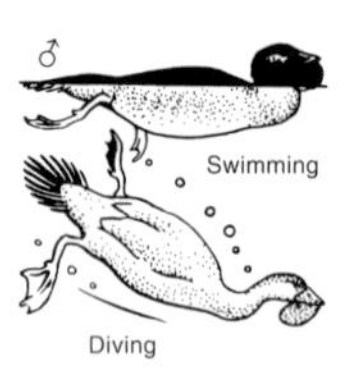

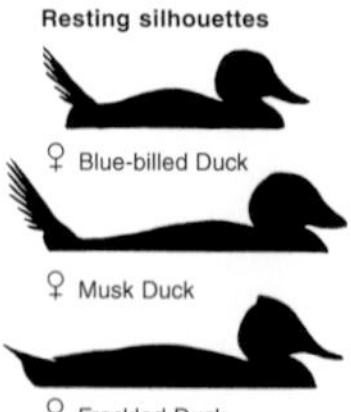

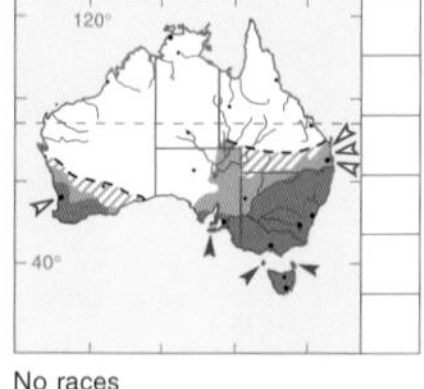

No races

Cotton Pygmy-goose ♂
Cotton Pygmy-goose ♀
Green Pygmy-goose ♀
Green Pygmy-goose ♂
Blue-billed Duck ♂
Musk Duck ♂
Musk Duck ♂
Displaying
Green Pygmy-goose ♀
Cotton Pygmy-goose ♀
Cotton Pygmy-goose ♂
Green Pygmy-goose ♂
Blue-billed Duck ♀
Blue-billed Duck ♂
Blue-billed Duck
Imm.
Musk Duck ♂
Musk Duck ♀
N. Day.

Buff-banded Rail *Gallirallus philippensis* **C** ♧

Often skulking behaviour. Bill brown, shorter than Lewin's. Long white eyebrow above chestnut eye-stripe, nape. Brown cap streaked black. Throat grey. Upperparts, wings, brown; blackish feather centres, edged with white spots. Upper chest to undertail black with white bars. Buffy-orange mid-chest band. Legs pink-brown. Population on Cape York Penin. smaller with narrower, darker breast band (but not including race *tounelieri* (B) on offshore islands). **Size** 30–33 cm. **Hatchling** Sooty-black. **Juv.** Duller, markings indistinct. **Voice** Piercing 'swit'; sibilant squeaks 'sswit sswit'; loud throaty croaks; at nest a low clucking. **Hab.** Grassy, reedy or thickly vegetated areas usually close to water; also offshore islands.

Hatchling

Related to NZ's Weka, Lord Howe Is. Woodhen.

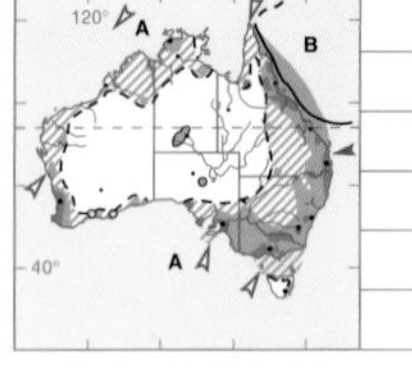

A = Race *mellori* **E** (includes former races *australis, yorki*)
B = Race *tounelieri* (Great Barrier Reef; Coral Sea)

Lewin's Rail *Rallus (Dryolimnas) pectoralis* **MC** ◎

Secretive. Much smaller, blacker, than Buff-banded Rail. Flicks tail as walks. Bill long, black-tipped, basal two-thirds reddish. Eyebrow and nape chestnut. Chestnut cap, black streaked. Throat, chest, plain olive-grey. Black feathers of upperparts margined olive-brown. Belly to undertail black, barred white. Undertail has two lateral streaks of white. Feet flesh-coloured. Race *brachipus* (B) Slightly larger birds on average. **Size** 20–27 cm. **Hatchling** Sooty-black. **Juv.** Black head; pale throat (paler than shown). White bars of underparts duller. **Voice** Wide variety of soft clicks, shrill 'deep-deep' or 'crek' in groups of calls; crowing, rapid drumming. Calls considered louder than Buff-banded Rail's. **Hab.** As Buff-banded Rail; prefers coastal regions. Race *brachipus* (B) Very numerous in Tas.

Flight

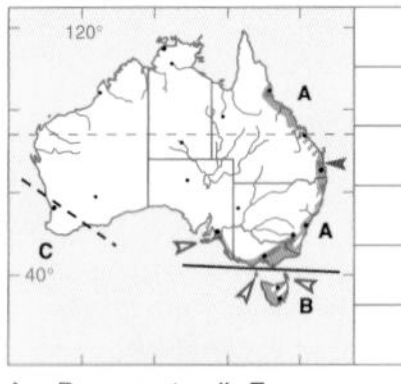

A = Race *pectoralis* **E**
B = Race *brachipus* **E**
C = Race *clelandi* **Extinct**

Chestnut Rail *Eulabeornis castaneoventris* **UC** ◎

Secretive, behaviour little known. Purple Swamphen size with 'ginger' body. Some variation in back colour across distribution (olive in west, chestnut in east). Bill green with horn tip. Head, nape grey. Throat pink-grey. Glossy pink-chestnut below, paler thighs. Legs olive-yellow. **Size** M 52; F 44–52 cm. **Hatchling** Bill black. Pale brown silky down; palest about lores. Legs, feet brown; claws pink. **Juv.** Bill base olive-yellow; pale pink-brown toward tip; all tinged white. Face, crown, nape, slaty-grey; browner on mantle. Back, rump, brown richly tinged hazel. Underparts uniform rich pink-chestnut. Tail uniformly chestnut. **Voice** Raucous screeches 'wack waka, wah-wah' rhythmically repeated; often alternated with grunting notes. **Hab.** Mangroves.

Calling

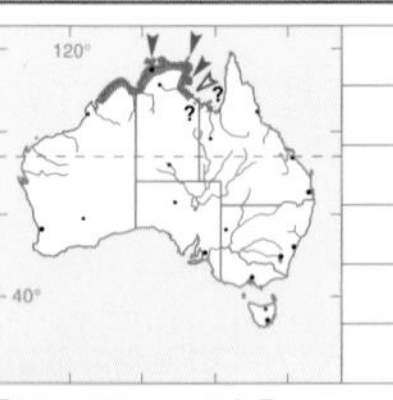

Race *castaneoventris* **E**
Map provisional; probably breeds throughout range

Red-necked Crake *Rallina tricolor* **UC** ◎

Normally appears a bi-coloured crake (despite Latin name). Flicks tail as walks. In flight, grey axilla, strongly barred underwing. Bill green. Head, neck and chest rich chestnut; throat buffy. Upperparts dark slate-grey. Abdomen, lower flanks, vent and undertail sooty-black with dull rufous cross bars. **Size** 23–29 cm. **Juv.** Bill dull green; duller chestnut and olive upperparts. Duller bars below. **Voice** Often calls at dusk. Loud, descending 'raak, rah-rah-rah'; 'kih'; 'toh, toh' or 'plop-plop-plop' often heard in wet season; grunts like piglet; single clicks. **Hab.** Rainforest near water.

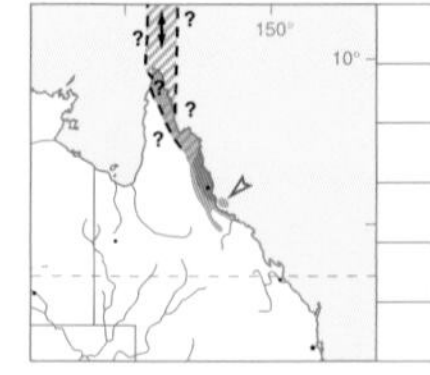

No races

Red-legged Crake *Rallina fasciata* see **Vagrant Bird Bulletin** p. 288.

Lewin's Rail
Juv.
Lewin's Rail
Lewin's
Rail
Hatchling
Buff-banded Rail
Red-legged Crake
Chestnut Rail
Red-necked Crake

Baillon's Crake *Porzana pusilla* **MC**

Smallest Aust. crake; sparrow-sized. Often walks over water weed. Swims, dives readily. Bill olive-brown. Eye red. Eyebrow light blue-grey. Eye-stripe ochre-brown. Cap, hind neck, upperparts, ochre-brown, streaked black. Wings have faint white spots on feather edges. Underparts light blue-grey, paler on throat, breast and abdomen. Flanks and undertail coverts barred black and white. Legs olive-brown. **Size** 15–18 cm. **Hatchling** Greenish-black. **Juv.** Browner below, duller bars on underparts. **Voice** 'chutt, krekk'; also a deep trill when alarmed. **Hab.** Well vegetated freshwater to brackish swamps.

Prior name was 'Marsh Crake'.

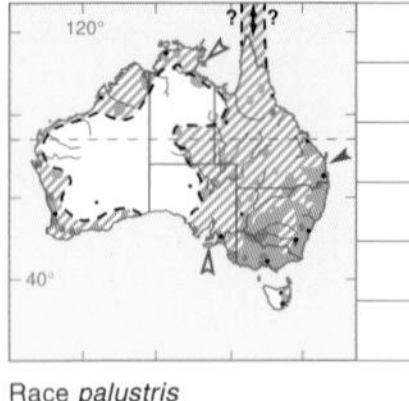

Race *palustris*

Australian Spotted Crake *Porzana fluminea* **C** E

Largest of Australian *Porzana* spp. More readily visible than other crakes. Bill olive-green, orange-red at base. Eye red. Lores black. Face, chest pale slate-grey. Cap, neck and upperparts dark olive-brown, streaked black and finely spotted white. Lower flanks black, barred white. Undertail coverts white. Legs olive-green. **Size** 19–23 cm. **Hatchling** Sooty-black. **Juv.** Bill may have a little red at base. Iris dull yellow. Upperparts brownish; buff feather edges. All underparts brown with white tips to feathers; abdomen, flanks, dull brown bars on white. **Voice** Many calls: 'doo-ik'; high-pitched 'chatter-chatter'; slow 'kirrik-kirrik-kirrik'; whirring. **Hab.** Well-vegetated freshwater swamps; estuary margins and brackish lagoons with saltmarsh.

Also known as 'Australian Crake', 'Spotted Crake'.

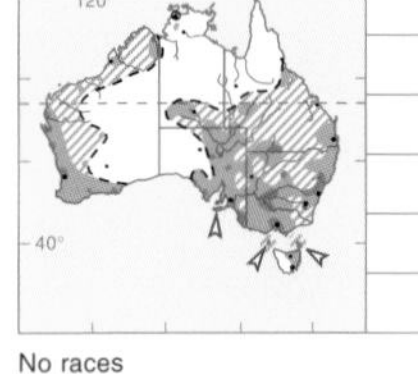

No races

Spotless Crake *Porzana tabuensis* **C–UC** ◎–

Plainer, darker, slightly smaller than Australian Spotted Crake. May appear black in the field. Bill black. Iris red. Dark slate-grey head, chin and underparts. Rest of upperparts chocolate-brown. Barred undertail. Legs red. **Size** 17–20 cm. **Juv.** Duller brown; iris black. **Voice** Slow 'kikk'; a sharp 'kikk, blop-blop-blop' like engine starting; 'bubbling' sounds. **Hab.** Reedy and grassy freshwater swamps.

Undertail pattern

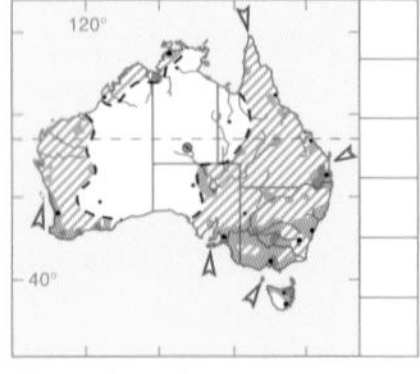

Race *tabuensis*

White-browed Crake *Porzana (Poliolimnas) cinerea* **LC** ◎

Walks on lilypads like a Jacana. Small. Bill olive-yellow, base red. Cap, lores and eye-stripe blackish. Face pattern (eyebrow, stripe below dark eye-stripe and throat, all white) diagnostic. Upperparts black with olive-brown feather margins. Cheeks, upper breast and upper flanks grey. Abdomen white; lower breast and undertail coverts sandy-buff. Legs olive-green. **Size** 17.5–20 cm. **Juv.** Facial markings duller; cap brown; neck buff. **Voice** Loud chattering. Squealing cackle in chorus; single 'yep'. **Hab.** Well-vegetated swamps.

Undertail pattern

No races

Corn Crake *Crex crex* **V**

Not reliably confirmed in Australia. Old and possibly unreliable records only (1893, 1944). **To be removed from the Field Guide in the future.**

Corn Crake
Baillon's Crake
Juv.
Baillon's Crake
Spotless Crake
Juv.
Spotless Crake
Australian Spotted Crake
Juv.
Australian Spotted Crake
White-browed Crake
Juv.
White-browed Crake
N. Day

Bush-hen *Amaurornis olivaceus* **MC–UC** ◎

Secretive. Bill green; small orange frontal shield. Iris brown. Cap to mantle olive-brown; browner to tail. Sides of head to abdomen pale slate-grey. Vent dull pink-chestnut. Legs yellow. **Size** 24–31 cm. **Hatchling** Black; at 5–6 weeks brown, black head. **Juv.** Paler; bill all green. **Voice** Call mostly at dusk, dawn. Long, shriek, repeated 'nee-u', then softer shuddering sound; possibly two birds in 'duet'. Also clicks and grunts; a single piping note, repeated. **Hab.** Swamps, flooded grassland, rainforest fringes.

Race now known to extend beyond Aust. No longer considered an Aust. endemic.

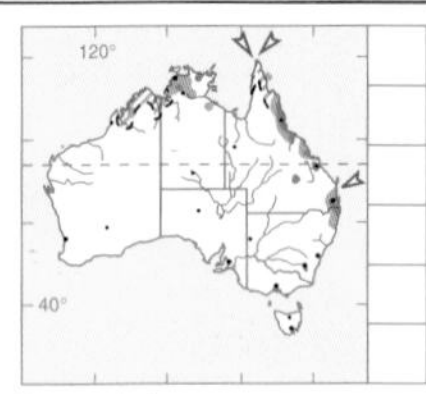

Race *ruficrissus*

Tasmanian Native-hen *Gallinula mortierii* **LC** ◎ E

Large olive-grey gallinule; almost size of Purple Swamphen. Flightless. Bill yellow. Iris ruby-red. Upperparts olive-brown, browner on wings. Underparts slate-grey. White flank patch. Tail, abdomen, black. Legs, feet dark grey. **Size** 43–51 cm. **Hatchling** Black down; white spot on flanks. **Juv.** Paler. **Voice** Harsh scream; drumming grunts. 'Wee-haw, wee-haw', braying chorus. **Hab.** Grassy areas, farmland, usually near water.

Calling

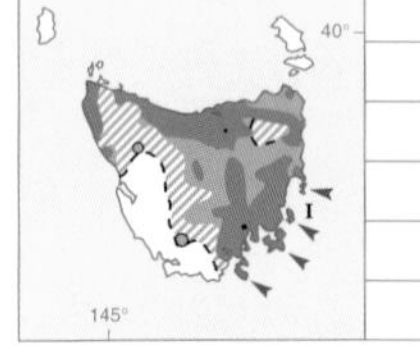

No races

Black-tailed Native-hen *Gallinula ventralis* **LA–C** ♧ E

Dusky Moorhen-sized, more upright. Tail black, erect, 'chicken'-like. Often in open. Groups run to shelter in bushes. Bill lime-green; lower bill-base orange. Iris yellow. Olive-brown above. Breast blue-grey. Belly, undertail coverts, black. White pear-shaped flank spots. Legs coral. **Size** 30–38 cm. **Hatchling** Greenish sheen. **Juv.** Paler; dull spots. **Voice** Quiet cackle; sharp 'chi-quik'. **Hab.** Near water; claypans, lignum swamps, dams.

Running tail down

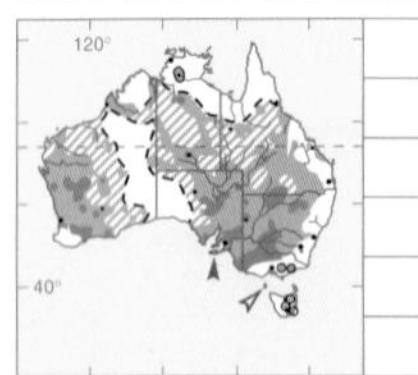

No races

Dusky Moorhen *Gallinula tenebrosa* **C** ◎–♧

Often swimming. Slightly smaller than Purple Swamphen. Bill, frontal shield, red, tip yellow. Iris olive. Body slate-grey. Wings, rump browner. Tail black. Faint white flank spots on some birds. White sides to undertail coverts. Legs yellow, scarlet and olive. **Size** 35–40 cm. **Hatchling** Black, white tips to chin, throat. Frontal shield red. Skin on cap bluish. **Juv.** Paler; bill green, horn or black. Legs green. **Voice** Shrill 'cheeah'; nasal 'tuk, tuk'; low honking. **Hab.** Fresh water, usually near reeds or dense cover.

Flight

Juv.

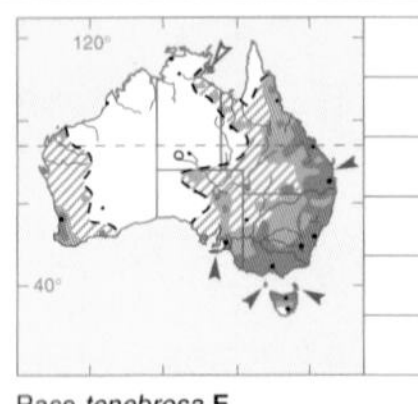

Race *tenebrosa* **E**

Purple Swamphen *Porphyrio porphyrio* **C** ♧

Large purple gallinule with stout brick-red bill, frontal shield. Flicks tail when walking. Red eyes. Head, upperparts black. Underparts, wings deep blue to purple-black. White 'triangular' undertail coverts. Legs red. Race *bellus* (B) Paler blue on underparts. **Size** 44–48 cm. **Hatchling** Black. Bill grey-white, black tip. Legs grey, become redder with age. **Juv.** Plumage, iris, bill, all browner. **Voice** Harsh screaming 'weeeah'. Querulous 'nee-ow?' Thuds. **Hab.** Swamps, marshy paddocks, urban lakes.

Flight

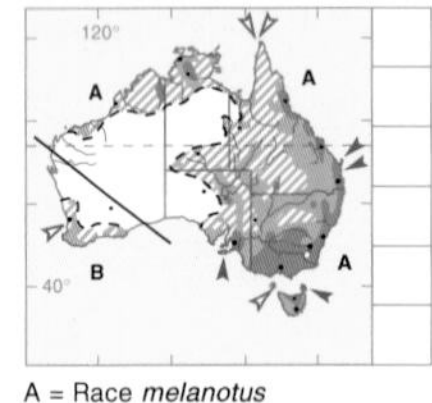

A = Race *melanotus*
B = Race *bellus* **E**

Eurasian Coot *Fulica atra* **LA–C** ♧

Often in large winter flocks (rafts) on water. Dives for food; favours deeper water. Body more 'rounded'. White bill, large frontal shield. Eyes red. Head black. All body dark slate-grey (no white undertail). Legs dark grey; toes lobed. During moulting, browner body, wing plumage. **Size** 35–39 cm. **Hatchling** Black down with yellow hair-like tips. Bill cream, face red. **Juv./Imm.** Pale throat; smaller, duller, than adults. **Voice** Reedy, nasal 'nerdip'; contact call a sharp 'pit, pit, pit'. **Hab.** Swamps, reservoirs, fresh or brackish lakes, estuaries, large garden ponds.

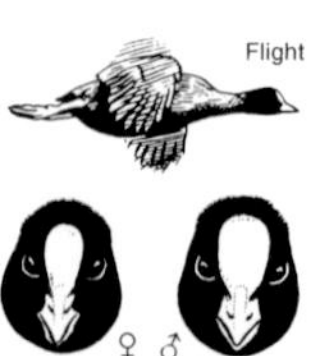

Head shields

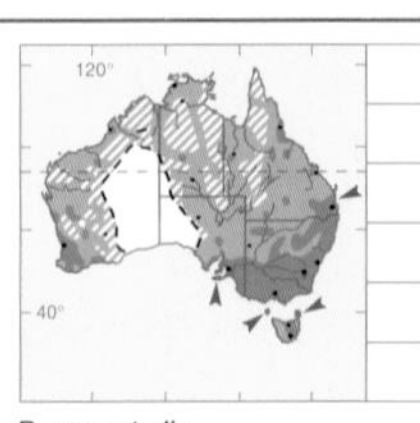

Race *australis*

Purple
Swamphen
Tasmanian
Native-hen
Purple
Swamphen
Purple
Swamphen
Hatchling
Black-tailed
Native-hen
Bush-hen
Dusky Moorhen
Eurasian
Coot
Eurasian Coot
Hatchling
Dusky Moorhen
Hatchling
Eurasian Coot
Dusky
Moorhen

Great-billed Heron *Ardea sumatrana* UC ◎

Huge bronze-brown heron. Bill long, stout and dark brown; paler at base of lower mandible. Entire plumage bronzy-brown with nuchal crest, hackles on foreneck and lanceolate plumes on back. Belly creamy-brown. Legs dark grey. **Non-br.** Face yellowish; plumes, hackles reduced. **Size** 100–110 cm. **Juv.** Rufous-brown; no crest, hackles or plumes. **Voice** Penetrating (and to the inexperienced, frightening) calls including loud guttural roars ('crocodile'-like) and groans, day and night. **Hab.** Mangrove-fringed tidal channels of tropical Australia; exposed mudflats, grassy verges along rivers.

Juv. Great-billed Heron

Juv. Black-necked Stork

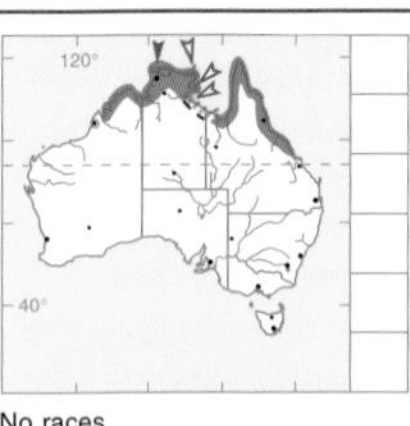

No races
Probably breeds throughout range

White-necked (Pacific) Heron *Ardea pacifica* MC ♣ Br. E

Large heron. The white 'shoulder' patch, visible both at rest and in flight (looks like headlights on flying bird), distinguishes it from juv. (much smaller) Pied Heron. Bill dark grey. Head and neck white. Back and wings sooty-black with a bluish sheen. Maroon lanceolate plumes on back and upper breast. Prominent white patch on shoulder of wing. Breast and belly grey-brown, streaked white. Legs dark grey. **Non-br.** A line of brown and black spots down the foreneck. Plumes reduced or absent. **Size** 76–106 cm. **Juv.** Neck has greyish wash; the foreneck is more heavily spotted and lanceolate plumes are absent. **Voice** Harsh deep croaks. **Hab.** Moist pasture, floodwaters and shallows of freshwater wetlands.

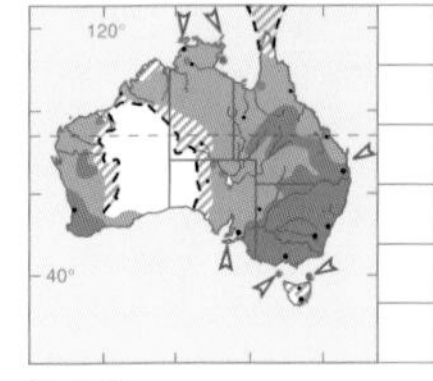

No races

Pied Heron *Ardea picata* LA–C ◎–?♣

Small black and white heron. Bill yellow. 'Cap' over head, nuchal plumes, dark blue-grey. Neck white. Blue-grey and white hackles frill the lower neck; slaty-grey lanceolate plumes on back. Body, wings, dark blue-grey. Legs yellow. **Non-br.** Plumes and hackles reduced. **Size** 43–55 cm. **Juv.** Head, neck white. Crown sometimes washed grey or brown. Hackles and plumes absent; back tinged brown. Belly whitish; flanks grey-brown. **Voice** Harsh croaks. **Hab.** Near-coastal swamps, billabongs, rubbish tips, sewage works and intertidal flats.

Roosting

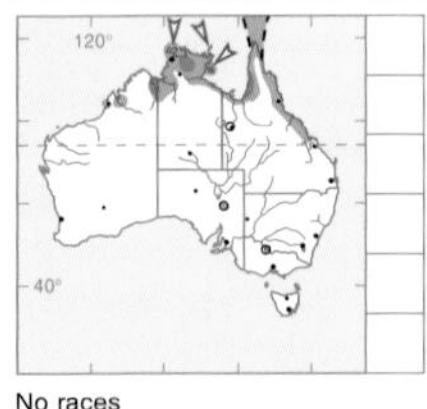

No races

White-faced Heron *Egretta (Ardea) novaehollandiae* C ◎–♣

Slender blue-grey heron. Heavy slow flight, neck retracted unless alarmed. Perches on trees, posts. Identify from grey morph of Eastern Reef Egret. Bill dark brown, paler at base of mandible. Face to just behind the eye, chin, white. Pale chestnut hackles on lower neck; lanceolate plumes on back. Upperparts and wings grey, belly paler. Flight feathers dark grey. Legs yellow-green. **Non-br.** Plumes and hackles reduced or absent. **Size** 66–68 cm. **Juv.** Face grey or with white only on chin. Dull fawn to brown wash on grey plumage; belly whitish or pale buff. Legs paler. **Voice** Harsh croaks. **Hab.** Pasture, farm dams, parkland, most wetlands including intertidal flats. Adapts to most urban areas.

Adult face pattern

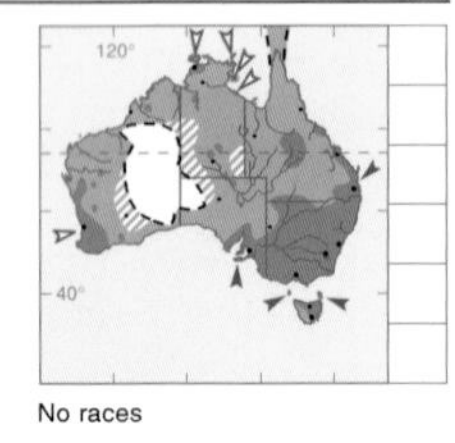

No races

Face comparisons

Adult White-faced Heron

Juv. White-faced Heron

Grey morph Eastern Reef Egret

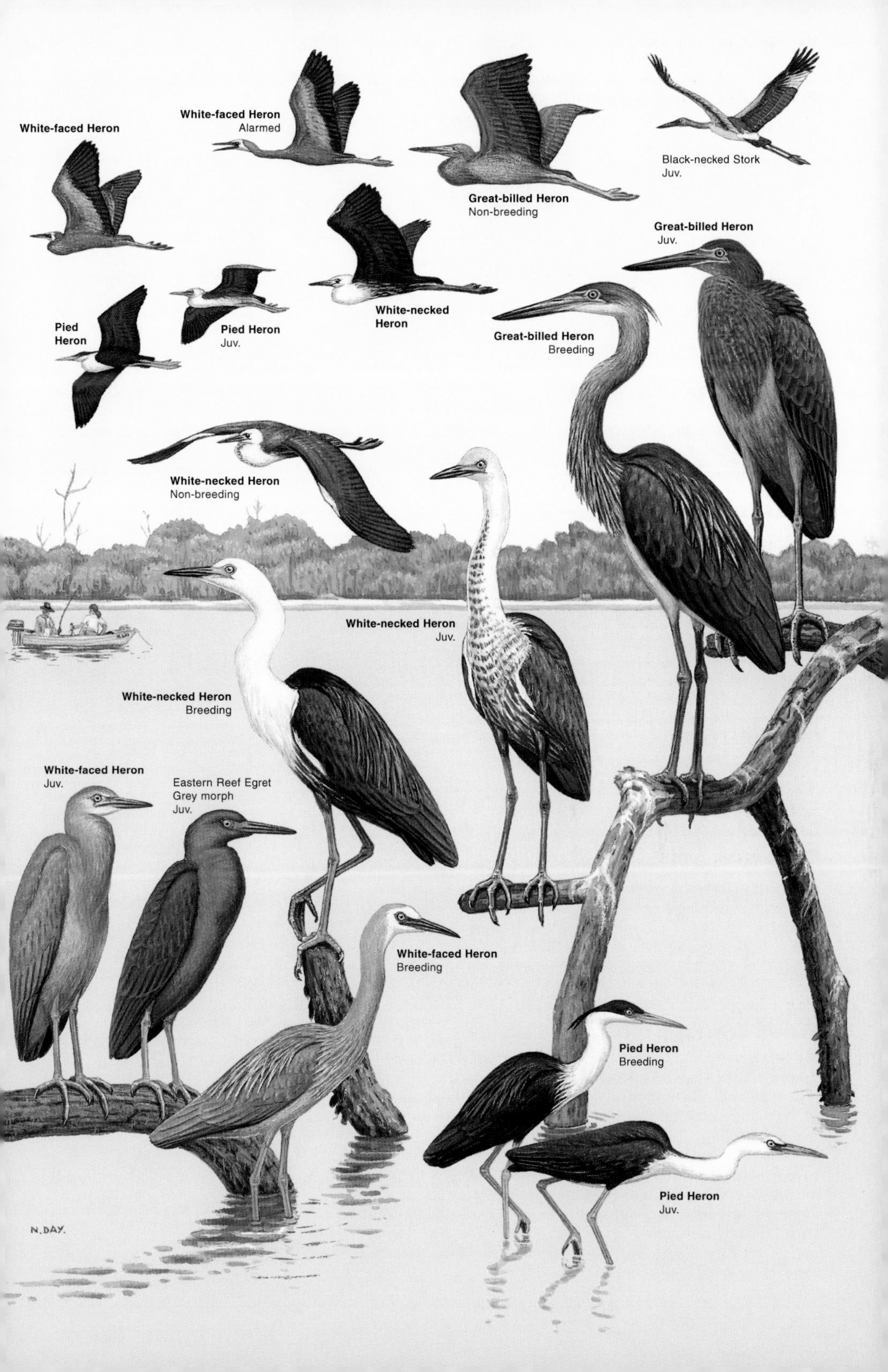
White-faced Heron
White-faced Heron
Alarmed
Great-billed Heron
Non-breeding
Black-necked Stork
Juv.
Great-billed Heron
Juv.
White-necked Heron
Pied Heron
Pied Heron
Juv.
Great-billed Heron
Breeding
White-necked Heron
Non-breeding
White-necked Heron
Juv.
White-necked Heron
Breeding
White-faced Heron
Juv.
Eastern Reef Egret
Grey morph
Juv.
White-faced Heron
Breeding
Pied Heron
Breeding
Pied Heron
Juv.
N. DAY.

Cattle Egret *Ardea ibis* **LA–C**

Often with grazing animals. Short, stocky appearance, rounded forehead, prominent feathers under lower mandible distinguish from other white egrets. In flight, may resemble corellas. Roosts communally in trees, on ground. Bill yellow or pinkish-yellow. In breeding plumage flush of orange-brown on head, neck. Long loose rusty-brown plumes on head. Neck, breast, back, rusty-brown; other plumage white. Legs greenish-grey. Bill base, face, orbital ring, legs, may turn red briefly prior to egg-laying. **Non-br.** Yellow-orange bill. Plumage snowy white. In Aust., rusty plumes acquired progressively from mid-August; traces may remain until May. **Size** 70 cm. **Voice** Harsh croaks. **Hab.** Pasture; shallows of freshwater wetlands.

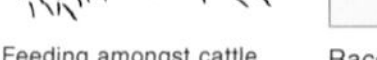
Feeding amongst cattle

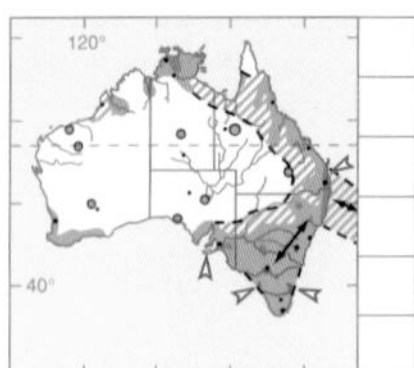

Race *coromanda*

Great Egret *Ardea alba* **C**

Legs extend well beyond tail in flight. Bill usually black; facial skin green. Body, wings, long lacy scapular plumes, white. Legs dark grey or black, slightly paler on tibia. **Non-br.** Bill usually yellow; facial skin yellow; plumes fewer or absent. Distinguished from other egrets, esp. Intermediate, by long bill and low, flat forehead, long neck with prominent kink (neck is 1.5 times body length). **Size** 83–103 cm. **Voice** Harsh croaks. **Hab.** Floodwaters, rivers, shallows of wetlands, intertidal mudflats.

Stalking

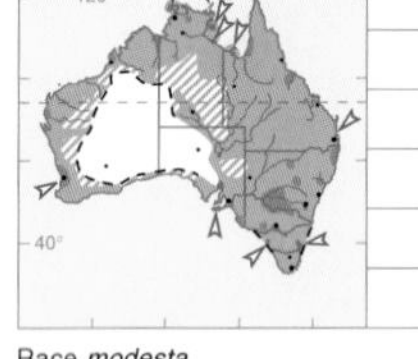

Race *modesta*

Little Egret *Egretta (Ardea) garzetta* **UC** ◎–

The only egret to run about when feeding, actively chasing prey. Bill black. Facial skin yellow to orange; more red in courtship. Entire plumage white. Two long thin nuchal plumes; lacy plumes on upper breast, wings, mantle. Legs black; soles of feet yellow. **Non-br.** Facial skin yellow; plumes few or absent. Identify by small size, black bill, yellow soles and slender build. **Size** 55–65 cm. **Voice** Harsh croaks, esp. when breeding. **Hab.** Shallows of wetlands, flooded pasture, intertidal mudflats.

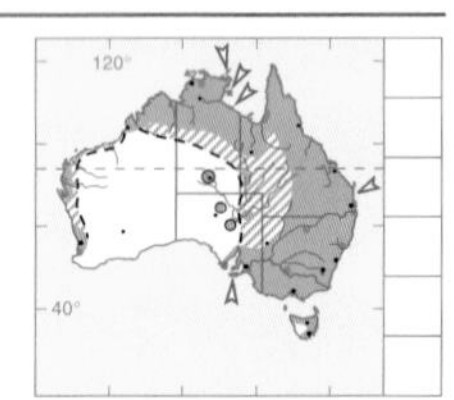

Race *nigripes*

Intermediate Egret *Ardea intermedia* **C** –?–

Bill orange or red; facial skin green. Plumage white with long lacy plumes arising from the upper breast and scapulars. Tibia red; tarsus black. **Non-br.** Bill orange-yellow; face yellow. Few or no plumes. Legs black. Distinguished from Great Egret by proportionately shorter and thicker bill; higher forehead; shorter, thicker and less-kinked neck (neck equals length of body). Legs appear shorter in flight. **Size** 56–70 cm. **Voice** Harsh croaks. **Hab.** Shallows of freshwater wetlands, intertidal mudflats.

Size comparison of adults

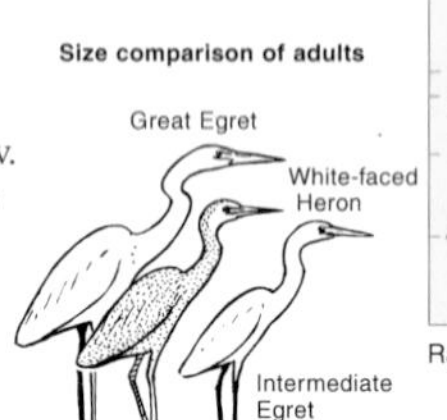

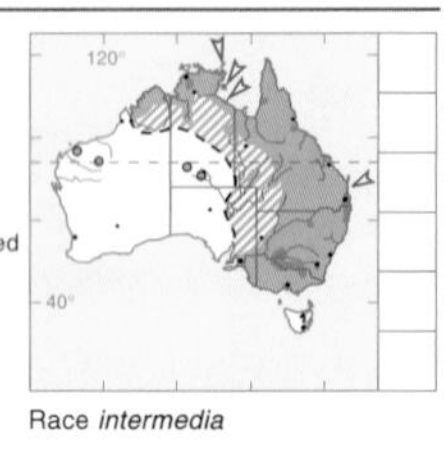

Race *intermedia*

Eastern Reef Egret *Egretta (Ardea) sacra* **C** ?◎

Roosts communally. Bill comparatively long and thick. Legs shorter, thicker than other egrets; appear very short in flight. Two colour morphs. **Grey morph** (commoner in south of range) Bill grey. Plumage dark sooty-grey except for some white on throat. Lanceolate plumes on back, hackles on lower neck. Legs vary; greyish- or greenish-yellow. Identify from White-faced Heron by darker plumage, no white on face. **Juv.** Brownish-grey, slightly brownish cap; identify from Striated Heron, juvenile White-faced Heron. **White morph** Bill pale horn to yellow. Entire plumage white. Identify from other egrets. **Juv.** White. **Non-br.** Few or no plumes. **Size** 60–65 cm. **Voice** Harsh croaks. **Hab.** Intertidal zone: rocks, coral reefs, mangroves, mudflats.

White morph: stalking

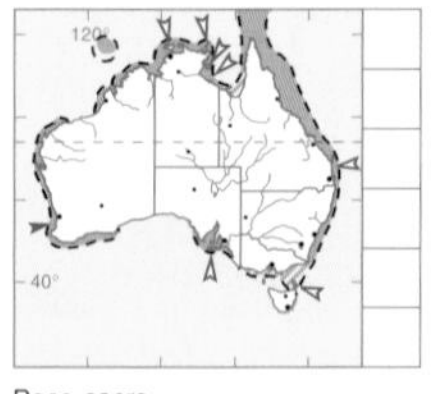

Race *sacra*
Probably breeds throughout range. White morph more common in N Aust.

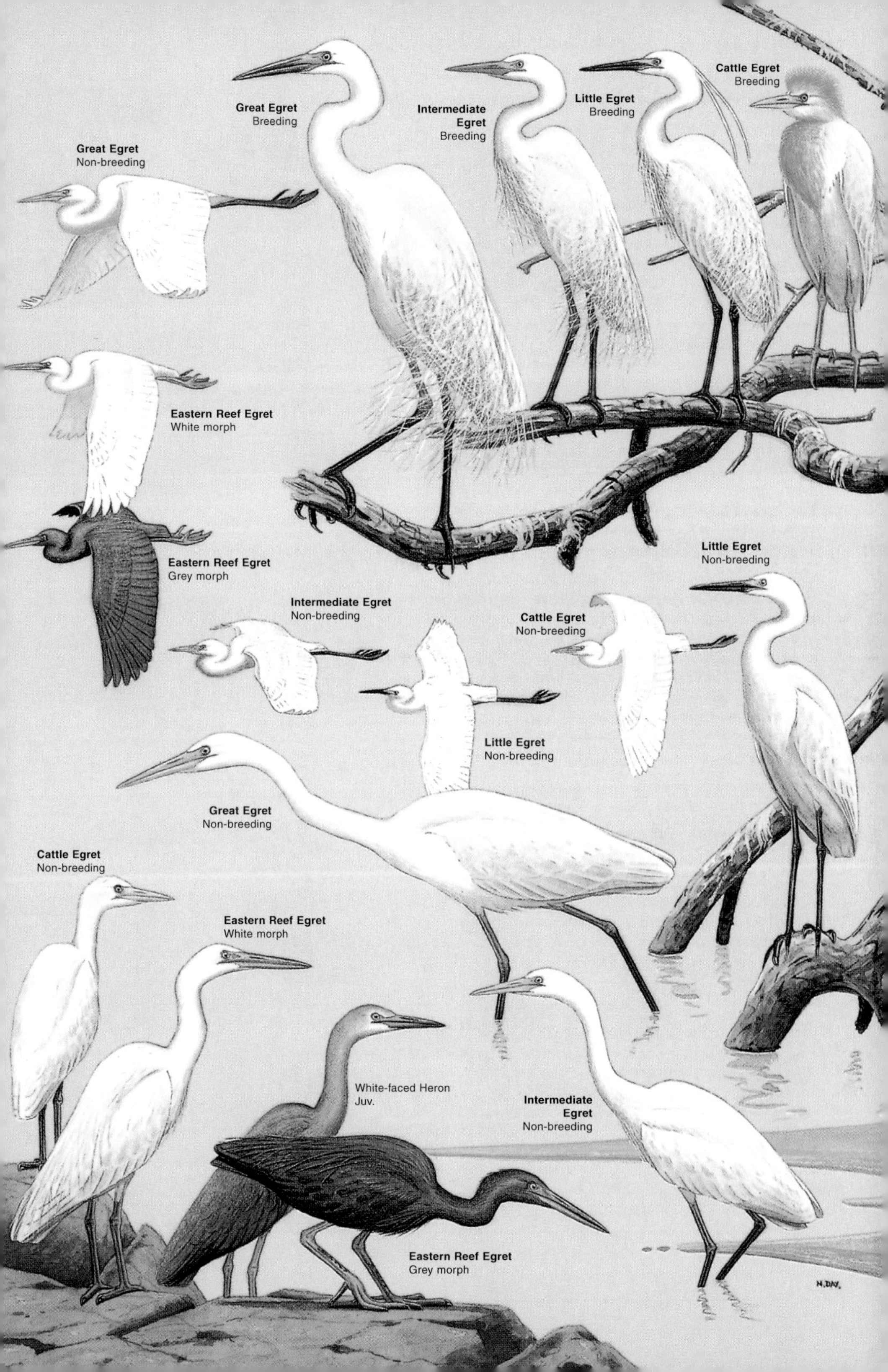
Great Egret
Breeding
Intermediate
Egret
Breeding
Little Egret
Breeding
Cattle Egret
Breeding
Great Egret
Non-breeding
Eastern Reef Egret
White morph
Eastern Reef Egret
Grey morph
Little Egret
Non-breeding
Intermediate Egret
Non-breeding
Cattle Egret
Non-breeding
Little Egret
Non-breeding
Great Egret
Non-breeding
Cattle Egret
Non-breeding
Eastern Reef Egret
White morph
White-faced Heron
Juv.
Intermediate
Egret
Non-breeding
Eastern Reef Egret
Grey morph
N.DAY.

Striated (Mangrove) Heron *Butorides (Ardeola) striatus* **LC** ◎

Crouches low, neck extended or retracted. 'Bittern-posture' when disturbed. Two Australian races each have glossy black crown, nuchal crest; body darker above than below. Metallic sheen on back; throat, foreneck, streaked black and dark brown. Race *macrorhyncha* (A) Dark-olive above, dusky-brown below. Race *stagnatilis* (B) Mostly rufous on Pilbara coast of WA but rarely elsewhere. Same subspecies becomes brownish-grey or paler grey in far NW and across N Australia, then dark grey-green in Gulf of Carpentaria. **Size** 43 cm. **Voice** Variety of sharp calls. **Hab.** Mangroves, intertidal flats.

Crouched stalking posture

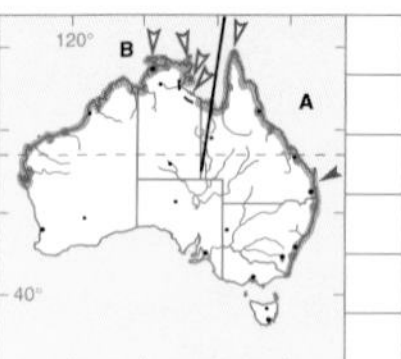

Previously 5 races in Aust., now 2:
A = Race *macrorhyncha* (incl. *littleri*)
B = Race *stagnatilis* (incl. *rogersi, cinerea*)

Nankeen (Rufous) Night Heron
Nycticorax caledonicus **C** ⁂–?–◎

Feeds nocturnally; roosts in trees close to water by day; also under jetties, wharves. Bill, crown black; two slender white nuchal plumes. Upperparts, wings, rufous. Belly white. **Non-br.** Lacks plumes. **Size** M 55–65; F 55–60 cm. **Juv.** Strongly mottled and streaked brown on white. **Imm.** Mottled rufous; black cap. **Voice** Deep croaks. **Hab.** Swamps, intertidal flats, estuaries, rivers, creeks, large ornamental ponds.

Dorsal flight

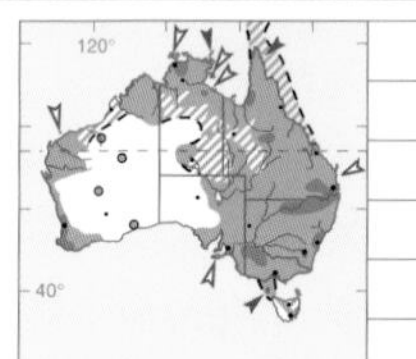

Race *hilli* **E**

Little Bittern *Ixobrychus minutus* **UC** O

Very secretive. In flight, dark wings, large buff wing-patches. Bill yellow; lores yellow flushed red. Crown, upperparts, black; hindneck deep red-brown. Long neck feathers cover throat. Buff breast centrally striped dark brown. Sides of breast, flanks, streaked dark brown. Vent, undertail, white. Legs, feet, green. **F** Black replaced by brown; underside more heavily streaked; wing patch brown–buff. **Size** 25–36 cm. **Juv.** Browner and streaked overall. Wing patch not obvious. **Voice** Deep frog-like repetitive croaks. **Hab.** Reedbeds, dense vegetation of freshwater swamps, creeks.

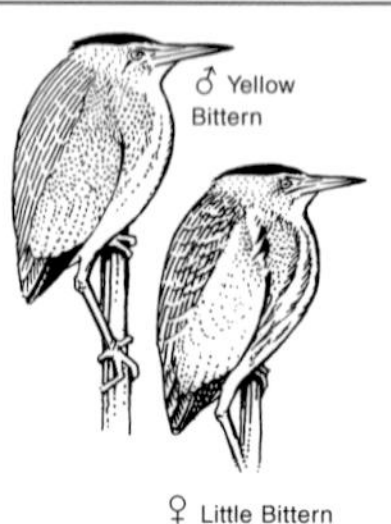

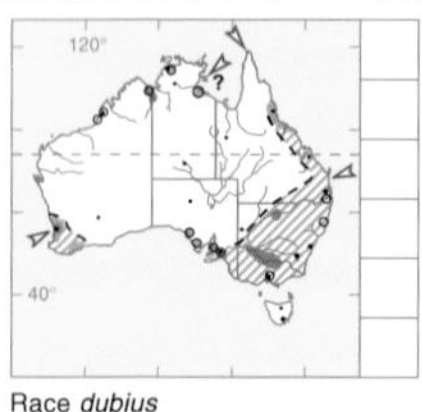

Race *dubius*

Black Bittern *Ixobrychus flavicollis* **LC–UC** ◎–?–⁂

Bill black above, yellow below. Upperparts sooty-black; side of neck yellow. Underparts white; prominent brown and black streaks down neck. Dark brown blotches on breast, belly. **F** Upperparts paler, browner; underparts more yellow. **Size** 54–66 cm. **Juv.** Like female; buff feather edges. **Voice** Deep repetitive booming. **Hab.** Mangroves, streamside vegetation including small creeks in forest.

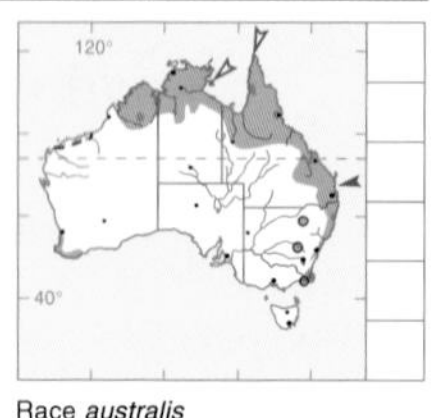

Race *australis*
Probably breeds throughout range

Australasian Bittern *Botaurus poiciloptilus* **UC** ⁂ Vulnerable

Secretive; labours into flight when disturbed. Identify from smaller Juv./Imm. Nankeen Night Heron. Bill straight, pointed, dull buff, dark culmen. Upperparts brown; cryptically streaked, mottled, cream and buff; more so on wing coverts. Brown stripe down side of neck edges the white throat. Underside cream-buff, streaked and barred dark brown. **Size** 66–76 cm. **Voice** Male in-drawn breath, then low-pitched 'booomph'. **Hab.** Reedbeds, swamps, streams, estuaries.

Cryptic posture

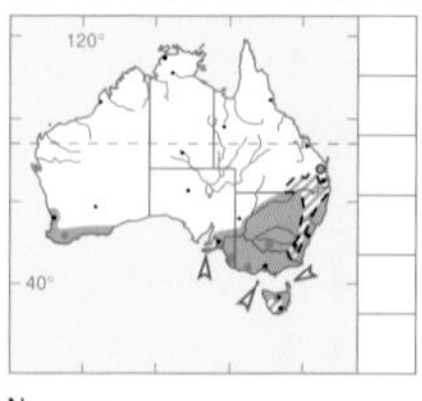

No races

Yellow Bittern *Ixobrychus sinensis* see **Vagrant Bird Bulletin** p. 288.

Australasian Bittern
Nankeen Night Heron
Nankeen Night Heron
Breeding
Nankeen Night Heron
Juv.
Striated Heron
Race stagnatilis
Grey morph
Black Bittern
Striated Heron
Juv.
Little Bittern
Striated Heron
Race macrorhyncha
Striated Heron
Race stagnatilis
Rufous morph
Little Bittern
Juv.
Little Bittern ♂
Yellow Bittern
Juv.
Black Bittern ♂
Australasian Bittern
Black Bittern
Juv.

Glossy Ibis *Plegadis falcinellus* **LA**

Distinctive on ground. In flight somewhat resembles Little Black Cormorant. Bill olive-brown. Reddish-brown body. Back, wings have purple-green sheen, changing with light and distance; may appear black. Legs variable, olive to dark brown. **Size** 55–65 cm. **Juv.** Duller; white and brown streaks on head, upper neck. **Voice** Croaking calls. **Hab.** Freshwater wetlands, pasture.

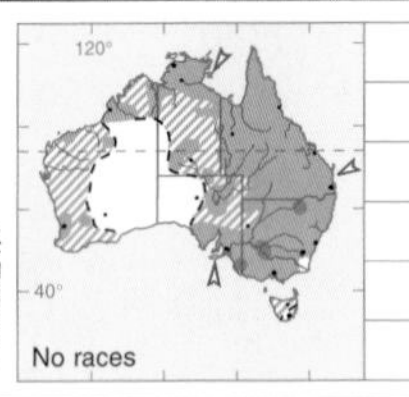

Australian White Ibis *Threskiornis molucca* **LA–C**

Soars, often with other ibis. In flight note black head, white body and wings. Roosts in trees in or near water, bullrush beds, mangroves. Bright pink bands across nape, red naked skin under wing to sides of breast. Yellow upper tail. **Non-br.** Black bill; naked skin on head, upper neck. Duller nape, underwing skin. Body, wings white (often stained dirty brown). Black wing tips. White upper tail. Black inner secondary plumes appear as a black 'tail'. Legs reddish brown. **F** Shorter bill. **Size** 65–75 cm. **Juv.** Head duskier; bill shorter. **Voice** Harsh croaks. **Hab.** All but very saline wetlands; pasture; tidal flats; rubbish dumps, urban parks.

Breeding colony

Called for a time 'Sacred Ibis' Threskiornis aethiopica.

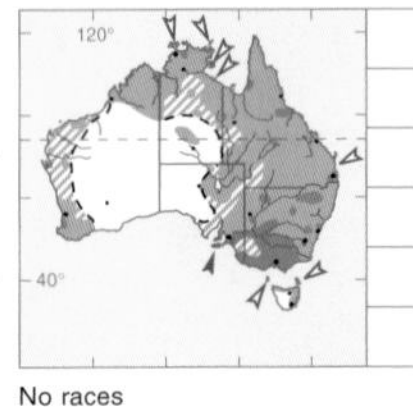

No races

Straw-necked Ibis *Threskiornis spinicollis* **C** E

In flight note white body and black wings. Soars in loose groups in thermals; flies directly in 'V' formation or long lines. Bare head, bill, upper neck, black. Back, tail and wings black with metallic sheen. Neck, belly, white; yellow straw-like breast plumes not visible at distance. Legs black; reddish 'tibia'. **Size** 60–70 cm. **Juv.** Bill shorter. **Voice** Low croaks. **Hab.** Shallow freshwater wetlands, pasture, rarely tidal flats.

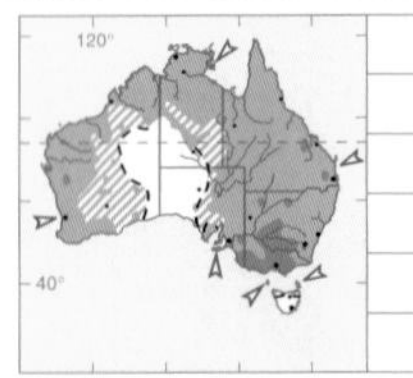

No races

Royal Spoonbill *Platalea regia* **C**

Feeds by sweeping submerged bill from side to side. Bill black, distinctive. Plumage 'whiter' than Yellow-billed; always looks 'clean'. Black skin on head to just behind eye. Small patch of red on forehead; yellow skin above each eye. White erectile nuchal plumes. Body, wings, very white. Legs black. **Non-br**. Lacks plumes, coloured patches on face. **Size** 74–81 cm. **Hab.** Shallows of fresh and saltwater wetlands including tidal flats, mangroves.

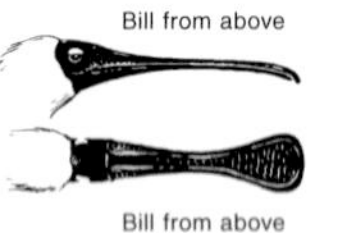

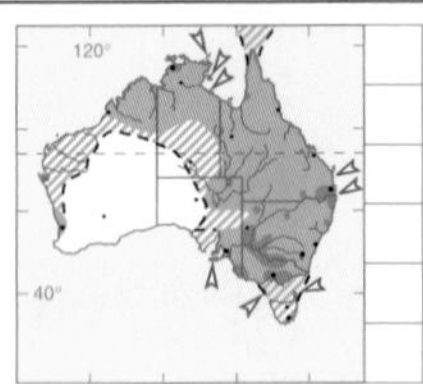

No races

Yellow-billed Spoonbill *Platalea flavipes* **C** E

Often solitary; roosts in trees. Plumage often 'grubbier' than Royal. Bill yellow, distinctive. Grey facial skin edged black. Body creamy-white except for black lace-like plumes on inner secondaries. Hackles on upper breast. Legs yellow. **Non-br.** Face yellow, without black edge. Hackles, plumes, reduced or absent. **Imm.** Birds show black markings on tertials. **Size** 76–92 cm. **Voice** Deep reedy grunt; bill clattering. **Hab.** Shallows of freshwater wetlands, occasionally on dry pasture, farm dams.

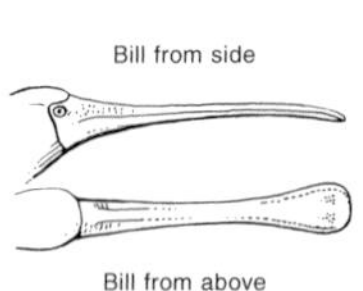

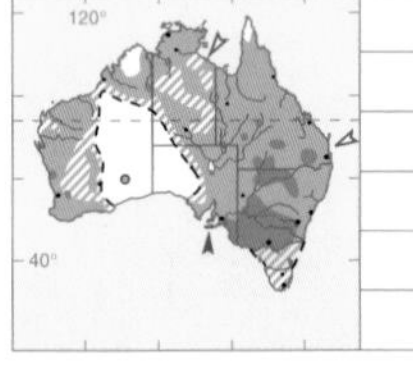

No races

Black-necked Stork *Ephippiorhynchus asiaticus* **LC**

Striking long-legged pied bird with thick, black, straight bill. Soars expertly with neck extended and legs trailing. At height, check Australian Pelican. Head, neck, broad wing-stripe, tail, are all glossy black. Iris colours differ (diagram). Body, remainder of wings, white. Very long red legs. **Size** 110–137 cm; stands to 120 cm; wingspan 190–218 cm. **Juv.** Dull brown. **Voice** Seldom calls; clappers with bill. Some booming notes recorded (but unconfirmed). **Hab.** River pools, swamps, tidal flats.

Yellow iris = Ad. female
Black iris = Ad. male

Formerly called 'Jabiru'.

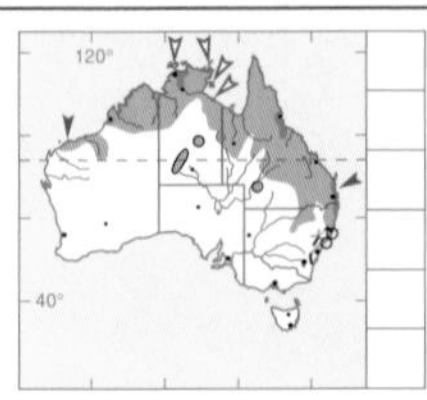

Race *australis*

Little Black Cormorant
Australian White Ibis
Black-necked Stork ♂
Glossy Ibis
Royal Spoonbill
Straw-necked Ibis
Australian White Ibis Juv.
Straw-necked Ibis Juv.
Yellow-billed Spoonbill
Glossy Ibis Imm.
Glossy Ibis
Australian White Ibis
Straw-necked Ibis
Black-necked Stork Juv.
Black-necked Stork ♀
Royal Spoonbill Non-breeding
Royal Spoonbill Breeding
Australian White Ibis Stained plumage
Yellow-billed Spoonbill Breeding
Yellow-billed Spoonbill Imm.

Brolga *Grus rubicunda* **C–UC** ◎–♣ E

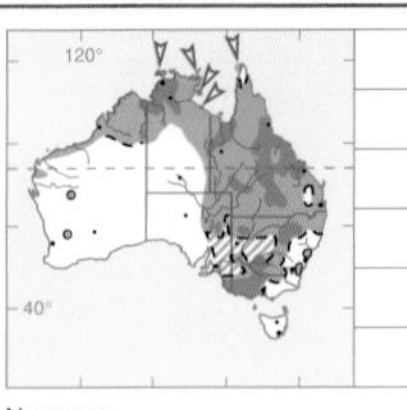

No races

Stately long-legged grey crane. Pairs or parties. Soars in thermals. In flight, neck, legs, extended; shallow wing beats with upward flick. Dancing displays of leaps, bows, high steps and loud trumpeting calls performed by both sexes. Eye yellow. Ear coverts grey. Head bare; pale grey skin on frons; scarlet on rear of head, nape. Black 'haired' dewlap under chin. Neck, back silver-grey. Back often has brown wash. 'Bustle' of secondary feathers falling over rump. Wings grey, black primaries. Underparts grey. Legs dark grey-brown to black. **F** Smaller. **Size** M 105–134; F 77–113 cm. Stands up to 140 cm. **Hatchling** Downy; grey, paler markings. **Imm.** Skin of face, nape, fleshy-pink. **Voice** Whooping bugle- or trumpet-like calls uttered in flight and on ground; also harsh croaks. **Hab.** Ephemeral wetlands, saltmarsh, open grassland, crops.

Sarus Crane *Grus antigone* **LMC** ◎–♣

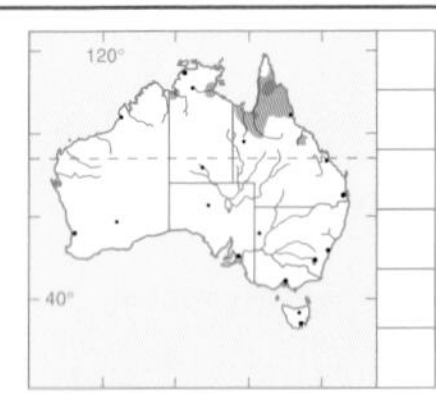

Race *gilliae* **E**

Stately, long-legged, grey crane. Often in mixed flocks with Brolgas. Distinguish from Brolga by scarlet skin on face, upper neck; no dewlap under chin. Eye red. Grey ear coverts, crown. Head, upper neck bare. Back, wings, grey. Paler 'bustle' of secondary feathers over rump sometimes has white feathers in it. Underparts grey. Legs, feet, pink. **Size** Stands to approx. 145 cm. **Imm.** Skin on head, upper neck, pale rufous. **Voice** Rather like Brolga. **Hab.** Wetlands, open grassland, pasture.

Australian Bustard *Ardeotis australis* **UC–LMC** ◎–♣

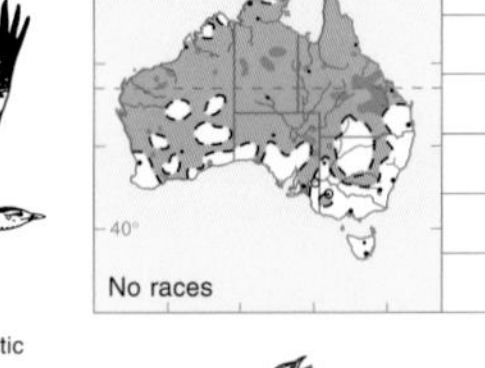

No races

Stands motionless in erect posture, head tilted upward. Strong slow flight; extends neck, legs. Crown black. White eyebrow. Neck white, finely vermiculated. Back, wings, tail, brown, fine buff marks. Upperwing coverts black and white. Black breast band. Underparts white to grey. Legs, feet, pale yellow to grey or olive; has three toes. **F** Narrow brown crown. Neck, breast, off-white to grey. Thin breast band less visible. Less black and white on wing. **Size** M 110–120; F 80–90 cm. M stands to 100 cm; F to 70 cm. **Hatchling** Downy; striped buff and brown. **Voice** Mainly silent. Guttural roars during spectacular male breeding display. Harsh barking alarm. **Hab.** Tropical open grassland, grassy woodland, pastoral land, crops.

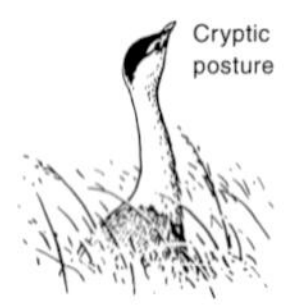

Plains-wanderer *Pedionomus torquatus* **R** ◎ E Endangered

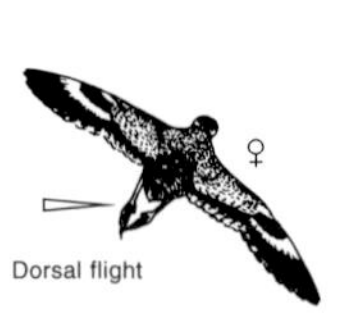

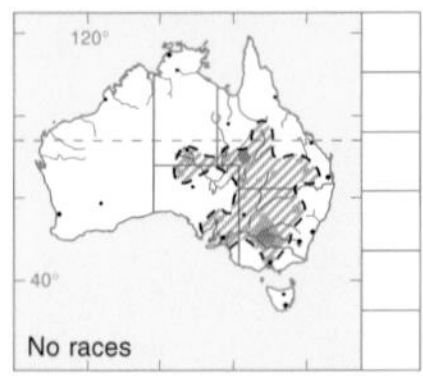

No races

Check Stubble, Brown Quail, button-quails. Runs 'crouched', may spread wings; stands erect; crouches motionless; seldom flies. Plumage soft. Buff and white; no obvious collar. Bill long, thin; long narrow nasal apertures. Iris faint yellow. Wings rounded, soft. Legs, feet, yellow to greenish-yellow; legs longer than button-quails'. Toes long; hind toe short, prominent. **F** Larger, darker; face, chin have sandy-red feathers, with fine black lines. Chestnut breast patch. Collar 'chequered' (black and white). Small black crescents on breast, upper abdomen. **Size** M 15–17; F 17–19 cm. **Juv.** As male, finer markings. **Voice** Repetitive 'oom'. **Hab.** Native grasslands, old stubble.

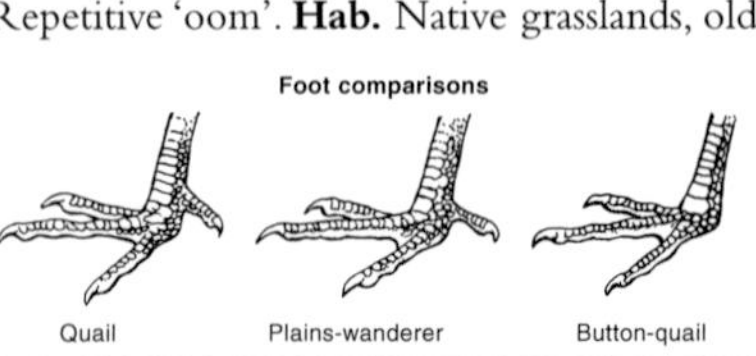

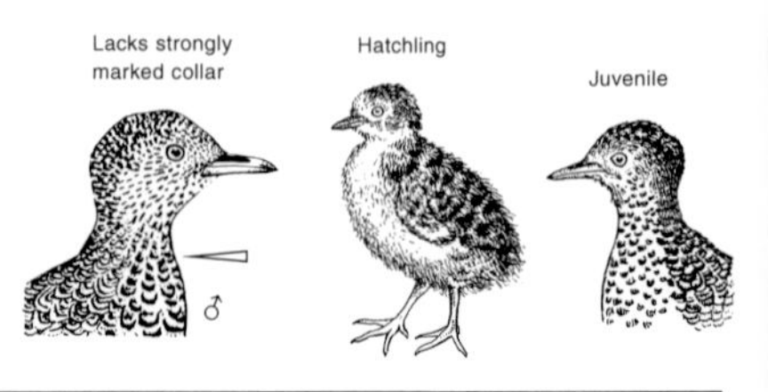

Sarus
Crane
Brolga
Sarus Crane
Brolga
Dancing
Brolga
Brolga
Imm.
Australian
Bustard
♂
Australian
Bustard
♀
Brolga
Hatchling
Australian
Bustard
Hatchling
Plains-
wanderer ♂
Plains-
wanderer ♀
Australian Bustard
Juv.
N.D.

Ruddy Turnstone *Arenaria interpres* **MC**

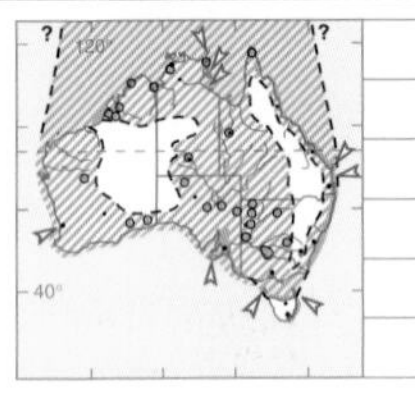
Race *interpres*

'Bulldozes' weed, gravel, shells. Distinctive, thickset, black and white wader (especially in flight). Short, wedge-shaped bill. Pied head, streaked crown, black breast. Short orange legs.
F br. Crown more streaked. **Non-br.** Dark-headed. Dusky black, less chestnut, mottled. White underparts. **Size** 22–24 cm. **Juv.** Dark brown above, breast band. **Voice** Loud rattle. **Hab.** Rocky shores with seaweed.

Eastern Curlew *Numenius madagascariensis* **MC–UC**

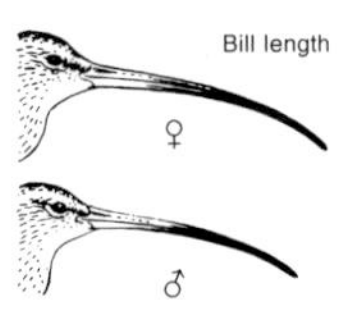

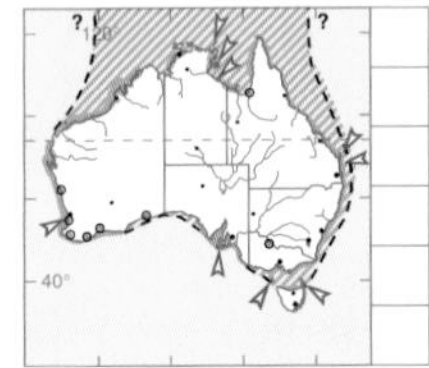
No races

Female is world's largest wader (in body size, bill length). Very long down-curved black bill with pink base. Upperparts, breast, light brown washed rufous, streaked black. Paler below. **Non-br.** Indistinct pale eyebrow. Upperparts buff, streaked grey-brown; rump darker. Underwing brown, finely barred white. Slightly paler below. **Size** 60–66 cm. **Voice** Mournful 'karr-er'; higher 'kerlee-kerlee'; musical bubbling calls. **Hab.** Coastal estuaries, mudflats, mangroves, sandspits.

Whimbrel *Numenius phaeopus* **MC**

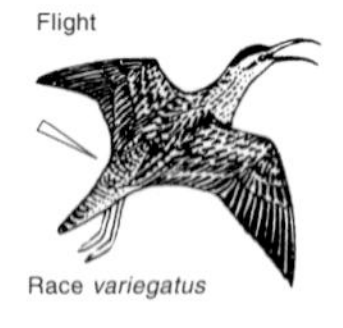

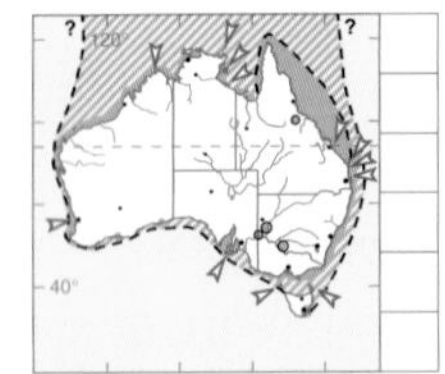
Races *variegatus, hudsonicus* in Aust.

Race *variegatus* like 'small, short-billed Eastern Curlew'. Underwing brown, finely barred white. **F** Bill longer than male's. Paler eye-stripe, crown stripe. Rump normally brown, speckled, grading to pale grey inverted 'V' on back. Lower back may be darker colour than plate (diagram). Some birds have more white on rump and back (plate). Race *hudsonicus* Darker brown rump (rare). **Size** 40–45 cm. **Voice** Shrill chattering 'tee-tee-tee-... '. **Hab.** Coastal estuaries, mudflats, mangroves.

Little Curlew *Numenius minutus* **LA–MC**

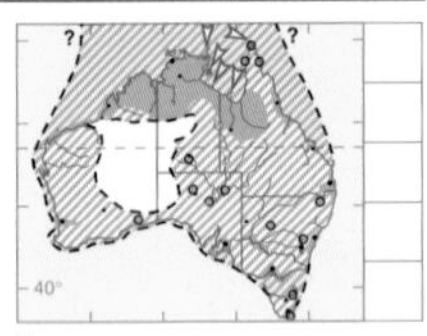
No races

Often in huge flocks in N Australia. Straggles to southern Australia. More buff than Whimbrel. Slightly larger than Pacific Golden Plover. Shortish down-curved grey bill; lower base pink. Brown, washed rich buff; diffuse russet breast band. **Non-br.** Plainer, less buff. Fine dark barring on buff underwing. **Size** 28–31 cm. **Voice** Distinctive flute-like double whistle. **Hab.** Open plains, grassland, sports-fields, parkland, mudflats.

Wood Sandpiper *Tringa glareola* **MC–UC**

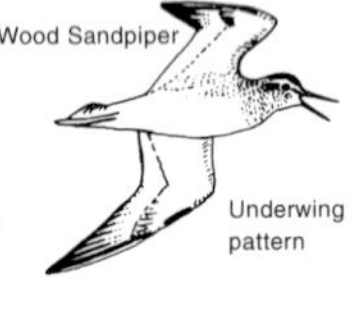

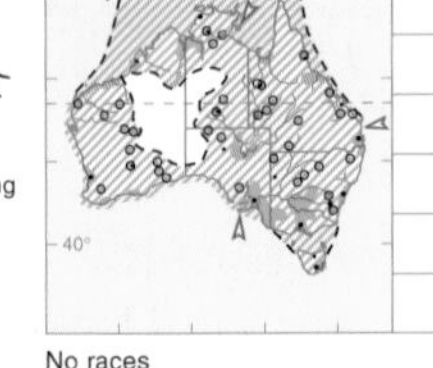
No races

Bobs. High zigzag flight. Sharp-tailed Sandpiper-sized; longer legs. Medium, straight, black bill. Longish neck. Dark brown back, wings, boldly spotted white. Short fine dark barring on sides of breast near wing-bend. **Non-br.** Narrow pale eyebrow to behind eye. Brown back; dark wings, spotted white. White rump. Tail thinly barred black. Pale underwing. Yellow-greenish legs. **Size** 19–23 cm. **Juv.** Wing spots buff. **Voice** Loud, rapid whistle 'ziss-iss-iss'. **Hab.** Mainly on fresh water; sometimes brackish.

Eurasian (European) Curlew *Numenius arquata,* **Upland Sandpiper** *Bartramia longicauda,* **Green Sandpiper** *Tringa ochropus,* **Spotted Redshank** *Tringa erythropus* see **Vagrant Bird Bulletin** pp. 289, 290.

Ruddy Turnstone
Breeding
Ruddy Turnstone
Breeding
Ruddy Turnstone
Non-breeding
Eurasian Curlew
Eastern
Curlew
Eastern
Curlew
Whimbrel
Race *variegatus*
Upland
Sandpiper
Little
Curlew
Whimbrel
Little
Curlew
Upland
Sandpiper
Wood
Sandpiper
Juv.
Wood
Sandpiper
Wood
Sandpiper
Green
Sandpiper
Green
Sandpiper

Grey-tailed Tattler *Heteroscelis (Tringa) brevipes* **C** ○

Bill straight, grey; short nasal groove. White eyebrow. Light to mid-grey above. Fine grey barring on sides of abdomen to flanks. Undertail coverts white. Legs yellow. **Non-br.** Grey breast; white from belly to undertail coverts. **Size** 25 cm. **Voice** Fluty 'troo-eet'; 'weet-eet'. **Hab.** Estuaries, mangroves, rocky coasts, reefs.

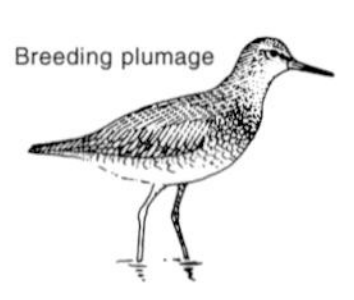

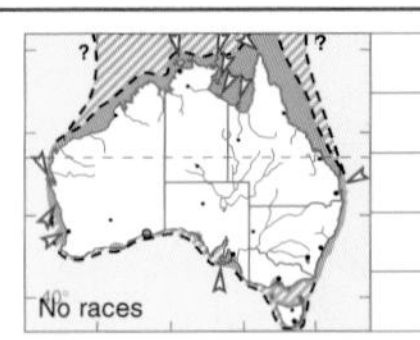

Wandering Tattler *Heteroscelis (Tringa) incana* **UC** ○

In field, voice identifies from Grey-tailed Tattler. In hand, deep section of nasal groove longer. Grey-brown above. Underparts boldly barred brown-grey to undertail coverts. **Non-br.** Face paler; white underparts. **Size** 27 cm. **Voice** Rapid trill 6–10 notes 'whee-wee-wee'. **Hab.** Open reefs, rocks ('coastal').

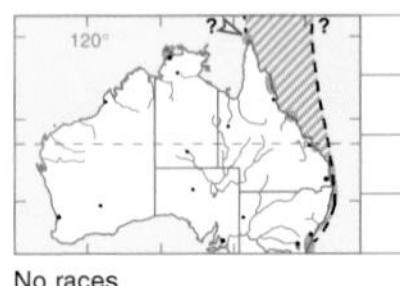

No races

Common Sandpiper *Actitis hypoleucos* **MC–UC** ○

In flight, broad white wing bar; dark centre to rump, white tail edges barred brown. Low jerky flight. Deep bobs of head, tail. Perches on rocks, piers, boats. White eyebrow, shoulder mark. Back bronze-green, scaled black. Breast dark. White below. **Non-br.** Paler, duller. **Size** 19–21 cm. Banks, rocks, sandy beaches.

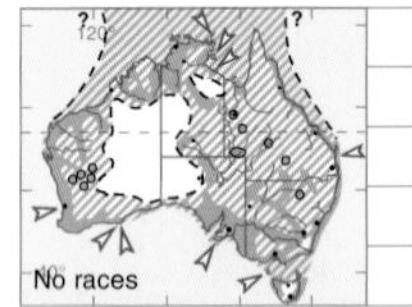

Common Greenshank *Tringa nebularia* **C** ○

Tall stance, wary. Often solitary. Bobs head. In flight, extensive white rump extends up in long 'V'; long green or dull yellow legs trail. Black bill slightly upturned, paler base. Upperparts grey, mottled black/white. White head, neck, breast, dark-streaked. **Non-br.** Paler, no black. Grey streaks on crown, upper breast. Barred underwing. **Size** 30–35 cm. **Voice** Ringing 'tew-tew-tew', when taking flight. **Hab.** Estuaries; inland lakes, open swamps.

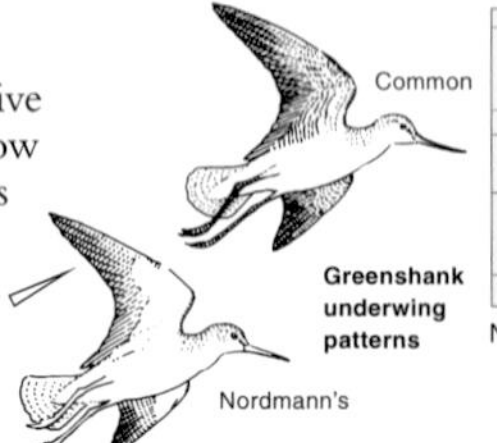

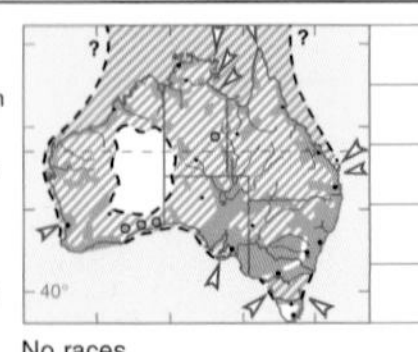

No races

Common Redshank *Tringa totanus* **R–LUC**

Jerky, erratic flight; white upper rump, broad white trailing edges to wings. More compact, browner than Common Greenshank. Red bill base, legs. Head, neck, underparts, dark-streaked. **Non-br.** Paler, duller. **Size** 27–29 cm. **Voice** Yelping 'thee-hu-hu'. **Hab.** Sheltered estuaries, inlets, saltmarsh, sewage farms. More common in NW of Australia.

Breeding plumage

Race visiting Aust. not yet identified

Marsh Sandpiper *Tringa stagnatilis* **MC–UC** ○

'Little Greenshank'. In flight, dark outer wings, long white rump, tail tip lightly barred. Paler; longer legs and bill than Wood Sandpiper. Bill straight, needle-like. Frons, underparts white. Darker above, blackish spots on neck, sides. Legs long, greenish; trail in flight. **Non-br.** Appears pale-headed, grey-capped. **Size** 22–26 cm. **Voice** Strident 'yip yip'. **Hab.** Fresh or saltwater.

Breeding plumage

No races

Terek Sandpiper *Xenus cinereus* **MC–UC** ○

In flight, flight feathers blackish; bold white trailing edge to wings. Runs with legs strongly flexed when feeding. Distinctive long, slightly upturned black bill, orange base. Dark grey above; white below. Prominent dark scapular bar. Grey rump, tail. Short yellow–orange legs. **Non-br.** Plainer. Pale grey above. Scapular bar less obvious. **Size** 22–24 cm. **Voice** Fluty 'weeta-weeta-weeta'; rapid 'tee-tee-tee'. **Hab.** Mudflats, beaches; rare inland.

Breeding plumage

No races

Nordmann's (Spotted) Greenshank *Tringa guttifer*, **Lesser Yellowlegs** *Tringa flavipes* see **Vagrant Bird Bulletin** p. 290.

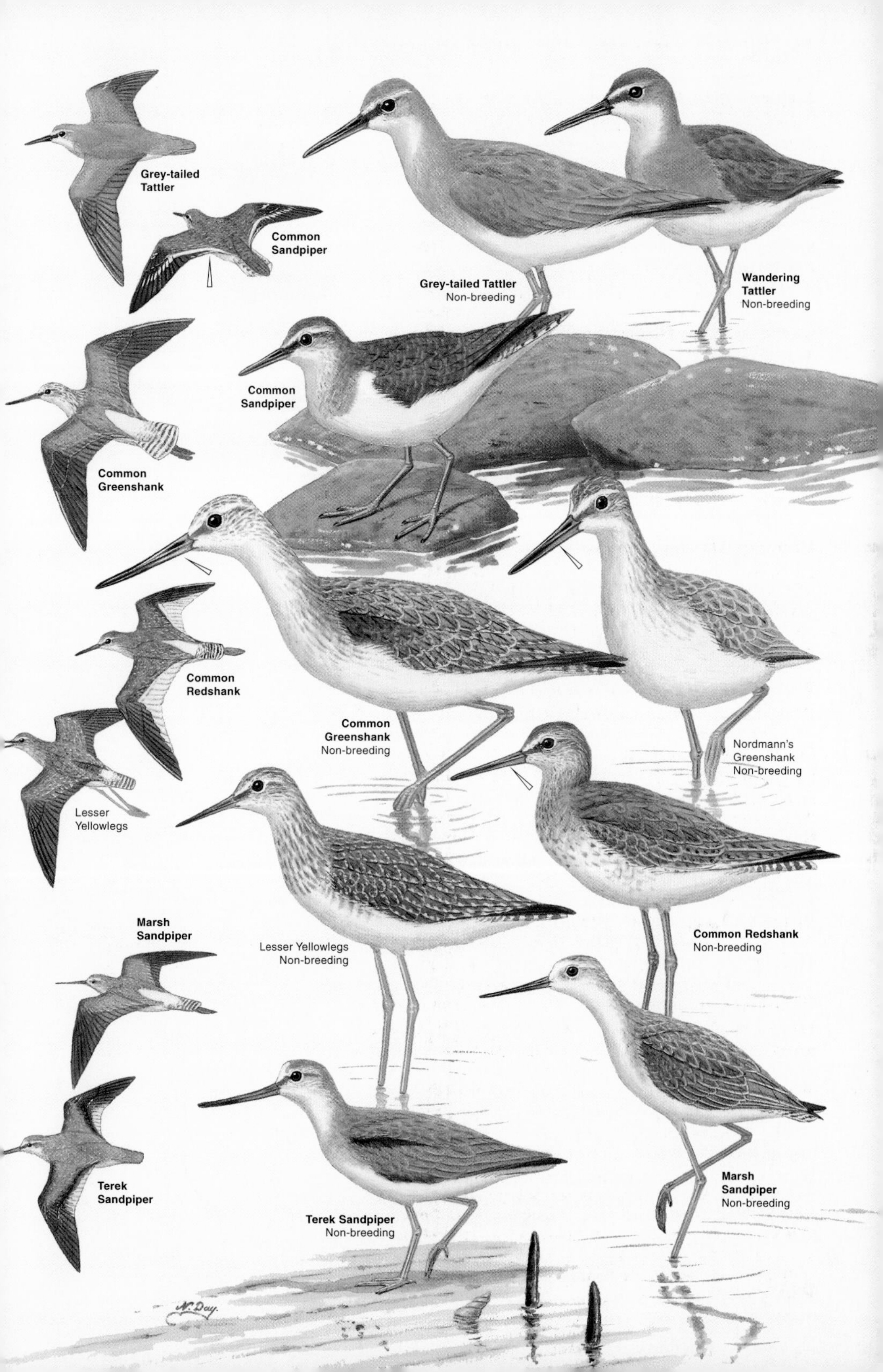

Grey-tailed
Tattler
Common
Sandpiper
Grey-tailed Tattler
Non-breeding
Wandering
Tattler
Non-breeding
Common
Sandpiper
Common
Greenshank
Common
Redshank
Common
Greenshank
Non-breeding
Nordmann's
Greenshank
Non-breeding
Lesser
Yellowlegs
Marsh
Sandpiper
Lesser Yellowlegs
Non-breeding
Common Redshank
Non-breeding
Terek
Sandpiper
Terek Sandpiper
Non-breeding
Marsh
Sandpiper
Non-breeding
N. Day.

Latham's (Japanese) Snipe *Gallinago hardwickii* **LC**

Erratic flight if flushed; drops sharply. Long bill; brown base. Dark brown crown, eye-stripe, cheek stripe. Pale cream face. Body cryptically mottled; scapulars pale-edged. Pale belly, barred flanks. Rufous sub-terminal tail band, white tip projects beyond wing-tips. **Non-br.** Plainer, less contrast. **Size** 29–33 cm. **Voice** Rasping 'shek'. **Hab.** Fresh wetlands, saltmarsh.

Tail patterns

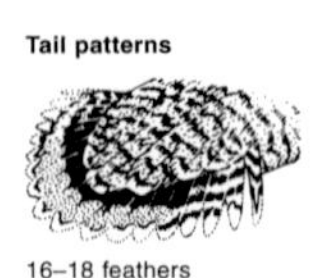

16–18 feathers

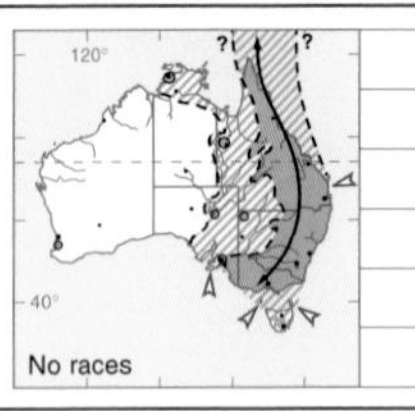

Pin-tailed Snipe *Gallinago stenura* **UC**

In flight, pale area on upperwing. Indistinct barring on back. Shorter wings, tail. **Size** 25–27 cm. **Voice** When flushed; abrupt nasal 'charp'. **Hab.** Freshwater wetlands. Rare migrant to N Aust.

24–28 feathers

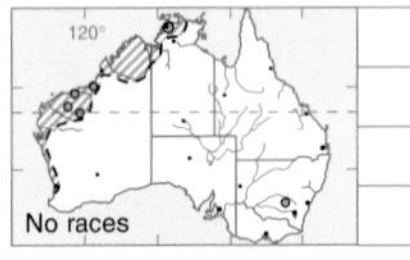

Swinhoe's Snipe *Gallinago megala* **MC**

Three snipe species hard to separate in field unless hand-held, tail pattern studied (see diagrams). Shape, size, intermediate between Latham's and Pin-tailed. **Size** 27–29 cm. **Voice** Short 'shrek'. **Hab.** Drier areas than Pin-tailed; fresh and brackish wetlands.

20–24 feathers

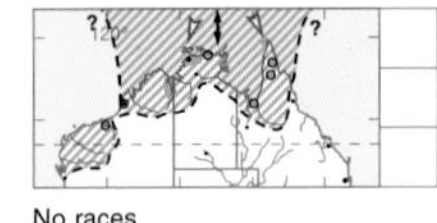

No races

Asian Dowitcher *Limnodromus semipalmatus* **R**

Larger than Great Knot. Diagnostic long, straight black bill; tip 'swollen'. Bold white eyebrow. Almost all brick-red; upperparts richer, heavily mottled black. Pale belly, undertail coverts, faintly scalloped. Legs black. **Non-br.** Lacks red tone. Check Bar-tailed Godwit. Whitish below; breast, flanks, mottled brown. **Size** 33–36 cm. **Voice** Single yelp. **Hab.** Coastal flats; sometimes inland.

Breeding plumage

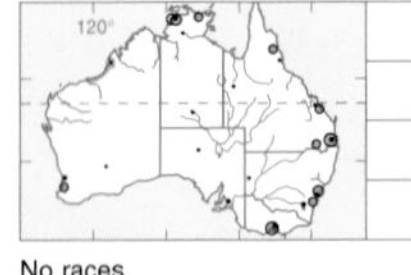

No races

Black-tailed Godwit *Limosa limosa* **MC**

In flight, bold pattern: white wing bar, rump; black border to white underwing. Long straight bill; pink base. Russet head, mantle, upper breast. White tail, black sub-terminal bar; dark feet protrude beyond tail in flight. **Non-br.** Uniform grey-brown, grey to white below. **Size** 40–44 cm. **Hab.** Tidal flats, inland wetlands.

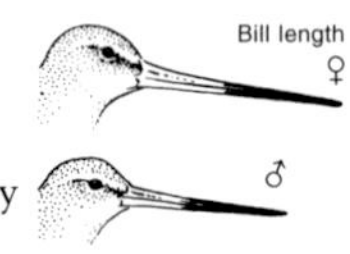

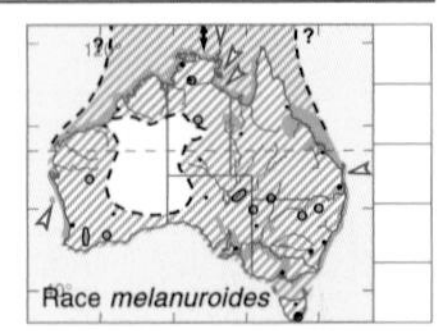

Bar-tailed Godwit *Limosa lapponica* **C**

Flocks. Large, stocky wader. Bill long, slightly upturned; pink base. Head, belly, rich chestnut-red. Underwing heavily barred. Upper tail, lower rump, heavily barred brown. Legs dark grey. **F** Larger; longer bill. **Non-br.** Upperparts patterned grey-brown. **Size** 37–39 cm. **Juv.** Paler, buffer. **Voice** Sharp contact call. **Hab.** Intertidal flats, sand banks.

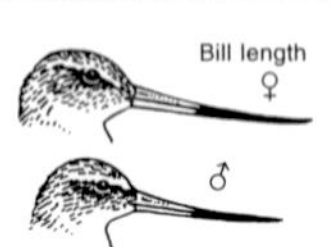

A = Race *menzbieri* particularly in NW of WA
B = Race ? *baueri* in E Aust.

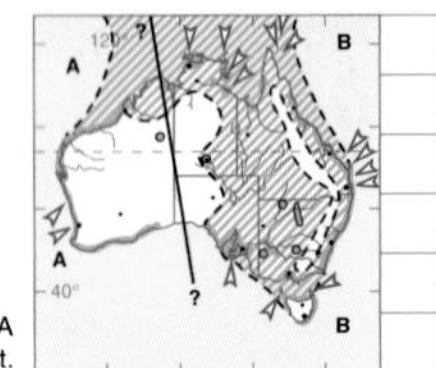

Red Knot *Calidris canutus* **C**

Often in flocks. Dumpy. Straight, robust, 3 cm bill. Red-brown, mottled black; rust-red below. Narrow white wing bar, pale grey rump. Legs dull olive. **Non-br.** Plain grey above; white below. **Size** 23–25 cm. **Juv.** Fine buff edges above. **Voice** Throaty 'knut' or 'kloot kloot'. **Hab.** Tidal sands, mudflats. Rare inland.

Races visiting Aust. not reliably identified; *rogersi*, and probably *canutus*, most likely.

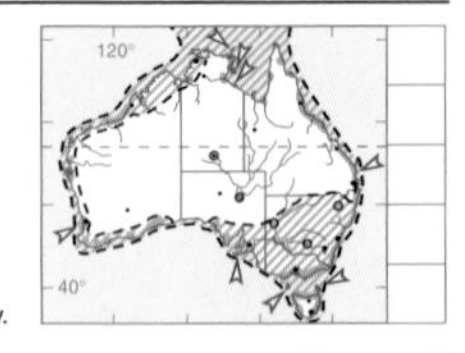

Great Knot *Calidris tenuirostris* **LA–UC**

Larger than Red Knot. Longer, faintly decurved, bill (4–5 cm). Head, neck, heavy black streaks. Black breast spotted white; no red below. Chestnut scapulars. **Non-br.** No red, black tones. **Size** 26–28 cm. **Voice** Occasional 'nyut-nyut'. **Hab.** As Red Knot.

Juv. has whitish fringes to scapular feathers, contrasting with dark centres; brown-buff in chest.

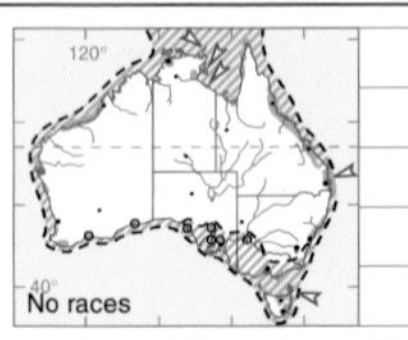

Short-billed Dowitcher *Limnodromus griseus*, **Hudsonian Godwit** *Limosa haemastica* see **Vagrant Bird Bulletin** pp. 289, 290.

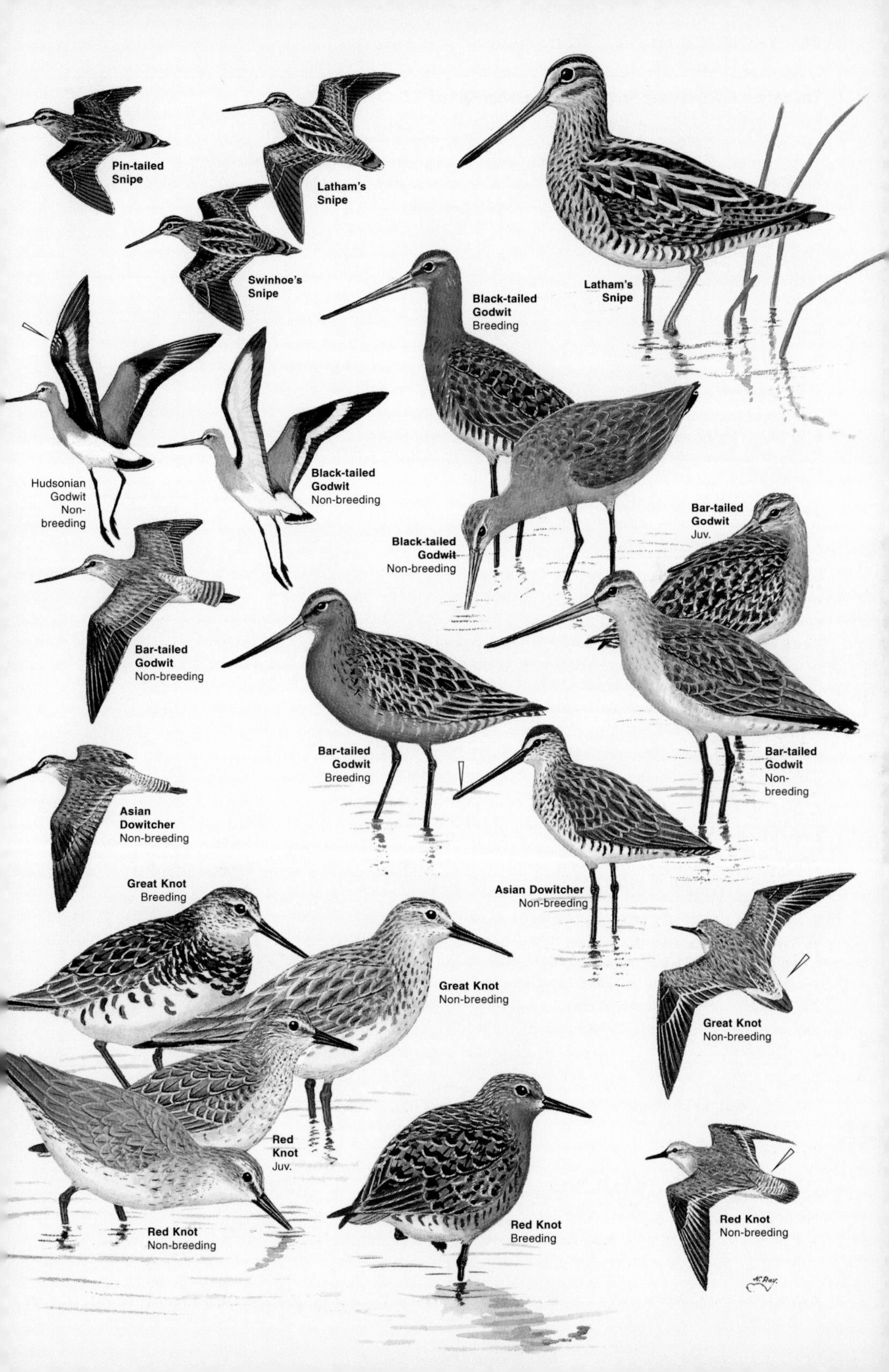
Pin-tailed Snipe
Latham's Snipe
Swinhoe's Snipe
Latham's Snipe
Black-tailed Godwit Breeding
Hudsonian Godwit Non-breeding
Black-tailed Godwit Non-breeding
Black-tailed Godwit Non-breeding
Bar-tailed Godwit Juv.
Bar-tailed Godwit Non-breeding
Bar-tailed Godwit Breeding
Bar-tailed Godwit Non-breeding
Asian Dowitcher Non-breeding
Asian Dowitcher Non-breeding
Great Knot Breeding
Great Knot Non-breeding
Great Knot Non-breeding
Red Knot Juv.
Red Knot Non-breeding
Red Knot Breeding
Red Knot Non-breeding
N. Day

Sharp-tailed Sandpiper *Calidris acuminata* **C**

Short straight black bill; dull olive base. Chestnut crown, rich rufous upperparts. Rich rufous chest, dense overlay of black spots, chevrons. Indistinct wing bar. Tail has white inner sides. Black central line from lower back to black terminal tail band. White belly. Olive-yellow legs. **F** Smaller. **Non-br.** Back feathers black-centred, buff edges. Dark streaked breast, flanks, to undertail sides. **Size** 17–22 cm. **Juv.** Brighter crown, upperparts. Buff breast. **Voice** 'wit wit wit-it-it'. **Hab.** Widespread; coastal, interior wetlands.

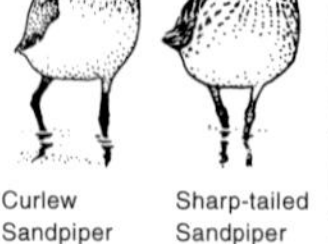
Curlew Sandpiper   Sharp-tailed Sandpiper

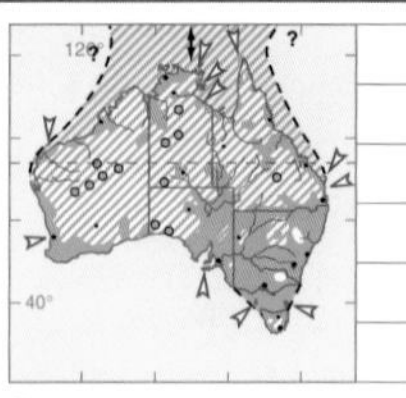

No races

Pectoral Sandpiper *Calidris melanotos* **UC**

Like Sharp-tailed but smaller head. In flight, dark rump, tail, white sides; narrow white wing bar. Bill longer; faintly decurved; base yellow. Crown brown, streaked dark, not chestnut. Breast streaking dense, dark, forming slightly inflatable 'pouch' when courting. Heavily streaked shallow 'V' on breast, distinct from white belly. Legs yellow. **F** Smaller. Breast streaks not as dense. **Non-br.** Duller, greyer; markings less distinct, but breast to belly demarcation still evident. **Voice** Reedy, rasping 'krrrt'. **Size** 19–24 cm. **Hab.** Grassy or lightly vegetated coastal and inland swamps.

And see hybrid 'Cox's Sandpiper', p. 290.

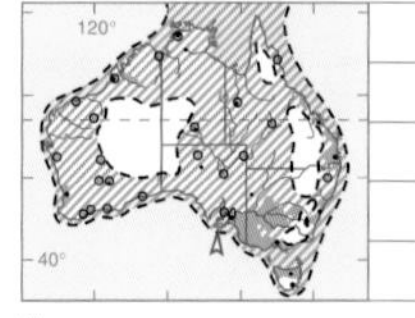

No races

Little Stint *Calidris minuta* **UC**

Small. Obvious white throat. Back feathers have black centres, chestnut edges. Cream 'V' on mantle. Incomplete orange breast band has dark streaks. **Non-br.** As Red-necked Stint. **Juv.** Streaked black, chestnut above. White 'V' on mantle. **Voice** 'wit'. **Size** 12–14 cm. **Hab.** As Red-necked.

Most identified in Aust. are in breeding or juvenile plumage. Non-breeding birds more difficult to identify.

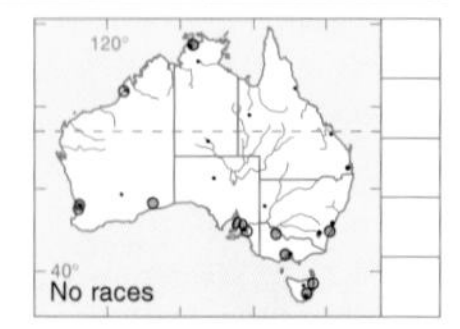

Red-necked Stint *Calidris ruficollis* **A–C**

Often in very large flocks. Small. Short, dark bill. Back feathers have black centres, chestnut edges. Head, neck, breast, pinkish chestnut. Thin black line through rump. Fine white wing bar. Legs black. **Non-br.** Grey above; white below, washed grey at sides of breast. **Size** 13–16 cm. **Voice** 'chit, chit'; high trill. **Hab.** Coastal and estuarine inland shores; saltworks.

Red-necked Stint   Curlew Sandpiper

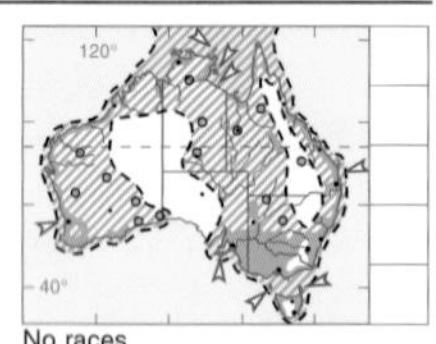

No races

Long-toed Stint *Calidris subminuta* **UC**

Tiny wader; a 'stint-sized Sharp-tailed Sandpiper'. Stands erect. Solitary; seldom in large flocks; small flocks in WA. Upperparts edged chestnut. Rump black centre, sides white. Long legs, greenish-yellow toes trail in flight. **Non-br./Imm.** No rufous on back. Head more heavily marked in eclipse than other 'pale-faced' stints. **Size** 13–16 cm. **Voice** Rapid ringing 'chre-chre-chre'. **Hab.** Coastal and inland swamps.

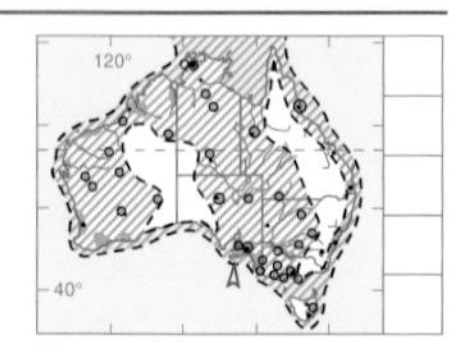

No races

'Cox's Sandpiper' *Calidris paramelanotus,* **Baird's Sandpiper** *Calidris bairdii,* **White-rumped Sandpiper** *Calidris fuscicollis,* **Western Sandpiper** *Calidris mauri* see **Vagrant Bird Bulletin** pp. 290, 291.

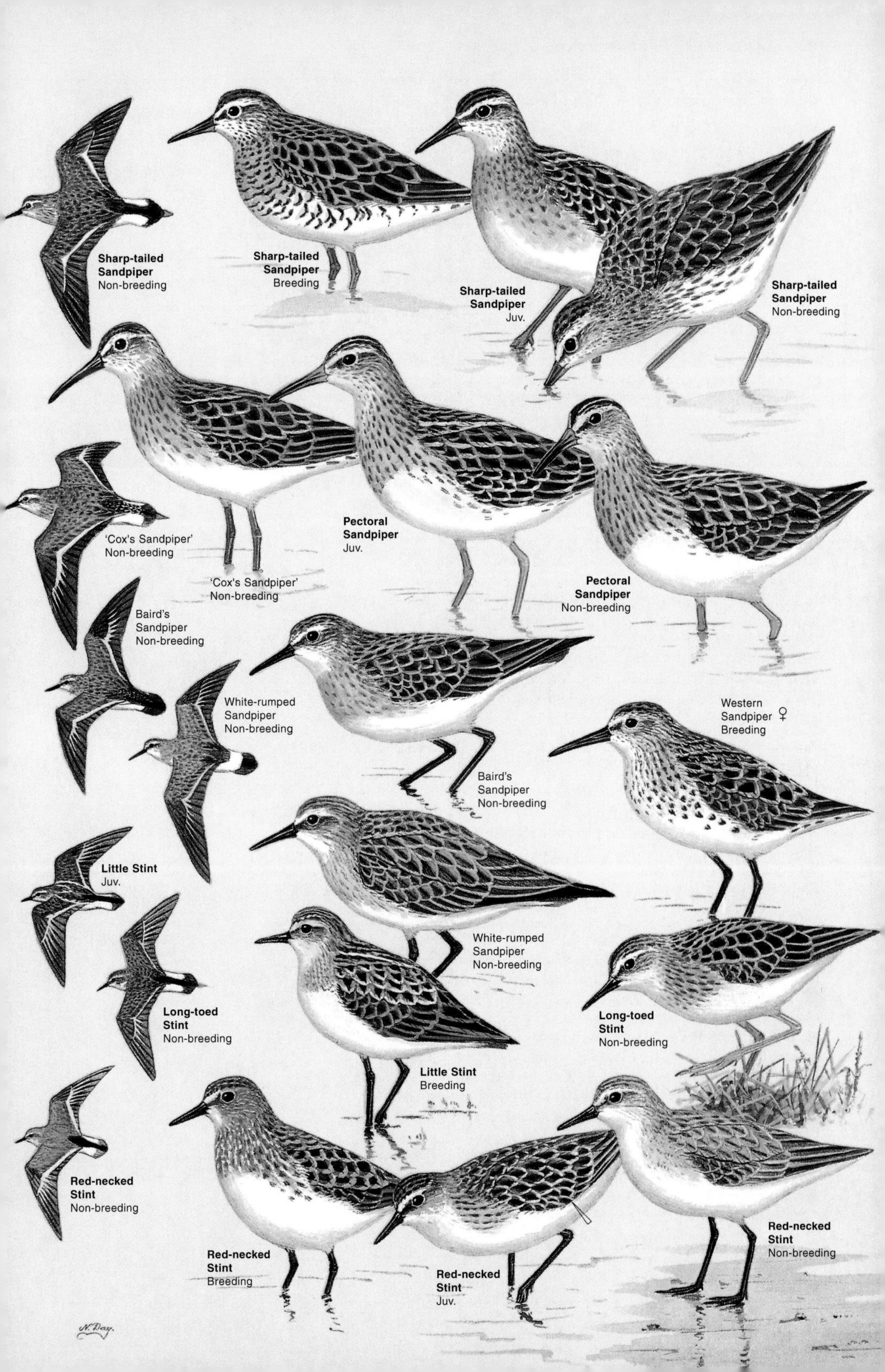
Sharp-tailed Sandpiper
Non-breeding
Sharp-tailed Sandpiper
Breeding
Sharp-tailed Sandpiper
Juv.
Sharp-tailed Sandpiper
Non-breeding
'Cox's Sandpiper'
Non-breeding
'Cox's Sandpiper'
Non-breeding
Pectoral Sandpiper
Juv.
Pectoral Sandpiper
Non-breeding
Baird's Sandpiper
Non-breeding
White-rumped Sandpiper
Non-breeding
Baird's Sandpiper
Non-breeding
Western Sandpiper ♀
Breeding
Little Stint
Juv.
White-rumped Sandpiper
Non-breeding
Long-toed Stint
Non-breeding
Long-toed Stint
Non-breeding
Little Stint
Breeding
Red-necked Stint
Non-breeding
Red-necked Stint
Breeding
Red-necked Stint
Juv.
Red-necked Stint
Non-breeding
N. Day.

Curlew Sandpiper *Calidris ferruginea* **A–C** ○

Frequently feeds with, close to, Sharp-tailed Sandpipers, Red-necked Stints. Bill long, black, down-curved. **Br.** Rich chestnut-red head and neck, back, underparts. Side of breast, flanks, thinly barred black. Undertail coverts white, dark spotting. Birds tend to be changing plumage at time of entering or leaving Australia. **Non-br.** Grey-brown above, white below. Broad white wing bar; white rump. Legs black. **Size** 18–23 cm. **Juv.** As adult non-br.; feathers of upperparts pale-edged. Rufous wash on breast. **Voice** Loud 'chirrup'. **Hab.** Coastal, inland, mudflats; saltworks.

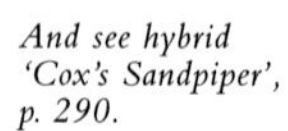
And see hybrid 'Cox's Sandpiper', p. 290.

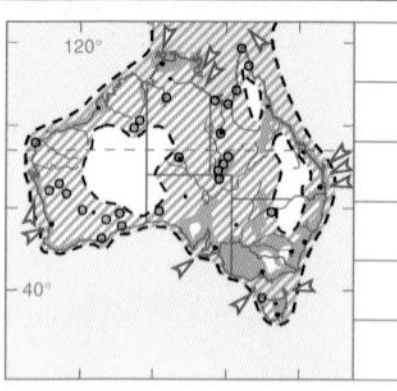

No races

Sanderling *Calidris alba* **MC** ○

Small flocks run up and down at edge of breaking waves. Palest calidrid. Larger than Red-necked Stint; longer bill. Chestnut face, breast. **Non-br.** In flight, broad white wing bar, blackish forewing. White face, underparts. Silver-grey back. Dark shoulder patch may be visible. Wide, bright white margins to dark grey central line on upper tail. Lacks hind toe. **Size** 20–21 cm. **Juv.** Blackish on crown, back. **Voice** 'twik twik'. **Hab.** Sandy coastal beaches, rare inland.

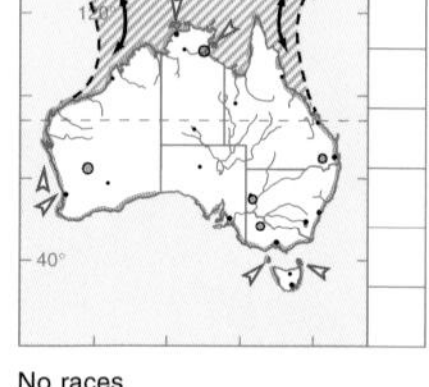

No races

Buff-breasted Sandpiper *Tryngites subruficollis* **R** ○

Medium-sized; 'plover-like' stance. Small round head. Short, straight black bill. Pale eye-ring. Rich buff-brown upperparts, breast. Bold black spots on crown, upperparts, sides of breast. Rear underparts whitish. Legs long, yellow-orange. **Non-br.** Duller, pale buff-brown. No wing bar. Underwing white; dark bar on greater primary coverts. **Size** 18–20 cm. **Juv.** Dark above; lighter breast. Check juv. Inland Dotterel. **Voice** Harsh 'krik'; 'tik'. **Hab.** Open grassland; sometimes near water.

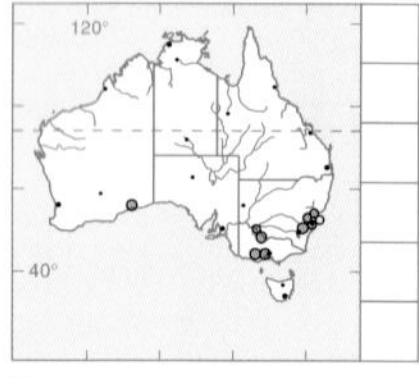

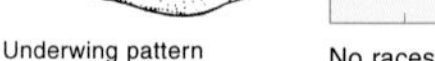
Underwing pattern

No races

Broad-billed Sandpiper *Limicola falcinellus* **MC–UC** ○

Larger 'stint'; with long, black bill, heavy base, drooped tip. Feathers of upperparts black-centred, buff or rufous edges. **Non-br.** Crown streaked black with double white eyebrow. Shoulder sometimes darker. Dark line through rump. Dark forewing; slender white wing bar in flight. Legs dark olive. **Size** 16–18 cm. **Juv.** Similar; buffer. **Voice** Sharp trilling. **Hab.** Mostly on coastal mudflats, sometimes inland.

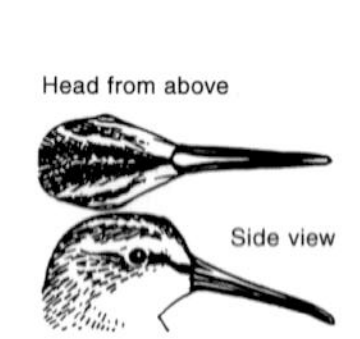

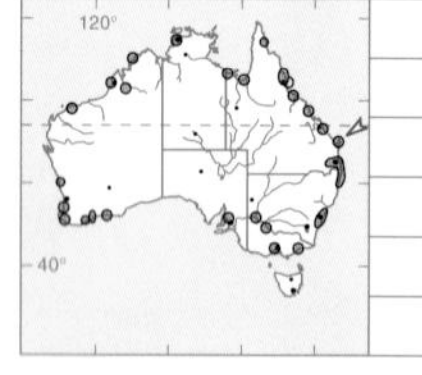

Race *sibirica*

Ruff *Philomachus pugnax* **UC** ○

Much larger than Sharp-tailed Sandpiper. Small head; long neck; long legs. **M br.** ('Ruff') Erectile ruff, ear tufts of various colours. **F br.** ('Reeve') Dark barring above. **Non-br.** Bill straight. Dark brown, buff above (variable); 'scaly' look. Head plain. Pale feathers circle bill. Neck light grey-brown, streaked darker. Breast light greyish-brown. Whitish below. In flight, white ovoid patches on side of dark rump. Legs vary: grey, green, yellow, red. **Size** M 26–32, F 20–25 cm. **Juv.** More buff; richer below. **Voice** Unlikely to be heard in Australia; 'tu-whit' when flushed (breeding areas). **Hab.** Inland wetlands; rarely on coast.

♂ breeding plumage

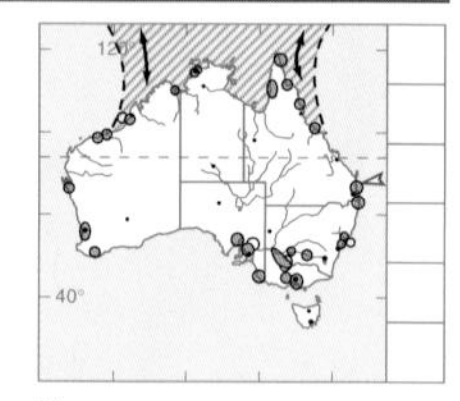

No races

Dunlin *Calidris alpina*, **Stilt Sandpiper** *Micropalama himantopus* see **Vagrant Bird Bulletin** pp. 291, 292.

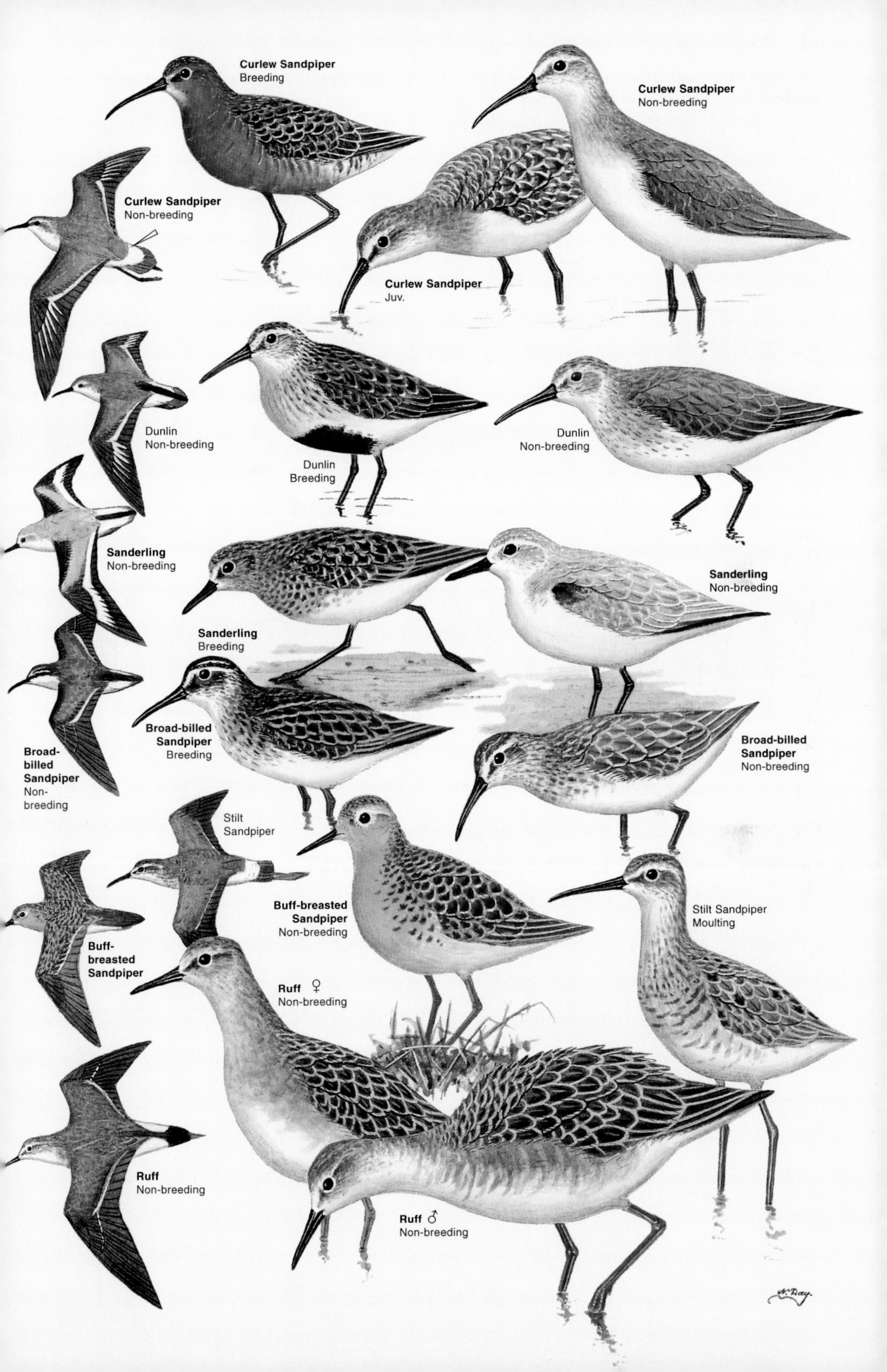
Curlew Sandpiper
Breeding
Curlew Sandpiper
Non-breeding
Curlew Sandpiper
Non-breeding
Curlew Sandpiper
Juv.
Dunlin
Non-breeding
Dunlin
Breeding
Dunlin
Non-breeding
Sanderling
Non-breeding
Sanderling
Non-breeding
Sanderling
Breeding
Broad-billed
Sandpiper
Breeding
Broad-billed
Sandpiper
Non-breeding
Broad-
billed
Sandpiper
Non-
breeding
Stilt
Sandpiper
Buff-breasted
Sandpiper
Non-breeding
Stilt Sandpiper
Moulting
Buff-
breasted
Sandpiper
Ruff ♀
Non-breeding
Ruff
Non-breeding
Ruff ♂
Non-breeding

Red-necked Phalarope *Phalaropus lobatus* **R–UC** O

Mostly swims for food, bobs head, spins around in circles. Smallest of world's three species. **M br.** Much duller than female. **F br.** Broad bright rufous neck stripe. Rest of head black. White throat. Blackish above with buff streaks. **Non-br.** Bill black, needle-like. Crown black. Broad black eye patch from before eye to ear coverts. Slender neck. Pale to dusky grey above, striped white. Pure white below. White wing bars and 'braces' in flight. Black line through rump. Feet lobed. **Size** 18–19 cm. **Juv.** Buffer, golden-buff pattern on wings. **Voice** 'chek' or 'chik-chik-chik'. **Hab.** Oceans, bays, lakes, swamps.

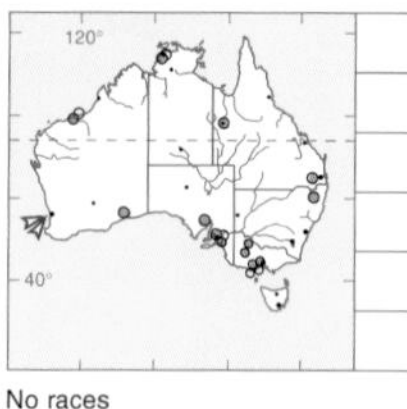

No races

Oriental Pratincole *Glareola maldivarum* **LA–UC** O

Huge flocks in N Australia. Hawks insects. In flight, swallow-like: chestnut underwing coverts, black trailing edge. Check juv. Common Starling (on ground). Bill, gape, red. Thin black border to light buff throat. **Non-br.** Bill black, red at gape. Olive-brown above, whitish below. Throat buff, edged with broken line of black streaks. Breast dusky grey. Tail white, dark-tipped, shallow fork. White rump. Legs short, black. **Size** 23–24 cm. **Juv./Imm.** Feather edges of upperparts scaly buff; lost with wear. Whitish throat. **Voice** Tern-like 'chik chik'; soft 'towheet-towheet'. **Hab.** Open plains, bare ground around swamps, claypans.

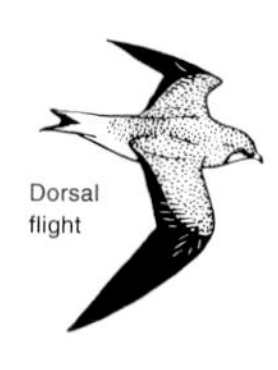

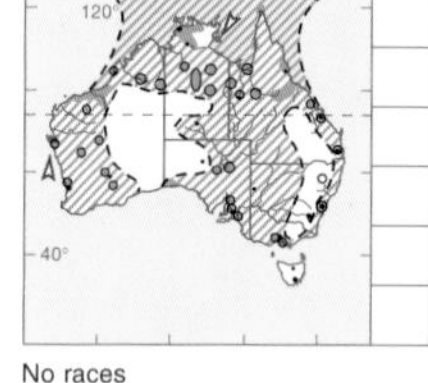

No races

Australian Pratincole *Stiltia isabella* **C–UC** O Br. E

Flocks. Slender body, long wings, flight tern-like. Bill red, black tip. Golden buff above and on upperwing coverts; grey back. Black primaries. Dark chestnut flanks. Square tail white; triangular black sub-terminal mark. Wings project well beyond tail when perched. Legs long, grey. **Juv./Imm.** Similar; bill lacks colour. Check Oriental Pratincole. **Size** 19–24 cm. **Voice** Variety of chirruping whistles; repeated loud, sharp alarm 'weetitit'. **Hab.** Semi-arid open plains; winters on coast in N Australia.

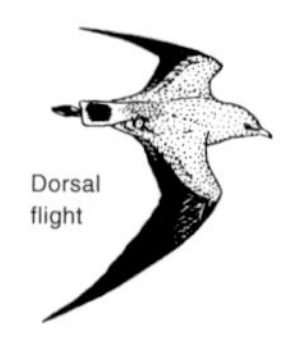

Also colloquially called 'Rainbird', based on 'persistent calls during summer storms'.

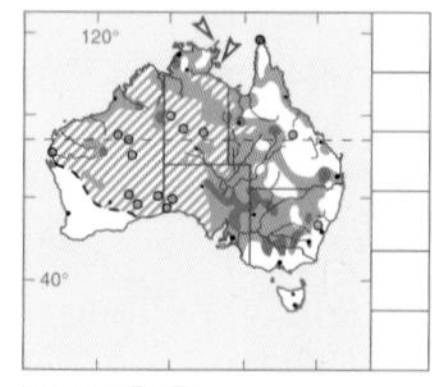

No races **Br. E**

Grey Phalarope *Phalaropus fulicarius*, **Wilson's Phalarope** *Steganopus (Phalaropus) tricolor* see **Vagrant Bird Bulletin** p. 292.

Australian
Pratincole
Oriental
Pratincole
Breeding
Oriental Pratincole
Breeding
Australian
Pratincole
Oriental
Pratincole
Non-breeding
Australian
Pratincole
Juv.
Marsh Sandpiper
Non-breeding
Red-necked
Phalarope
Non-breeding
Grey Phalarope
Non-breeding
Red-necked
Phalarope ♀
Breeding
Wilson's Phalarope
Non-breeding
Grey
Phalarope ♀
Breeding
Wilson's
Phalarope ♀
Breeding
Marsh
Sandpiper
Non-breeding
Red-necked
Phalarope
Non-breeding
Grey Phalarope
Non-breeding
Wilson's Phalarope
Non-breeding
N. Day.

Painted Snipe *Rostratula benghalensis* **MC** Vulnerable

Likely to 'freeze' when approached. Flight fast; rail-like. Wings outspread, curved forward in a threat display. Long, drooped, pinkish bill. **M/Imm.** Smaller, duller; more grey than female. Eye patch, crown stripe, buff. Wings predominantly spotted. **F** Delicate black, green, grey and buff patterns above. Chestnut-black hood. White eye patch, crown stripe. Curved white collar. **Size** 24–30 cm. **Voice** Booming in display; buzzing when threatened. **Hab.** Marsh with moderate cover.

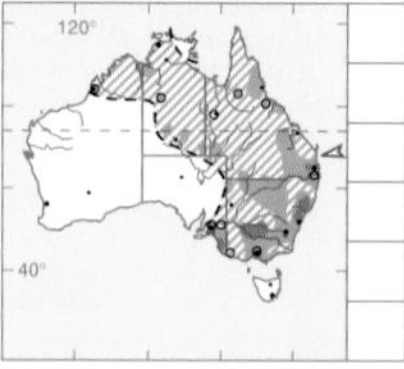

Race *australis* **E Vulnerable**

Comb-crested Jacana *Irediparra gallinacea* **C** ◎

Walks on floating plants. Adults put downy chicks under wings when threatened; carry them with chicks' legs, toes, trailing. Red forehead, comb. Bill green-yellow, tipped brown. Cheeks golden-yellow. Crown, hind neck, breast band, black. Brown upperparts. Belly, neck, white. Long, dull green legs; extremely long slender toes. Wings wholly dark in flight. **Size** M 20–21; F 24–27 cm. **Imm.** Comb small; crown brown; breast white. **Voice** Squeaky 'pee pee pee'; shrill alarm call. **Hab.** Swamps, lakes, lagoons.

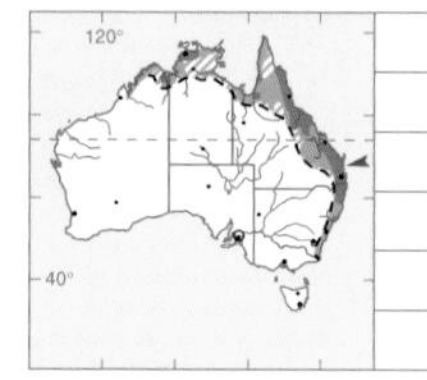

Race *novaehollandiae*

Bush Stone-curlew *Burhinus grallarius* **MC–LUC** ◎– Vulnerable

Large cryptically plumaged wader. Singly, pairs; loose flocks up to 100+. Active at night. 'Skulking' habits; 'rigid' movements. 'Freezes' to escape notice. Medium black bill. Forehead buff; pale buff eyebrow. Large yellow eye. Black eye-stripe through to neck. Black streaking on grey-brown upperparts; buff-white underparts. Whitish shoulder patch. N Australian arid country birds more rufous-grey; 'rufous morph'. **Size** 54–59 cm. **Voice** Mournful, wailing 'wee-loo' usually at night. **Hab.** Open woodland, often near beaches; on some offshore islands.

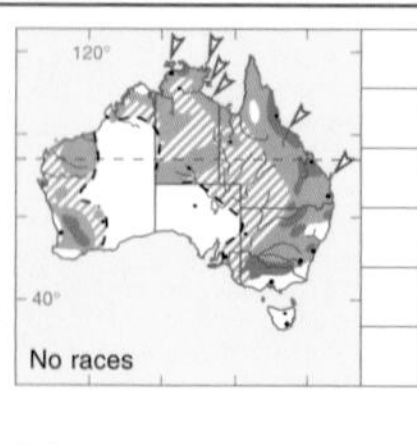

Prior name 'Bush Thick-knee'.

Beach Stone-curlew *Esacus neglectus* **UC** ◎–

Large, tall, cryptically plumaged wader. Wary, nervous – avoid disturbing. Large black bill has yellow base. Large yellow eye. Broad black eye patch; white bands above and below. Upperparts brown; darker shoulder. White wing patches. Throat, breast grey; white below. Legs olive-yellow. **Size** 54–56 cm. **Voice** Repeated, mournful, wailing 'wee-loo'; higher, harsher than Bush Stone-curlew. **Hab.** Reefs, beaches, coastal mudflats.

Prior name 'Beach Thick-knee' E. magnirostris.

Patchy distribution.

Pied Oystercatcher *Haematopus longirostris* **C**

In flight, boldly patterned. White of lower back 'square' across. Black with white half wing-stripe, rump, belly, vent. Bright red eye, eye-ring and bill. Pink legs. **Size** 42–50 cm. **Juv.** Duller bill, tipped black. Eyes brown. Upperparts edged brown. Grey legs. **Voice** Loud 'pleep pleep' in flight; rapid 'pee-pee-pee-pee'. **Hab.** Coastal; prefers sandy beaches, tidal flats and estuaries.

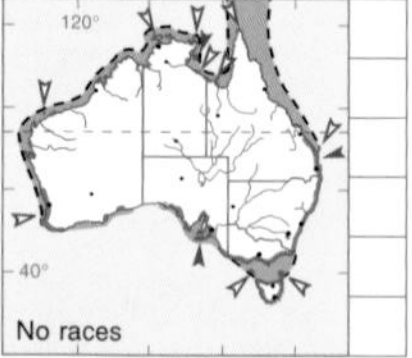

Sooty Oystercatcher *Haematopus fuliginosus* **MC** E

All black. Red eye, eye-ring and bill. Pink legs. Race *opthalmicus* (B) Slightly longer bill, broader red eye-ring. **Size** 40–52 cm. **Juv.** Duller bill, tipped black. Eyes brown. Upperparts edged brown. Grey legs. **Voice** More mournful than Pied. **Hab.** Coastal; prefers rocky coastline; occasionally estuaries.

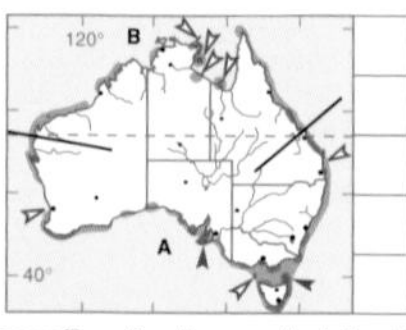

A = Race *fuliginosus* **E** B = Race *opthalmicus* **E**

Pheasant-tailed Jacana *Hydrophasianus chirurgus*, **South Island Pied Oystercatcher** *Haematopus finschi* see **Vagrant Bird Bulletin** pp. 292, 293.

Comb-crested
Jacana
Comb-crested Jacana
Imm.
Pheasant-tailed
Jacana
Non-breeding
Painted Snipe ♂
Painted Snipe ♀
Painted Snipe ♀
Bush Stone-curlew
Beach Stone-curlew
Pied Oystercatcher
Pied Oystercatcher
Juv.
Sooty Oystercatcher
Race *opthalmicus*
Pied Oystercatcher
Sooty Oystercatcher
Race *fuliginosus*

Masked Lapwing *Vanellus miles* C ◎–♧

Pairs usually seen on ground. Flies, calls loudly at night. Large flocks in Tasmania. Brown above; white below. Prominent yellow facial wattle extends behind eye; wing spurs. Black crown, flight feathers, hind neck and sides of breast. Race *novaehollandiae* (B) 'Spur-winged Plover' Smaller, rounded wattle. Black hind neck to breast sides. Hybrids. **Size** 30–37 cm. **Juv.** Buff tips to all black/brown dorsal plumage. **Voice** Loud cackling 'kerr-kick-ki-ki-ki'; single 'kek'. **Hab.** Grassland, mudflats, urban parks.

Hatchling

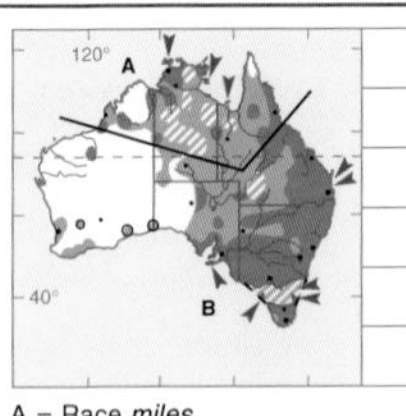

A = Race *miles*
B = Race *novaehollandiae*

Banded Lapwing *Vanellus tricolor* MC ◎–♧ E

Usually seen in pairs. Calls, flies at night. White wing stripe in flight. Red lore wattle. Yellow bill, eye-ring. White line behind eye. Black crown, side of neck, breast band. Brown above; white below. **Size** 25–29 cm. **Juv.** Crown brown. Mantle, wing coverts, etc. edged buff. **Voice** Crying 'er-chill-char'; less harsh than Masked's. **Hab.** Open grassland, bare plain and arable land.

Hatchling

Previous name 'Banded Plover'.

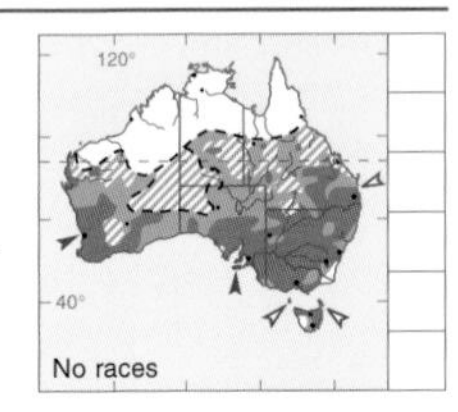

No races

Grey Plover *Pluvialis squatarola* MC ↻

Larger, greyer, plumper, than Pacific Golden Plover; often with them. Large head. **Br.** Marbled silver and dark grey above. Black from throat to belly; white vent. **Non-br.** Bill black, longer, bulkier than Pacific's. Small, pale eyebrow. Mottled grey back. In flight, axilla (armpit) black. Underparts white. White wing bar, rump. White tail, barred black. Legs dark grey. **Size** 27–31 cm. **Voice** High 'pee-oo-eer'. **Hab.** Like Pacific Golden Plover.

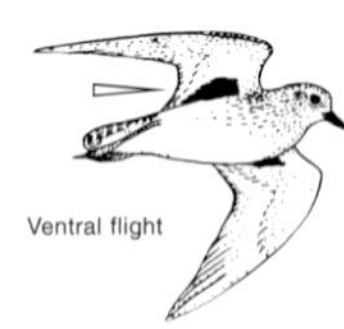
Ventral flight

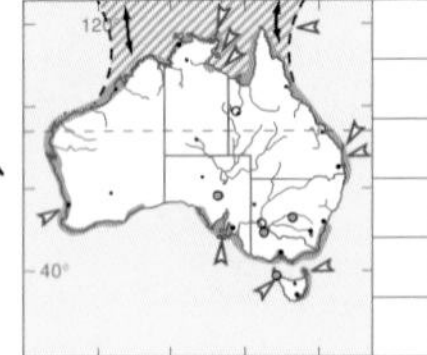

No races

Pacific Golden Plover *Pluvialis fulva* MC ↻

Bright gold above, dark mottling. Black from throat to white-sided undertail coverts. White line, eyebrow to flanks. Standing, wing-tips project slightly beyond tail. **Non-br.** Bill black. Eye large. Broad eyebrow, buff to whitish. Golden buff to cream spots over dark upperparts to tail. Breast golden-brown to cream. Underwing dark grey. Indistinct wing bar. White underparts. Legs dark grey-black. **Size** 23–26 cm. **Voice** Triple 'too-wheet-u'. **Hab.** Beaches, also mudflats; among rocks; also inland.

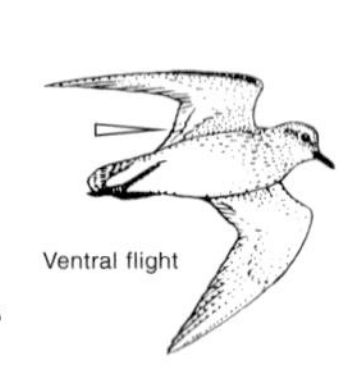
Ventral flight

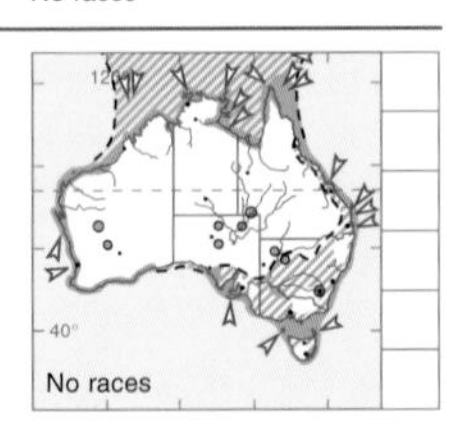

No races

The American Golden Plover Pluvialis dominica *is now considered a full species. It is not recorded for Australia.*

Red-kneed Dotterel *Erythrogonys cinctus* C ♧ Br. E

Distinctive. Stocky. Rich dark brown above; white below. Black hood, nape, breast band. White throat (obvious even at distance). Flanks chestnut, edged white. White trailing wing-edge in flight. Legs brown-grey; red knees. **Size** 17–19.5 cm. **Juv.** Brown head, nape; no breast band. **Voice** 'chet chet-chet'; loud trills in flight. **Hab.** Swamp edges and shallows.

Hatchling

Now known to be allied to the lapwings.

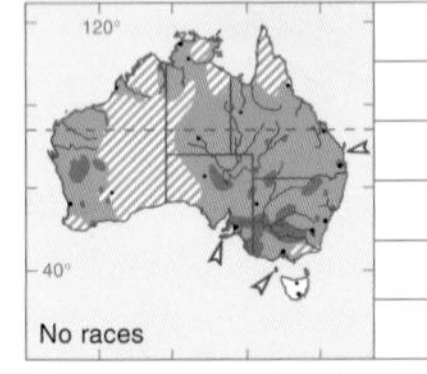

No races

Hooded Plover *Thinornis (Charadrius) rubricollis* UC–R ◎ E Vulnerable

Avoid disturbing breeding birds! Pairs, families on beaches. Distinctive. In flight, broad white wing bar; tail, rump black, edged white. Black-hooded, pale-bodied plover. Red bill, black tip. Red eye-ring. Black head; white collar. Lower neck, side of breast, black. Back pale grey-brown. **Size** 19–23 cm. **Juv.** Paler overall, brown where adult black. **Voice** Piping 'pee-oo', 'prip, prip'. **Hab.** Ocean beaches, rarely coastal lakes. Inland salt lakes of WA.

Hatchling

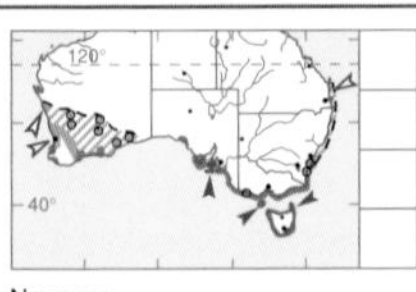

No races
Declining. Former range in eastern Aust. shown.

American Golden Plover *Pluvialis dominica,* **Eurasian Golden Plover** *Pluvialis apricaria* see **Vagrant Bird Bulletin** p. 293.

Masked Lapwing
Race *miles*
Masked Lapwing
Race *novaehollandiae*
Masked
Lapwing
Race *miles*
Banded
Lapwing
Banded
Lapwing
Pacific
Golden
Plover
Breeding
Grey
Plover
Breeding
Grey Plover
Non-breeding
Pacific
Golden Plover
Non-breeding
Grey Plover
Non-breeding
Eurasian
Golden Plover
Non-breeding
Pacific
Golden Plover
Non-breeding
Red-kneed
Dotterel
Red-kneed
Dotterel
Juv.
Red-kneed
Dotterel
Hooded Plover
Black-fronted
Dotterel
Juv.
Hooded Plover
Hooded Plover
Juv.

Ringed Plover *Charadrius hiaticula* R

Grey-brown above; white below. Orange bill, black tip. Thin orange eye-ring. Black eye-band, lores. Black band over white frons. White collar, black breast band. White wing bar. Legs orange. **F** Duller. **Non-br.** Black areas dull. White eyebrow complete. Wide brownish breast band often incomplete. **Size** 18–20 cm. **Juv.** As palest non-br. adult. Breast band small; its centre may be joined. **Voice** 'too-li', 'coo-eep'. **Hab.** Shores.

Breeding plumage

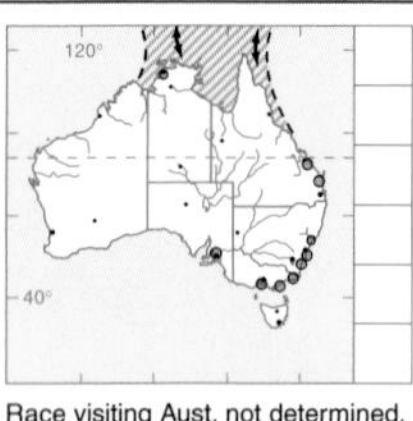

Race visiting Aust. not determined.

Little Ringed Plover *Charadrius dubius* R–UC

Like Ringed; smaller, browner. Slightly smaller than Black-fronted Dotterel. Bill black-tipped. Prominent yellow eye-ring. Lacks white wing bar. Legs orange. Duller. **Non-br.** Bill black. Small breast band incomplete. **Size** 14–17 cm. **Juv.** Smaller, browner. No white frons; thin eyebrow. Divided brown breast bar. **Voice** 'pee-oo'. **Hab.** Shores, marshes.

Breeding plumage

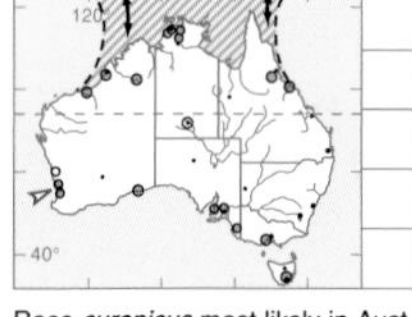

Race *curonicus* most likely in Aust.

Lesser Sand (Mongolian) Plover *Charadrius mongolus* MC

Chestnut-red nape, breast. Throat white, cut off from breast by thin black line. Bold black eye patch, edge to white forehead. Narrow white wing bar. Legs greyish. **F** Duller. **Non-br.** Small. Black bill. Lores dark brown. Dark eye patch. Dark brown-grey above; white below. Faint grey breast band. **Size** 18–21 cm. **Juv.** As non-br.; breast browner; buff-edged scapulars, tertials. **Voice** 'derrit drit'; short trills. **Hab.** Coastal; rarely inland.

Juv. head pattern

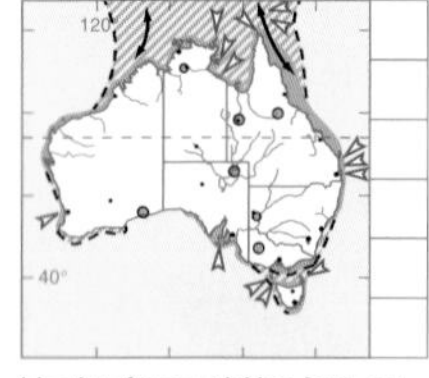

Identity of races visiting Aust. not reliably established

Double-banded Plover *Charadrius bicinctus* C

Grey-brown above; white below. Bill short, slender, black. Forehead, eyebrow white. Upper chest band black; lower band broader, chestnut. White wing bar. Legs yellow-grey or grey-green. **F** Duller. **Non-br.** Tinged buff; browner than Lesser and Greater Sand Plovers. Remnants of two breast bars may show. **Size** 18–21 cm. **Juv.** Golden-buff nape, eyebrow, shoulder; fringes to upper feathers. **Voice** Loud, staccato 'pit-pit'; rapid trill. **Hab.** Beaches, mudflats, grassland, bare ground.

Juv. head pattern

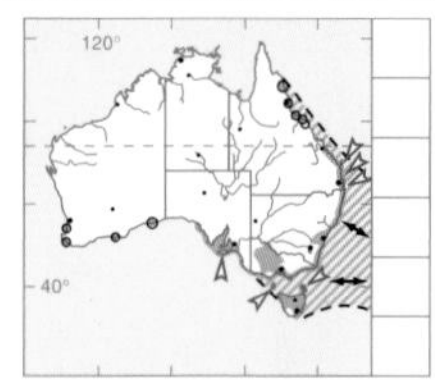

Race *bicinctus*
Only the breeding NZ alpine population winters in Aust.

Greater (Large) Sand Plover *Charadrius leschenaultii* UC–MC

Often with Lesser Sand Plover. Narrow chestnut chest band. **F** Duller. **Non-br.** Like Lesser. Bill larger. Face paler; lores often partly marked grey-brown. Uniform pale grey-brown above; white below. Broader wing bar. Legs paler, longer, thinner. **Size** 22–25 cm. **Juv.** As Lesser, slightly larger. **Voice** 'preep-preep'; longer trills than Lesser. **Hab.** Also as Lesser.

Juv. head pattern

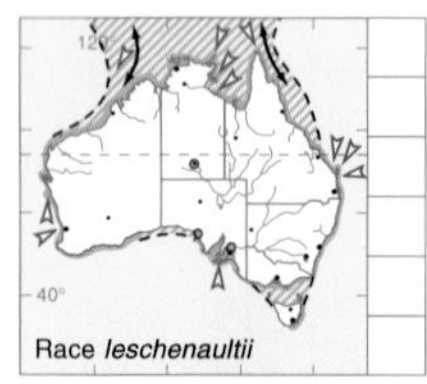

Race *leschenaultii*

Oriental Plover *Charadrius veredus* LA–UC

Slender, long-legged. White head; faint brown cap, ear coverts. Black line between chestnut breast, white belly. **F** Duller; fawn breast well defined. **Non-br.** Fine black bill. Buff-white throat, eyebrow. Grey-brown above. No wing bar. Black sub-terminal tail band. White below, faint chest band. All dark underwing. Legs greenish to dull yellow. **Size** 21–25 cm. **Juv.** As non-br., paler. Check non-br. Pacific Golden. Buff eyebrow, breast. **Voice** Nasal 'chit-chit'; 'chrreep'. **Hab.** Dry plains; coastal.

Underwing patterns

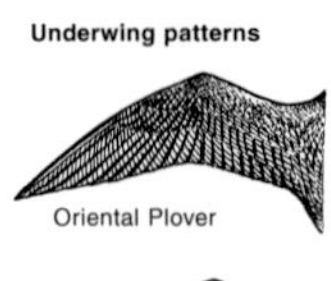

Oriental Plover

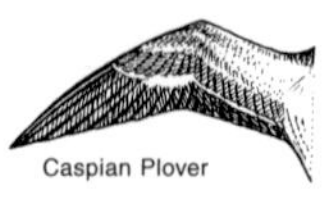

Caspian Plover

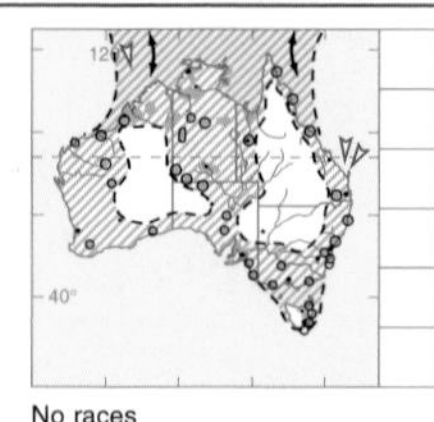

No races

Caspian Plover *Charadrius asiaticus*, **Kentish Plover** *Charadrius alexandrinus* see **Vagrant Bird Bulletin** p. 294.

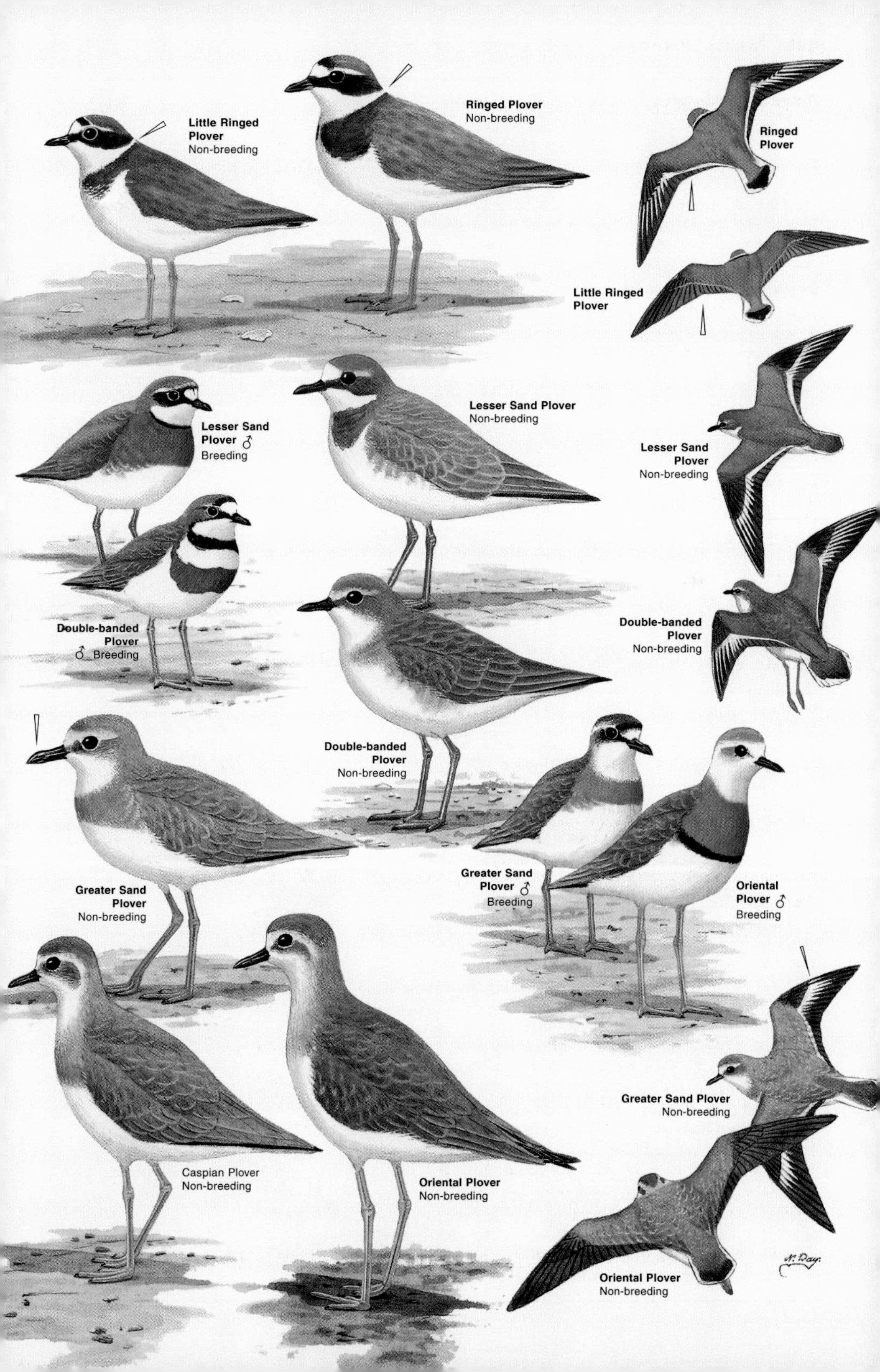

Little Ringed Plover
Non-breeding
Ringed Plover
Non-breeding
Ringed Plover
Little Ringed Plover
Lesser Sand Plover ♂
Breeding
Lesser Sand Plover
Non-breeding
Lesser Sand Plover
Non-breeding
Double-banded Plover
♂ Breeding
Double-banded Plover
Non-breeding
Double-banded Plover
Non-breeding
Greater Sand Plover
Non-breeding
Greater Sand Plover ♂
Breeding
Oriental Plover ♂
Breeding
Greater Sand Plover
Non-breeding
Caspian Plover
Non-breeding
Oriental Plover
Non-breeding
Oriental Plover
Non-breeding

Red-capped Plover *Charadrius ruficapillus* **MC** ◎–♣ Br. E

Runs in short spurts. Small. Bright rufous crown, nape, collar, all partly edged black. Black eye-stripe; black bill, legs. White forehead. Upperparts brown. White wing bar and black rump line in flight. **F** Similar; crown duller; black less distinct. **Non-br.** Upperparts plain grey-brown. **Size** 14–16 cm. **Juv.** Upperparts edged buff. **Voice** Sharp 'twink'; piping. **Hab.** Estuaries, beaches; coastal and inland lakes.

Compare with Kentish Plover; see Vagrant Bird Bulletin, p. 294.

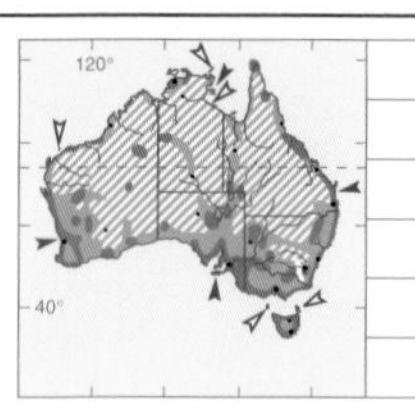

No races

Black-fronted Dotterel *Elseyornis (Charadrius) melanops* **C** ◎–♣

Small plover. Flight jerky, reveals white wing bars; alights, runs. Brown upperparts. Sexes alike. Bill bright red, tipped black. Red eye-ring. Face white; black frons and black eye-line. Pale streaked wing coverts; chestnut shoulder patch. Underparts white with broad black chest 'V'. **Size** 16–18 cm. **Juv.** Plainer. No black 'V' on chest. **Voice** Metallic 'pink'; trilling calls. **Hab.** Freshwater lake margins, farm dams; rarely tidal areas.

Hatchling

Front on

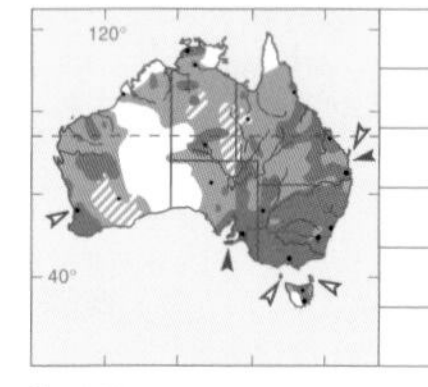

No races

Inland Dotterel *Charadrius (Peltohyas) australis* **MC** ◎–♣ E

Small, well camouflaged. Largely feeds at night. Often flushed from roadsides by vehicles. Check Black-fronted Dotterel. Bill short, black. Frons, face, upper breast white-buff. Black bar over crown becomes 'tear-drop' below large eye. Upperparts yellowish-buff, streaked dark grey-brown. Thin black line behind eye joins black collar, extends to deep 'V' on chest, dividing pale upper breast from rich chestnut lower breast. White abdomen, undertail. Legs buffy-grey. **Non-br./Juv.** May lack black markings. **Size** 20 cm. **Voice** Mostly silent; short, sharp or soft calls. **Hab.** Ploughed ground, open sparse plains, gibber.

Front on

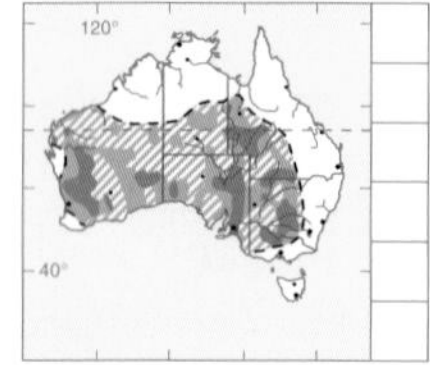

No races

Black-winged Stilt *Himantopus himantopus* **C** ◎–♣

'Tall' stance. Long fine black bill. Red eye. White-headed. Black nape patch. Back, wings black. Very long coral-pink legs trail in flight. **Size** 33–37 cm. **Imm.** Head, nape patch greyish. **Juv.** Ashy crown; neck white; no black on nape. Back, wings brownish, feathers edged buff. **Voice** Sharp puppy-like yelps. **Hab.** Fresh- and saltwater marshes. Flooded paddocks.

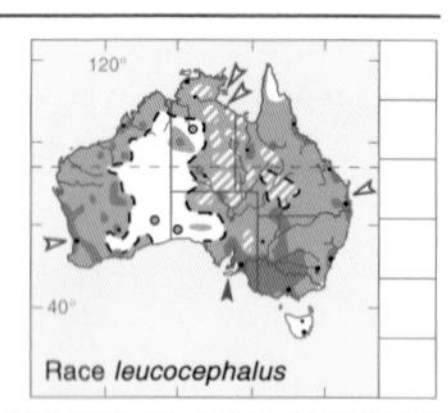

Banded Stilt *Cladorhynchus leucocephalus* **LA–UC** ♣–? E

'Tall' stance. Often in dense flocks; often swims. Associates with Black-winged Stilt, Red-necked Avocet. White. Long, fine black bill. Eye dark brown. Wings brown-black; white trailing edge in flight. Bold red-brown breast band above deep brown mid-belly patch (looks black in field). Long legs are flesh-pink; shorter than Black-winged Stilt; trail in flight. **Non-br.** Breast band mottled or absent. **Size** 35–43 cm. **Juv.** Underparts white; legs duller. **Voice** 'chowk'. **Hab.** Freshwater, saltwater marshes, tidal mudflats. Ephemeral inland lakes where salinity is increasing.

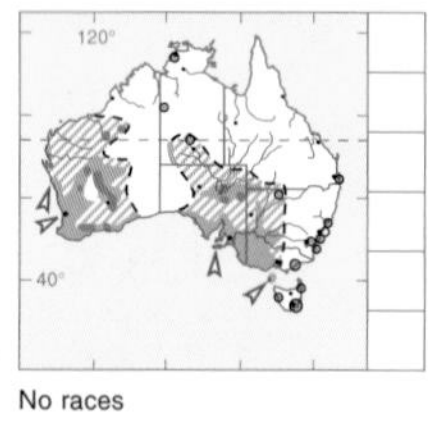

No races

Nomadic/?migratory. In good conditions, breeds colonially. Weather heavily influences movements.

Red-necked Avocet *Recurvirostra novaehollandiae* **LA–C** ♣

'Tall' stance. Gregarious; roosts in tight-packed groups. Often swims. White. Head, neck, chestnut. Long black up-curved bill (female's more steeply). Black wing bar, wing tips, stripes down side of back, distinctive in flight. Long pale blue-grey legs trail in flight. Partly webbed feet. **Size** 40–48 cm. **Juv.** Paler; grey on scapulars. **Voice** Yelps, wheezes; musical 'toot toot'. **Hab.** Tidal flats, marshes, saltworks, shallow inland salt lakes.

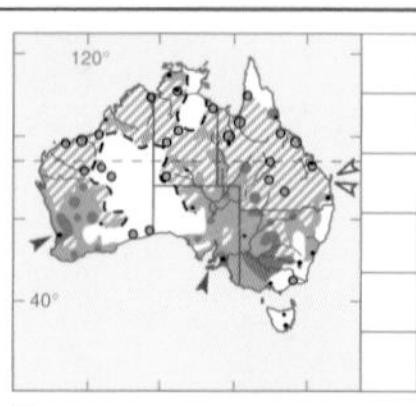

No races

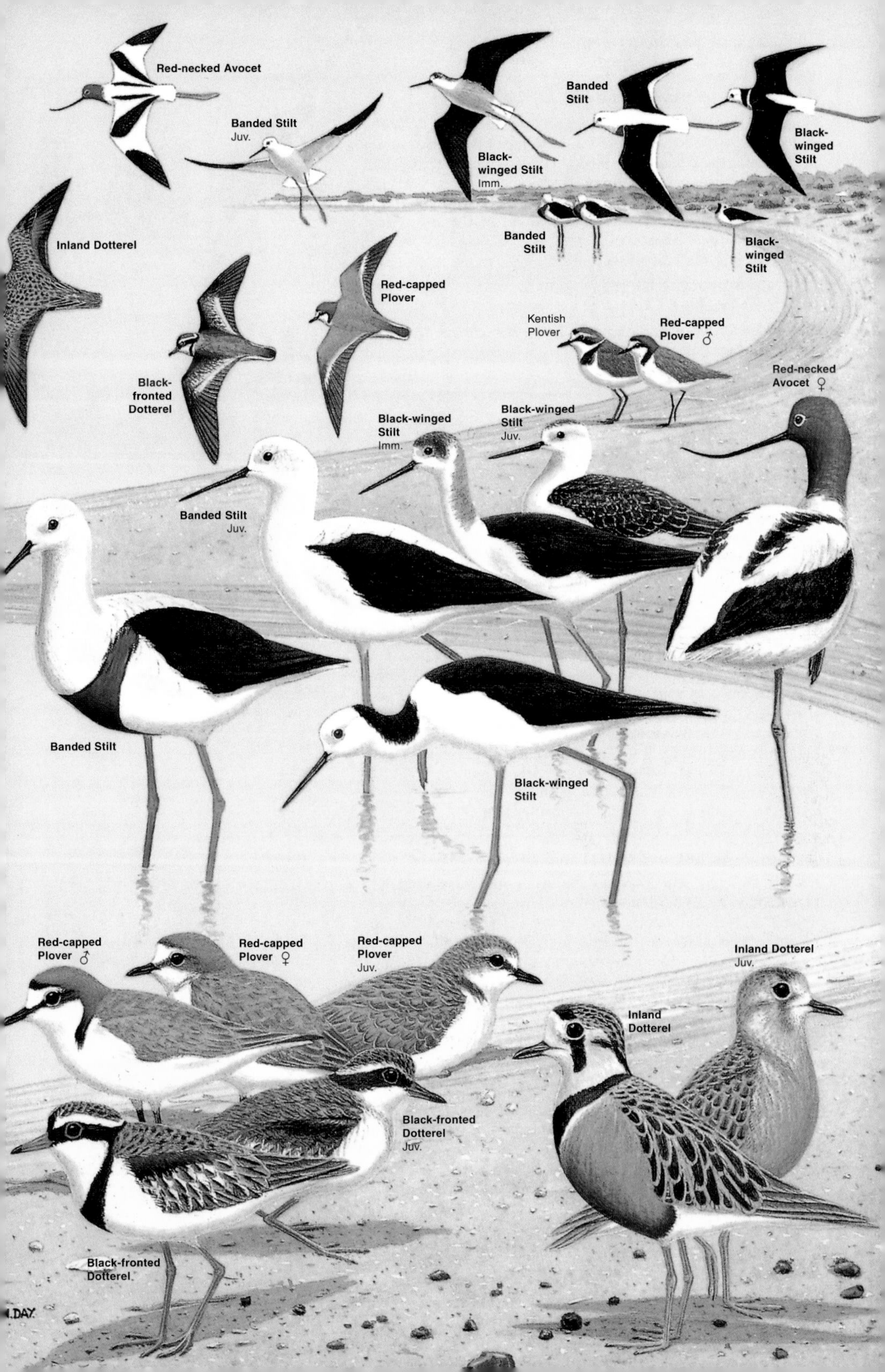
Red-necked Avocet
Banded Stilt
Juv.
Black-
winged Stilt
Imm.
Banded
Stilt
Black-
winged
Stilt
Banded
Stilt
Black-
winged
Stilt
Inland Dotterel
Red-capped
Plover
Black-
fronted
Dotterel
Kentish
Plover
Red-capped
Plover ♂
Red-necked
Avocet ♀
Black-winged
Stilt
Imm.
Black-winged
Stilt
Juv.
Banded Stilt
Juv.
Banded Stilt
Black-winged
Stilt
Red-capped
Plover ♂
Red-capped
Plover ♀
Red-capped
Plover
Juv.
Inland Dotterel
Juv.
Inland
Dotterel
Black-fronted
Dotterel
Juv.
Black-fronted
Dotterel
.DAY

Great Skua *Catharacta skua* **MC** ⟲ Vulnerable

Flight direct, powerful flapping and gliding. Large, stocky. Some resemblance to juvenile Pacific Gull. Bill black. Chocolate-brown, flecked buff. Back boldly streaked buff. Dark brown wings with broad white primary bases; these show in flight. Short tail. Legs black. **Size** 64 cm. **Juv.** Upper body tinged copper-red. **Voice** Generally silent in Australian seas. At nest territory, both sexes give strong challenge calls, wings raised; sharp screeches in aerial attack. **Hab.** Coastal, oceanic.

Wing moult

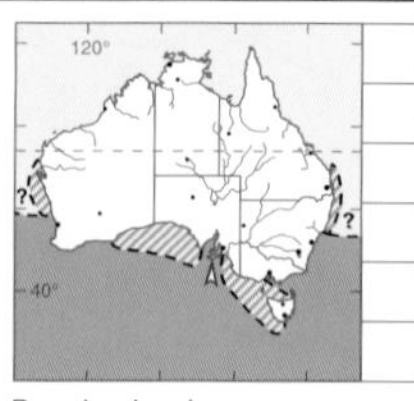

Race *lonnbergi*

South Polar Skua *Catharacta maccormicki* **R–UC** ⟲

Like Great Skua but smaller. **Light morph** Light grey-brown body; pale buff collar contrasts with dark upperparts. **Dark morph** Dark brown to blackish; nape sometimes paler; paler around bill. **Size** 53 cm. **Juv.** Bill base, legs blue. Chin, throat, paler. **Hab.** Oceanic. A few Aust. records, mostly E coast.

Dark morph

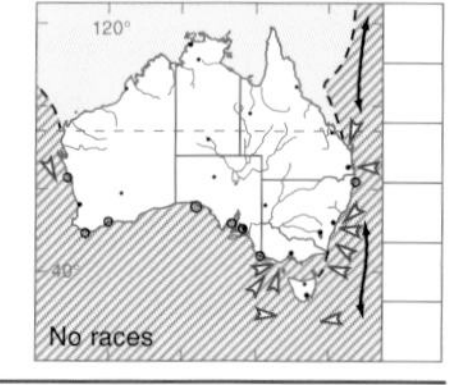

Arctic Jaeger *Stercorarius parasiticus* **C** ⟲

Fast, acrobatic flight when chasing terns, gulls. A small jaeger. Small head. Slender wings. Normally two long, pointed, central tail streamers (often lacking). **Light morph br.** Bill, cap black. Collar, throat, upper breast, buff. Brown breast band. Belly white. Upperparts, wings, brown-grey, little contrast with trailing edge. Underwing dark grey. Bases of primaries white. Tail black, white base. Legs black. **Light morph non-br.** Head paler. Black and white barred flanks, upper and undertail coverts. Often lacks tail streamers. **Light morph juv.** Like non-breeding. Bill base paler. Brown above, barred buff and rufous. Underwing coverts barred brown, rufous and white. Short pointed tail streamers. Legs black and blue. **Dark morph br.** Dark brown; cap black; yellowish collar, cheeks. **Dark morph non-br.** White bars on rump. **Dark morph juv.** Faint buff to rufous bars below. **Size** 46–67 cm (incl. tail streamers) (cf. Crested Tern 40–50 cm). **Hab.** Oceanic, coastal, enters bays. Rarely in large sub-coastal wetlands. Summer migrant to Australian coastal seas.

Juv.

Underwing pattern

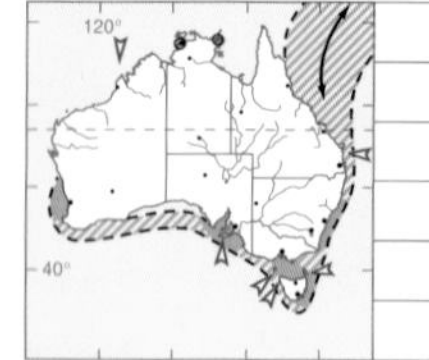

No races

Resting on drifting plank

Most jaegers in Aust. seas are in non-br., juv., or imm. plumage; many subtleties in these plumages, therefore wide variation in appearance.

Pomarine Jaeger *Stercorarius pomarinus* **MC–LC** ⟲

Like Arctic, larger; often hard to identify from it. Head, bill, bigger; body bulkier. All plumages as Arctic, but wing flashes usually larger. Tail streamers short, rounded; twisted when fully grown. Legs black and blue. **Light** and **Dark morphs** recognised. **Non-br.** Broader white bars on rump. **Size** 65–78 cm (incl. streamers; 10% larger than Crested Tern). **Juv.** Upperparts brownish; faint to pale barring; no rufous bars. Brown and white bars on underwing coverts. **Hab.** Enters bays. Normally more oceanic than Arctic Jaeger. Mostly seen off SE Aust. coast.

All skuas and jaegers are parasites of other seabirds, chasing and robbing them of food. Some (possibly imm.) over-winter in Aust. seas.

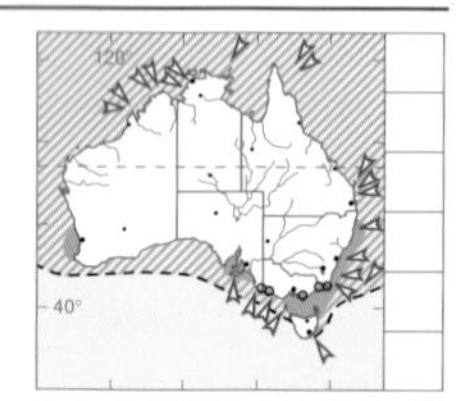

No races

Long-tailed Jaeger *Stercorarius longicauda* **UC** ⟲

Like Arctic, body smaller. Slender wings; tern-like flight. Long tail with double-length streamers, finer near tips. Bill sheath blue to horn-colour. **Br.** Upperparts pale blue-grey, contrasting black secondaries and primaries (usually no white in wing). Legs black to black and blue. **Non-br.** Pale head. Barred flanks, tail coverts. **Size** 38–58 cm (incl. streamers). **Juv.** Greyish to dark brown above (no rufous), scaled buff-white. Rump, flanks, underwing coverts, barred grey and white. White crescents on primary bases. Short central tail feathers rounded. **Hab.** Oceanic.

Non-breeding underwing pattern

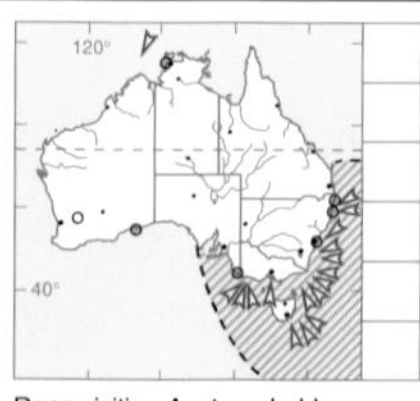

Race visiting Aust. probably *pallescens*

Arctic Jaeger
Breeding
Light morph
Great Skua
Arctic Jaeger
Breeding
Dark morph
Arctic Jaeger
Non-breeding
Light morph
Crested Tern
Great Skua
South Polar
Skua
Light morph
Pomarine Jaeger
Non-breeding
South Polar Skua
Light morph
Pomarine Jaeger
Juv.
Long-tailed
Jaeger
Breeding
Pomarine Jaeger
Breeding
Dark morph
Pomarine Jaeger
Breeding
Light morph
Long-tailed Jaeger
Juv.
Wedge-tailed Shearwater
Long-tailed Jaeger
Juv.
Arctic
Jaeger
Juv.

Silver Gull *Larus novaehollandiae* **LA–C** ◎–

Scavenges trawlers, beaches, seabird colonies, cities. Mature plumage after 6 partial or full moults in 3 years. Body white, incl. tail. Bill, feet, eye-ring, red. Iris white. Mantle grey. Upperwings, inner primaries, medium grey. Outer wing region from carpal, white. Black sub-terminal band; white-tipped black primaries become white 'mirrors' (spots) when wings folded. **Non-br.** Dark bill tip. Duller red parts. **Size** 43–44 cm. **Juv.** Bill, iris, legs, dark. Faint brown ear patch, marks on crown, before eye. Grey above, heavily mottled brown, buff tips. Smaller wing mirrors. Sub-terminal tail band brownish. **Imm.** (2nd yr)/**Sub-ad.** (3rd yr) Dark bill becomes browner, then yellowish, dark-tipped. Over 2 years becomes dull to bright red. Legs, toes, webs, lighten with age. **Voice** Harsh. Repeated fast squeals, short cackles; soft mewings. **Hab.** Coastal, inland waters; farmland, urban.

Hatchling

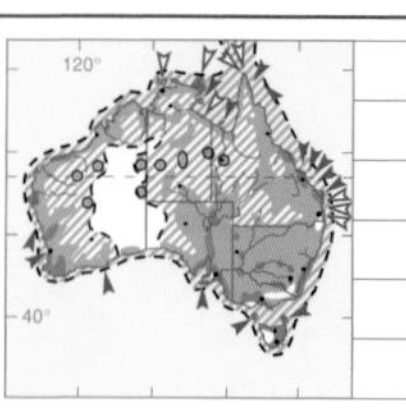

Race *novaehollandiae*

Pacific Gull *Larus pacificus* **MC** ◎– E

Roosts on boats, piles, reefs; on open beaches, cruises along dunes. Flies up, drops shellfish, to break them. Mature plumage after 8–10 partial or full moults in 5 years. Massive yellow bill; both mandibles tipped red. Iris pale. Orbital ring orange. Body white. Black mantle, outer primaries, wings, with white trailing edge. Tail white; bold black sub-terminal band. Legs yellow. **Non-br.** Bill orange-yellow, orange-red tip. Orbital ring, legs, feet, yellow to orange-yellow. Race *georgii* (B) Iris varies white (SA) to dark (west WA). Less red on bill tip. **F** (both races) Smaller, bill less massive. **Size** 50–67 cm. **Juv.** Dark bill, iris, legs. Body largely dark brown, slightly mottled. Tail black, tip white. Pale undertail coverts. **Imm.** (1st yr)/**Sub-ad.** (3rd, 4th yrs) White increases on face, head, neck, body; black on back, wings. Bill changes from dark horn to pale with reddish tip. Legs pale. **Voice** Carrying 'kow kow kow'; honks. **Hab.** Coastal, nearby rubbish tips.

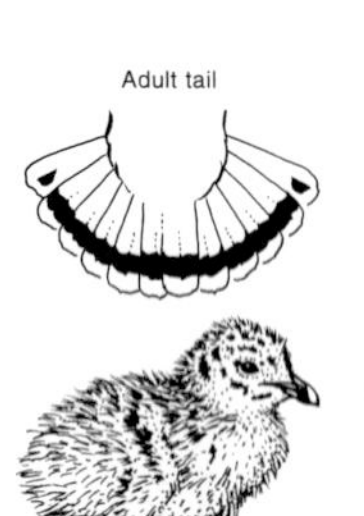

Hatchling

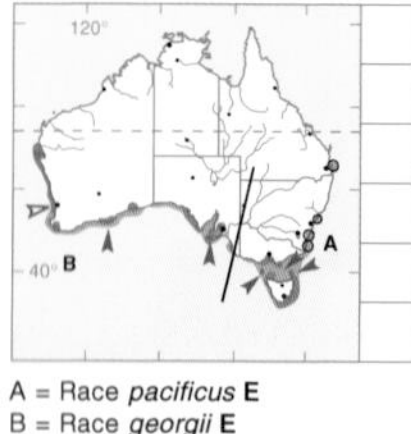

A = Race *pacificus* **E**
B = Race *georgii* **E**

Kelp Gull *Larus dominicanus* **UC** ◎–

Mature plumage after 8 partial to full moults in 4 years. As Pacific Gull, smaller. Broader white trailing edge in flight. Finer, paler lemon-yellow bill, red spot on lower mandible. White mirrors on folded wings; tertials show as two thin white bars. White-tipped secondaries. Tail all white (no band). Legs olive-yellow; appear short in field. **Size** 49–62 cm. **Juv.** Like juv. Pacific; paler, more heavily mottled. Dark bill, iris. Black band on secondaries. **Imm.** (1st yr)/**Sub-ad.** (3rd yr) Aging sequence very like Pacific Gull. Both mandibles, dark sub-terminal tip. Dusky about head until breeding plumage. **Voice** Short series 'ow ow ow ow'; crying. **Hab.** Coastal; often rocky shores. Colonised southern Aust. from 1950s.

Hatchling

Race *dominicanus*
Recent (*circa* early 1950s) coloniser in southern Aust.

Comparison of dorsal wings

Silver Gull adult

Franklin's Gull adult

Laughing Gull adult

Black-headed Gull adult

Sabine's Gull adult

Black-tailed Gull adult

Black-tailed (Japanese) Gull *Larus crassirostris*, **Black-headed Gull** *Larus ridibundus*, **Laughing Gull** *Larus atricilla*, **Franklin's Gull** *Larus pipixcan*, **Sabine's Gull** *Larus (Xema) sabini* see **Vagrant Bird Bulletin** pp. 294, 295, 296.

Pacific Gull
Imm. 3rd yr
Pacific Gull
Imm. 1st yr
Silver Gull
Ad.
cific Gull
Pacific Gull
Imm. 2nd yr
Silver Gull
Imm. 1st yr
p Gull
Ad.
Silver Gull
Ad.
Juv.
Imm. 2nd yr
Kelp Gull
Imm. 1st yr
Pacific Gull
Imm. 3rd yr
Gull
2nd yr
cific Gull
Juv.
Pacific Gull
Race
georgii
Pacific Gull
Imm. 2nd yr
Race
pacificus
Kelp Gull
Imm. 2nd yr
Kelp Gull
Ad.
Kelp Gull
Juv.

Whiskered (Marsh) Tern *Chlidonias hybridus* **A–C**

Large head, chunky body. Perches on posts in water; roosts on ground. In flight, short forked tail; 'dips' as feeds over water. Short, thick, crimson bill. Dark iris. Black cap; white cheek. Pearl-grey above. Chin pale, grading to black belly; white undertail coverts. Dark red legs, feet. **Non-br.** Bill black, base dusky red. Head white; black eye-band to nape; rear crown finely streaked. White below. **Size** 23–25 cm. **Juv.** Blackish bill; larger black cap than non-br.; mantle dusky-buff. Dark-brown terminal tail band. **Voice** Harsh shrieks. **Hab.** Shallow freshwater wetlands with emergent vegetation; flooded saltmarsh; estuaries.

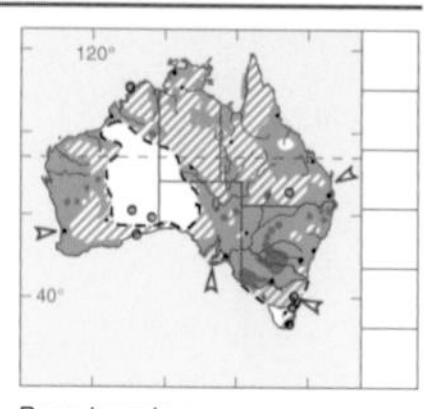

Race *javanicus*

White-winged Black Tern *Chlidonias leucopterus* **MC–UC**

Perches on posts in water. Smaller, whiter, than Whiskered Terns; often with them. Short dark red bill. Head, mantle, breast, belly, black. Upperwing mid-grey; silver shoulder bars. Short, almost square tail, less forked than Whiskered. Underwing coverts black, primaries grey. Some birds change to this breeding plumage near end of summer migration. **Non-br.** Birds look 'whiter'. Bill black; black crown extends in 'sideburns' behind, below, eye; white mask. Crown, nape, black, streaked white. White hind-neck, mid-grey mantle. Dusky shoulder bar. Rump, sides of tail, underparts, white. Underwing white, trailing edge grey. Often retains black line along tips of greater coverts. In transition to br. plumage, black underbody, wing lining. **Size** 20–24 cm. **Juv.** As non-br. adult; blackish-brown mantle contrasts with pale wings. **Voice** Noisy screech. **Hab.** Lakes, estuaries, coastal seas.

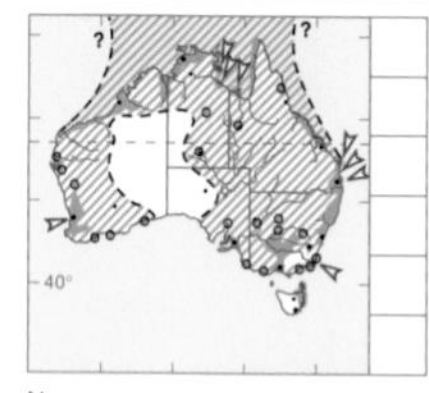

No races

Caspian Tern *Sterna caspia* **MC**

World's largest tern; size distinctive. Shallow wing beats. 'Patrols' rivers, lakes, stretches of coast, at about 20–40 m height. Dives for prey. Massive red bill has dusky sub-terminal mark. Cap black. Pale grey upperparts; white below. Primaries entirely blackish below. **Non-br.** Black eye, ear coverts. Forehead, crown, white; fine black streaks increasing to nape. **Size** 47–54 cm. **Juv.** Like non-br. adult. Bill paler; forehead to nape grey-buff, streaked black. Mantle variegated ('chequered') dusky and buff. **Hab.** Coastal; also inland watercourses; saline, brackish lakes.

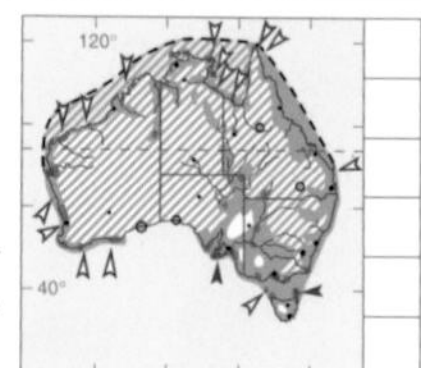

No races

Gull-billed Tern *Sterna nilotica* **LC–UC**

Tern-shaped but almost Silver Gull-sized. In flight, slow, gull-like. Dipping flight when feeding over water, like marsh terns. Very pale, chunky tern; slightly forked tail. Short, thick, black bill. Dark iris. Black cap. Upperparts whitish-grey; underparts white. Blackish trailing edge to most primaries. Long black legs. **Non-br./Imm.** Head white; usually with faint, dark crown streaks. Black mask from eye to ear coverts. **Size** 35–38 cm. **Juv.** Like non-br. adult but crown greyish-brown, finely streaked, darker than adult. Mantle variegated; dusky/pale buff. Some pale birds may be plainer, more buff. **Voice** Usually quiet. Bleating alarm, given only when breeding. **Hab.** Coastal seas, tidal flats, shallow lakes, ploughed, fallowed and flooded fields, crops.

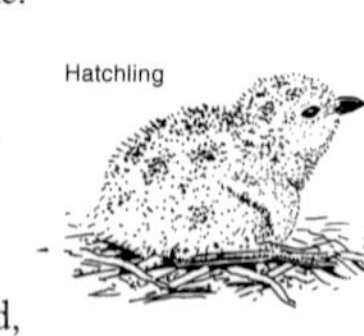

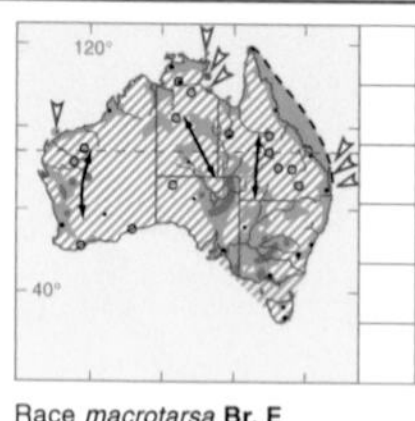

Race *macrotarsa* **Br. E**

Black Tern *Chlidonias niger* see **Vagrant Bird Bulletin** p. 296.

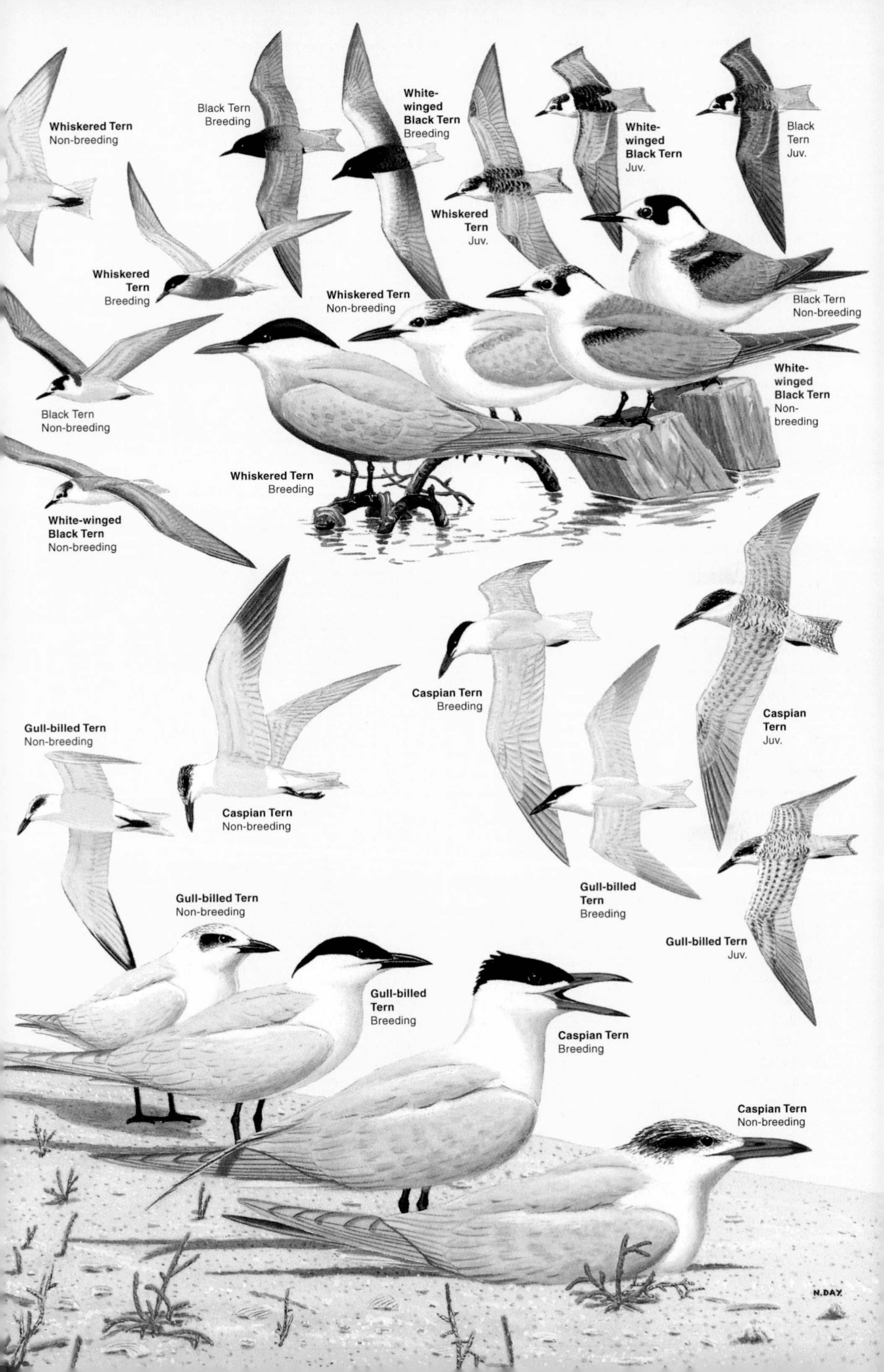

Whiskered Tern
Non-breeding
Black Tern
Breeding
White-winged Black Tern
Breeding
White-winged Black Tern
Juv.
Black Tern
Juv.
Whiskered Tern
Juv.
Whiskered Tern
Breeding
Whiskered Tern
Non-breeding
Black Tern
Non-breeding
Black Tern
Non-breeding
White-winged Black Tern
Non-breeding
Whiskered Tern
Breeding
White-winged Black Tern
Non-breeding
Caspian Tern
Breeding
Caspian Tern
Juv.
Gull-billed Tern
Non-breeding
Caspian Tern
Non-breeding
Gull-billed Tern
Breeding
Gull-billed Tern
Non-breeding
Gull-billed Tern
Juv.
Gull-billed Tern
Breeding
Caspian Tern
Breeding
Caspian Tern
Non-breeding
N.DAY

Common Tern *Sterna hirundo* MC ○

Black, mid-length bill. Cap to bill black. Body light grey. White rump. Tail streamers shorter than folded wings. Against light, white underwing has small rear central translucent patch only, dark trailing edge on primaries. Brown, mid-length legs. **Non-br.** Black bill. Frons to above eye, white. Front crown mottled black; black rear crown, nape, ear coverts, patch in front of eye. Black shoulder bar (wedge-shaped) when perched. Back, rump, tail, pale greyish, no contrast between them. Underparts white. Tail shorter. Race *hirundo* (B) Black-tipped red bill; red legs. **Size** 32–37 cm. **Voice** 'Ki-ork'; 'kik-kik-kik'. **Hab.** Oceans, bays.

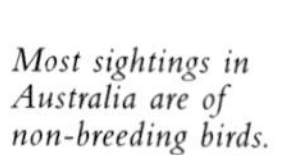
Most sightings in Australia are of non-breeding birds.

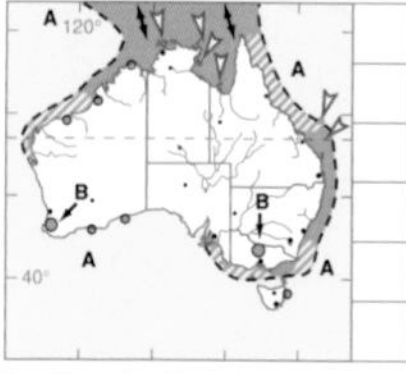

A = Race *longipennis*
B = Race *hirundo*
Race *hirundo* (B) extremely rare; just two single European-banded terns recorded (1956, 1968).

Arctic Tern *Sterna paradisaea* UC ○

Like Common; smaller body. Red bill. Crown more domed. In flight appears 'short-necked'. Contrasting white rump. Shorter legs. Tail streamers project past primaries (longer in Roseate). Legs red. In flight, against light, all primaries strongly translucent with black trailing edge of constant width. **Non-br.** Bill black. Head white; black band, eye to nape. Rear crown black streaked. Tail shorter than wing-tips. Legs dark. **Size** 27.5–35 cm. **Imm.** As non-br. No dark shoulder (cubital) bar. **Hab.** Oceans, coastal.

Most stragglers reaching the coast are from more pelagic migration routes. Spot localities in SW and SE Aust. seem to be concentration points for both living and beachwashed birds.

Some individuals reach Aust. in juv. plumage.

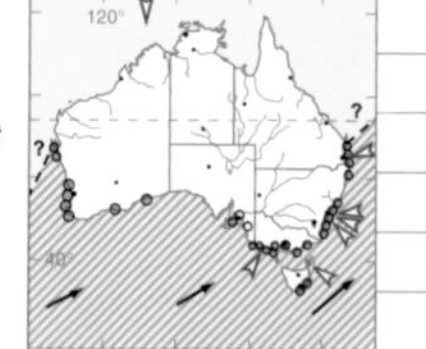

No races

Roseate Tern *Sterna dougallii* C–UC ◎–⅄

Most slender Australian 'commic' tern. At rest, streamers extend beyond wing-tips. Bill as long as head, slender, varies: black-tipped red to red-based black. Black cap, bill to nape (incl. eye). Pale grey back, wings, tail; rump white, little contrast. Underwing white, no dark trailing edge. Legs red. White below; soft pink tinge. **Non-br.** Streamers retained. Black bill. Slender upperwing, outer primaries black (due to suspended moult). White below; variably pink (roseate) on belly. Legs brownish. **Size** 31–38 cm. **Juv.** No streamers. Dark streaked crown. Scapulars grey, scaled black. Tail short; blotched black sub-terminally. **Imm.** Almost no carpal bar. **Voice** 'chew-ich'; grating 'aach'. **Hab.** Oceanic.

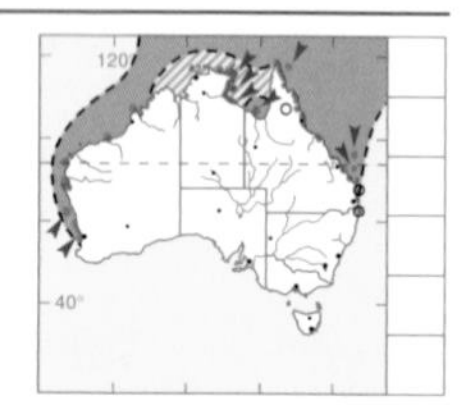

Race *gracilis*

White-fronted Tern *Sterna striata* MC–UC ○

Bill stout; cap black, separated by white frons. Pale grey above; little rump contrast. Folded primaries show white line along upper edge. White below. Deeply forked white tail, a little longer than primaries, outer edge blackish. Legs dusky-red. **Non-br.** Frons like non-br. Common, but heavier bill, white underwing, paler above. **1st yr** Dark shoulder bar. **Size** 35–43 cm. **Juv.** Upperparts, central tail feathers, boldly barred blackish. Upperwing has broad dark shoulder triangle. Dark outer primaries; the rest whitish. **Voice** 'kech kech'; 'kee-ech-kee-ech'. **Hab.** Oceanic; rocky reefs, sandspits and bars; jetties, groynes.

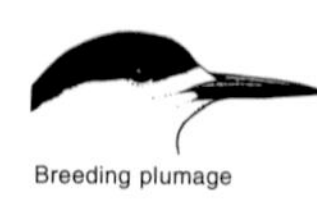
Breeding plumage

Largest 'commic' tern. Most birds seen over-wintering in southern Aust. are from NZ.

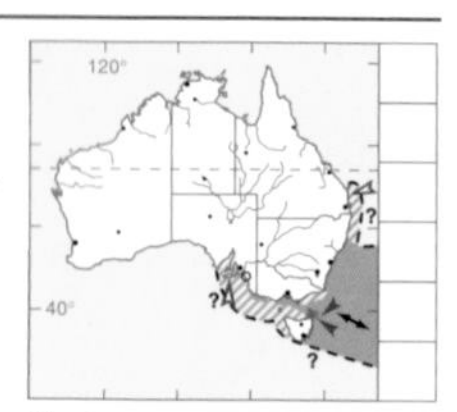

No races

Black-naped Tern *Sterna sumatrana* LC ◎–⅄

Adults gleam white. Larger than non-br. Little Tern; whiter than non-br. Roseate. Black bill. White head (no black cap). Thin black line from triangle before eye to nape. Wings, back, very pale grey. Black 1st primary shows in flight and when wings folded. White tail deeply forked. White below (some pink-tinged). Black legs. **Size** 30–32 cm. **Juv.** Bill base dusky-yellow. Identify from juv. Roseate by grey nape, whitish bases to dark-fringed dorsal feathers; bulkier body, shorter legs. **Hab.** Coastal.

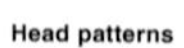
Head patterns

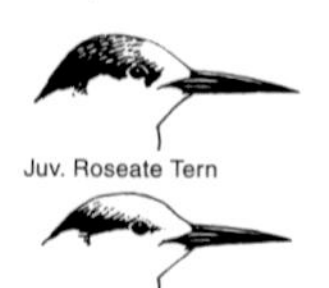
Juv. Roseate Tern

Juv. Black-naped Tern

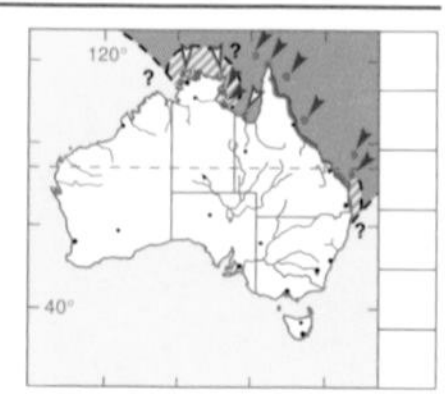

Race *mathewsi*

Antarctic Tern *Sterna vittata* see **Vagrant Bird Bulletin** p. 296.

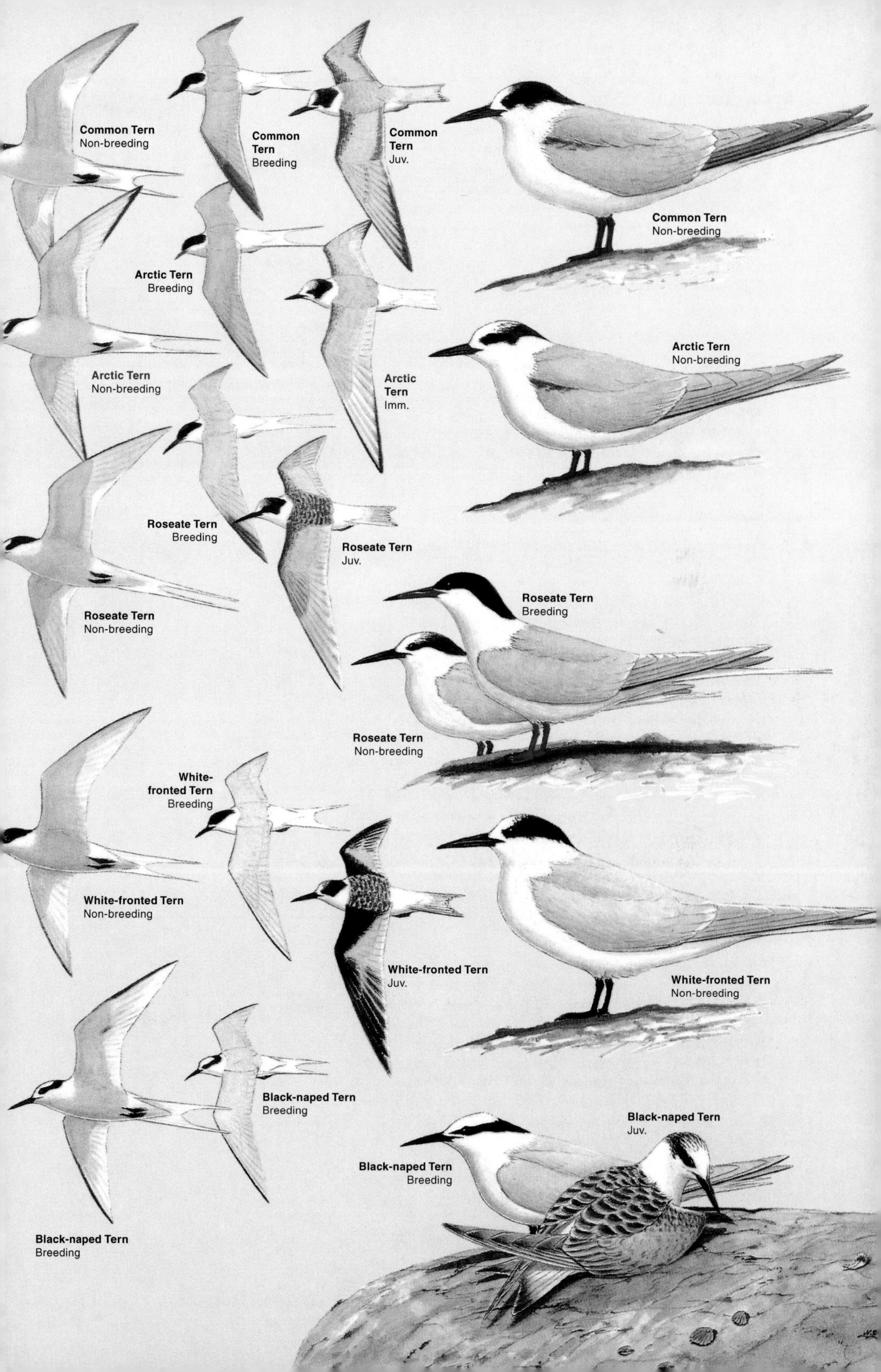
Common Tern
Non-breeding
Common Tern
Breeding
Common Tern
Juv.
Common Tern
Non-breeding
Arctic Tern
Breeding
Arctic Tern
Non-breeding
Arctic Tern
Imm.
Arctic Tern
Non-breeding
Roseate Tern
Breeding
Roseate Tern
Juv.
Roseate Tern
Non-breeding
Roseate Tern
Breeding
Roseate Tern
Non-breeding
White-fronted Tern
Breeding
White-fronted Tern
Non-breeding
White-fronted Tern
Juv.
White-fronted Tern
Non-breeding
Black-naped Tern
Breeding
Black-naped Tern
Juv.
Black-naped Tern
Breeding
Black-naped Tern
Breeding

Sooty Tern *Sterna fuscata* **A O**

Bill, legs, feet, black. Broad, white, triangular forehead patch. Upperparts black. Tail deeply forked, outer tail streamers white. Underparts white; faint grey on belly when breeding. Underwing white; primaries, secondaries black. **Size** 33–36 cm. **Juv.** Dark brown upperparts; feathers tipped pale buffish to white. Underwing coverts pale grey; vent white. Tail short. **Voice** Chatter like corellas. Hoarse cries. **Hab.** Pelagic: oceans, islands.

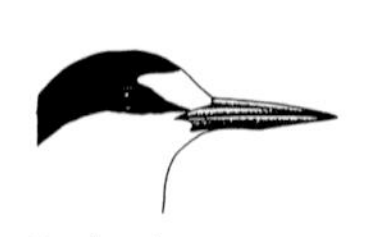

Breeding plumage

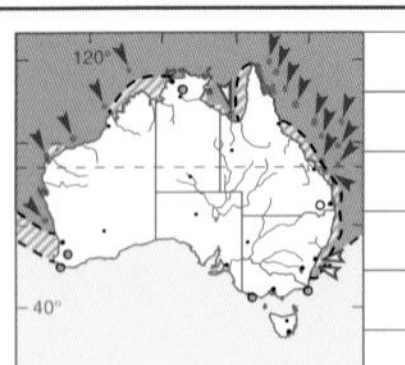

Race *serrata*

Bridled Tern *Sterna anaethetus* **C O**

Like Sooty Tern, larger; less white on forecrown. Underwing like Sooty but primary bases slightly silvery-grey. Bill, legs, black. White extends as eyebrow behind eye. Upperparts dark grey-brown. Darker plumage when breeding. **Size** 30–32 cm. **Juv.** Cap strongly streaked white. Lores white with a buff mark in front of eye. Upperparts grey-brown, buffy-tipped. Underparts white; underwing same as adult. Tail shorter, less deeply forked. **Voice** Stilt-like yaps. **Hab.** Oceans, coasts, islands.

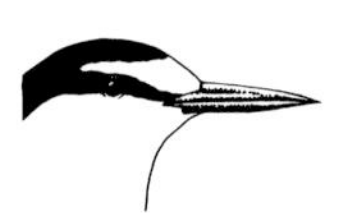

Breeding plumage

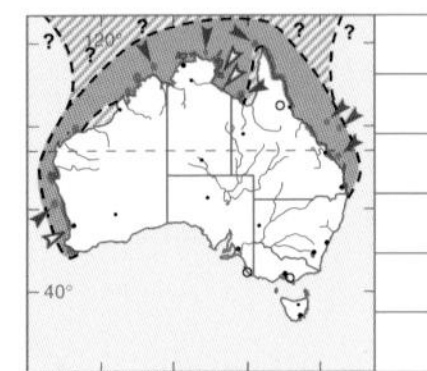

Race *anaethetus*

Little Tern *Sterna albifrons* **MC–UC O** Endangered

Race *sinensis* Very small grey and white tern with long, narrow wings; rapid wing beats. Smaller head, flatter crown, noticeably longer legs and body more slender than Fairy Tern. In tropical areas, check larger Black-naped Tern. Bill mid-yellow, usually black tip. Triangular white forehead from bill to above eye. Black line through lores to bill. Rest of cap black. Pale grey upperparts contrast with forked white tail. Upperwing pale grey, contrasts with blackish outer three or four primaries. Legs yellow to orange-yellow. **Non-br.** Bill black. Lores, forecrown, white; crown mottled grey. Black band remains from eye to nape, bold black spot in front of eye. Upperwing has dusty-greyish shoulder (cubital) bar. Outer primaries slightly darker than rest of wing; these wear (abrade) to black. Legs blackish-brown. **Size** 20–28 cm. **Juv.** Bill black, brownish base. Cap streaked dusky and buff; dark ear patch. Upperparts grey with dark sub-terminal feather bands and buffish fringes. Darker, broader shoulder bar than non-breeding birds. Secondaries grey, tipped white. **Voice** Short, harsh squeaks. **Hab.** Coasts, estuaries. Australian birds breed on sandy beaches and sand spits.

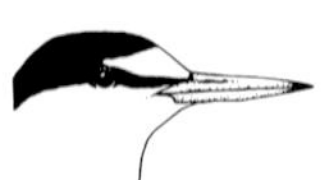

Breeding plumage

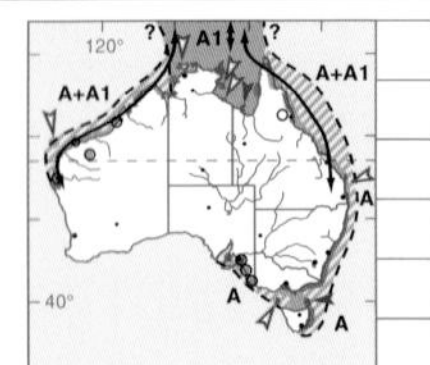

Race *sinensis*

In northern Aust., the locally breeding yellow-billed population is masked by arrival of a black-billed non-br. (wintering) migratory population from the Northern Hemisphere (area A1 on map). They are also of race sinensis. *These birds spread south, mostly within the tropics (long arrows).*

Fairy Tern *Sterna nereis* **C–MC O–**

Like Little Tern but slightly larger head with more rounded profile. Bill bright orange and often black at base of upper bill. Also, noticeably bulkier body, giving round-bellied appearance; shorter, thicker legs. Larger white forehead area. Lores white with black patch in front of eye. Black crown, nape. Pearl-grey upperparts give less contrast with whitish rump, tail. Legs bright orange. **Non-br.** Bill dusky orange-brown, blackish at tip. Crown white (check Black-naped Tern). Upperwing as breeding adult but outer primaries less contrasting; no dark shoulder bar. **Size** 22–27 cm. **Juv.** Like juv. Little Tern but generally darker and no dark wing bar. Outer wing dark greyish, grading to pale grey inner wing, secondaries whitish (grey in Little Tern). Bill, legs, dark brown. **Voice** Three-note squeak. **Hab.** Coasts, estuaries; breeds on sandy beaches and sand spits.

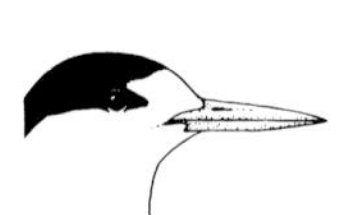

Breeding plumage

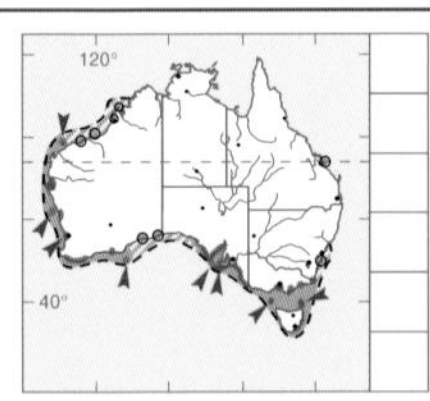

Race *nereis* **E**

Bridled Tern
Sooty Tern
Sooty Tern
Juv.
Bridled Tern
Juv.
Sooty
Tern
Bridled Tern
Sooty Tern
Bridled Tern
Juv.
Bridled Tern
Fairy Tern
Breeding
Fairy Tern
Early breeding
Little Tern
Early breeding
Little Tern
Breeding
Little Tern
Breeding
Common Tern
Non-breeding
Fairy Tern
Juv.
Little Tern
Juv.
Fairy Tern
Late breeding
Little Tern
Non-breeding
Fairy Tern
Early breeding
N. Day

Crested Tern *Sterna bergii* C

Bill lemon-yellow (rarely tinged orange). Frons white. Cap black; short, shaggy crest on nape. Body, wings, grey above, white below. Legs, feet, black. **Non-br.** Forecrown white, scalloped black; rest of cap black. **Size** 40–50 cm. **Juv.** Bill green-yellow; as non-br. but black cap extends as collar to sides of throat sides. Upperparts 'chequered', dark grey and white. Black shoulder. **Voice** Harsh 'kurraak'. **Hab.** Coastal seas, continental shelf.

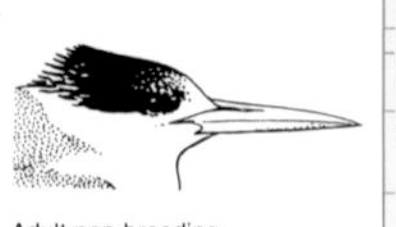
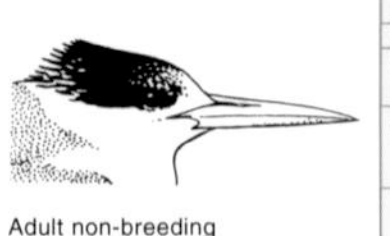

Adult non-breeding

Race *cristata*

Lesser Crested Tern *Sterna bengalensis* C

As Crested; smaller. Bright orange bill. Black frons; black cap from bill to nape (few have white frons, cap speckled white). **Non-br.** Frons, centre crown, face, white. **Size** 38–43 cm. **Juv.** Bill dull orange. 'Chequered' above, paler than Crested. Forehead, crown, whiter. Shoulder bar paler grey. Feet, legs, dull orange. **Voice** Higher than Crested; staccato. **Hab.** Coastal areas.

Adult non-breeding

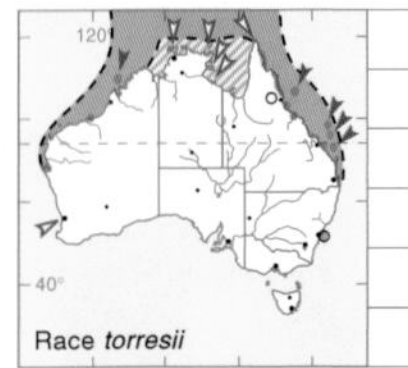

Race *torresii*

Common (Brown) Noddy *Anous stolidus* A –?O

Largest noddy. Colonial. Glides low to sea, wings forward, slow wing beats. Bill shorter, thicker than other noddies. Black lores. Indistinct grey-white crown. Body, wings, brown; black primaries; upper wing looks 'two-toned'. In flight, tail long, wedged, with shallow central notch. **Size** 40–45 cm. **Juv.** Darker grey-brown cap. Upperparts have fine, pale feather fringing. **Voice** Purring; 'kraaa, kraaa'. **Hab.** Tropical seas, islands.

Hatchling

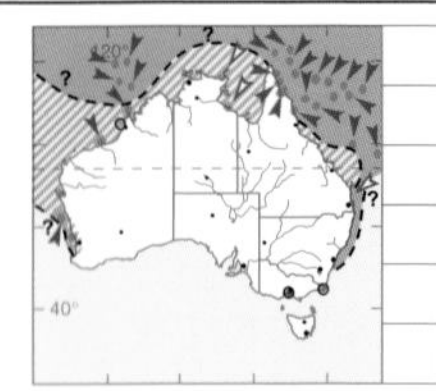

Race *pileatus*

Lesser Noddy *Anous tenuirostris* LA –?O Vulnerable

Colonial. Like Black Noddy, but shorter black bill. Lores pale grey. Pale grey cap grades into nape, face. Dark body, wings, tail. **Juv.** Browner; cap may be whiter, or more sharply defined. **Size** 29–34 cm. **Voice** Rattling alarm; purring call. **Hab.** Oceans, coastal islands. Many breed Ashmore Reef; Houtman Abrolhos.

Hatchling

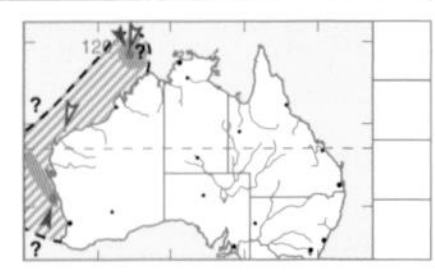
Race *melanops* ? **Br E**

Black Noddy *Anous minutus* C –?O

Colonial. Smaller than Common Noddy. Longer, finer bill. Lores black. Distinguish in flight from Common by white cap, blackish body, black underwing, short tail with wider fork. **Juv.** Browner. Cap white; sharply demarcated. **Size** 35–40 cm. **Voice** 'kirr'; cackling 'krik-krik-krik'. **Hab.** Oceans, coastal islands.

Hatchling

Previous name 'White-capped Noddy'.

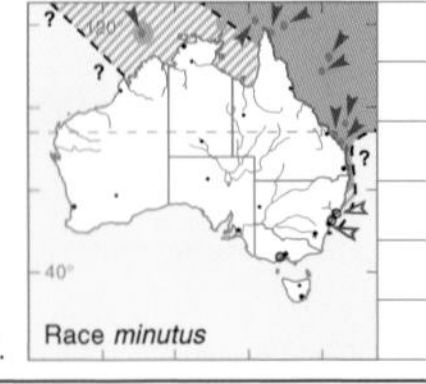

Race *minutus*

Grey Ternlet *Procelsterna cerulea* V–LC

'Blue-grey noddy'. Small. Shape like Black Noddy. Feeds by bouncing on sea, like storm-petrel. Black bill. Head, underparts, pale greyish-white. Upperwing blue-grey, trailing edge darker. Rump, uppertail coverts, white. Underwing grey, flight feathers darker. Long black legs, toes; pale webs. **Size** 25–30 cm. **Juv.** Brownish wash on upperparts. **Voice** 'kirrr, kirrr'. **Hab.** Oceans. Common at br. islands (incl. Lord Howe, Norfolk).

Feeding

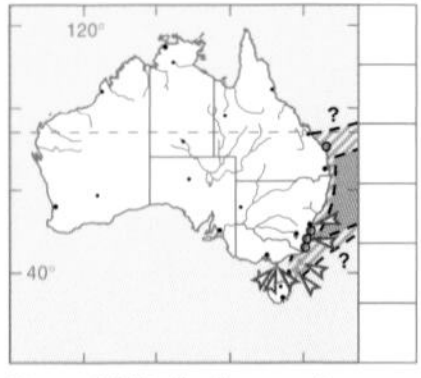

Race *albivitta* **Endangered**

White Tern *Gygis alba* V–LC

White. Black eye. Upturned black bill; bluish base. Primaries, tail shafts, dark brown; barely seen in flight. Translucent wings. Tail short; legs bluish. **Size** 28–33 cm. **Juv.** Dusky ear coverts. Soft light brown mark behind eye. Fresh plumage speckled ginger on nape, mantle, upperwings. **Voice** Rolling 'krip, krip'. **Hab.** Oceans, tropical islands (incl. Lord Howe, Norfolk).

Tree 'nest'

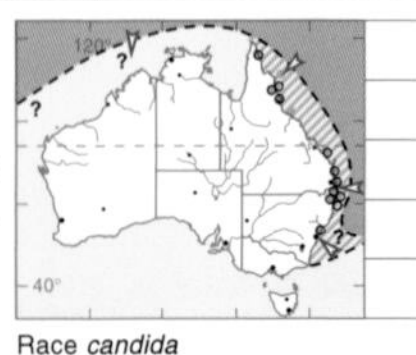

Race *candida*

White Tern
Sooty Tern
Juv.
Black Noddy
Lesser Noddy
Common Noddy
White-winged Black Tern Non-breeding
Grey Ternlet Race *albivitta*
Common Noddy
Lesser Noddy Juv.
Lesser Noddy
Black Noddy
White Tern Juv.
Grey Ternlet Race *albivitta*
Lesser Crested Tern Juv.
Lesser Crested Tern Breeding
Crested Tern Non-breeding
Crested Tern Juv.
Lesser Crested Tern Non-breeding
Crested Tern Breeding

Pacific Baza *Aviceda subcristata* **UC** ◎

Flight buoyant, leisurely; moves inconspicuously among trees; sometimes hovers around tree canopies or hangs from foliage with beating wings. Soars on flat or slightly drooped wings; performs undulating diving display flight with wings held in a stiff 'V'. Identify from imm. Brown Goshawk. Short crest. Slate-grey upperparts and chest. Underwings have pale rufous lining; boldly barred 'fingers'. Belly whitish with bold dark bars. Thighs, vent, pale rufous. **Size** 35–45 cm. **Juv.** Much browner upperparts. Pale rufous chest. **Voice** Shrill double whistle, rising and falling; quieter whistles and trills, soft chatter. **Hab.** Coastal and subcoastal closed and open forests; urban trees and parklands.

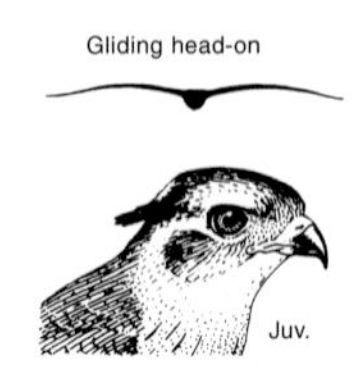

Prior name 'Crested Hawk'.

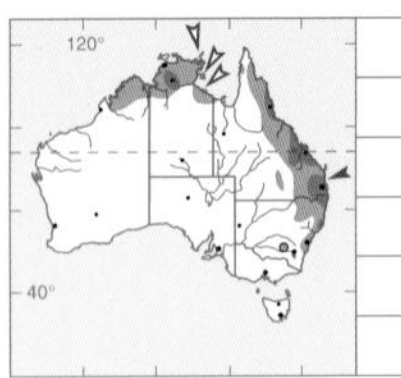

Race *subcristata* **Br. E**
Includes former race *njikena* (NW of WA, and NT), which is smaller, darker, forming a cline across N Aust., with larger, paler birds in east Aust.

Black-shouldered Kite *Elanus axillaris* **C** ◎–♧ E

Hunts from perches or by hovering over tall grasses. Often a dusk and dawn hunter; hovers with faster wing beats than Letter-winged Kite, soars with elevated wings. Perches singly or in family groups in tops of dead trees. Black patch from lores above and behind eye forms 'brow'. Body white with grey wings; prominent black shoulders; underwings white, black carpal spot, dark tips. **Size** 35 cm. **Juv.** Spotted brown to golden-tan on head, neck, breast, back. **Voice** Harsh wheezing 'kar'; quiet whistling 'chep'. **Hab.** Open woodland, grassland, crops, parkland.

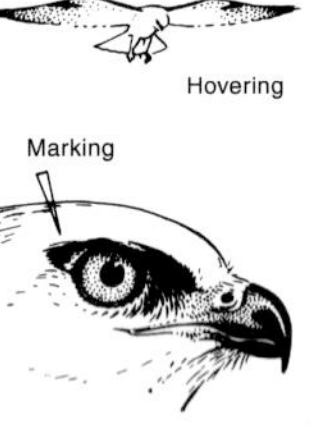

Previous name Elanus notatus.

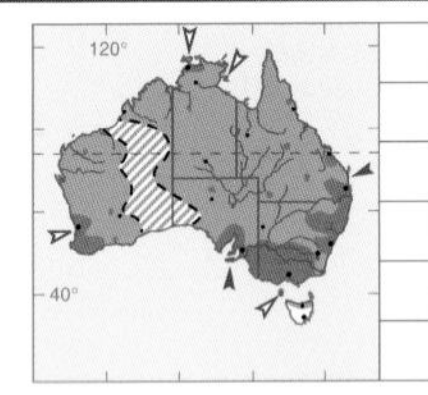

No races

Letter-winged Kite *Elanus scriptus* **LA–UC** ♧ E

Hunts at night – the only Australian hawk to do so habitually. Hovers; soars with elevated wings; wing beat is slower than Black-shouldered Kite. Roosts communally in daylight. Identify from Barn Owl, Grass Owl, at night. Large eyes ringed by black give 'owl-like' appearance. Prominent black bar along almost translucent white underwings. **F** Greyer crown, back. **Size** 35 cm. **Juv.** White with mottled brown to tan-orange on head, back, breast. **Voice** Harsh wheezing 'kar-kar' or whistling 'chip-chip'. **Hab.** Desert grasslands and timbered watercourses. Distribution, population numbers, influenced by plagues of rodents, esp. Long-haired Rats, *Rattus villosissimus*.

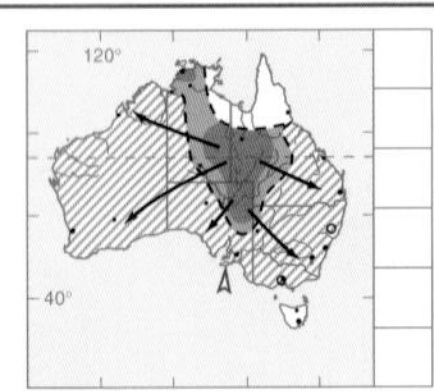

No races.
Map shows coastward dispersal during occasional population irruptions.

Osprey *Pandion haliaetus* **MC–UC** ◎

Soars on long, angled, bowed wings. Patrols over water; hovers, plunges feet-first. Identify from imm. White-bellied Sea-Eagle, and 1st year Brahminy Kite. Brown streak through eye and down sides of neck. Dark brown upperparts; white head and underparts. Band of brown mottling across chest light in male, heavier in female. Barring on underwings and tail. **F** Larger. **Size** 50–65 cm. **Juv.** Buff tips on upperparts; heavier chest band than adults. **Voice** Plaintive or ringing whistles. **Hab.** Mangroves, rivers and estuaries, inshore seas, coastal islands. Constructs large nests on prominent headlands, trees, communication towers.

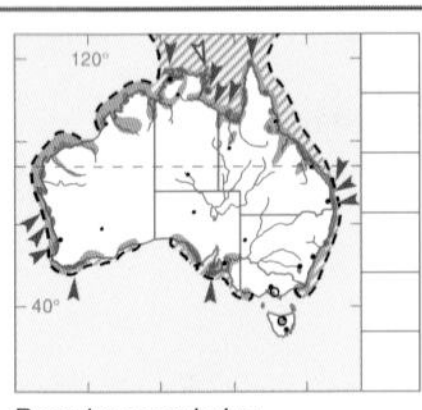

Race *leucocephalus*

Osprey adult

Juvenile

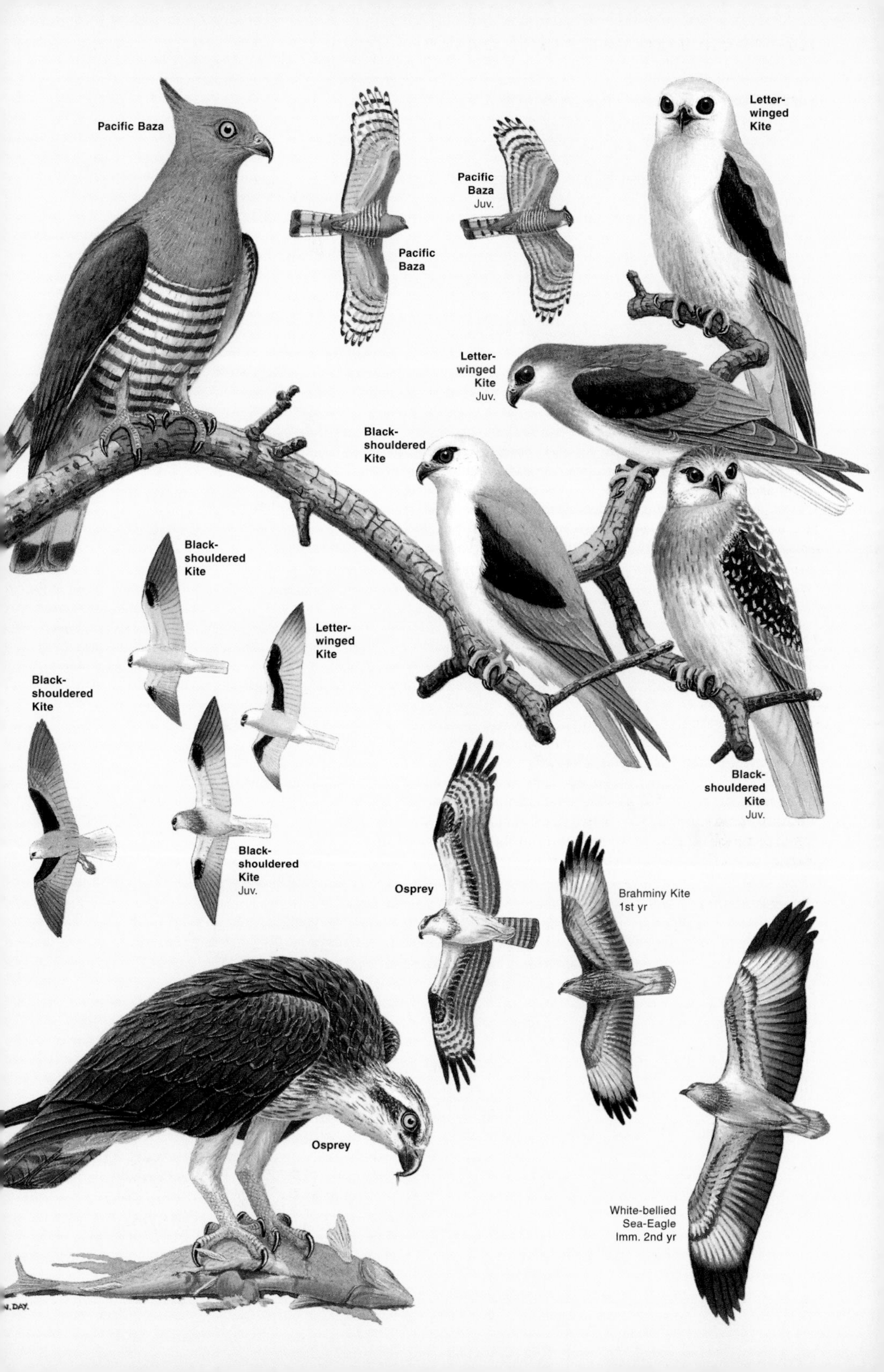
Pacific Baza
Pacific Baza
Pacific Baza
Juv.
Letter-
winged
Kite
Letter-
winged
Kite
Juv.
Black-
shouldered
Kite
Black-
shouldered
Kite
Letter-
winged
Kite
Black-
shouldered
Kite
Black-
shouldered
Kite
Juv.
Black-
shouldered
Kite
Juv.
Osprey
Brahminy Kite
1st yr
Osprey
White-bellied
Sea-Eagle
Imm. 2nd yr
N. DAY.

Square-tailed Kite *Lophoictinia isura* R ♧ E

Solitary; soars low over or through tree canopy on raised wings. Identify from Black Kite, 1st–3rd yr Black-breasted Buzzard, Red Goshawk, imm. harriers and female Swamp Harrier. Slender, very long-winged. White 'face'; pale eyes, heavily streaked breast. Underwings have rufous lining, dark carpal crescent, pale 'bull's-eye', boldly barred fingers. Long, square tail with dark sub-terminal band. **F** Slightly larger. **Size** 50–55 cm; wingspan 130–145 cm. **1st yr** Head, underparts, rich rufous; less streaked. **Voice** Hoarse or plaintive yelp; weak chatter. **Hab.** Open forests, riverine woodland, scrubs, heathland.

Gliding head-on

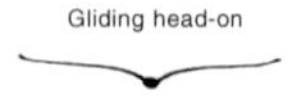

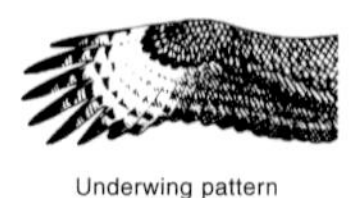

Underwing pattern

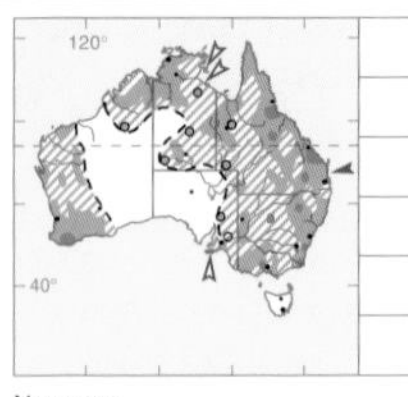

No races

Black-breasted Buzzard *Hamirostra melanosternon* UC ♧ E

Identify from dark morph of Little Eagle, juv. Swamp Harrier. Robust; short-tailed. Blackish above and below. Rufous nape, shoulder mottling, thighs and vent. Prominent white 'bull's-eye' in broad wings. Pale tail. **F** Larger. **Size** 50–60 cm; wingspan 145–155 cm. **1st yr** Rich rufous; dark wingtips, less distinct 'bull's-eyes'. **2nd–3rd yr** Birds paler than adults but darker than 1st yr; 'bull's-eyes' more prominent. **Voice** Short sharp calls; hoarse yelp, thin whistle, harsh sounds. **Hab.** Arid scrub, riverine and tropical woodland. Soars high on raised, swept-back wings.

Gliding head-on

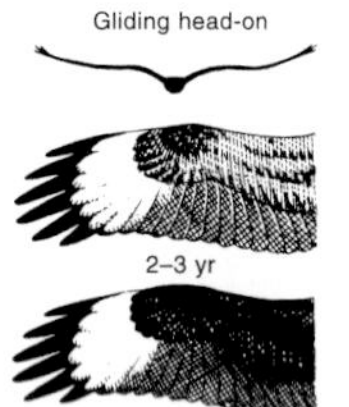

Adult
Underwing patterns

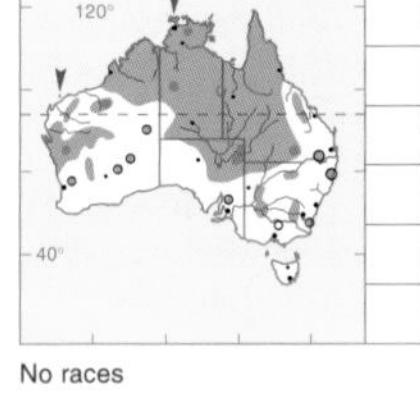

No races

Black Kite *Milvus migrans* A–LA ♧

Attends bush fires. Flocks soar effortlessly with frequently twisting forked tails. Identify from dark morph of Little Eagle; also resembles Square-tailed Kite and harriers but in flight wings are held flat or slightly bowed, seldom in a 'V'. Uniformly dark brown, appearing black in strong light. Pale shoulder bar. Wings without obvious pale patches. **Size** 45–55 cm; wingspan 120–140 cm. **1st yr** Paler than adults; upperwing surfaces lightly mottled. **Voice** Plaintive descending 'see-err'; whistles 'si-i-i-i-'. **Hab.** Open plains, timbered watercourses, rubbish dumps, abattoirs, cattle yards.

Gliding head-on

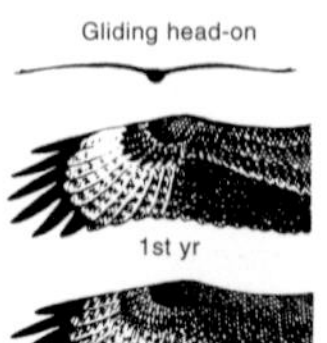

Adult
Underwing patterns

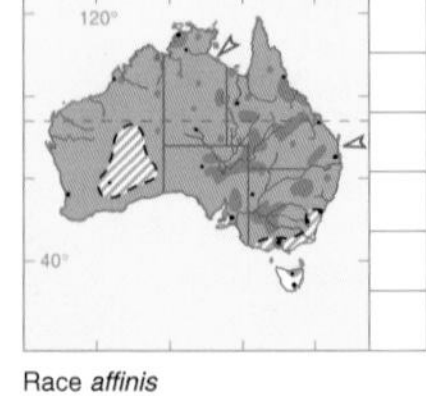

Race *affinis*

Prior name 'Fork-tailed Kite'.

Whistling Kite *Haliastur (Milvus) sphenurus* C ♧

Identify from Little Eagle, Black Kite, Square-tailed Kite, harriers. Head, underparts, light brown with pale streaks. Dark wings with pale wing linings; pale angled panel mid-wing. Long, rounded, plain pale tail. **Size** 50–60 cm; wingspan 120–145 cm. **1st yr** Brown back and wings, spotted with white. **Voice** Long descending 'seeo' followed by an upward staccato 'si-si-si-si'. **Hab.** Soars over open woodlands, plains, streams, swamps, seashores.

Gliding head-on

Light morph Little Eagle
Underwing patterns

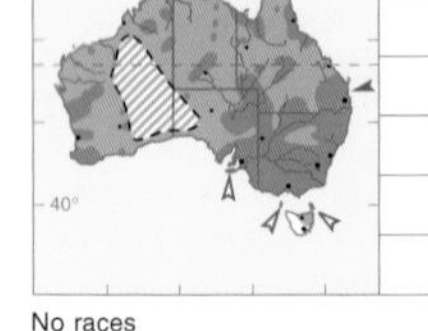

No races

Brahminy Kite *Haliastur (Milvus) indus* UC ◎

Chestnut and gleaming white with dark wing tips; short, rounded tail with pale tip. **Size** 45–50 cm; wingspan 110–125 cm. **1st yr** Browner, mottled, resembling Whistling Kite, but much shorter tail. Also identify 1st yr birds from Osprey, 1st yr White-bellied Sea-Eagle, Little Eagle. **2nd yr** Mottled mixture of faded 1st yr and 'dirty' adult. **Voice** Plaintive bleating 'pee-ah-ah-ah'. **Hab.** Coastal mudflats, mangroves, harbours, offshore islands.

Gliding head-on

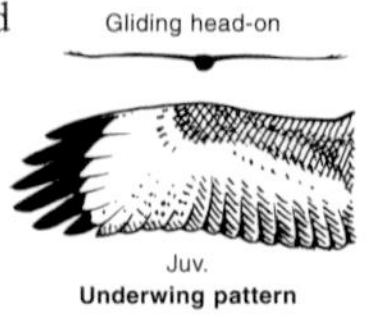

Juv.
Underwing pattern

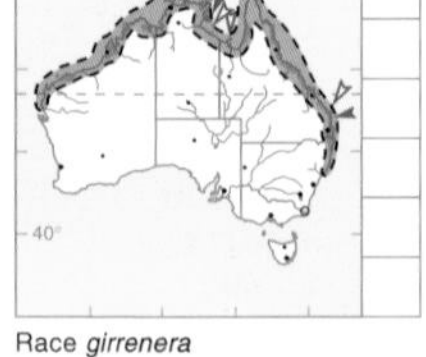

Race *girrenera*

Notes 1. Genera *Haliastur, Milvus* and *Haliaeetus* are closely related.
2. When perched, relative lengths of folded wings to tail can help differentiate between these kite species.

Square-tailed Kite 1st yr
Square-tailed Kite
Square-tailed Kite
Square-tailed Kite 1st yr
Square-tailed Kite
Black-breasted Buzzard 1st yr
Black Kite 1st yr
Black-breasted Buzzard 1st yr
Black-breasted Buzzard
Black-breasted Buzzard
Black Kite 1st yr
Black Kite
Black Kites Soaring
Black Kite
Black Kite
Whistling Kite
Whistling Kite
Whistling Kite 1st yr
Whistling Kite 1st yr
Whistling Kite
Brahminy Kite 1st yr
Brahminy Kite 1st yr
Brahminy Kite
Brahminy Kite
Brahminy Kite 1st yr
N.DAY

White-bellied Sea-Eagle *Haliaeetus leucogaster* **MC** ◎–♧

Wings broad and rounded, held stiffly upswept when soaring. Birds become lighter with age. Identify from soaring Australian Pelican. White, with grey back, rump, wings, base of tail. Bare whitish legs. **F** Larger. **Size** 75–85 cm; wingspan 180–220 cm. **1st yr** Brown with lighter markings; paler on head. Whitish 'bull's-eye' in wings. Tail short; rounded or wedge-shaped. Tail whitish, shading to light brown at tip. Identify **Imm.** from Wedge-tailed Eagle, Black-breasted Buzzard, Osprey. **Voice** Deep goose-like honking or cackling. **Hab.** Large rivers, fresh and saline lakes, reservoirs, coastal seas, islands.

Gliding head-on

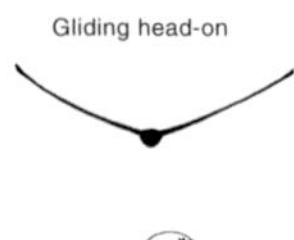

Ventral pattern

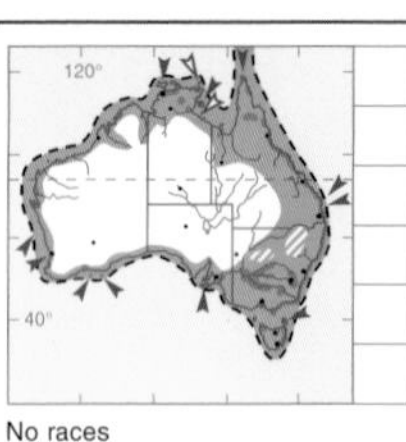

No races

Wedge-tailed Eagle *Aquila audax* **C** ◎–♧

Noted carrion-eater; often seen along roadsides. Soars on long, fingered, upswept wings. Birds become darker with age. Identify from Black-breasted Buzzard, imm. White-bellied Sea-Eagle. Sooty-black with tawny hackles on nape. Pale brown wing coverts and undertail coverts. Tail long and wedge-shaped. Feathered legs. Race *fleayi* (B) Pale nape. No rufous on dorsal surface. **F** Larger. **Size** 85–105 cm; wingspan 185–230 cm. **End of 1st yr to 4th or 5th yr** Usually paler than adults. Dark brown with rich golden-brown nape, uppertail coverts, wing coverts. Whitish undertail coverts. **Voice** Feeble yelps and squeals. **Hab.** Most types except closed forest.

Gliding head-on

Adult at nest

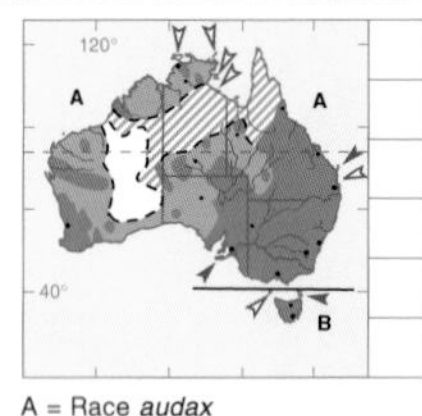

A = Race *audax*
B = Race *fleayi* **E Endangered**

Little Eagle *Hieraaetus morphnoides* **C** ◎–♧

Compact in flight: wings slightly drooped when gliding; held level to slightly raised when soaring. Identify from Whistling Kite, Square-tailed Kite. **Light morph** Head buff to pale rufous with blackish streaks on cheeks. Blackish crown feathers extending into a short crest. Upperparts brown, paler on nape and scapulars, with a distinct pale band across the wing. Tail barred, rather short and square-cut. Underwing has rufous leading edge and white oblique band, contrasting with grey-barred secondaries, black-tipped outer primaries. Underparts white with fine black streaks, washed buff to rufous, especially on breast. Legs feathered. **Dark morph** Head, underparts, light brown with black streaks. Leading edge and oblique band on underwing, dark brown. **F** Much larger. **Size** 45–55 cm; wingspan 110–135 cm. **1st yr light morph** Head, underparts, richer rufous, less streaked. **1st yr dark morph** More rufous-brown than adults; less streaked. **Voice** Loud, excited, high-pitched whistle, usually 2–3 notes uttered rapidly. Also a series of mellow or plaintive piping notes and long squeals. **Hab.** Most open forest, woodland and scrub types; open agricultural country.

Gliding head-on

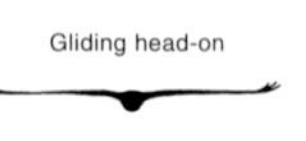

Dark morph Little Eagle

Light morph Little Eagle

Whistling Kite
Underwing patterns

Race *morphnoides* **E**

Little Eagle

Black-breasted Buzzard

Erect 'crests'

Wedge-tailed Eagle
Wedge-tailed Eagle 1st yr
White-bellied Sea-Eagle 2nd yr
White-bellied Sea-Eagle 1st yr
White-bellied Sea-Eagle Ad.
White-bellied Sea-Eagle 1st yr
White-bellied Sea-Eagle 1st yr
White-bellied Sea-Eagle Ad.
White-bellied Sea-Eagle Ad.
Little Eagle 1st yr
Little Eagle Ad. Light morph
Little Eagle Ad. Dark morph
Little Eagle Ad. Light morph
Little Eagle 1st yr
Little Eagle Ad. Light morph
Little Eagle Ad. Dark morph
Wedge-tailed Eagle 1st yr
Wedge-tailed Eagle 1st yr
Wedge-tailed Eagle Ad.
Little Crow
Little Crow
N.DAY.

Brown Goshawk *Accipiter fasciatus* C ◎–♣

Flat-winged glide; soars. Identify from smaller Collared Sparrowhawk. Eyes bright yellow. Head grey. Body slate-grey or dark brown above; rufous collar across nape. Wings rounded; slate-grey or dark brown above; buff and rufous below; wingtips darker. Tail long, rounded; slate-grey or dark brown above; light grey with dark barring below. Underparts finely barred rufous and white. Legs long, yellow; rufous feathering about thighs. Race *didimus* (B) Noticeably smaller, paler. **F** Much larger. **Size** 40–55 cm. **1st yr** Eyes yellow. Head streaked chocolate. No rufous collar. Body dark brown above, off-white below, with bold chocolate lower throat and breast streaking. Wings dark brown above; off-white with chocolate barring below. Tail long, rounded; dark brown above; light grey with darker barring below. Belly to undertail coverts strongly barred chestnut-brown. **2nd yr** More like adult; collar not prominent. Some pale streaks on face. Underparts darker; barring broader. These plumages variable; their time of retention varies. **Voice** Rapid, shrill chatter; female's generally lower-pitched; also upslurred squeals. **Hab.** Most timbered areas.

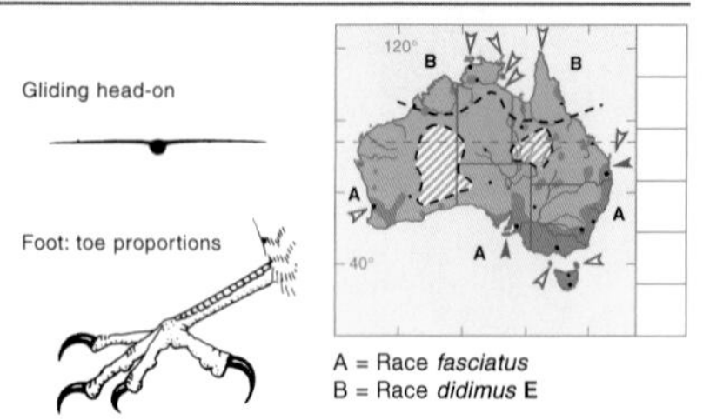

A = Race *fasciatus*
B = Race *didimus* E

Relative sizes

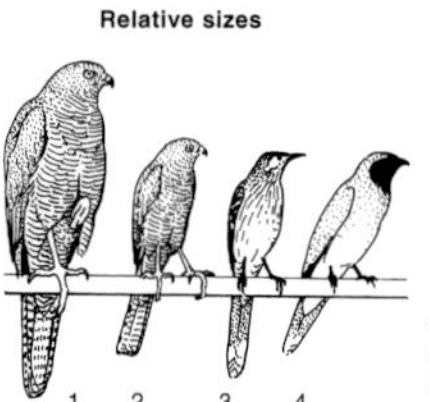

1 ♀ Brown Goshawk
2 ♂ Collared Sparrowhawk
3 Red Wattlebird
4 Black-faced Cuckoo-shrike

Collared Sparrowhawk *Accipiter cirrhocephalus* C ◎

Flat-winged glide; soars. Wings short, rounded. Identify from male of larger Brown Goshawk. Similar plumage to Brown Goshawk adult and 1st yr counterparts. Collared Sparrowhawk distinguished by squarer tail, less beetle-browed eyes, finer legs and toes. Race known as *quaesitandus* (B) across far northern Australia now believed invalid. Smaller, more rufous birds. **F** Much larger; approximates male Brown Goshawk in size. **Size** 30–40 cm. **Voice** Very rapid, shrill chatter, female lower pitch. Slower mewing calls. **Hab.** Most terrestrial habitats with trees.

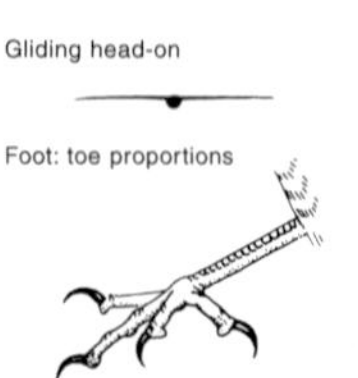

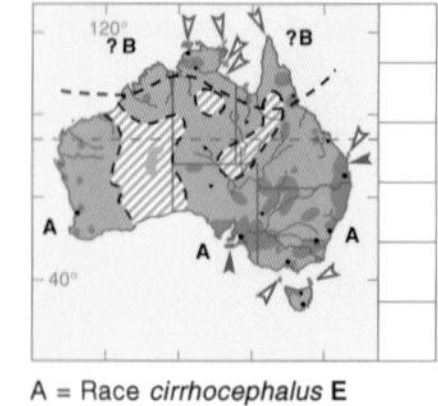

A = Race *cirrhocephalus* E
B = Race ?*quaesitandus* E

Grey (White) Goshawk *Accipiter novaehollandiae* UC ◎

Two morphs. White morph predominates in north-western WA, NT and coastal Vic. Only white morph in Tas. **Grey morph** Eye dark red. Head grey. Body grey above; white below, with fine grey chest barrings. Wings rounded; grey above; white below with darker wing-tips. Tail long, square or slightly rounded; grey above; white below with grey barring. Legs yellow. **1st yr** Similar but broader chest barring and often buff-washed collar. **White morph** Plumage pure white in all ages. **F** Much larger. **Size** 40–55 cm. **Voice** Repeated rising shrill whistle; also a rapid, shrill chatter. **Hab.** Various forests, esp. coastal closed forest.

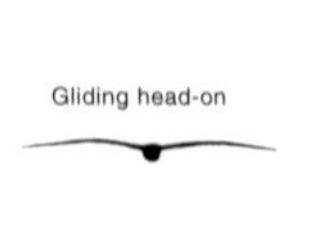

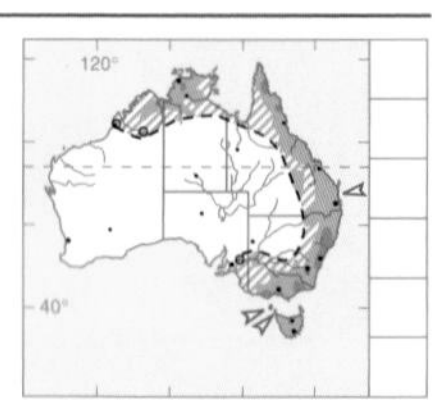

Race *novaehollandiae* E

Red Goshawk *Erythrotriorchis radiatus* R ◎ E Vulnerable

Rare; often confused with other rufous raptors. Identify from imm. harriers, also from Brown Goshawk, Black-breasted Buzzard, Little Eagle. Eyes yellow. Head rufous, streaked black and white; much white on face and throat. Body rufous above, with bold dark markings. Wings long, rounded, fingered at tips. Upperwings rufous, streaked with black above; much lighter below, with rufous underwing coverts, flight feathers darker barred. Tail long, broad; barred grey and rufous-brown above and below. Rufous belly. Legs powerful, yellow. **F** Much larger; pale belly. **Size** 45–60 cm. **1st yr** Head rufous, eyes brown. **Voice** Loud, harsh chatter; raucous yelps. **Hab.** Coastal, subcoastal forest, tropical woodland.

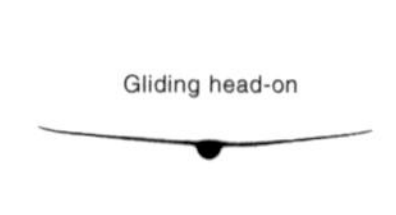

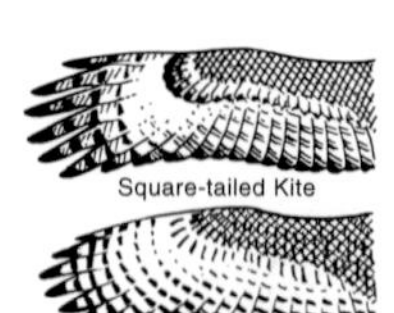

Underwing patterns

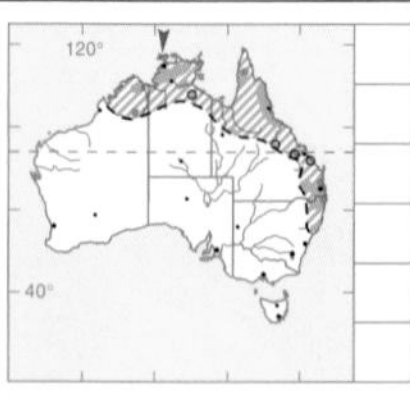

No races

Brown Goshawk ♂ Ad.
Yellow-tufted Honeyeater
Brown Goshawk ♀ 2nd yr
Brown Goshawk ♀ 1st yr
Brown Goshawk ♂ 1st yr
Collared Sparrowhawk ♂ 1st yr
Brown Goshawk ♀ Ad.
Collared Sparrowhawk ♂ Ad.
Collared Sparrowhawk ♀ 1st yr
Collared Sparrowhawk ♀ Ad.
Grey Goshawk ♀ 1st yr Grey morph
Grey Goshawk ♂ 1st yr Grey morph
Grey Goshawk ♀ Ad. Grey morph
Grey Goshawk ♂ Ad. White morph
Red Goshawk ♂ Ad.
Red Goshawk ♂ 1st yr
Red Goshawk ♀ Ad.
Grey Goshawk ♂ Ad. Grey morph
Grey Goshawk ♀ Ad. White morph
N. DAY.

Spotted Harrier *Circus assimilis* MC ♲

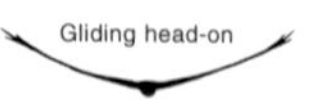
Gliding head-on

No races

Hunts low over vegetation. Soars with wings elevated. Upperparts blue-grey. Wings have prominent black tips. Tail prominently barred and slightly wedge-shaped. Face, underparts, chestnut spotted white. Long yellow legs. **F** Larger. **Size** 50–62 cm. **1st yr** Dark brown and buff above; pale buff with brown streaks below; has somewhat 'hooded' appearance during post-juvenile moult. **2nd yr** Like adults but white streaks (not spots) below. **Voice** Piercing squeaks, rapid chatter. **Hab.** Open grassland, crops, and windbreaks.

Swamp Harrier *Circus approximans* C ⟳

Gliding head-on

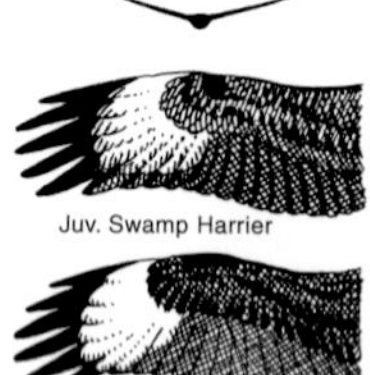
Juv. Swamp Harrier

Adult Black-breasted Buzzard

Underwing patterns

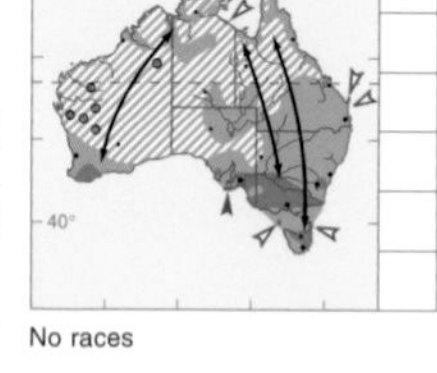

No races

Hunts low over vegetation. Soars with elevated wings; performs courtship dives high above swamps. Dark brown above; prominent white rump (uppertail coverts). Tail, wings, barred. Underparts off-white to buff. Long yellow legs. **F** Larger; underparts rufous. **Size** 50–60 cm. **1st yr** Darker brown; wings have pale primary bases; rump brownish. **Voice** High-pitched whistling 'seee-uh' during aerial food transfer between birds; loud mewing 'kee-a' during courtship flights. **Hab.** Tall grass, reeds, rushes, crops, and open water surfaces.

Black Falcon *Falco subniger* R ♲ E

Gliding head-on

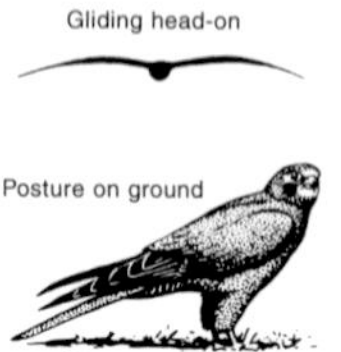
Posture on ground

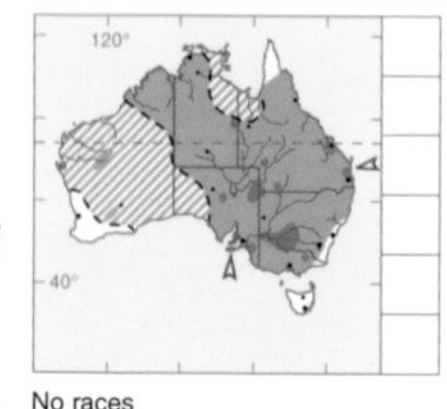

No races
Few breeding sites known.

Flight swift when hunting, otherwise leisurely. Glides on slightly drooped wings. Soars. Dark brown to sooty-black. Blue-grey bill. Pale chin and face; dark streak below eye; some birds have pale markings on forehead and throat, faint narrow bars under wings, tail. Heavy shouldered. Long tail usually square-cut. Legs short. **F** Larger. **Size** 45–55 cm. **1st yr** Darker than adults, some birds have pale forehead, cheeks. **Voice** Deep harsh chattering and slow whining calls. **Hab.** Woodland, scrub, shrubland and grassland types in arid and semi-arid zones.

Peregrine Falcon *Falco peregrinus* MC ◎–♲

Gliding head-on

Stooping

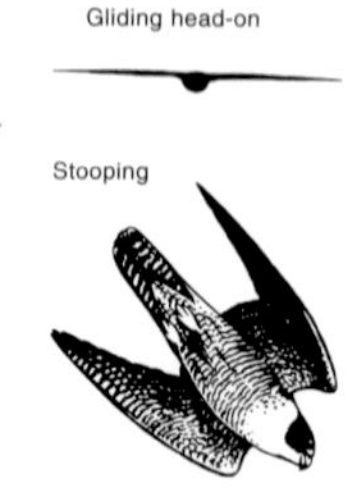

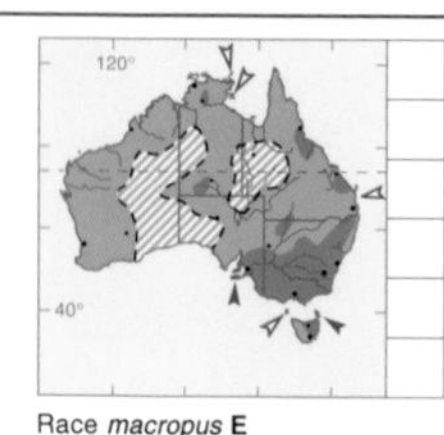

Race *macropus* **E**

Heavily built and compact. Flight powerful. Wings held stiffly outstretched when soaring; trailing edge usually straight. Identify from Australian Hobby. Head and cheeks black (hooded), upperparts blue-grey, underparts cream with dark barring on belly. **F** Much larger. **Size** 35–50 cm. **1st yr** Upperparts tinged brown; underparts buff with heavy dark streaks. **Voice** Hoarse chatter, clucking and whining sounds. **Hab.** Most land types, especially cliffs and rocky outcrops, rocky coastal islands.

Eastern Marsh (Papuan) Harrier *Circus spilonotus* see **Vagrant Bird Bulletin** p. 297.

Peregrine Falcon ♀
Peregrine Falcon ♂ 1st yr
Australian Hobby
Peregrine Falcon ♀ 1st yr
Peregrine Falcon ♂
Black Falcon
Brown Falcon Dark morph
Black Falcon
Black Falcon
Black Falcon 1st yr
Spotted Harrier 1st yr
Swamp Harrier 1st yr
Spotted Harrier
Spotted Harrier
Swamp Harrier
Eastern Marsh Harrier ♂
Spotted Harrier 2nd yr
Swamp Harrier
Swamp Harrier 1st yr
Spotted Harrier 1st yr

Australian Hobby *Falco longipennis* C ◎–

In flight, silhouette may resemble Oriental Cuckoo, White-throated Needle-tail. Slender and long-winged. Cap and 'mask' (hood) black, forehead and half-collar whitish. Upperparts blue-grey; underparts rufous, streaked darker. Birds in arid zone are paler. Race known as *murchisonianus* (B) now believed invalid. **F** Larger. **Size** 30–36 cm. **1st yr** Upperparts tinged brown. **Voice** Rapid peevish chatter, squeaky chittering, and loud chuckling call. **Hab.** Most open forest, woodland and scrub types, also urban areas.

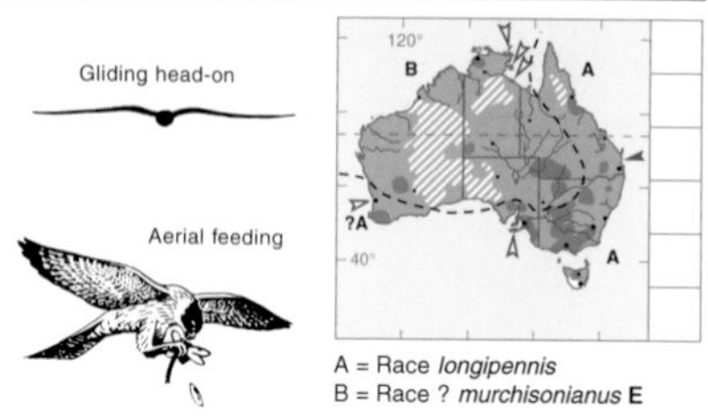

A = Race *longipennis*
B = Race ? *murchisonianus* **E**

Previously known as 'Little Falcon'.

Grey Falcon *Falco hypoleucos* R ◎– E

Heavy-shouldered, Peregrine-like in flight. Identify from *Elanus* kites; Grey Goshawk, Peregrine Falcon. Grey above with black streak under eye, black wing-tips; prominent yellow cere, eye-ring, feet. Tail grey, faintly barred. White below with fine dark streaks; underwings barred. **F** Larger. **Size** 30–45 cm. **1st yr** Darker with heavier streaks on underparts. **Voice** Hoarse chattering, clucking and whining sounds. **Hab.** Woodland and scrub types in arid zone.

Gliding head-on

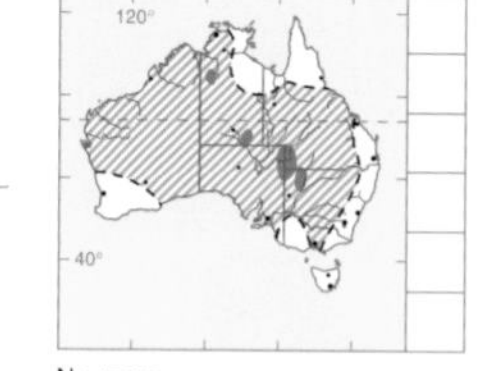

No races

Brown Falcon *Falco berigora* C ◎–

Glides on raised wings, flight heavy and slow. Hovers 'unsteadily'. Commonly perches with 'upright' posture, on wires, posts, fences. Check identity of paler birds from smaller Nankeen Kestrel when solitary birds observed perched. Brown above, with dark marks below and behind eye. Tail rounded. Underparts either whitish with dark streaks, or blotched brown and white, or wholly dark brown. Underwings pale, barred. Thighs always dark brown; may appear as leg-stripe on paler-bellied birds. Legs long. Birds from central Aust. are usually paler, and those from the tropical north are often very dark. **Dark morph** Almost entirely dark brown (see illustration p. 125). **Brown morph** Brown dorsally; pale or mostly brown ventrally. **Rufous morph** Rufous-brown dorsally; either pale or rufous-brown ventrally. **F** Larger. **Size** 40–50 cm. **1st yr** Usually darker underparts; buff face; broad buff collar (in brown morph only); lack flank spotting of adults. **Voice** Raucous cackles and screeches. **Hab.** Most land surface types except closed forest.

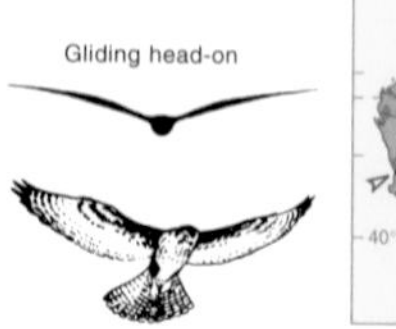

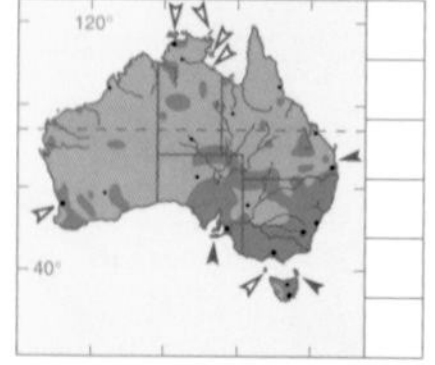

Race *berigora* **E**
The five former races – *berigora, tasmanica, centralia, occidentalis, melvillensis* – are now combined in the nominate race *berigora*.

Nankeen (Australian) Kestrel *Falco cenchroides* C ◎–

Slender, hovers with body horizontal, showing black band near tail-tip. Commonly perches on wires, posts, fences, building ledges. Bill dark grey. Cere yellow. Dark tear-drop mark under eye. Grey head, pale rufous back and wings. Most plumage lightly streaked black. Grey tail has broad black sub-terminal band; white tips. Buff underparts with fine dark streaks. Legs, feet yellow. **F** Slightly larger. Head and tail pale rufous, may have grey wash. Back, underparts, more heavily streaked black than male. **Size** 30–35 cm. **1st yr** As female, but more rufous; more streaked and barred with black. **Voice** Shrill, excited chatter. **Hab.** Most land surface types except dense forest.

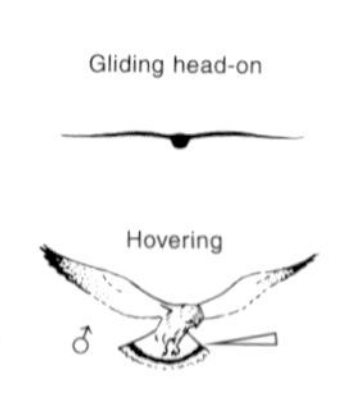

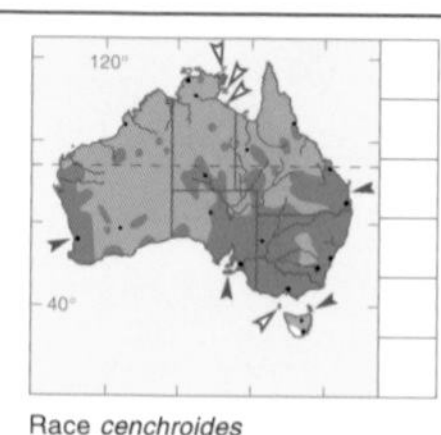

Race *cenchroides*

Nankeen
Kestrel
♂
Australian Hobby
Peregrine Falcon
1st yr
Peregrine
Falcon
Grey
Falcon
Australian
Hobby
Brown Falcon
Brown morph
(pale bird)
Grey
Falcon
Grey
Falcon
♂ 1st yr
Grey Falcon ♀
Nankeen
Kestrel
♀
Australian
Hobby
Australian
Hobby
1st yr
Nankeen
Kestrel
1st yr
Brown Falcon ♂
Brown morph
(pale bird)
Nankeen Kestrel ♂
Brown Falcon ♂
Brown morph
(intermediate bird)
Brown Falcon ♀
1st yr
Brown morph
Brown Falcon ♀
Rufous morph
N. Day

Banded Fruit-Dove *Ptilinopus cinctus* **UC**

Striking black and white. Head, neck white. Upperparts, breast band, black. Rump, belly mid-grey. Tail black, broad grey tip. **Size** 38–44 cm. **Juv.** Pale grey head, tail. **Voice** Strong, repeated low 'coo'. **Hab.** Forested gullies of rocky escarpments, woodland.

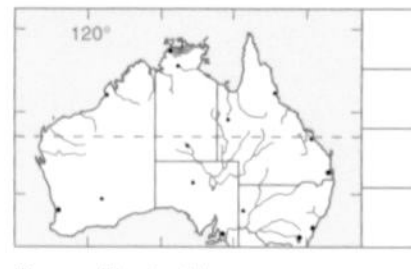

Race *alligator* **E**

Superb Fruit-Dove *Ptilinopus superbus* **MC** ◎–

Crown purple. Cheeks pale green. Hind neck, collar orange. Upperparts green, spotted black; tail tip white. Throat, breast, blue-grey. Black breast band; belly white. Green barred flanks. **F** Dull blue crown; lacks orange on neck and black breast band. **Size** 22–24 cm. **Juv.** As female, lacks crown patch. **Voice** 5–6 clear, deep, rising whoops. **Hab.** Rainforest, adjacent mangroves; eucalypt forest, scrubland with native fruits.

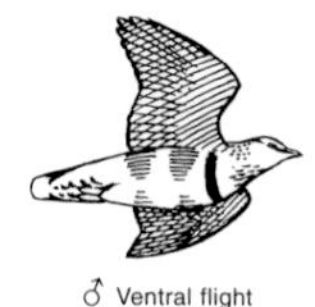

♂ Ventral flight

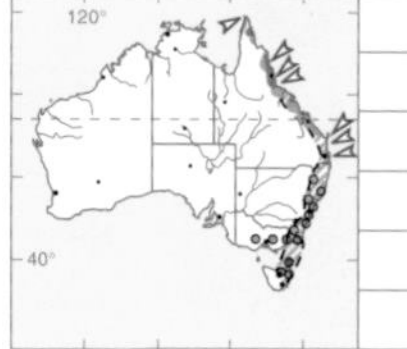

No races

Rose-crowned Fruit-Dove *Ptilinopus regina* **MC** ◎–

Difficult to locate in canopy. Crown rose, edged yellow. Rest of head and breast green-grey. Upperparts green. Tail tip yellow. Underparts orange; abdomen lilac. Long toes. **F** Duller. Race *ewingii* (B) Crown paler, rose-pink; underparts yellower. **Size** 22–24.5 cm. **Juv.** Mostly green, lacks rose crown. **Voice** Falling 'woop-whoop' repeated, becoming faster to rapid 'hoo-hoo-hoo'. **Hab.** Rainforest, monsoon and paperbark forests, mangroves, eucalypt woodland, vine groves, fruit trees.

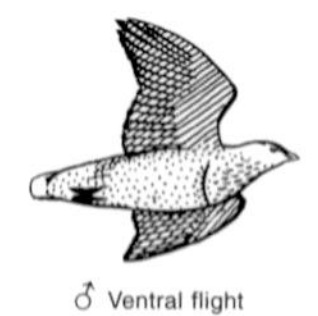

♂ Ventral flight

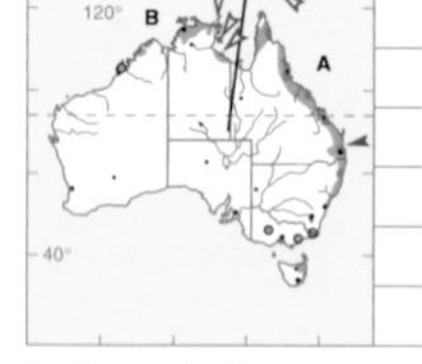

A = Race *regina* **E**
B = Race *ewingii* **E**

Wompoo Fruit-Dove *Ptilinopus magnificus* **LC** ◎–?

Large, spectacular. Eye red. Head, neck, light blue-grey. Back, upperparts, green; wing bar gold. Breast plum-purple; abdomen yellow. Races *assimilis* (B), and *keri* (C) Smaller and brighter. **Size** 35–45 cm. **Juv.** Duller; purple breast blotched green. **Voice** Deep, carrying, bubbly 'wallock-a-woo'; quiet 'wom-poo'. **Hab.** Rainforest.

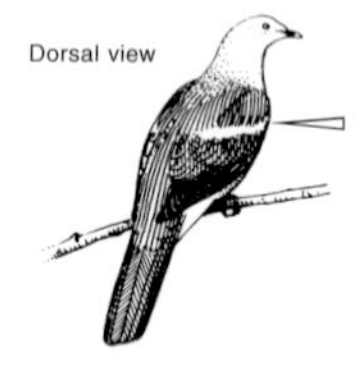

Dorsal view

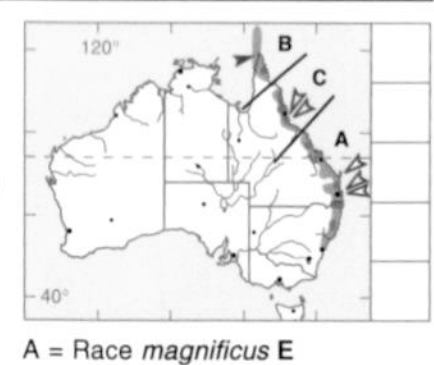

A = Race *magnificus* **E**
B = Race *assimilis* **E**
C = Race *keri* **E**

Pied (Torresian) Imperial-Pigeon *Ducula bicolor* **C–MC**

Strong flight in flocks; tends to travel at dawn, dusk, between coastal islands and mainland. Qld, NT population migratory; many to S New Guinea in autumn; return early spring to breed. NW Australian population may be sedentary/locally nomadic. Large. White. Pale bill. Black eye. Primaries, end of tail, blackish. Belly, undertail coverts scaled black. **Size** 38–44 cm. **Juv.** Undertail coverts little or no barring. **Voice** Deep falling 'woop-woooo'. **Hab.** Coastal rainforest, mangroves, islands.

Ventral flight

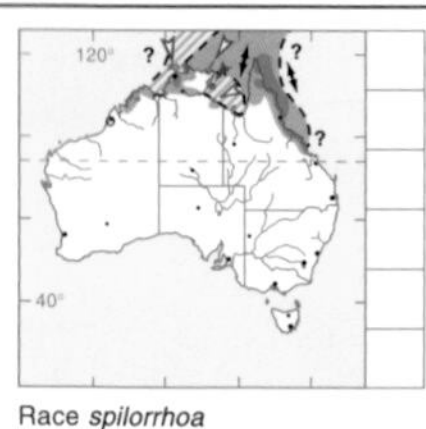

Race *spilorrhoa*

Topknot Pigeon *Lopholaimus antarcticus* **MC** ◎– E

Strong flight; identify from smaller Galahs. Mostly seen in flocks. Large, grey. Red bill, eye. Grey cere and fore-crest prominent; Rusty crest sweeps back from eye over crown to nape. Black primaries. Black tail with pale grey central band. **Size** 40–45 cm. **Voice** Rarely heard. Soft grunt 'errp, errp'. **Hab.** Rainforest, adjacent woodland or forest; palms, fruit trees.

Ventral flight

No races

Collared Imperial-Pigeon *Ducula mullerii*, **Elegant Imperial-Pigeon** *Ducula concinna* see **Vagrant Bird Bulletin** p. 297.

Superb
Fruit-Dove ♀
Superb
Fruit-Dove ♂
Banded
Fruit-Dove
Juv.
Banded
Fruit-Dove
Ad.
Superb
Fruit-Dove
Juv.
Rose-crowned
Fruit-Dove ♂
Pied
Imperial-Pigeon
Rose-crowned
Fruit-Dove
Juv.
Wompoo
Fruit-Dove
Ad.
Wompoo
Fruit-Dove
Juv.
Topknot Pigeon
Ad.
Topknot Pigeon
Juv.
Wompoo
Fruit-Dove

White-headed Pigeon *Columba leucomela* MC ♧ E

Often a ground-feeder under trees. Identify from Topknot Pigeon. Head, breast, white; often with buff or grey wash. Back, wings, tail, black; glossy margins to the feathers. Lower breast, abdomen, undertail, grey. **F** Generally has some grey mottling to head, neck and breast. Crown darker. **Size** 38–41 cm. **Juv.** Crown, sides of head, grey to brown; face paler. Mottled grey-brown below. **Voice** Slow, deep, 'wooop-wuk', second part a soft gulp. **Hab.** Rainforest, scrub, gardens.

Ventral flight

No races

Rock Dove (Feral Pigeon) *Columba livia* Intro. A ◎

Flocks of domestic racing pigeons may be seen. Noisy flight when taking off. Plumage immensely variable (see plate opposite) but has a basic pattern of blue-grey body, with glossy sheen on neck; wings black with a chequered pattern, or two black wing bars. **Size** 31–34 cm. **Voice** Bubbling 'racketty-coo' or 'co-roo-coo-coo'. **Hab.** Mainly urban areas, parks, city buildings, crop margins along roads; also railways, coastal cliffs.

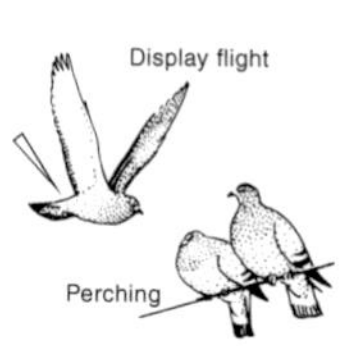

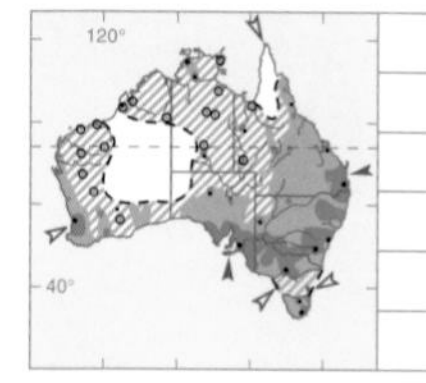

No races.
Wide variation among feral birds and escapes from avicultural breeding programmes.

Spotted Turtle-Dove *Streptopelia chinensis* Intro. A ◎

Raises and lowers tail on alighting. Head grey, tinged pink. Nape and back of neck black, spotted white. Wing, back and tail mottled dark and light brown. Underparts pinkish-fawn. Tail long. Undertail grey; outer feathers tipped white. Race *tigrina* (B) differs from *chinensis* (A) by having wing coverts streaked black, undertail coverts white and feathers on front of wings lighter grey. Hybrids now very common. **Size** 30–33 cm. **Juv.** Lacks spotted nape pattern. **Voice** Mellow, musical 'curoo, curoo'; 'cuckoo-crroooo-cuck'. **Hab.** Cities; suburban gardens, parks; established grain-growing areas of coastal, eastern Australia.

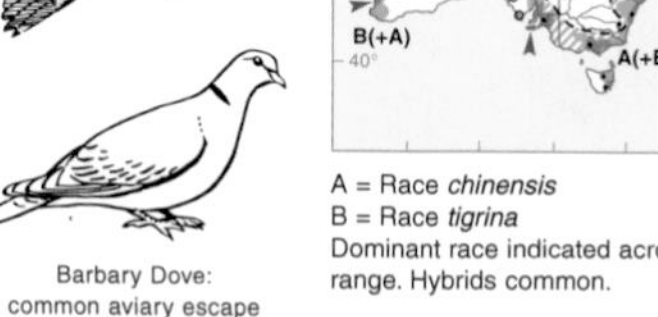

Barbary Dove: common aviary escape

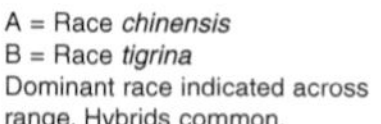

A = Race *chinensis*
B = Race *tigrina*
Dominant race indicated across range. Hybrids common.

Laughing Turtle-Dove *Streptopelia senegalensis* Intro. A ◎

Head, neck, mauve-pink. Back brown, mauve-pink tinge. Broad black-spotted buffish band on lower throat. Breast mauve-pink, shading to white on abdomen. Shoulder, wings, lower back and uppertail coverts slaty blue-grey. Outer tail tipped white. **Size** 25–27 cm. **Juv.** Duller; without blue-grey on wings. **Voice** Musical, 5-note chuckling 'curra coora coo'. **Hab.** City/suburbs of Perth and surrounding regions; Kalgoorlie and Esperance, WA.

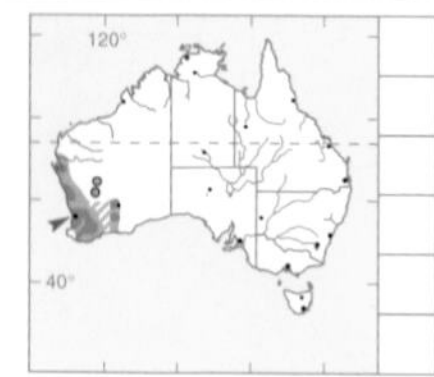

No races

Brown Cuckoo-Dove *Macropygia amboinensis* C ◎–♧

Dark copper-brown upperparts; iridescent on neck. Lighter cinnamon-brown underparts. **F** Chestnut on crown, dark mottling on throat and breast. Tail long. **Size** 39–45 cm. **Juv.** Crown chestnut. Neck and upper breast finely barred black. Wings mottled brown and chestnut. **Voice** Repeated questioning 'cuck-a-whooap?' (or 'didjawalk?'). **Hab.** Rainforest, forest margins, regrowth thickets.

Feeding

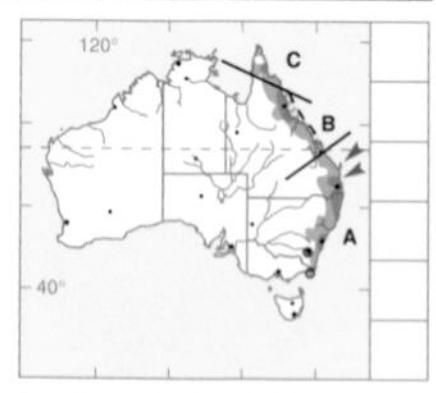

A = Race *phasianella* **E**
B = Race *quinkan* **E**
C = Race *robinsoni*

Brown Cuckoo-Dove ♀
Brown Cuckoo-Dove ♂
White-headed Pigeon ♂
White-headed Pigeon Juv.
Rock Dove
Rock Dove
Colour varieties
Rock Dove
Rock Dove
Rock Dove
House Sparrow ♂
Rock Dove
Rock Dove
Eurasian Tree Sparrow
Spotted Turtle-Dove Juv.
Laughing Turtle-Dove Juv.
Laughing Turtle-Dove
Spotted Turtle-Dove
Race *tigrina*

Peaceful Dove *Geopelia placida* (formerly *striata*) **C** ⁂

In flight, chestnut underwing coverts, dark flight feathers. Race *placida* (A) includes former race *tranquila*. Crown grey-brown, fine black streaks. Forehead, throat blue-grey. Back, wings, grey-brown, buff-toned; breast blue-grey; all barred black. Birds darker in N Aust. Race *clelandi* (B) Paler. **Size** 20–24 cm. **Juv.** Browner. **Voice** Carrying 3-note'woodle-oo'; descending 'wooorr'. **Hab.** Lightly timbered country near water.

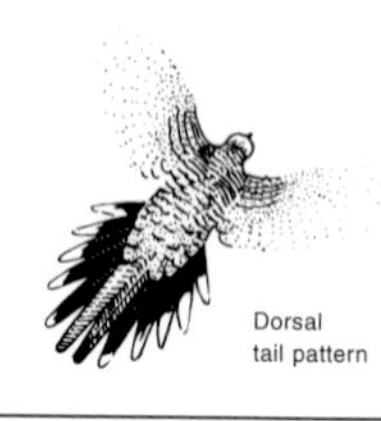

Dorsal tail pattern

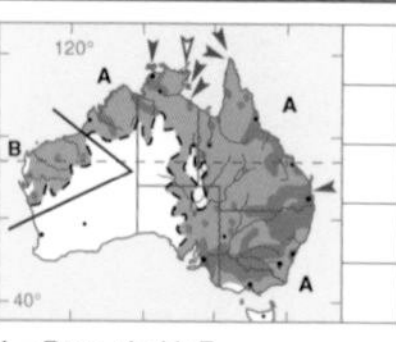

A = Race *placida* **E**
B = Race *clelandi* **E**
Probably breeds throughout range.

Diamond Dove *Geopelia cuneata* **C** ◎–⁂ E

Flight direct, shows white belly, outer tail; chestnut primaries. Red eye, eye-ring. Blue-grey head, breast. Smoky-brown back, wings. Fine white wing spots. White belly. **F** Browner. **Size** 19–24 cm. **Juv.** Browner; appears banded buff. **Voice** Flute-like slow 'coo-ah', 'coo-coo-ah'. **Hab.** Watercourses in woodland, hills.

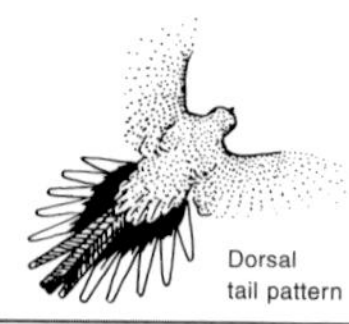

Dorsal tail pattern

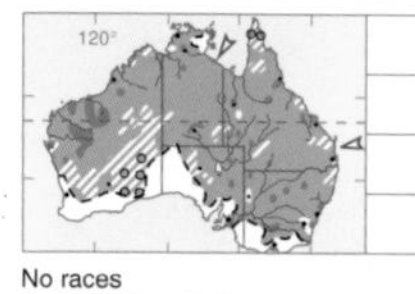

No races
Probably breeds throughout range.

Bar-shouldered Dove *Geopelia humeralis* **C** ◎–⁂

Face, head blue-grey; crown flecked black. Hind neck, mantle, bronze, scalloped black. Upperparts dark grey-brown, scalloped black. Wings in flight chestnut. Throat, upper breast, blue-grey, grading to cream. Clinal colour changes occur across range. **M br.** Red eye-ring. **Size** 27–30 cm. **Juv.** Duller. Bronze areas brown. **Voice** 4-note 'cuckoo-cuck-oop'; cooing chuckle. **Hab.** Scrubby bush, mangroves, eucalypt woodland, urban settlement.

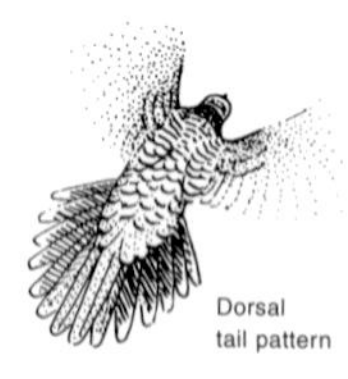

Dorsal tail pattern

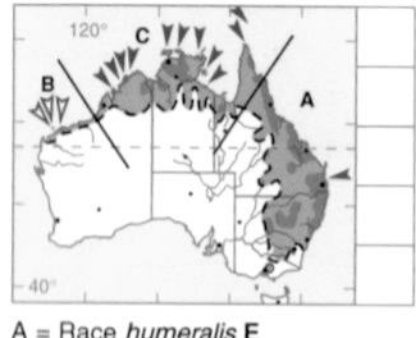

A = Race *humeralis* **E**
B = Race *headlandi* **E**
C = Race *inexpectata*

Emerald Dove *Chalcophaps indica* **C** ◎

Race *longirostris* (A) Grey-mauve crown. Head, breast, tinged soft purple. Mauve-brown body, iridescent emerald wings. White shoulder patch, bars across back. Underwing chestnut. Bill, legs, reddish. **F** Paler, browner. Race *rogersi* (B) Deeper wine below. **F** Grey shoulder patch. **Size** 23–27 cm. **Juv.** Chestnut, dark green wings; barred black. **Voice** 'croo, curroo, curroo', increasing in speed, volume. **Hab.** Rainforest, wet eucalypt forest, mangroves.

Race longirostris *incl. race* melvillensis. *Race* rogersi *formerly named* chrysochlora.

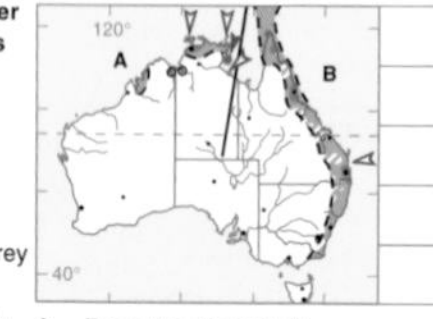

A = Race *longirostris* **E**
B = Race *rogersi*

Common Bronzewing *Phaps chalcoptera* **C** ◎ E

Forehead rich cream. Crown, sides of nape purple-brown. Extended white line under eye. Back brown, feathers pale edged. Varying metallic spots on wings, back. Breast pink-brown. **F** Forehead grey. White line under eye wider. Breast grey-buff. **Size** 28–36 cm. **Juv./Imm.** More buff, little iridescence. **Voice** Resonant, deep 'whoom'. **Hab.** Dry and wet forest, woodland, mallee, farmland margins, heath, coastal scrub.

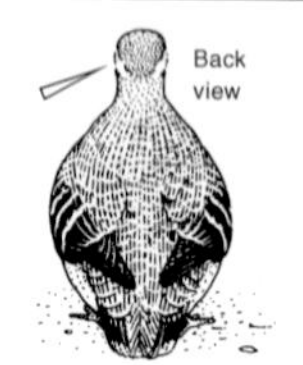

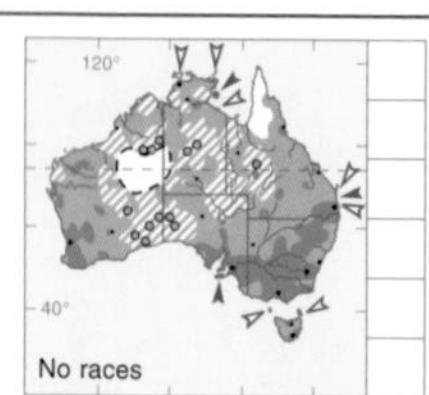

Prior races *chalcoptera*, *murchisoni* and *consobrina* dropped, as species shows clinal variation.

Brush Bronzewing *Phaps elegans* **C** ◎ E

Stockier than Common. Rich buff crown. Eye-stripe, throat, back of neck, shoulder, rich chestnut. Back, wings, chestnut to brown, metallic wing feathers tipped white. Breast blue-grey. **F** dark grey-brown upper, not chestnut. **Size** 25–33 cm. **Voice** Muffled 'whoom', higher, quicker repeat than Common. **Hab.** Woodland, wet forest, heathland; some mallee, coastal areas.

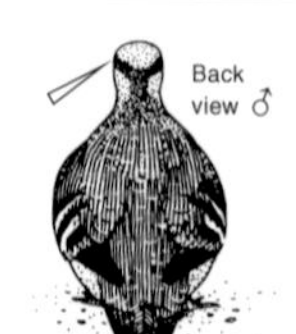

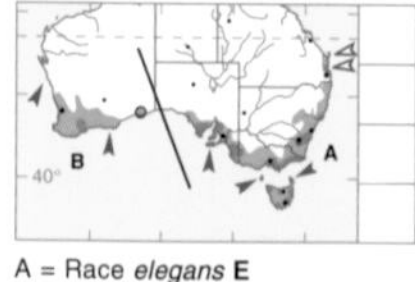

A = Race *elegans* **E**
B = Race *occidentalis* **E**

Flock Bronzewing *Phaps histrionica* **LC–UC** ⁂ E

May be in huge flocks near water. Black head; white frons, ear-mark, throat. Rich sandy-brown back, wings. Grey underparts. **F** Duller; head brown; white areas less distinct. **Juv.** As female; scalloped light brown. **Size** 28–31 cm. **Voice** Low meditative cooing, only when breeding. **Hab.** Arid zone grassy plains.

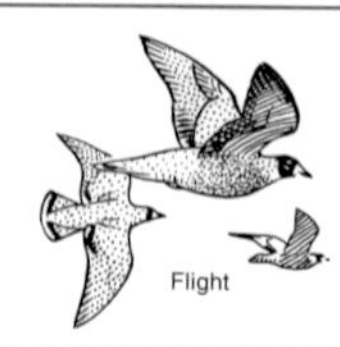

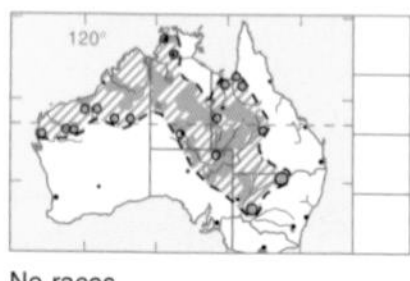

No races

Diamond Dove
Bar-shouldered Dove
Peaceful Dove
Emerald Dove
Juv.
Diamond Dove
Juv.
Emerald
Dove ♂
Race
longirostris
Flock Bronzewing ♀
Brush
Bronzewing
♀
Flock
Bronzewing
♂
Brush
Bronzewing
♂
Common
Bronzewing ♀
Common
Bronzewing ♂

Crested Pigeon *Ocyphaps (Geophaps) lophotes* **C** ♧ E

Flies with alternate bursts of fast flapping, long planing glides. Sociable. Feeds on ground. Upright crest is long, black, slender. Eye, eye-ring red. Grey body. Brown wings have bold black bars, metallic green to purple patch. Tail tip white. Race *whitlocki* (B) Narrower black wing bars; less white on tail tip. **Size** 31–36 cm. **Juv.** Duller. **Voice** Explosive 'whoop'; low 'coo'. **Hab.** Lightly wooded grassland near water; farms, rail yards, towns in grain-crop areas. Range expanding in SE Aust.

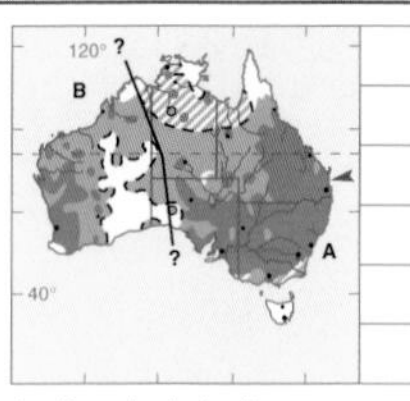

A = Race *lophotes* **E**
B = Race *whitlocki* **E**

Squatter Pigeon *Geophaps scripta* **LC** ◎ E

Crown, back, brown. Black and white face. Wings brown; pale feather margins give mottled effect. Breast blue-grey, deep white 'V' below. Race *peninsulae* (B) Red eye-ring. **Size** 26–32 cm. **Juv.** Upperparts chestnut flecked. **Voice** Rapid falling 3–5 notes; cooing chuckle; rising 'whoop'. **Hab.** Grassy plains; woodland.

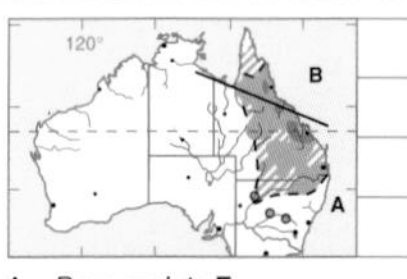

A = Race *scripta* **E**
B = Race *peninsulae* **E**

Partridge Pigeon *Geophaps smithii* **LC** ◎ E

Heavy black bill. Bare facial skin red. Crown, neck, back, wings, tail brown. Throat white. Breast pink-brown. Black scallops on purple-grey breast patch. Deep white 'V' below. Race *blaauwi* (B) Facial skin yellow. **Size** 25–28 cm. **Juv.** Upperparts fine-flecked chestnut. **Voice** Two-note 'coo?-coop'; 'whoop' in chorus. **Hab.** Grassy woodland; open areas by water.

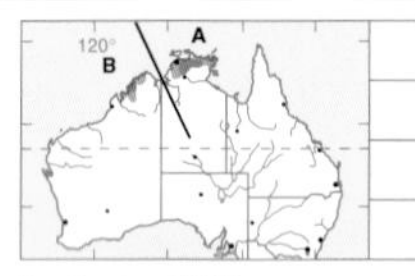

A = Race *smithii* **E**
B = Race *blaauwi* **E Vulnerable**

White-quilled Rock-Pigeon *Petrophassa albipennis* **LC** ◎ E

Uniform dark brown with light scalloping. Throat black, white spots. Outer primary bases show white (variable) in flight. Some reddish populations. Race *boothi* (B) Reddish, smaller; almost no white wing patch. **Size** 28–30 cm. **Juv.** More rufous. **Voice** Loud 'coo-corook'; querulous 'whooop?'. **Hab.** Sandstone gorges.

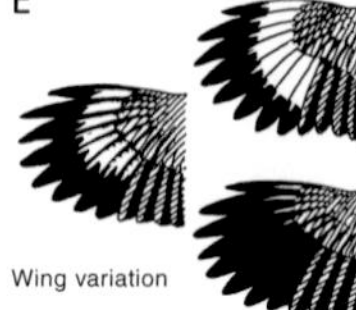

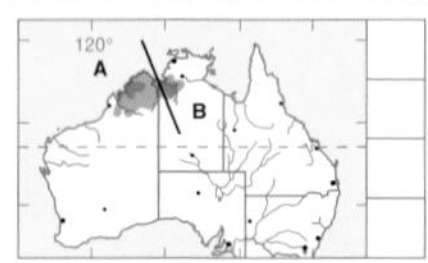

A = Race *albipennis* **E**
B = Race *boothi* **E**

Chestnut-quilled Rock-Pigeon *Petrophassa rufipennis* **LC** ◎ E

Head, face, neck spotted grey. Dark brown, light scalloping. Throat off-white. Chestnut wing patch in flight. **Size** Approx. 30 cm. **Voice** Staccato, repetitive. **Hab.** Sandstone cliffs, rubble.

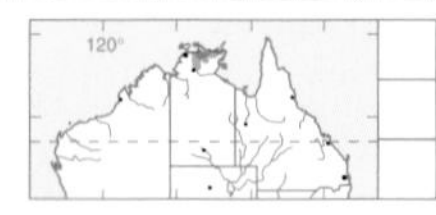

No races

Spinifex Pigeon *Geophaps plumifera* **C** ◎ E

Distinctive red-brown, tall crest. Flocks, groups, forage on bare ground. Frons blue-grey. Strong face pattern: red eye-skin, black throat. Upperparts, tail, wings, red-brown; wing coverts strongly barred black, grey. Bronze-green wing patch. Breast red-brown, thin dark bar. Whitish abdomen. Race *ferruginea* (B) Abdomen red-brown. No white above black breast band. Race *leucogaster* (C) Lower breast, abdomen, very white; flanks brown, back more rufous. **Size** 20–24 cm. **Juv.** No wing bars, head marks faint. **Voice** Low 'woo coo-up coo-up'; deep 'coo-rrr'. **Hab.** Spinifex grassland; rocky hills, by water.

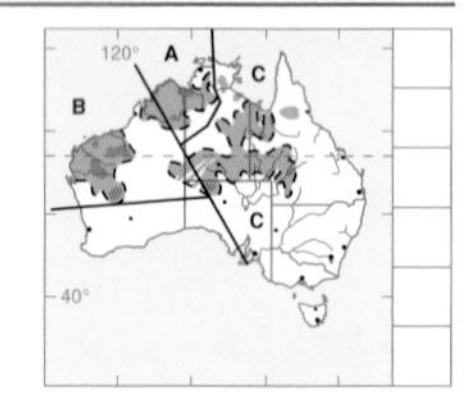

A = Race *plumifera* **E**
B = Race *ferruginea* **E**
C = Race *leucogaster* **E**

Wonga Pigeon *Leucosarcia melanoleuca* **C** ◎–♧ E

Mostly on ground; calls from trees. Generally grey. White frons. Upper breast has broad white 'V'. Lower breast, abdomen, flanks, undertail, white, bold black marks (cryptic). **Size** 38–45 cm. **Juv.** Upperparts browner; 'V' duller. **Voice** High resonant 'woohp woohp woohp'; repeated monotonously in breeding season. **Hab.** Coastal, dense forests, scrubs, rainforest.

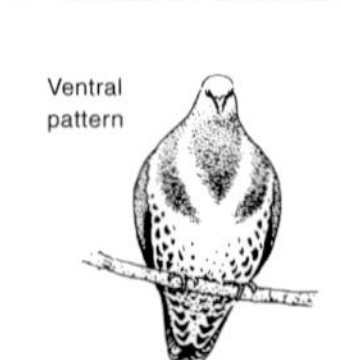

No races

Spinifex Pigeon
Race leucogaster
Chestnut-quilled
Rock-Pigeon
White-quilled Rock-Pigeon
Race boothi
White-quilled
Rock-Pigeon
Race albipennis
Spinifex
Pigeon
Race
ferruginea
Chestnut-quilled
Rock-Pigeon
Partridge Pigeon
Race blaauwi
Partridge Pigeon
Race smithii
Crested Pigeon
Wonga Pigeon
Squatter Pigeon
Race scripta
Squatter Pigeon
Race peninsulae

Palm Cockatoo *Probosciger aterrimus* UC ◎

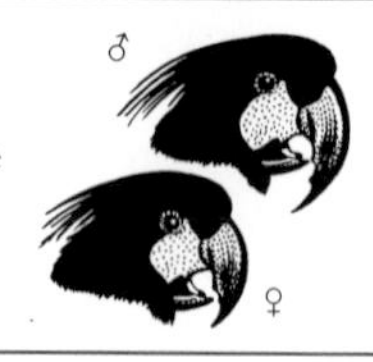

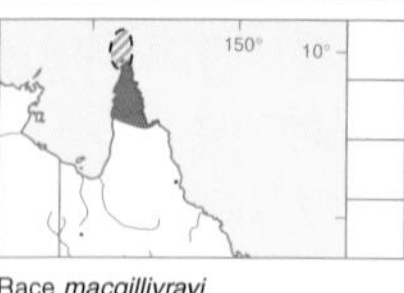

Race *macgillivrayi*

Largest, only wholly dark-feathered cockatoo. Broad wings; deep slow beat in flight. Prominent crest. Red facial skin. Massive pointed bill. **F** Bill smaller. **Size** 56 cm. **Juv.** Bill tip, face, pale. **Voice** Metallic whistle; wailing in flight. **Hab.** Closed tropical forest; adjacent savannah woodland.

Red-tailed Black-Cockatoo *Calyptorhynchus banksii* C–UC ♧ E

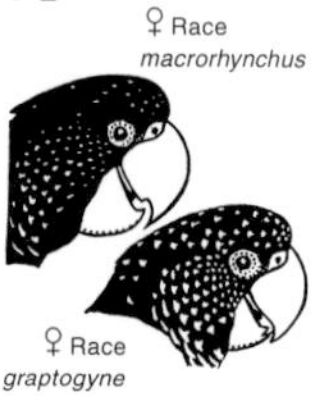

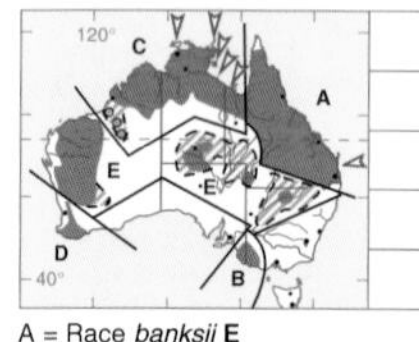

A = Race *banksii* **E**
B = Race *graptogyne* **E Endangered**
C = Race *macrorhynchus* **E**
D = Race *naso* **E**
E = Race *samueli* **E**

Noisy, often large flocks. Buoyant slow flight. Rounded helmet-like crest, massive bill diagnostic. Sooty-black. Red panels in tail. **F** Duller, spotted, barred yellow. Bill whitish. Tail orange-yellow, barred black. Markings, bill sizes vary racially. **Size** 55–60 cm. **Juv./Imm.** As female. Bill dusky. Black breast; tail barring broader. **Voice** Harsh, metallic, rolling, far-carrying 'creee creee'. **Hab.** Coastal forest, woodland. Inland, open shrubland near water, open forest in SE Aust.

Glossy Black-Cockatoo *Calyptorhynchus lathami* UC ◎–♧ E

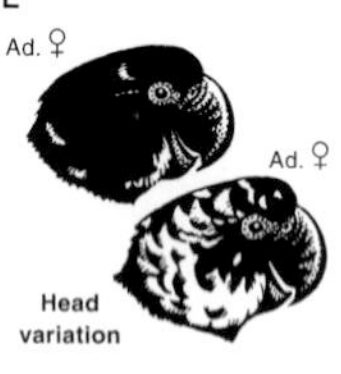

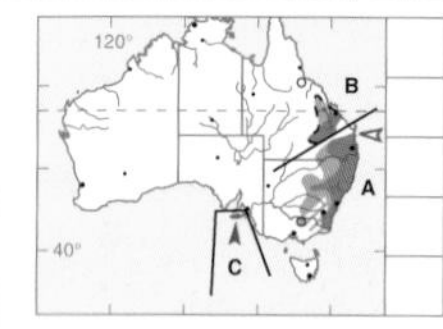

A = Race *lathami* **E**
B = Race *erebus* **E**
C = Race *halmaturinus* **E Endangered**

Smallest black-cockatoo. Like Red-tailed Black-Cockatoo but brownish-black, less red in tail, shorter crest, more bulbous bill. **F** Irregular yellow blotches on head, neck. Bill paler. Red tail panels generally have black bars, yellow edges on inner webs. **Size** 48 cm. **Juv.** As female, head darker. Often small spots on breast, shoulder. **Voice** Low 'growls' when feeding; soft wailing 'tarrr'. **Hab.** Open forest, especially she-oaks, where feed quietly.

Yellow-tailed Black-Cockatoo *Calyptorhynchus funereus* C ◎–◔ E

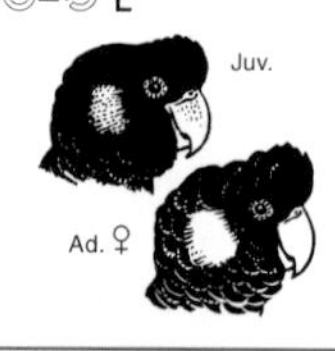

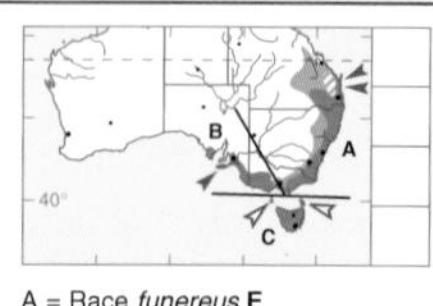

A = Race *funereus* **E**
B = Race *whiteae* **E**
C = Race *xanthanotus* **E**

Flocks. Buoyant flight, slow wingbeat. In flight, tail very long, yellow tail panels. Dark bill. Pink eye-ring; yellow cheek patch. Most body feathers edged pale yellow. **F** Pale bill, grey eye-ring; larger cheek patch. **Size** 56–65 cm. **Juv.** Bill pinkish. When with parents, wail continuously. **Imm.** As female. **Voice** Wailing 'kee-aaah'; staccato 'growl'. **Hab.** Open forest, pines, farms.

Short-billed (White-tailed) Black-Cockatoo *Calyptorhynchus latirostris* C ♧ E Vulnerable

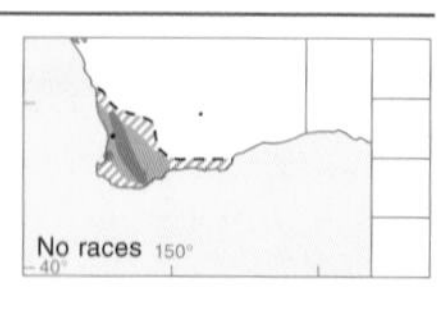

Also called 'Carnaby's Black-Cockatoo'.

Dark bill, pink eye-ring. White tail panels, cheek patches. **F** Pale bill, grey eye-ring. Plumages of WA species very similar; identify from Long-billed Black-Cockatoo by bill, contact calls. **Size** 54–56 cm. **Juv./Imm.** As female. **Voice** Long drawn-out 'wee-la', softer than Red-tailed. **Hab.** Sandplain woodland, mallee.

Long-billed Black-Cockatoo *Calyptorhynchus baudinii* C ♧ E

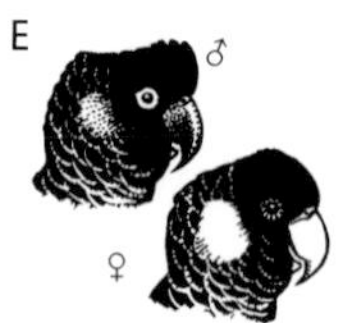

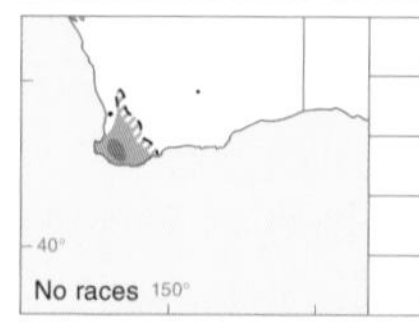

Also called 'Baudin's Black-Cockatoo'.

Smaller than Short-billed, bill longer. Dusky brown-black. Black bill, pink eye-ring, white cheek patch. **F** Pale bill; grey eye-ring. Larger white cheek patch. **Size** 52–57 cm. **Juv./Imm.** As female. Male bill darkens gradually. **Voice** Shorter wails than Short-billed. **Hab.** Largely confined to karri and marri open forests; surrounding farmland, wandoo woodland.

Gang-gang Cockatoo *Callocephalon fimbriatum* C ◎–♧ E

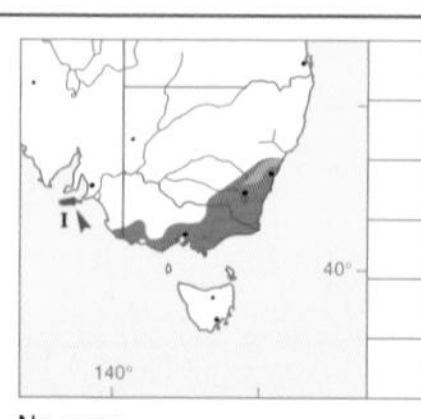

No races

Pairs, families, feed quietly. Rocking flight. Scarlet head with filamentous crest. Slate-grey; feathers pale-edged. **F** Grey head; body strongly barred lemon-grey. Cheeks, feathers of underparts, edged salmon. **Size** 32–36 cm. **Juv./Imm.** As female. Males slowly gain red head. **Voice** Distinctive 'creaky door' screech. Soft, short 'creaks' when feeding. **Hab.** Open forest; move in autumn/winter to woodland, farms, suburbs.

Palm
Cockatoo
Juv.
Palm
Cockatoo ♂
Palm
Cockatoo
Red-tailed
Black-Cockatoo ♂
Race *macrorhynchus*
Red-tailed
Black-Cockatoo ♀
Glossy
Black-Cockatoo ♀
Glossy Black-
Cockatoo Juv.
Red-tailed
Black-
Cockatoo ♀
Red-tailed
Black-
Cockatoo ♂
Yellow-tailed
Black-Cockatoo
♂
Glossy Black-
Cockatoo ♀
Yellow-tailed
Black-Cockatoo
♀
Glossy
Black-
Cockatoo
♂
Glossy Black-
Cockatoo ♂
Yellow-tailed
Black-Cockatoo
♂
Long-billed
Black-Cockatoo
♂
Short-billed
Black-
Cockatoo
♀
Long-billed
Black-Cockatoo
♀
Gang-gang
Cockatoo ♀
Gang-gang
Cockatoo ♂
Imm.
Gang-gang
Cockatoo ♂
Gang-gang
Cockatoo ♀
Gang-gang
Cockatoo ♂

Galah *Eolophus (Cacatua) roseicapillus* C ◎–♧ E

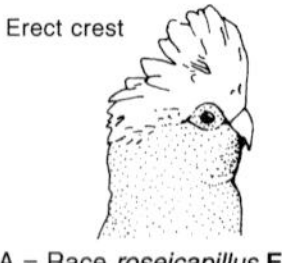

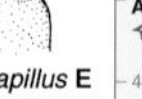

Grey and pink cockatoo, almost white in sunlight. Permanent pairs. Brown iris. Race *roseicapillus* (includes *assimilis*) (A) Grey eye-ring. Race *albiceps* (B) Red eye-ring. Race *kuhli* (C) Smaller. Wide hybrid zones. **F** Red iris (all races). **Size** 35 cm. **Imm.** Iris brown. Duller; grey about face, breast. **Voice** Shrill 'chri-chri'. **Hab.** Woodland, open shrubland, grassland, parks.

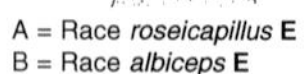

Galah taxonomy from Schodde & Mason (1997).

Long-billed Corella *Cacatua tenuirostris* C ♧ E

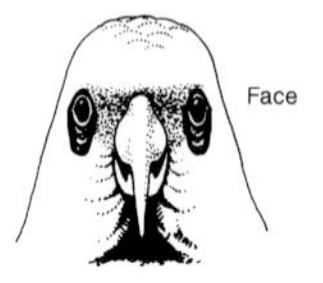

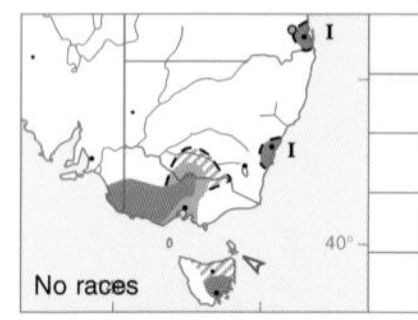

Large flocks feed on ground. White. Distinctive long upper bill. Bluish bare skin around eye. Orange-red lores, forehead, splashes at throat, breast ('Cut-throat'). Underwing, undertail, pale yellow. **Size** 38–40 cm. **Voice** High-pitched quavering 3-note call in flight. **Hab.** Red gum woodland, farmland.

Little Corella *Cacatua sanguinea* C–LC ♧–◎

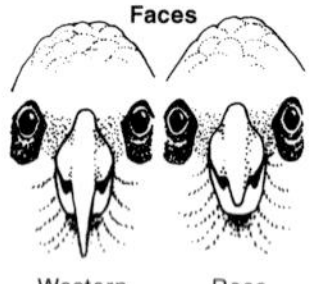

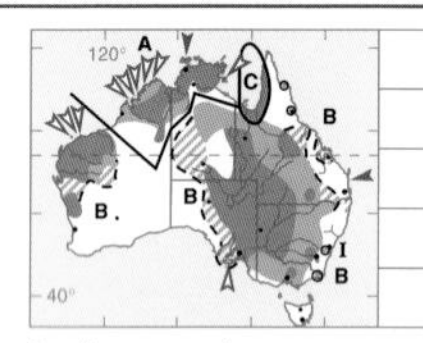

Check flying Cattle Egrets. Often vast, noisy flocks. Corellas' flight more pigeon-like than Sulphur-crested Cockatoo. White. Short whitish bill. Short erectile crest. Bare bluish eye skin. Salmon-pink lores. Underwing, undertail, pale yellow. No red on breast. **Size** 35–40 cm. **Voice** Low; short, 2-note. **Hab.** Semi-arid, monsoon woodland, shrubland; farms, stock tanks, watercourses; increasingly urban.

A = Race *sanguinea*
B = Race *gymnopis*
C = Race *normantoni*

Western Corella *Cacatua pastinator* C–LC ♧–◎ E

Previously considered a race of Little Corella, C. sanguinea. Also called 'Muir's Corella'.

Long upper mandible. Bright red lores. Rich yellow under wings, tail. **Size** 40–45 cm. **Hab.** Remnant woodland.

A = Race *pastinator* **E Endangered**
B = Race *derbyi* (includes former race *butleri*) E

Major Mitchell's (Pink) Cockatoo *Cacatua leadbeateri* MC ◎–♧ E

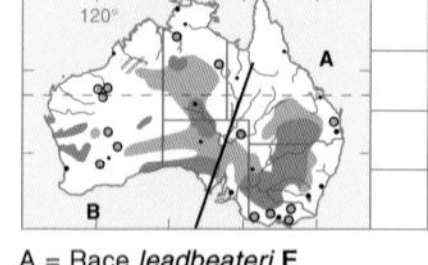

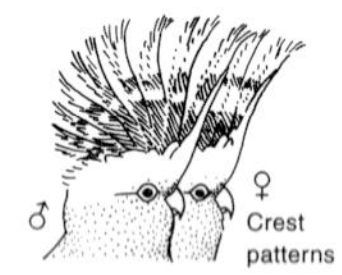

Usually small flocks; buoyant flight. Long white crest, banded red, yellow. Iris brown. White above; head, breast pink. **F** Less red in crest. Iris red. Race *mollis* (B) No yellow in crest. **Size** 39 cm. **Voice** Lighter than Galah, 2-note quaver more like corella. **Hab.** Mallee, mulga, Murray Pine, she-oak.

A = Race *leadbeateri* E
B = Race *mollis* E

Sulphur-crested Cockatoo *Cacatua galerita* LA–C ♧–?◎

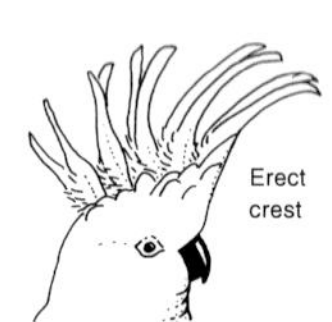

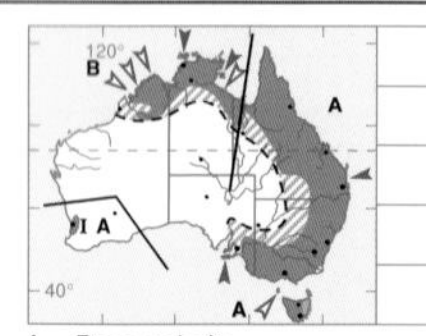

Flocks feed on ground. White; distinctive in flight: uneven wing beat (flap, flap, glide) on stiff, broad, rounded wings. Erectile, forward-curving sulphur crest. Underwing, undertail, washed yellow. **Size** 48–55 cm. **Voice** Extremely raucous screech; single squawk in flight. **Hab.** Many, varied vegetation types.

A = Race *galerita*
B = Race *fitzroyi* E

Eclectus Parrot *Eclectus roratus* UC ◎

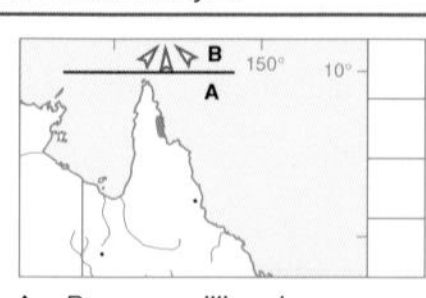

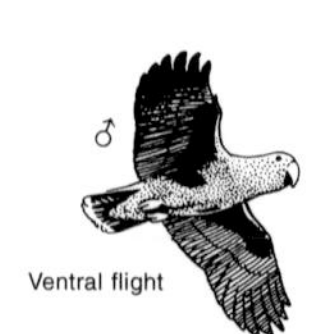

Ventral flight

Fast flight, broad dark wings; short tail. Slow shallow wingbeat. Unusual dimorphism. **M** Bright green. Bill orange above, black below. Scarlet underwing coverts, sides of abdomen. **F** Scarlet. Bill black. Blue mantle, broad breast band. **Size** M 42–48; F 40–45 cm. **Juv.** Brownish bill; plumage as adults. **Voice** Quavering screech. Soft 'peerroo'. **Hab.** Rainforest; woodland.

A = Race *macgillivrayi*
B = Race *polychloros*

Red-cheeked Parrot *Geoffroyus geoffroyi* UC ◎

Fast flight (underwing pale blue)

Active. Flight swift, direct, like Common Starling. Bright green. Bright red face, forehead. Blue-violet crown. Blue underwing. Upper bill red, lower bill grey. **F** Head brownish; bill grey. **Size** 22–25 cm. **Juv.** Head greenish. **Voice** Metallic screeching 'hink hink'. **Hab.** Rainforest.

Race *maclennani*

Little Corella
Western Corella
Long-billed Corella
Red-cheeked Parrot ♂
Red-cheeked Parrot ♀
Red-cheeked Parrot Juv.
Eclectus Parrot ♀
Eclectus Parrot ♂
Grey Goshawk White morph
Sulphur-crested Cockatoo
Galah
Galah
Major Mitchell's Cockatoo
Western Corella
Long-billed Corella
Sulphur-crested Cockatoo
Sulphur-crested Cockatoo
Little Corella
Little Corella
Galah
Major Mitchell's Cockatoo ♂
Long-billed Corella
Galah ♀ Race roseicapillus
Galah ♂ Race albiceps
Major Mitchell's Cockatoo ♀
N.DAY

Rainbow Lorikeet *Trichoglossus haematodus* **A–C**

Sociable, noisy, acrobatic. Bright red bill. Blue head. Lime-green half-collar. Breast red/yellow; abdomen blue. Underwing coverts red; yellow underwing bar. **Juv.** Duller; bill brown. **Size** 30 cm. **Voice** Strong 'screet, screet', noisy chattering. **Hab.** Rainforest, open forest, woodland, heath, gardens, urban parks.

Rainbow, Red-collared Lorikeets are long-tailed in flight.

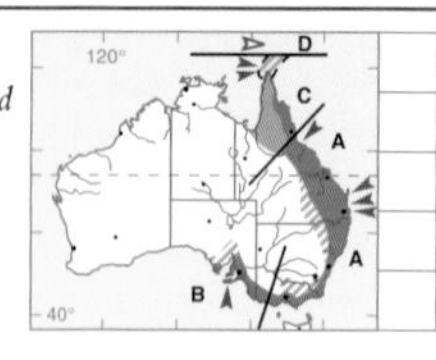

A = Race *moluccanus*
B = Race *eyrei*
C = Race *septentrionalis*
D = Race *caeruleiceps*

Red-collared Lorikeet *Trichoglossus rubritorquis* **A–C**

Sociable, noisy, obvious. Bright red bill. Dark blue head. Orange-red collar extends to orange breast. Dark blue nape. Blackish-blue band across lower belly. Broad yellow underwing bar. **Juv.** Duller; bill brown. **Size** Approx. 30 cm. **Voice** Screeching, chattering. **Hab.** Tropical open forest, gardens, settlements.

Lorikeets are acrobatic foragers

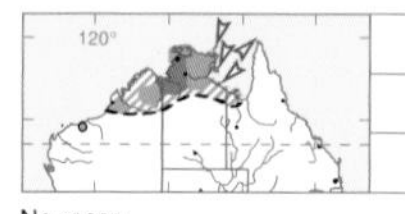

No races

Scaly-breasted Lorikeet *Trichoglossus chlorolepidotus* **C** E

Behaviour like Rainbow; sometimes hybridises with it. Identify from Musk, Varied Lorikeets. Only lorikeet with all-green head. Red bill. Orange-red underwing. Yellow crescents on hindneck, breast, flanks, thighs. **Size** 24 cm. **Juv.** Bill brown. **Voice** Very shrill chittering. **Hab.** Coastal open forest; modified habitat.

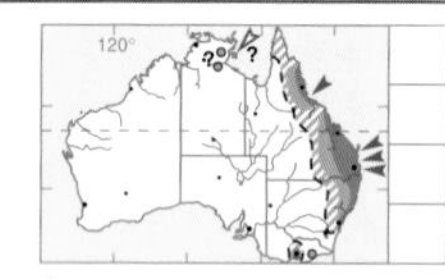

No races

Varied Lorikeet *Psitteuteles versicolor* **C** E

Orange-red bill. White eye-ring, cere. Crown, frons, lores, bright red. Ear lime-yellow. Blue on nape. Body bright green, breast pale pink, all finely streaked yellow-green. Green underwing. **F** Pale red crown. **Size** 19–20 cm. **Juv.** As female; green crown, brown bill. **Voice** More staccato, less strident, than other lorikeets. **Hab.** Monsoon woodland, melaleuca swamp, riparian open forest.

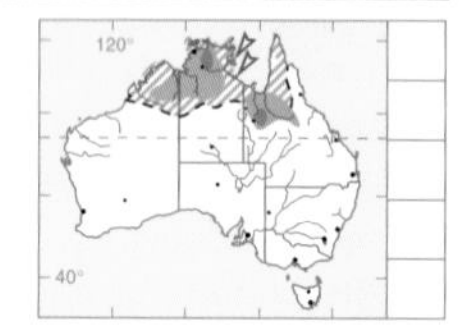

No races

Musk Lorikeet *Glossopsitta concinna* **C** E

Small, noisy, fast flocks. Bill tipped red. Scarlet frons, lores, ear band. Green-blue crown. Olive-brown mantle. Green below; sides of breast yellow. **Size** 20–23 cm. **Juv.** Dark bill. **Voice** Tinny, higher than Rainbow. **Hab.** Forest, woodland; farms, urban.

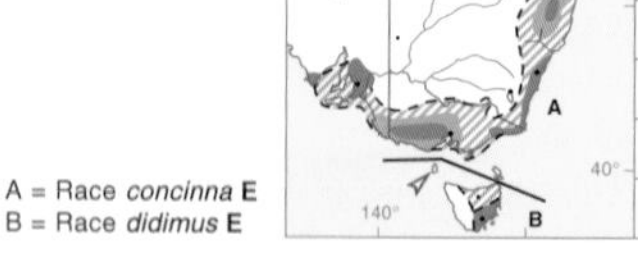

A = Race *concinna* **E**
B = Race *didimus* **E**

Purple-crowned Lorikeet *Glossopsitta porphyrocephala* **C** E

Bill black. Crown purple (often looks black). Forehead, lores, ear coverts, orange. Bright green back, brown mantle. Underwing crimson, blue shoulder. Pale blue below, yellow undertail. **F** Dark brown hood. **Size** 17–18.5 cm. **Juv.** Green head. **Voice** Sharp, buzzing 'zit-zit-zit'. **Hab.** Drier open forest, woodland, mallee.

Juv.

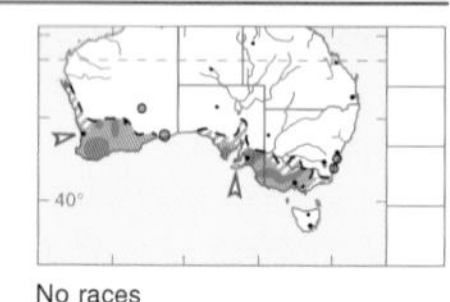

No races

Little Lorikeet *Glossopsitta pusilla* **C** E

Bright green. Bill black. Red face, forehead, throat. Light brown upper mantle. Green underwing coverts (no red), red/yellow undertail. **Size** 16–18 cm. **Voice** High, acid 'zit, zit-zit' in flight. **Hab.** Tall open forest, woodland, orchards, parks, street trees.

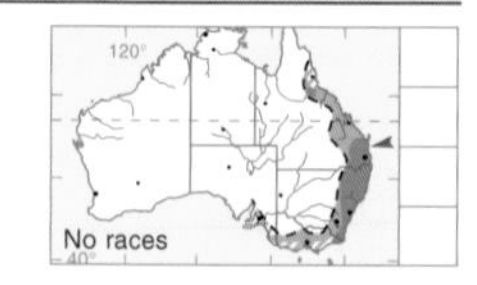

No races

Double-eyed Fig-Parrot *Cyclopsitta diopthalma* **UC** ◎

Speeding flocks fly high over canopy. Smallest Australian parrot. Bright green. Yellow sides to breast. Facial pattern varies with sex and race. **F** Races *marshalli* (A), *macleayana* (B) Pale face. Race *coxeni* (C) As male. **Size** 13–15 cm. **Voice** Thin twittering 'zeet-zeet' in flight. **Hab.** Rainforest; soft fruit trees in gardens.

Feeding on figs

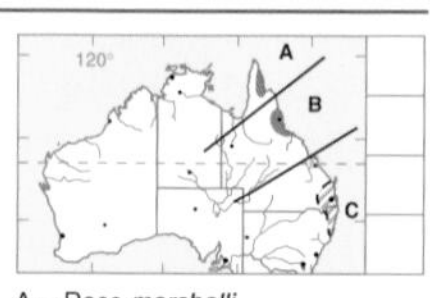

A = Race *marshalli*
B = Race *macleayana* **E**
C = Race *coxeni* **E Endangered**

Double-eyed Fig-Parrot ♂ Race marshalli
Double-eyed Fig-Parrot ♀ Race marshalli
Double-eyed Fig-Parrot ♂ Race macleayana
Double-eyed Fig-Parrot ♀ Race macleayana
Double-eyed Fig-Parrot ♀ Race marshalli
Double-eyed Fig-Parrot ♂ Race coxeni
Purple-crowned Lorikeet
Little Lorikeet
Varied Lorikeet ♂
Musk Lorikeet
Purple-crowned Lorikeet
Little Lorikeet
Varied Lorikeet
Musk Lorikeet
Rainbow Lorikeet
Scaly-breasted Lorikeet
Swift Parrot
Red-collared Lorikeet
Scaly-breasted Lorikeet
Rainbow Lorikeet
Red-collared Lorikeet
N. DAY.

Australian King-Parrot *Alisterus scapularis* **C** ◎–♧ E

Small flocks. Strong rocking, undulating flight. Distinctive, dimorphic. Red and black bill. Bright yellow eye. Head, neck, underparts, brilliant flame-scarlet. Dark green mantle, wings. Light green inner wing coverts ('shoulder' stripe). Dark blue hindneck, back, rump. Tail blackish-blue. Green-black crescents on red undertail coverts. Yellow spotted feathers on some birds are areas lacking melanin. **F** Greyish bill. Red-brown eye. Green head, neck; little or no 'shoulder' stripe. Tail narrow pink tips. **Juv./Imm.** Brownish bill, chest, throat. **1st yr** No blue on back. **Size** 40–45 cm. **Voice** Loud 'carrak-carrak' in flight. Far-carrying, shrill piping whistle by male. **Hab.** Moist, tall forest; nearby farmland. Orchards, parks, gardens, autumn/winter.

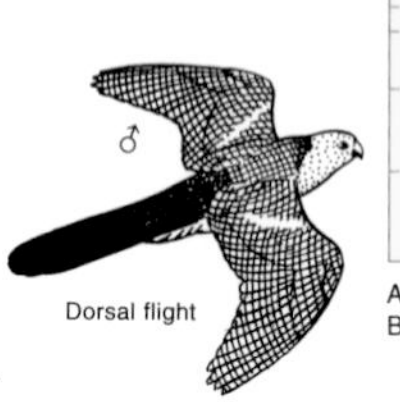

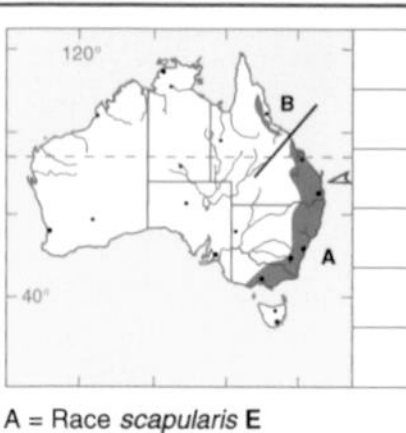

A = Race *scapularis* **E**
B = Race *minor* **E**

Red-winged Parrot *Aprosmictus erythropterus* **C** ♧

Strong, erratic, rocking flight; deep wing beat. Arboreal, noisy, wary. Dimorphic. Bright green head tinged blue. Large scarlet shoulder patch. Black to bottle-green upper back, wings. Blue lower back grades to lime-green uppertail coverts. Tail tips yellow. Lime below. **F/Juv.** Duller, no black saddle, thin shoulder patch. **Size** 32 cm. **Voice** Brassy 'crillik-crillik' in flight. **Hab.** Subtropical, semi-arid eucalypt, casuarina woodland, mulga.

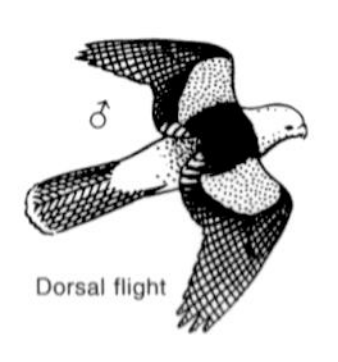

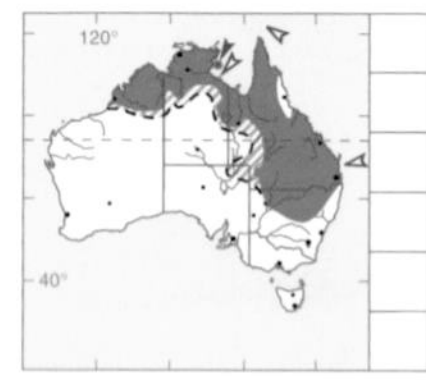

No races

Superb Parrot *Polytelis swainsonii* **LC** ◎–♧ E Vulnerable

Small flocks; ground feeder. In flight, swift, slender, long-tailed. Yellow forehead, cheeks, throat. Broad scarlet border to throat. Brilliant green body. **F** Green. Variable blue on cheeks, pink-washed throat. Red thighs. Pink undertail feather edges. **Size** 40 cm. **Juv.** Like female, duller. **Voice** Rolling 'currak-currak' in flight; not as harsh as Regent. **Hab.** Riverine, flood-plain open forest/woodland, particularly River Red Gum; stubble, roadsides.

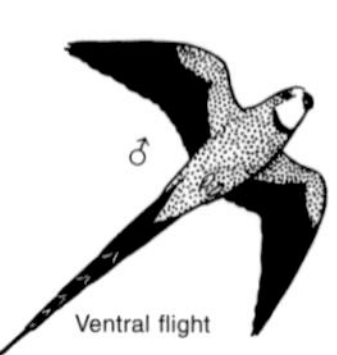

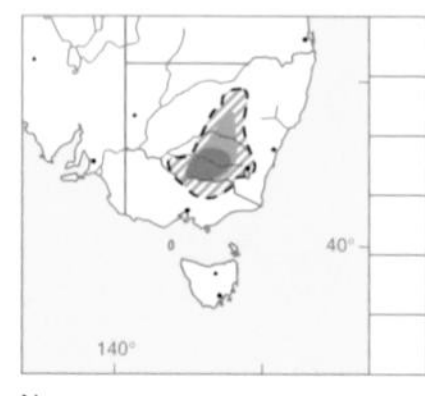

No races

Regent Parrot *Polytelis anthopeplus* **LC** ◎–♧ E

Check 'Yellow Rosella', a race of Crimson Rosella. Pairs or small groups. Flight graceful, swift, erratic. Slender, mostly yellow, with contrasting blue-black flight feathers, tail. Pinkish-red bill. 'Smoky' olive-yellow head, neck, underparts. Dark green mantle. Yellow shoulder patch. Red bands across wing. Race *monarchoides* (B) Brighter yellow. **F** Greener; duller markings. Wing colours more subtle. **Juv.** As female, faintly duller. **Size** 40–42 cm. **Voice** Loud, harsh 'currak-currak' in flight. Rapid chatter. **Hab.** River Red Gum, Black Box and casuarina woodland, mallee and acacia shrubland, farmland.

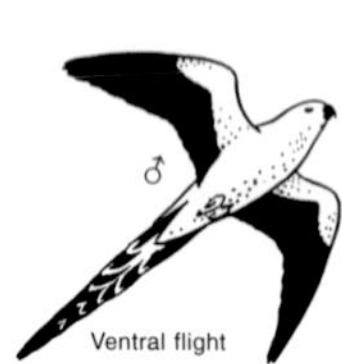

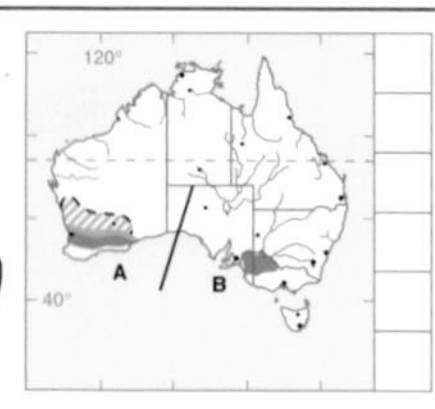

A = Race *anthopeplus* **E**
B = Race *monarchoides* **E**
Endangered

Princess (Alexandra's) Parrot
Polytelis alexandrae **UC** ♧ E Vulnerable

Pairs or small parties. Flight undulating. Reasonable chance of sightings along northern Canning Stock Route, WA. Crown and side of head violet, grading to pale blue. Cheek, throat, rose-pink. Upperparts light olive; lime-green shoulder (conspicuous in flight). Violet back, rump. Breast yellow-grey. Abdomen pinkish-mauve. Underwings lime green, dark edged. Very long tail, olive above, black below with pink centre. **F/Juv.** Duller; shorter tail. **Size** 40–45 cm. **Voice** Prolonged call; chattering; 'queet-queet' alarm. **Hab.** Arid shrubland, particularly mulga, Desert Oak and spinifex country. Trees along watercourses.

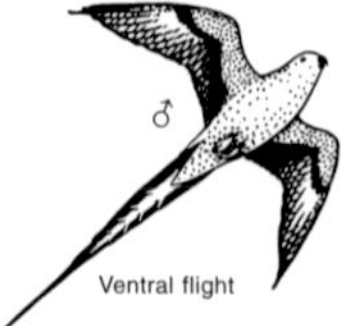

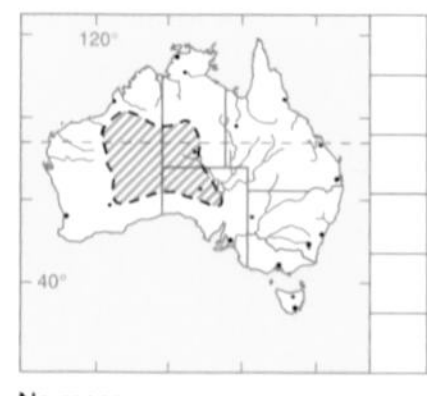

No races
Precise breeding areas not known.

Australian King-Parrot ♀
Australian King-Parrot ♂ Imm.
Australian King-Parrot ♂ Ad.
Australian King-Parrot Juv.
Red-winged Parrot ♀
Red-winged Parrot ♂
Red-winged Parrot Juv.
Superb Parrot ♂
Regent Parrot ♂ Race *monarchoides*
Superb Parrot ♀
Regent Parrot ♀ Race *monarchoides*
Princess Parrot ♀
Princess Parrot ♂

Cockatiel *Nymphicus hollandicus* **C** ♧ E

Flocks. Graceful undulating flight; pointed wings, long tail, flashing white shoulders. Long yellow and grey crest. Grey-brown body; white shoulder patch. Lemon forehead, face, throat, cheeks; orange ear patch. Escaped domestic varieties, yellow or white, most common. **F/Juv.** Paler yellow face; dull ear patch. Grey crest. Rump, upper tail, barred pale yellow. **Size** 29–32 cm. **Voice** High, far-carrying, rolling 'cweeree'. **Hab.** Semi-arid to arid country; usually near water; cereal crops.

Flight patterns

Now known from DNA work to be a small cockatoo.

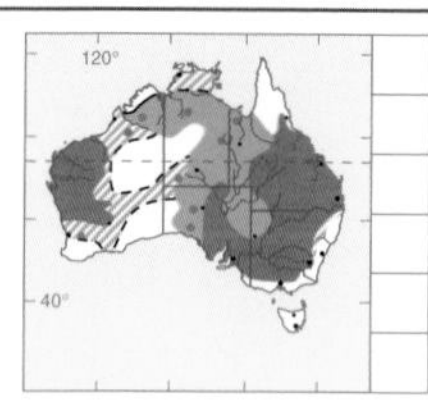

No races

Ground Parrot *Pezoporus wallicus* **UC** ◎ E

Terrestrial. Flies swiftly if flushed. Flight 'snipe-like'; plunges into thickets, then runs. Red frons diagnostic. Black streaks on crown, neck. Bright green above, barred and spotted yellow, black. Prominent pale yellow wing bar; long tail barred yellow and green. Legs, toes, long. Sexes alike. Race *flaviventris* (B) Plainer yellow belly. **Size** 30 cm. **Juv.** Frons green. **Voice** Bell-like, distinctive repetition; mostly at dawn, dusk. **Hab.** Coastal, tableland heath; sedgeland; 'button-grass plains' (Tas.).

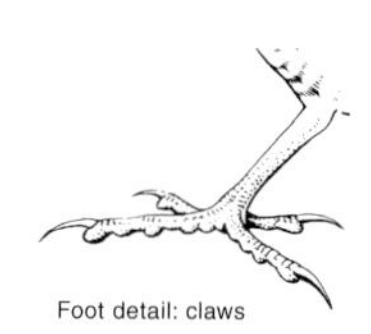

Foot detail: claws

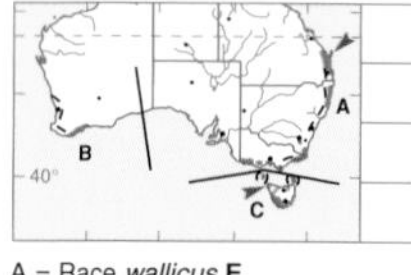

A = Race *wallicus* **E**
B = Race *flaviventris* **E**
Endangered
C = Race *leachi* **E**
Former range shown.

Night Parrot *Pezoporus occidentalis* **R** ◎–?♧ E Endangered

Shy. By day believed to hide in dense saltbush and spinifex, emerging at dusk. Flight reportedly 'quail-like'; drops after short distance, runs to cover. Thick-set; short-tailed. No red on forehead. Upperparts dull yellowish-green, mottled and barred black, dark brown. Underparts yellowish; primaries brown. **Size** 22–25 cm. **Juv.** Browner; more so on head, neck. **Voice** Peculiar croaking alarm; drawn-out mournful whistle. **Hab.** Inland plains, breakaways, samphire about salt lakes. Only modern specimen (1990) dead beside highway near Boulia, W Qld.

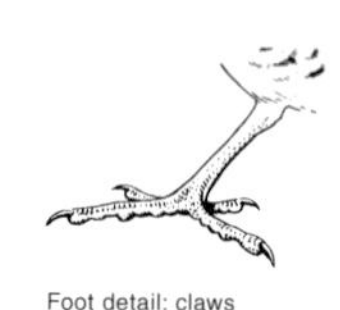

Foot detail: claws

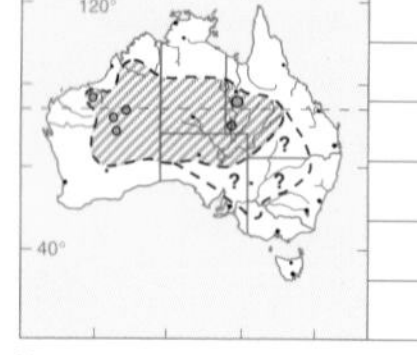

No races

Budgerigar *Melopsittacus undulatus* **C**–LA ♧ E

Densely packed, fast-wheeling flocks. Nomadic. Small, slender-bodied; bright green parrot ('parakeet'). Dark blue cere. Yellow throat, forehead. Blue, black, throat spots. Pale wing bar in flight. **F** Pale blue to brown cere. **Size** 18 cm. **Juv.** Iris brown; black barring on frons, cheeks. **Voice** Continuous 'chirrup'; 'zitting' alarm call. **Hab.** Arid and semi-arid woodland, grassland, farms.

Juv.

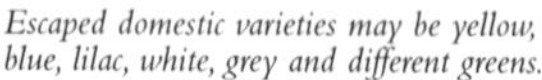

Escaped domestic varieties may be yellow, blue, lilac, white, grey and different greens.

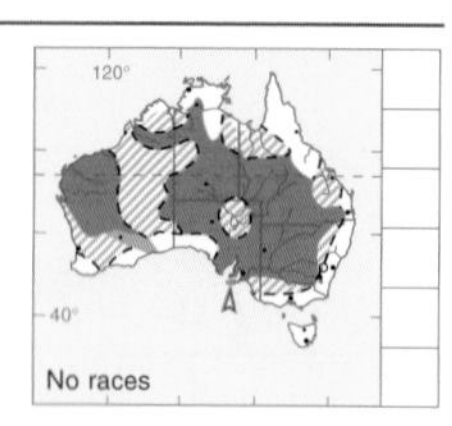

No races

Swift Parrot *Lathamus discolor* **UC** ʘ E Vulnerable

Slender-tailed, lorikeet-like. Often flying, feeding, with lorikeets. Swift erratic flight. Pale bill, iris. Bright green body, red shoulders. Crown bluish-purple. Frons, throat, red edged yellow. Greater coverts blue; red underwing coverts obvious in flight (cf. lorikeets). Tail dull red. **F/Juv.** Duller; less red on face. Brown iris. Undertail coverts green. **Size** Approx. 25 cm. **Voice** High, distinctive 'swit, swit'. **Hab.** Drier open forest, woodland, parks, gardens. Winter migrant to SE Aust.

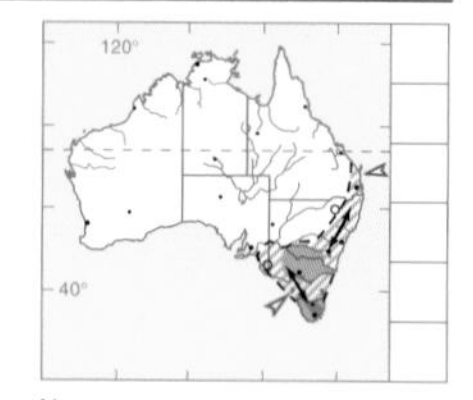

No races

Red-capped Parrot *Purpureicephalus spurius* **LC** ◎ E

Undulating rosella-like flight. Forehead, crown, dark red. Bill pale grey; upper bill elongated. Dark lores. Dark green above. Face, throat, rump, lime-green. Purple breast, upper abdomen. Red lower abdomen, undertail coverts. Tail dark green above, light blue below. **F** Similar; duller. **Size** 34–38 cm. **Juv.** Crown green, red frons. Violet-grey breast, abdomen. **Voice** Harsh 'shrek shrek'. **Hab.** Open forest, woodland, orchards, gardens.

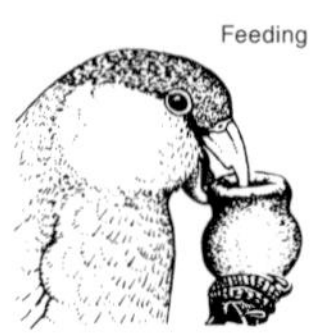

Feeding

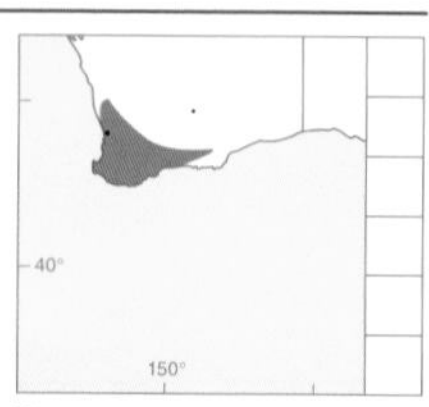

No races

Swift Parrot
Juv.
Swift Parrot
Swift Parrot
Cockatiel
♂
Cockatiel
♀
Red-capped
Parrot
Juv.
Red-capped
Parrot
♂
Red-capped
Parrot
♂
Budgerigar
Cockatiel
Domestic variety
Cockatiel
♂
Cockatiel
♀
Ground Parrot
Budgerigar
Domestic
varieties
Ground
Parrot
Ground
Parrot
Juv.
Night
Parrot
Budgerigar
Night
Parrot
N.DAY.

Green Rosella *Platycercus caledonicus* C ◎ E

Blue cheeks, throat, shoulder patch. Red band over bill. Bright yellow head. Dark green above. Yellow below. **F** Variable red wash on breast, undertail coverts. **Size** 29–36 cm. **Juv./Imm.** Duller; greener. Less black in mantle. **Voice** Loud 'cussick cussick' (in flight); triple, bell-like (perched). **Hab.** Dense mountain forests, farmland, gardens. Breeds throughout range. Race *brownii* (B) restricted to southern King Is.

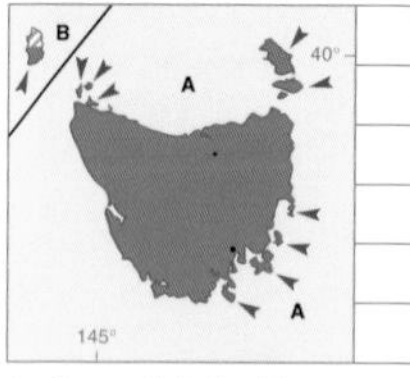

A = Race *caledonicus* **E**
B = Race *brownii* **E Vulnerable**

Crimson Rosella *Platycercus elegans* C ◎–♧ E

Blue cheeks, shoulders, tail. Rich crimson body. Race *nigrescens* (B) Smaller, darker-backed. Race *flaveolus* (C) 'Yellow Rosella' Crimson is replaced by yellow except red frontal band. Races *subadelaidae* (D), *fleurieuensis* (E) (together called 'Adelaide Rosella') Variable orange replaces yellow of *flaveolus* on head, neck, underparts. **F** (all races) White underwing bar. **Size** 35–38 cm. **Juv./Imm.** *elegans*, *subadelaidae* Green with crimson; *flaveolus* duller, greener; *nigrescens* much like adults. **Voice** Local dialects. Brassy 'kweek-kweek' in flight; 'p-link, p-link'; bell-like whistle, perched. **Hab.** Race *elegans* Moist forests, farmland, parks. Race *nigrescens* Sub-coastal mountains. 'Yellow Rosella' Riparian forest, red gum woodland. 'Adelaide Rosella' Woodland, farmland, orchards, parks.

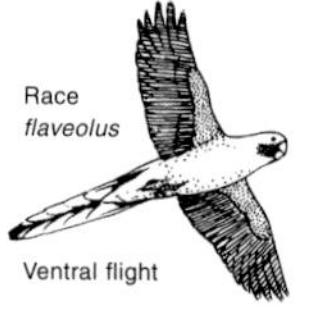
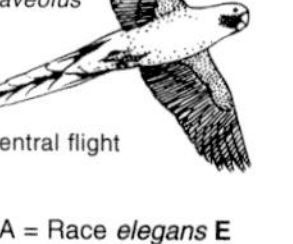

Race *flaveolus*
Ventral flight

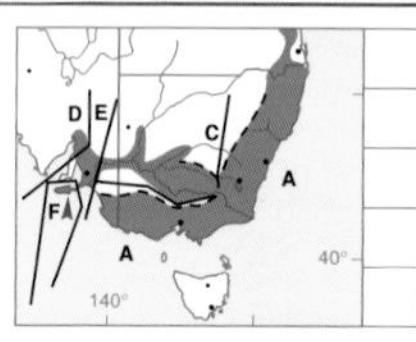
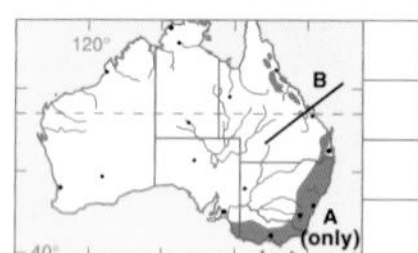
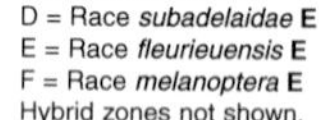

A = Race *elegans* **E**
B = Race *nigrescens* **E**
C = Race *flaveolus* **E**
D = Race *subadelaidae* **E**
E = Race *fleurieuensis* **E**
F = Race *melanoptera* **E**
Hybrid zones not shown.

Eastern Rosella *Platycercus eximius* C ◎–♧–?○ E

White cheeks. Red head, breast. Back yellow-green, scaled black. Rump lime-green. Tail dark blue-green, outer feathers blue, white tips. Lower breast yellow, belly lime-green; undertail coverts red. Race *elecica* (C) Yellower back, rump paler. **F/Imm.** White underwing bar. **Size** 28–33 cm. **Juv.** As dull female, nape green; two pale underwing bars. **Voice** Bell-like 'pee-pity, pee-pity' on one note. High 'clink-clink' in flight. One or two birds chattering sound like a crowd. **Hab.** Woodland, farmland, parks, gardens.

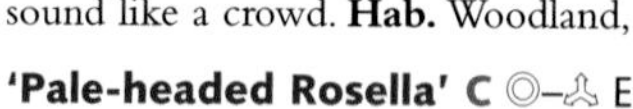

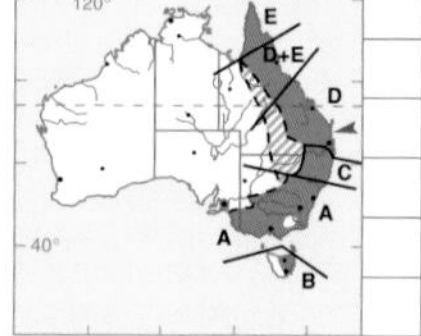

Eastern Rosella
A = Race *eximius* **E**
B = Race *diemenensis* **E**
C = Race *elecica* **E**
Hybrid zones occur between all races; only one (D + E) shown.

'Pale-headed Rosella' C ◎–♧ E

Race *palliceps* (D) White cheeks, faint blue edge. Golden yellow head, nape (occasional red feathers); local name 'Custardhead'. Lower back, rump, variable yellowish, washed dusky blue. Wings blue. Breast yellowish; rest dusky blue. Red undertail coverts. Race *adscitus* (E) White/violet-blue cheeks; pale head. **F** Duller, paler; off-white underwing bar. **Size** 28–34 cm. **Voice** Strong 'crik, crik'. **Hab.** Woodland, farmland, parks, gardens.

'Pale-headed Rosella'
D = Race *palliceps* **E**
E = Race *adscitus* **E**

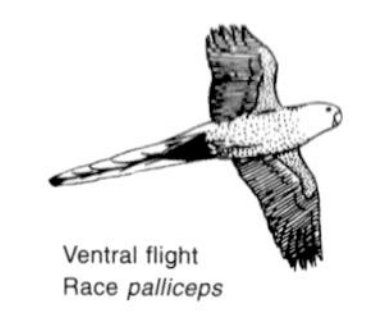

Ventral flight
Race *palliceps*

Northern Rosella *Platycercus venustus* MC ◎–?♧ E

Variable white/blue cheeks. Black cap. Back yellow, boldly marked black. Wings blue. Uppertail blue-green, edged blue. Rump, underparts, yellow, fine black scallops. **F** More red on head, breast. **Size** 29–32 cm. **Juv./Imm.** As female, duller. **Voice** As Eastern. **Hab.** Eucalypt, woodland; scrub, grassland, gardens.

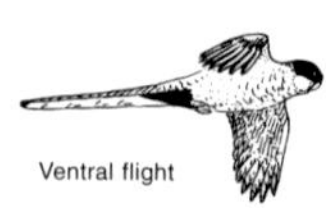

Ventral flight

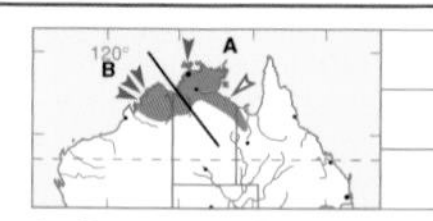

A = Race *venustus* **E**
B = Race *hilli* **E**

Western Rosella *Platycercus icterotis* MC–LC ◎ E

Yellow cheeks; red head, underparts. Wings, uppertail greenish-black, deep blue shoulder. Rump yellow-green. **F** Green head, red forecrown; breast. More green below; bold cream underwing bar. Race *xanthogenys* (B) More red, both sexes. Paler cheeks. **Size** 25–30 cm. **Juv./Imm.** As female; no cheek patch. **Voice** Soft 'clink-clink'; 4-note bell. **Hab.** Open forest, woodland, farms.

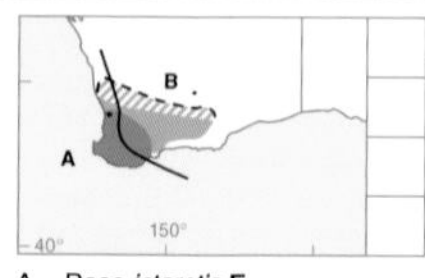

A = Race *icterotis* **E**
B = Race *xanthogenys* **E**

Crimson Rosella
Race elegans
Crimson
Rosella Juv.
Race
fleurieuensis
Crimson
Rosella Juv.
Race elegans
Crimson Rosella
Race fleurieuensis
Green Rosella
Juv.
Green
Rosella
Crimson
('Yellow')
Rosella Juv.
Race flaveolus
Crimson ('Yellow')
Rosella
Race flaveolus
Northern Rosella
Western Rosella
Juv.
Western
Rosella
♀
Eastern
'Pale-
headed'
Rosella
Race
adscitus
Eastern
Rosella
Race eximius
Eastern
Rosella ♂
Race
eximius
Western
Rosella ♂
Eastern ('Pale-
headed') Rosella
Race palliceps
Eastern Rosella ♀
Race eximius
N. Day

Australian Ringneck *Barnardius zonarius* **C** ◎ E

Race *zonarius* (A) 'Port Lincoln Parrot' Bright green with brown-black head, dark blue cheeks. No red frontal band. Yellow collar, belly. Light green undertail coverts. Primaries dark blue. **F** Browner hood, duller. Race *semitorquatus* (B) 'Twenty-eight Parrot' Largest. Darker green. Black head. Red frontal band. **F** Dull head. Light underwing bar. Race *barnardi* (C) 'Mallee Ringneck' Green head, blue cheeks; red frontal band. Collar yellow. Dark blue mantle. Orange-yellow lower breast. **F** Darker, plainer. Belly orange. Race *macgillivrayi* (D) 'Cloncurry Parrot' Smaller, paler; plain head, no red frontal band; yellow below, no orange on breast. **Size** M 32–44; F 28–41 cm. **Voice** 'Twenty-eight Parrot' named from its call. Port Lincoln more strident than 'Mallee', 'Cloncurry'. Ringing 'kling'. Mellow whistles. **Hab.** (A), (C), (D) Dry woodland, mallee, roadsides; (B) tall, wet forest.

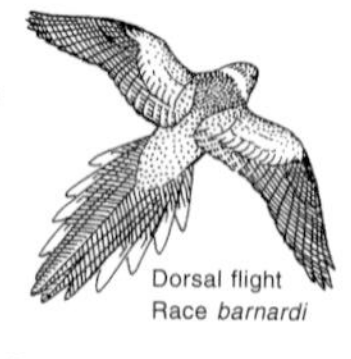

Dorsal flight
Race *barnardi*

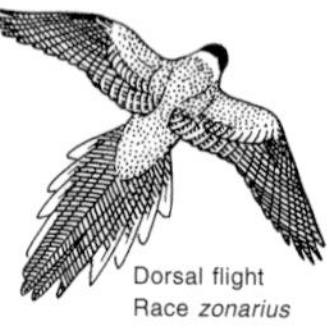

Dorsal flight
Race *zonarius*

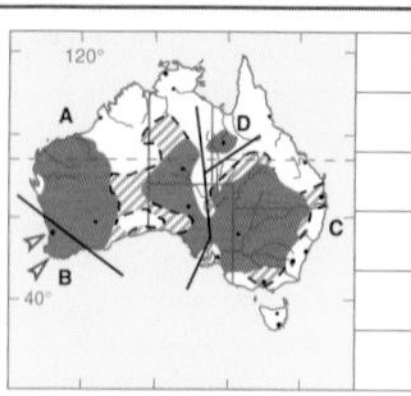

A = Race *zonarius* (includes former race *occidentalis* of Pilbara region) **E**
B = Race *semitorquatus* **E**
C = Race *barnardi* **E**
D = Race *macgillivrayi* **E**
Hybrid zones not shown.

Red-rumped Parrot *Psephotus haematonotus* **C** ◎–♧ E

Brilliant green; red 'rump' when taking flight. Head turquoise. Shoulder patch, belly, yellow. **F** Dull olive-green; pale underwing bar. Race *caeruleus* (B) Greyer. Orange 'rump'. **Size** 24–30 cm. **Juv./Imm.** Duller. **Voice** Very high, squeaky 'sweet-swit, sweet-swit'. **Hab.** Open woodland, red gums, grassland, urban parks.

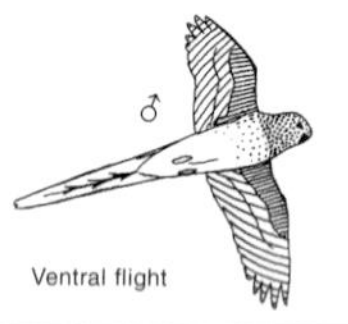

Ventral flight

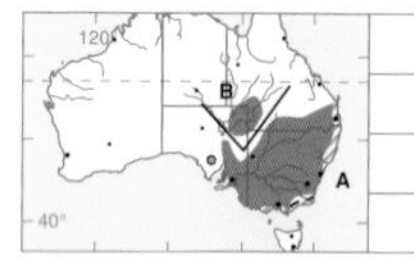

A = Race *haematonotus* **E**
B = Race *caeruleus* **E**

Mulga Parrot *Psephotus varius* **MC** ◎ E

Emerald green. Banded green/black/red 'rump' diagnostic. Frons, shoulder, vent, yellow. Nape, belly patch, red. **F** Much duller; pale brown-olive; dull orange frons, dull red shoulder. **Size** 27–32 cm. **Juv.** Duller than adults. **Voice** Slow flute-like 'sweet-sweet'; rapid 'swit-swit-swit-swit'. **Hab.** Arid shrubland, mallee.

Dorsal flight

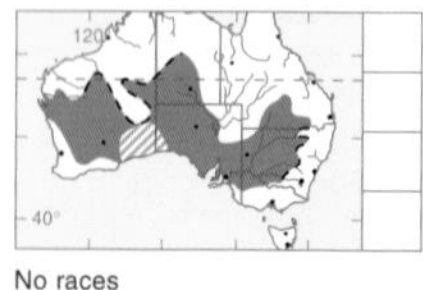

No races

Golden-shouldered Parrot *Psephotus chrysopterygius* UC ◎ E Endangered

Black crown. Yellow frons. Turquoise face, breast. Brown wings, golden shoulder. Reddish vent. **F** Light yellow-green. Pale yellow frons, dusky crown. Lower underparts pale blue; some red on vent. **Size** 23–28 cm. **Juv.** As Hooded. **Voice** 'preep-preep'. **Hab.** Savannah woodland with termite mounds.

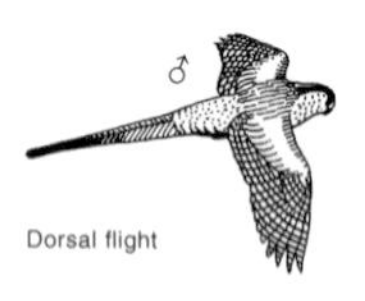

Dorsal flight

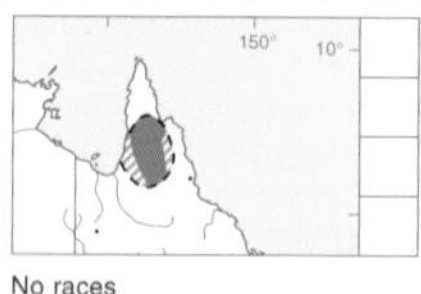

No races

Hooded Parrot *Psephotus dissimilis* **UC** ◎ E

Like Golden-shouldered. Black hood to lower bill; shoulder patch larger, brighter. **F** Dull olive. Frons, crown, abdomen, dull turquoise. **Size** 26–28 cm. **Juv.** As female. Orange bill at fledging. **Hab.** Savannah woodland with termite mounds.

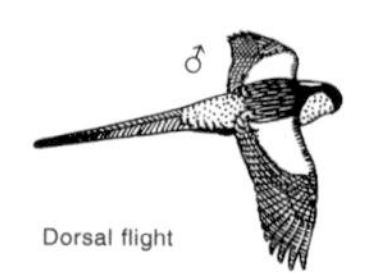

Dorsal flight

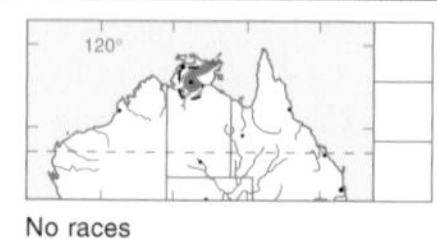

No races

Paradise Parrot *Psephotus pulcherrimus* ○ E Presumed extinct

Brown above. Red frontal band, shoulder, abdomen, undertail coverts. Turquoise rump, underparts. **Size** 27 cm. **Voice** Musical whistle. **Hab.** Grassy eucalypt woodland with termite mounds.

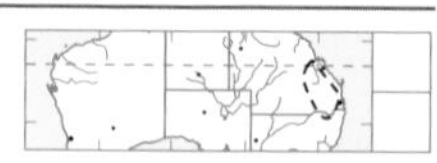

No races. **Presumed extinct**
Dotted lines = probable former range

Blue Bonnet *Northiella haematogaster* **C** ◎ E

Brown, blue-faced parrot, black in poor light. Wing band blue; upperwing coverts olive-yellow; belly red; vent yellow. Race *haematorrhous* (B) Wing band green; upperwing coverts, vent, red. Race *pallescens* (C) Paler. Race *narethae* (D) 'Naretha Blue Bonnet' Smaller; blue face, frons turquoise; belly yellow, vent red. **F/Juv.** Duller. **Size** M 28–35; F 26–32 cm. **Voice** Harsh 'chack chack'; piping whistle. **Hab.** Semi-arid woodland.

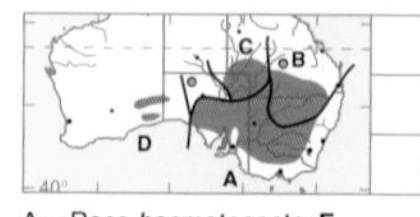

A = Race *haematogaster* **E**
B = Race *haematorrhous* **E**
C = Race *pallescens* **E**
D = Race *narethae* **E**
Hybrid zones not shown.

Australian
Ringneck
Race macgillivrayi
Blue Bonnet
Race haematorrhous
Blue Bonnet
Race narethae
Blue Bonnet
Race
haematogaster
alian
eck
rdi
Australian Ringneck
Race zonarius
Australian Ringneck
Race semitorquatus
Red-
rumped
Parrot ♂
Red-
rumped
Parrot
♀
Mulga
Parrot
♀
Red-
rumped
Parrot
♂
Red-rumped
Parrot ♀
Golden-
shouldered
Parrot ♂
Golden-shouldered
Parrot
♀
Mulga
Parrot
♂
Paradise
Parrot ♂
Hooded
Parrot
♀
Hooded
Parrot
♂
Paradise Parrot
♀

Bourke's Parrot *Neopsephotus bourkii* **C–UC** ◎ E

Check Diamond Dove. Distinctive pinkish-brown. Variable blue frontal band. White about eye, face. Grey-brown above; wing feathers edged yellowish-white. Salmon-pink below; face to breast finely scalloped. Undertail coverts pale blue; undertail whitish. **F/Juv.** Dull; no frontal band. **Size** 20–23 cm. **Voice** Soft twitter. **Hab.** Arid to semi-arid scrubland, mainly mulga.

Previously in genus Neophema.

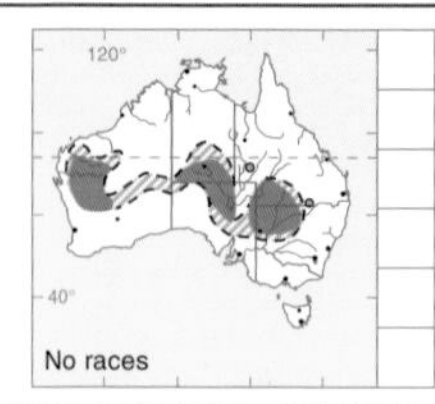

Blue-winged Parrot *Neophema chrysostoma* **C** ⁂ E

Yellow lores, face, short eyebrow. Deep blue frontal band but not over eye. Olive-green above. Shoulder brilliant deep blue. Breast green, grading to yellow abdomen, which may be orange-centred. **F** Duller; greener. **Juv.** Indistinct frontal band. **Size** 21–24 cm. **Voice** High tinkling in flight; alarm, sharp 's-wit, s-wit'. **Hab.** Open forest, woodland, grassland, coastal heath, saltmarsh.

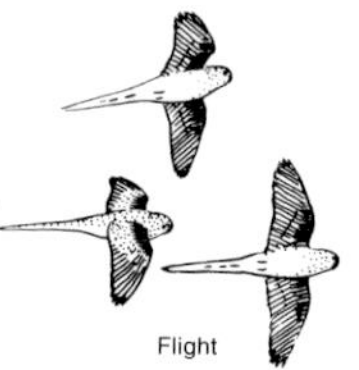

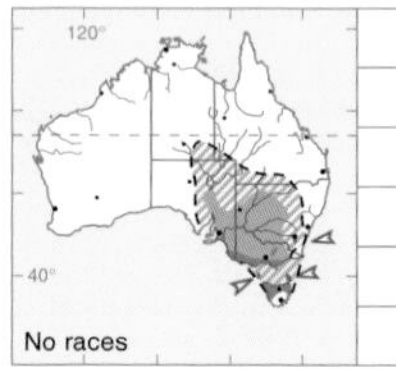

Elegant Parrot *Neophema elegans* **C** ⁂ E

Like Blue-winged, but yellow-olive above; brighter yellow rump, uppertail coverts, outer tail. Blue frontal band extends over eye. Less deep blue in wing. **F** Darker blue, duller. **Juv.** Dull frontal band. **Size** 22–25 cm. **Voice** Sharp 'zwit, zwit, zwit' in flight; soft twitters when feeding. **Hab.** Open country; semi-arid scrublands.

All Neophema *parrots are primarily 'ground feeders'.*

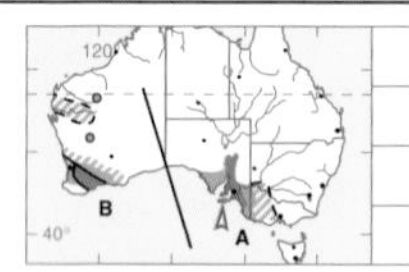

A = Race *elegans* **E**
B = Race *carteri* **E**

Rock Parrot *Neophema petrophila* **MC** ◎ E

Dullest *Neophema.* Dark olive above; yellowish-olive below. Frontal band deep blue, pale-edged; some blue about eye. Light blue lores. Bright yellow undertail coverts. **F/Juv.** Less blue on face. **Size** 22–24 cm. **Voice** Double 'swee-swee' in flight. **Hab.** Coastal dunes, saltmarsh, rocky islands. Race *petrophila* Breeds on offshore islands/islets; visits adjacent WA coast.

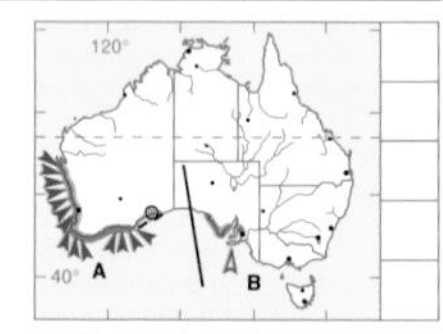

A = Race *petrophila* **E**
B = Race *zietzi* **E**

Orange-bellied Parrot *Neophema chrysogaster* **R O** E Endangered

Rich grass-green above. Broad two-tone blue frontal band to eye. Narrow deep violet-blue edge to folded wing. Greenish-yellow face, throat, breast. Yellow abdomen; variable orange centre, not always visible. **F** Light blue frontal band. **Juv.** Olive head, breast. **Size** 22–25 cm. **Voice** Rapid buzzing alarm call (diagnostic). **Hab.** Breeds (SW Tas.) in open-forest copses in heath. Winters in SE mainland coastal saltmarsh, dunes, damp grasslands.

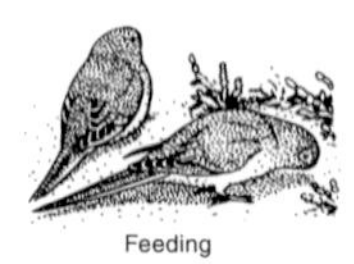

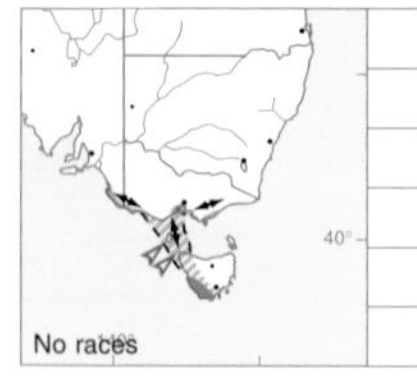

Turquoise Parrot *Neophema pulchella* **UC** ⁂ E

Turquoise blue crown, face. Bright green above. Two-tone blue on shoulder. Upperwing patch chestnut-red. Deep blue flight feathers. Upper breast has orange tint. Yellow abdomen may have orange centre. **F** Duller; whitish lores; no red on shoulder. **Size** 20–22 cm. **Juv.** Males some orange on shoulder. **Voice** Cicada-like buzzing. Fast 'zwee-zwee-zwee'. **Hab.** Open forests.

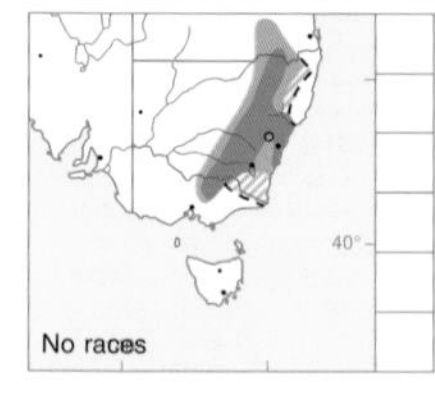

Scarlet-chested Parrot *Neophema splendida* **UC** ⁂ E

Bright blue face; darker on chin. Brilliant green above. Light blue shoulder. Breast scarlet; bright yellow below. **F/Juv./Imm.** Face, crown, less blue. Breast greenish. **Size** 19–21 cm. **Voice** Quiet twittering. Also 2-note 'pu-lick'. **Hab.** Mulga, mallee.

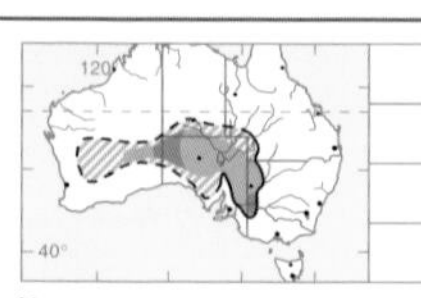

No races
Two possible breeding areas shown.

Bourke's Parrot ♂
Scarlet-chested Parrot ♀
Turquoise Parrot ♂
Turquoise Parrot ♀
Scarlet-chested Parrot ♂
Orange-bellied Parrot Juv.
Elegant Parrot
Orange-bellied Parrot
Blue-winged Parrot
Rock Parrot Juv.
Rock Parrot

Oriental Cuckoo *Cuculus saturatus* UC

Large cuckoo. Grey above; paler grey breast. Whitish belly, strongly barred black. Eye-ring, bill base, legs, feet, all bright yellow. Primaries grey, barred black. Long, dark grey tail, spotted edges, tipped white. Underwing white, barred black; leading edge white. **F** Like male. Some are **rufous morphs**, upperparts barred chestnut and black; strongly barred black below. **Size** 30–32 cm. **Juv.** Scalloped white above. **Voice** Allegedly silent in Aust. **Hab.** Forest, woodland. Palaearctic summer migrant to N Aust.

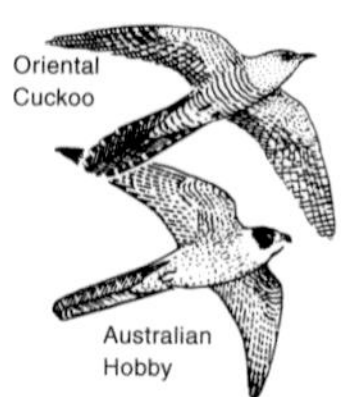

Flight comparison

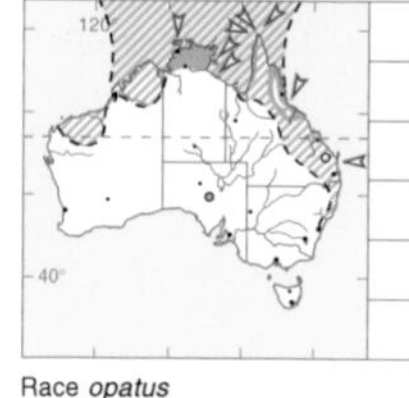

Race *opatus*

Pallid Cuckoo *Cuculus pallidus* MC E

Large cuckoo. Raises, lowers, tail on alighting. Grey above; white below. Black bill; dark grey eye-stripe. Yellow eye-ring. Pale eyebrow, nape. Tail dark grey, notched white. **F grey morph** As male. **F rufous morph** Heavily mottled brown, chestnut above. **Size** 31 cm. **Juv.** Boldly streaked dark brown, white. Grey below; buff breast, barred brown. **Voice** Male gives diagnostic mournful whistle, 8–10 notes dip, then ascend, accelerate. **Hab.** Woodland.

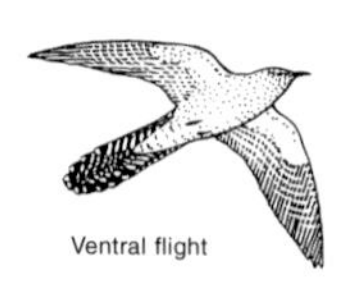
Ventral flight

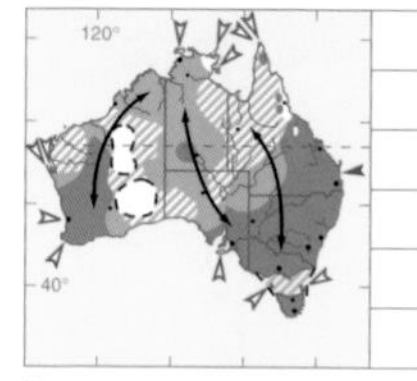

No races

Brush Cuckoo *Cacomantis (Cuculus) variolosus* MC

Grey eye-ring. Grey-brown above; pale grey below, tinged buff. Tail square, tipped white, no notches above; shorter than Fan-tailed. Undertail broadly barred brown, thin whitish notching on inner web. **F** Some have upperparts flecked white; barred below. **Size** 20–23 cm. **Juv./Imm.** Rufous, barred dark brown above (incl. tail); paler below. **Voice** 6–7 slow descending 'peee-up, peee-up'; mournful 'ther-er-weee' accelerating. **Hab.** Wetter forest, brush. Race *variolosus* migrates; *dumetorum* may not.

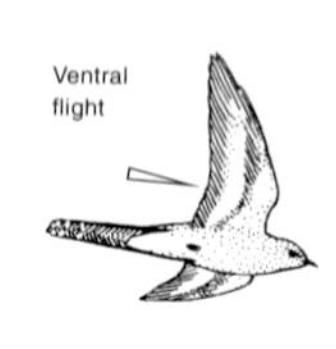
Ventral flight

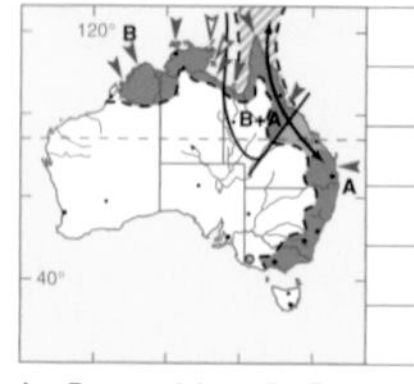

A = Race *variolosus* **Br. E**
B = Race *dumetorum* **Br. E**

Chestnut-breasted Cuckoo
Cacomantis (Cuculus) castaneiventris UC ◎ ?

Like Fan-tailed; smaller, rich chestnut below. Yellow eye-ring. Undertail bands broad. **Size** 22 cm. **Juv.** Grey-brown eye-ring. Chestnut above; pale cinnamon below. **Voice** Descending pulsing whistle, repeated after pause; 3-note 'chirryoo'. **Hab.** Rainforest.

Juv.

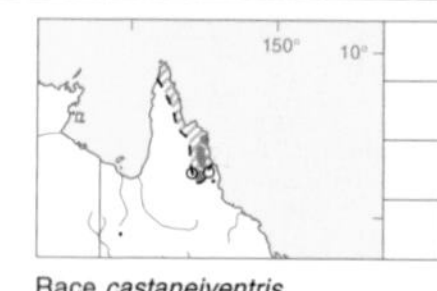

Race *castaneiventris*

Fan-tailed Cuckoo *Cacomantis (Cuculus) flabelliformis* C

Yellow eye-ring. Distinguish from Brush Cuckoo by notched, wedge-shaped tail, larger size, often brighter underparts. Dark grey above. Dull fawn-chestnut below. Tail wedge-shaped, strongly notched white. Undertail barred black and white. **Size** 24–28 cm. **Juv.** Dark brown above, barred reddish-brown. Head streaked dark brown. Finely barred grey and brown below. Distinguish from juv. Brush by yellow eye-ring; tail shape. **Voice** Mournful descending trill, repeated. Female contact call 'pree-ou-eeee, pree-ou-eeee', rising at end. **Hab.** Forest, woodland.

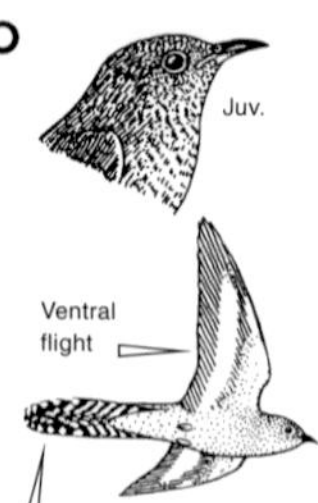
Juv.
Ventral flight

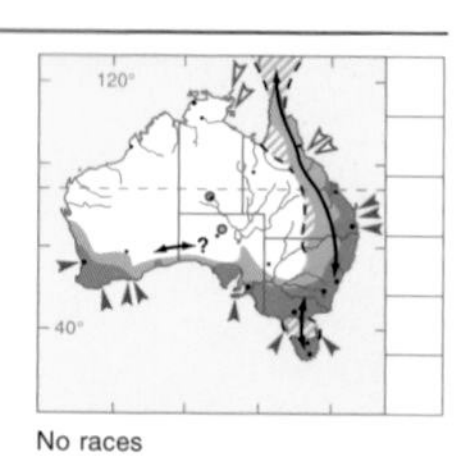

No races

Black-eared Cuckoo *Chalcites (Chrysococcyx) osculans* UC

Black eye-stripe, broadest behind eye. Whitish eyebrow, throat. Greyish above, with slight metallic sheen. Pale rump. Tail grey, tipped white. Cream below. Undertail barred black and cream. Check Tawny-crowned Honeyeater. Identify from juv. Horsfield's Bronze-Cuckoo by lack of rufous on tail, broader black eye-stripe, larger size. **Size** 19 cm. **Juv.** Duller brown eye-stripe. **Voice** Descending 'feeeuw' singly or repeated; lower, longer, more mournful than Horsfield's; rather like Brush Cuckoo call. Low 'pee-u-wu'. **Hab.** Inland; low bushes to dry forest.

Juv.
Ventral flight

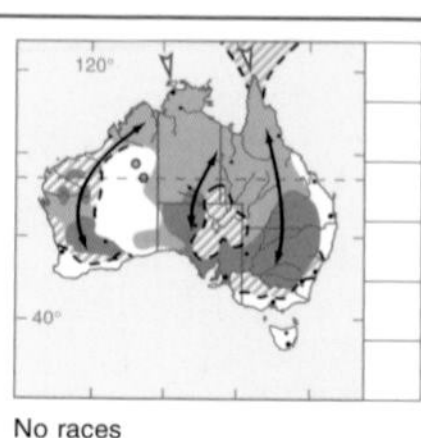

No races

Oriental Cuckoo ♀
Rufous morph
Oriental
Cuckoo ♂
Pallid Cuckoo ♀
Rufous morph
Pallid
Cuckoo
♂
Brush
Cuckoo
♂
Pallid
Cuckoo
Juv.
Fan-tailed
Cuckoo
Chestnut-
breasted
Cuckoo
Fan-tailed
Cuckoo
Juv.
Brush
Cuckoo
Juv.
Black-eared
Cuckoo

Horsfield's Bronze-Cuckoo
Chalcites (Chrysococcyx) basalis **C** Br. E

Check Black-eared Cuckoo. Bronze-sheen on back. Cap dull brown. Pale eyebrow. Eye-stripe dusky brown. Tail edged rufous. Cream below; incomplete bronze chest bars. Undertail black and white, rufous centre. **Size** 16 cm. **Juv.** Duller; sometimes lacks chest bars. **Voice** Descending whistle 'fee-ew'; shorter, higher than Black-eared. **Hab.** Open country, woodland.

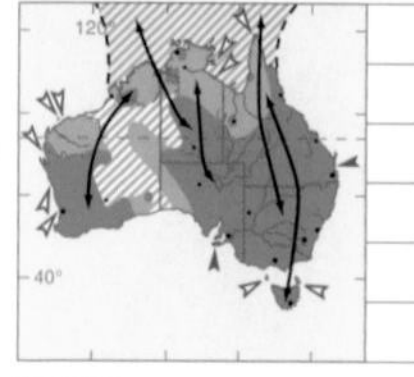
No races

Shining Bronze-Cuckoo *Chalcites (Chrysococcyx) lucidus* **C**

Metallic green 'cap'. No head contrast; white flecks on forehead prominent. Face, underparts white, complete green chest bars. Undertail black, white. Race *plagosus* (B) 'Golden Bronze-Cuckoo' Copper 'cap'. Bill more slender. May be pale spots on crown. Metallic green above. Complete bronze chest bars. No rufous in tail. **Juv.** Duller; flank bars only. **Size** 13–18 cm. **Voice** Tone more varied than Horsfield's. Repeated upward 'pweee, pweee', like whistling a dog. Falling 'pe-ee-ee-er'. **Hab.** Forest.

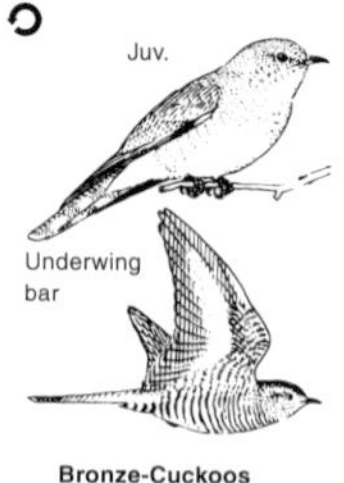

Bronze-Cuckoos

A = Race *lucidus*
B = Race *plagosus* **Br. E**
Both races migrate, with mixing in E. Aust.

Little Bronze-Cuckoo *Chalcites (Chrysococcyx) minutillus* **UC**

Metallic green above. Red eye-ring, eyes. White eyebrow. White below; chest bars complete. 3–4 black bars on white outer tail feathers; inner ones rusty, black sub-terminally, white tips. **F** Duller. Cream eye-ring; brown eye. **Size** 14–17 cm. **Juv.** As female; duller; flank bars only. **Voice** Six clear notes, falling fast in long trill. **Hab.** Forest, mangroves. Race *barnardi* (B) Migrant to NE Aust.

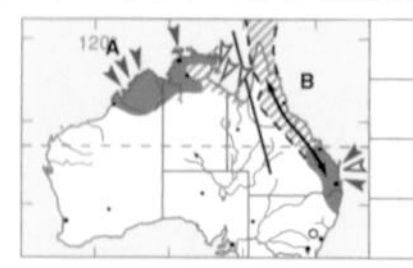
A = Race *minutillus* **E**
B = Race *barnardi* **Br. E**

Species composition and relationships of genus Chalcites *still under review. Little and Gould's hybridise. Previously* C. (C.) malayanus.

'Gould's Bronze-Cuckoo'
Chalcites (Chrysococcyx) minutillus russatus **UC**

Like Little; upperparts edged bronze. Side of chest pale to bright rust; chest bars bronze. Eyebrow buff. Rusty outer webs to tail. **F** Rusty breast, tail. **Size** As Little. **Juv.** As female, duller; bars only on flanks. **Voice** Shorter trill. **Hab.** Forest, mangroves.

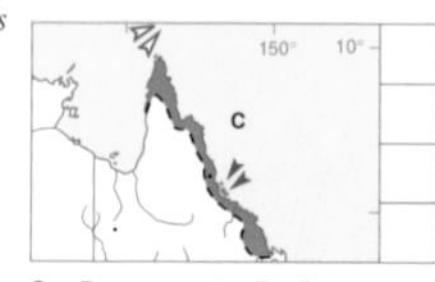
C = Race *russatus* **Br. E**
A race of Little Bronze-Cuckoo

Common Koel *Eudynamys scolopacea* **MC**

Glossy black; red eye; long tail. **F** Black cap. Brown above; spotted, barred white. Throat dark. White to buff below, thin brown bars. Some females mottled rufous-brown crown. **Size** 41 cm. **Juv.** Crown cream. Eye dark. Barred rufous above, large white spots. **Voice** Slow 'ko-weel, ko-weel'. Fast, rising 'wurra wurra wurra' from thick cover. **Hab.** Forest, tall trees, thickets.

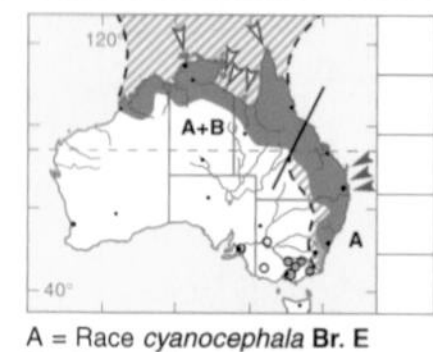
A = Race *cyanocephala* **Br. E**
B = Race *subcyanocephala* **Br. E**

Channel-billed Cuckoo *Scythrops novaehollandiae* **MC**

Very large. Often calls loudly in flight. Huge pale bill. Red iris, eye-ring. Grey, dark scalloped wings, long tail. White below, faintly barred black. **F** Belly strongly barred. **Size** 57–70 cm. **Juv.** Head, neck, wing-marks, pale buff. Some juv. overwinter in NE Qld. **Voice** Hoarse trumpet 'hoink, hoink'. **Hab.** Tall trees.

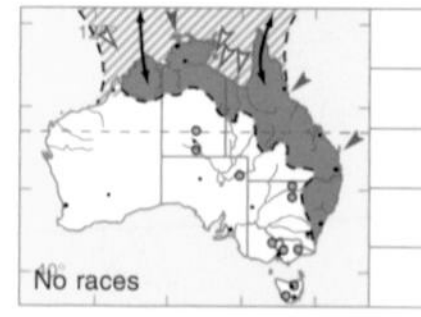
No races

Pheasant Coucal *Centropus phasianinus* **C**

Short bill. Red eye. Black head; underparts. Black barred rufous, cream, above. Long, pheasant-like tail. **Non-br.** Pale eye. Head, tail, rufous brown, streaked white. **Juv.** Head brown, spotted buff. **Size** M 54–63; F 54–68 cm. **Voice** Falling, quickening, deep 'boop boop boop' about 15 times (summer). Sharp, hissing 'physchit' (winter). **Hab.** Thick growth near streams, canefields.

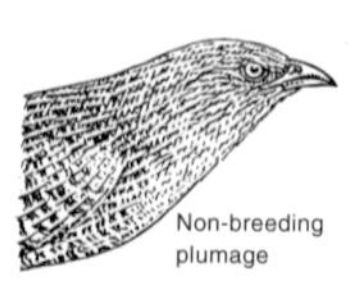

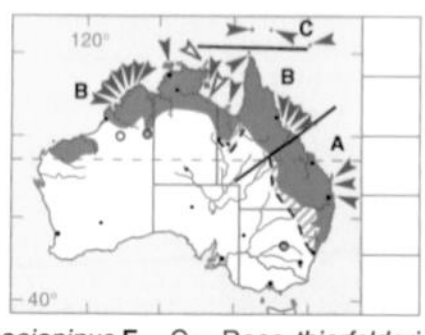
A = Race *phasianinus* **E** C = Race *thierfelderi*
B = Race *melanurus* **E**

Horsfield's Bronze-Cuckoo
Horsfield's Bronze-Cuckoo
Little Bronze-Cuckoo ♀
Race minutillus
Little Bronze-Cuckoo ♂
Race minutillus
Shining Bronze-Cuckoo
Race plagosus
Shining Bronze-Cuckoo
Race lucidus
'Gould's Bronze-Cuckoo' ♂
Race russatus
'Gould's Bronze-Cuckoo' ♀
Race russatus
Channel-billed Cuckoo ♂
Common Koel ♀
Common Koel ♂
Pheasant Coucal

Rufous Owl *Ninox rufa* **UC** ◎

Note All members of the Hawk Owl group have pale eyes.

Very large; rufous coloration. Often perched in pairs. Head large, rounded when feathers raised. Greenish-yellow eyes in indistinct facial mask. Upperparts very closely barred dark rufous-brown, buff. Underparts closely barred brownish-rufous and whitish. **F** Smaller. Race *meesi* (B) Smaller than *rufa*. Race *queenslandica* (C) Darker than *rufa*. **Size** M 55; F 46 cm. **Juv.** Head, underparts pure white, except distinct dark facial discs. **Voice** Slow double hoot; second note shorter. Female higher pitched. **Hab.** Closed forest, other dense vegetation, e.g. riparian monsoon forest.

Ventral flight

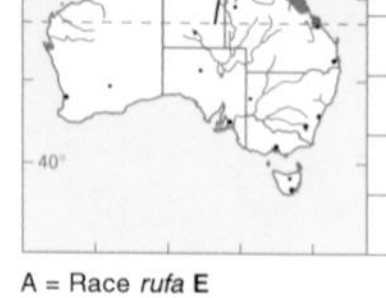

A = Race *rufa* **E**
B = Race *meesi* **E**
C = Race *queenslandica* **E**

Powerful Owl *Ninox strenua* **MC** ◎ E

Largest Australian owl. Pale with smallish, yellow eyes. Short, broad head. Often roosts in pairs in shaded parts of large trees of gullies; may be clutching part-eaten prey item. Slow, deliberate flight on huge wings. Upperparts, tail dark greyish-brown with indistinct off-white bars. Underparts whitish with dark greyish-brown chevrons. **F** Smaller. **Size** M 67; F 58 cm. **Juv.** White underparts and crown contrast with small dark streaks and dark eye patches. **Voice** Slow, resonant double hoot; second note lower in male. Female has upward inflection on higher second note of call. **Hab.** Tall open forest, woodland.

Ventral flight

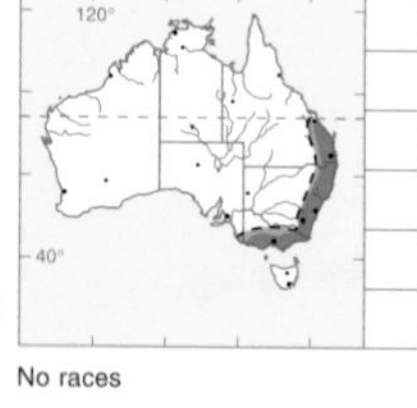

No races

Southern Boobook *Ninox boobook (novaeseelandiae)* **C** ◎

Goshawk-like flight. Eyes green-yellow or grey-green. Distinct, dark facial discs contrast sharply with surrounding pale borders. Upperparts dark chocolate-brown; upperwing coverts, scapulars spotted white. Underparts reddish-brown. Upper breast mottled buff, becoming reddish-brown. White-streaked belly. Small grey feet. Great variation within and between races. Race *ocellata* (B) North-western and central Aust. birds paler, more reddish; less clearly marked; south-western birds darker. Race *leucopsis* (C) Smaller, darker; mantle, breast more spotted. Eyes yellow. Some dispersal to mainland. Race *halmaturina* (D) Kangaroo Is.; adj. mainland. Race *lurida* (E) NE rainforests; small, darker, less spotted than *boobook*. **F** (all races) Larger; richer colour. **Size** 30–35 cm. **Juv.** Crown whitish, streaked darker centrally; facial discs very distinct. Underparts downy white; tawny wash on upper breast. **Voice** Falsetto double-hoot 'boo-book'; second note lower. Continuous croaking hoot. **Hab.** Woodland, forest, scrub.

Ventral flight

Southern Boobook

Tawny Frogmouth

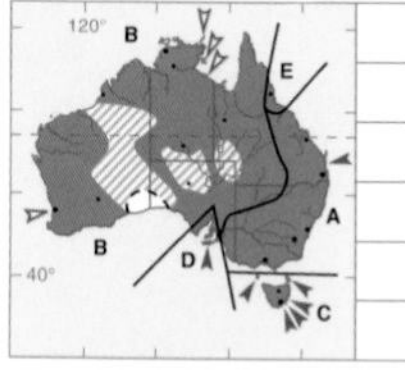

A = Race *boobook* **E**
B = Race *ocellata*
C = Race *leucopsis* **E**
D = Race *halmaturina* **E**
E = Race *lurida* **E**

Barking Owl *Ninox connivens* **MC** ◎

Large pale owl. Large bright yellow eyes. Almost no facial mask. Upperparts brownish-grey, coarsely spotted white. Flight feathers, tail, barred lighter. Underparts white, streaked brownish-grey. Large yellow feet. Race *peninsularis* (B) Smaller; underparts streaked rich rufous-brown. **F** Smaller. **Size** 39–44 cm. **Juv.** Incomplete white collar; flanks, breast streaked like adults. **Voice** Dog-like double bark; male at lower pitch, 'grr woof-woof', 'grr woof-woof'. Also wavering 'human' scream, rising grating trill, short yaps. **Hab.** Forest, woodland.

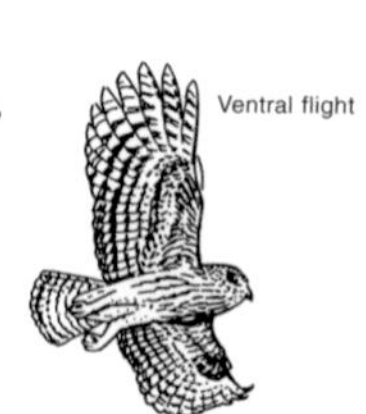
Ventral flight

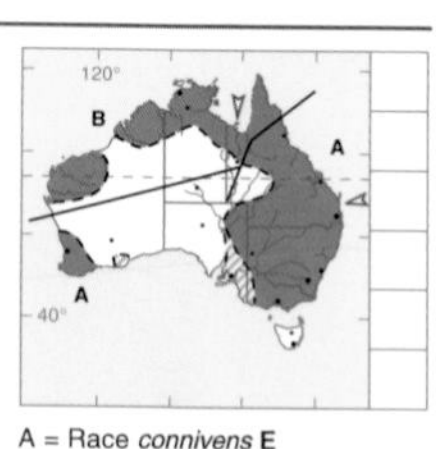

A = Race *connivens* **E**
B = Race *peninsularis* **E**

Brown Hawk-Owl *Ninox scutulata* see **Vagrant Bird Bulletin,** p. 297.

Rufous Owl
Rufous Owl
Juv.
Powerful Owl
Juv.
Powerful Owl
Southern Boobook
Race *lurida*
Southern Boobook
Race *leucopsis*
Southern
Boobook
Race *ocellata*
Southern
Boobook
Race
boobook
Barking Owl Juv.
Race *connivens*
Barking Owl
Race *connivens*
Barking Owl
Race
peninsularis
Southern
Boobook Juv.
Race *boobook*

Sooty Owl *Tyto tenebricosa* MC ◎

Note All members of the Barn Owl group have black eyes.
Active in canopy at night. Dark sooty-grey, spotted white. Round to heart-shaped pale to sooty grey disc, outlined black; very large eyes. Belly paler, mottled whitish. Stumpy tail. Strong feathered legs, powerful feet. **Size** M 33–36; F 38–43 cm. **Juv./Imm.** As adult. **Voice** Female has long descending whistle or scream (the famous 'falling bomb' call). Male call shorter than female's, less drop in pitch. Harsh screech like Masked. **Hab.** Well-vegetated gullies in tall wet forest. By day roosts in tree hollows, caves.

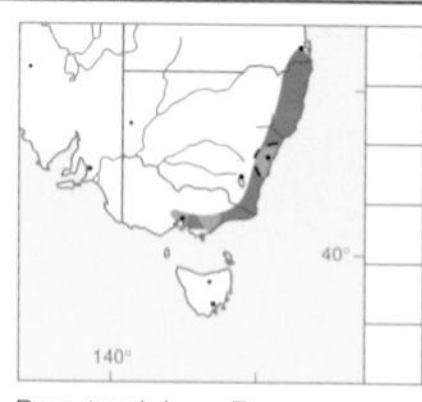

Race *tenebricosa* **E**

Lesser Sooty Owl *Tyto multipunctata* UC ◎ E

Much smaller than Sooty Owl; paler plumage, more spots, lighter feet. Disc outlined black, whitish near border, darkest near eyes. Upperparts coarsely, densely spotted. White breast washed grey. Underparts greyish-white, barred blackish-grey. Legs paler.
F Usually slightly larger than male. **Size** M 31–35; F 35–38 cm.
Voice Higher-pitched than Sooty. **Hab** Tropical rainforest.

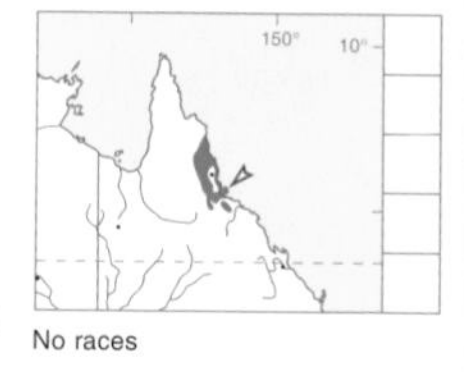

No races

Masked Owl *Tyto novaehollandiae* UC–R ♧

Active in middle storey. Round, dark-bordered mask. Dark 'tear-drop' near eyes. Powerful feet; crouched posture. Legs feathered. Plumage variable. In S Aust. 'dark' females, 'intermediate' males predominate. In N Aust. smaller 'intermediate' females, 'light' or 'white' males predominate. Three morphs may occur in range of each race: dark or tawny; intermediate; light or white.
Dark morph Chestnut disc. Upperparts blackish-brown, washed rufous, speckled white. Underparts pale rufous, coarsely dark-spotted. **Intermed. morph** Off-white disc. Upperparts blackish-brown, washed yellow, densely speckled white. Underparts off-white, coarsely dark-spotted. **Light morph** White disc. Pale grey upperparts, washed yellow, dark and white speckled. Underparts white, sparsely grey-flecked. **F** Larger, heavier, esp. bill, feet.
Size M 33–41; F 39–50 cm. **Voice** Male aerial display with chattering calls. Both sexes strong, harsh hissing 'kwooosh'; or more musical version. **Hab.** Forest, woodland. Caves, mature trees with hollows for roosting, nesting; by open, foraging areas.

Observers need be aware of Masked Owl sexual sizes and colour dimorphism, and also morph differences in the field.

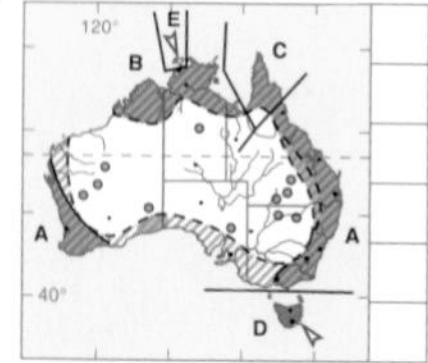

A = Race *novaehollandiae* **E**
B = Race *kimberli* **E**
C = Race *galei*
D = Race *castanops* **E Endangered**
E = Race *melvillensis* **E Endangered**
Probable breeding areas marked but overlain with hatching because extremely rare across whole of mainland range. More common in Tas.

Barn Owl *Tyto alba* C ♧

Only toes protrude beyond tail in flight. May hover. Almost white in spotlight; slim; upright posture. Small eyes. Rounded heart-shaped mask; narrow border, dark 'tear-drop'. Upperparts soft grey, patchily washed golden-fawn; fine black spots, white-tipped. Underparts white, sparsely dark-flecked. **F** Slightly brighter above; heavier spotting below. **Size** 29–38 cm.
Voice Rasping screech, as cockatoo. **Hab.** Grassland, crops, open and riparian woodland. Roosts tree hollows, out-buildings, caves.

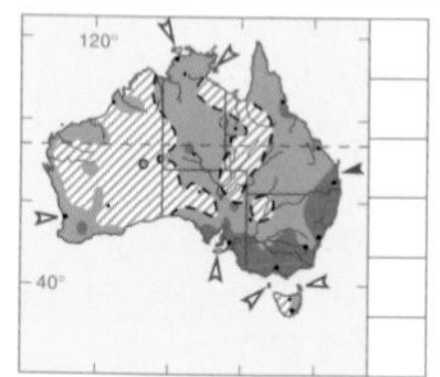

Race *delicatula* **Br. E**

Grass Owl *Tyto capensis* UC ♧

In flight, back darker than Barn; very long lower legs protrude well beyond tail. Slim; upright posture. Very small, black eyes. 'Long', heart-shaped mask; pale disc bordered brown and white. Dark tear marks. Upperparts dark brown, washed orange, white-spotted. Underparts white, finely dark-spotted. **F** Larger; disc, underparts, washed rufous. **Size** 30–38 cm. **Juv.** Dark, as female; face washed chocolate. **Voice** Harsh hissing (as Masked); cricket-like prolonged trilling. **Hab.** Swampy heath, tussock grassland, canefields, crops. Usually roosts and always breeds on ground.

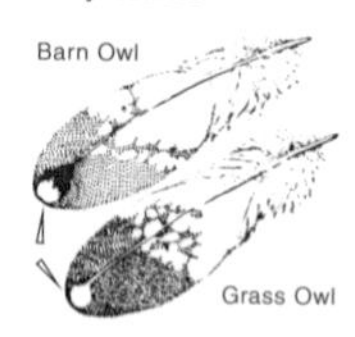

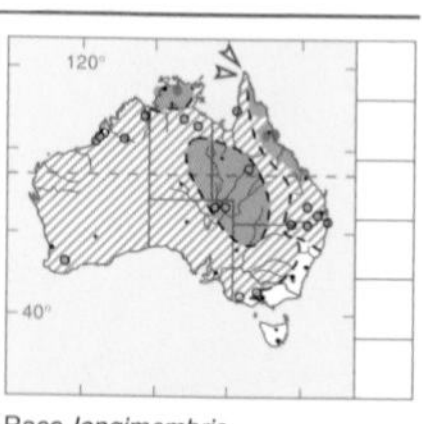

Race *longimembris*
Three isolated breeding populations. Occasional widespread dispersal.

Sooty Owl ♂
Lesser Sooty Owl ♂
Masked Owl ♀
Race *castanops*
Masked Owl ♀
Race *novaehollandiae*
Grass Owl
Barn Owl
Masked Owl ♂
Race
novaehollandiae
Barn Owl
Grass Owl ♀
Grass Owl ♂
Masked Owl ♂
Race *kimberli*
N. DAY.

Tawny Frogmouth *Podargus strigoides* **C** ◎ E

Cryptic grey-brown plumage like stringybark; marbled silver-grey with dark streaks. Flat crown. Broad bill; bristled frons. Yellow eye; pale brow. Long black malar stripe. Ungraduated short tail. Race *phalaenoides* (C) Very small. **F** Long brown malar stripe; no marbling below. **Rufous, chestnut morphs** All female. Check female Papuan, Marbled. **Size** 35–50 cm. **Nestl.** Speckled grey down. **Juv.** Sides of breast streaked. **Voice** Repeated low, resonant 'oom-oom ...'. **Hab.** Open woodland.

Ventral flight

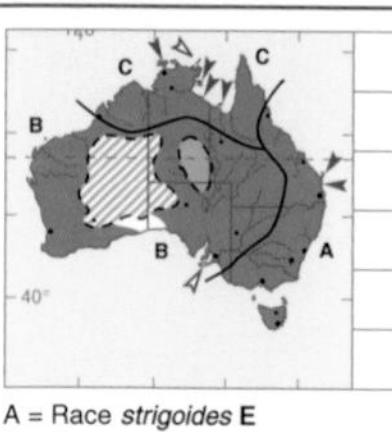

A = Race *strigoides* **E**
B = Race *brachypterus* **E**
C = Race *phalaenoides* **E**

Papuan Frogmouth *Podargus papuensis* **LMC** ◎

Largest frogmouth; biggest head, stoutest bill. Red eyes. Cream eyebrow. Grey to dark brown above, paler below; marbled white with black streaks. Long graduated barred tail. **F** Smaller, plainer, more rufous, finer markings. **Size** 50–60 cm. **Nestl.** Downy white to off-white. **Voice** Deep slow 'oom'; snaps bill. Hisses. **Hab.** Rainforest margins, gallery forest, mangroves. Often near water.

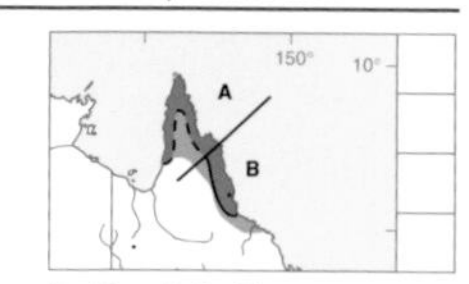

A = Race *baileyi* **E**
B = Race *rogersi* **E**

Marbled Frogmouth *Podargus ocellatus* **UC** ◎

Solitary. Race *plumiferus* (A) 'Plumed Frogmouth' Long, banded facial plumes. Black crown, malar stripes. Buff-white eyebrow. Deep rufous-brown to greyish above, speckled brown, softly marbled cream. Pale marbling below, finely edged black. Long graduated tail. Race *marmoratus* (B) 'Marbled Frogmouth' Smaller; longer tail. **F** Browner, plainer. **Size** 30–45 cm. **Juv.** Downy; rufous brown; dark loral stripe. **Voice** Repeated 'coo-lew'. 'Coop-coop' before gobbles, then bill-clap. Rapid drumming. **Hab.** Rainforest.

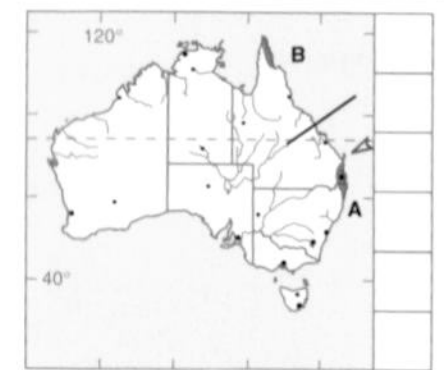

A = Race *plumiferus* **E**
B = Race *marmoratus* **E**

White-throated Nightjar *Eurostopodus mystacalis* **MC** ↻

Some loose flocks. Bill black. Eye brown; most highly reflective of our nightjars. Dark grey above; black, sandy, whitish spots, patches, bars. Pointed wings; primaries have small white spots. Black throat; white patches at sides. Dark below, fine grey bars on breast, grading to cinnamon undertail coverts. **Size** 30–35 cm. **Juv./Imm.** Duller, redder. **Voice** Rising 'whook-whook-whook' accelerates to 'laughter'. Low crooning. **Hab.** Forest, woodland.

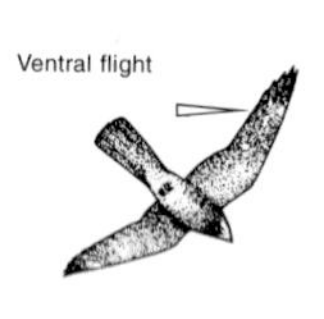
Ventral flight

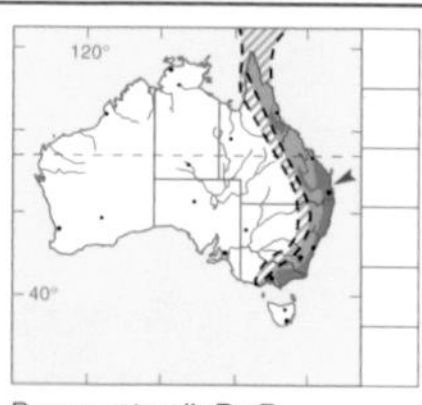

Race *mystacalis* **Br. E**

Spotted Nightjar *Eurostopodus argus* **MC** ↻ ? Br. E

May flock. Like White-throated; smaller. All-white throat. Large white wing spot. Rounded wings. **Size** 30 cm. **Juv./Imm.** Paler, duller, more rufous. **Voice** Higher than White-throated. Rising 'wook-wook-wook-pukka-pukka-pukka'. Low staccato thudding. **Hab.** Open forest, woodland, scrubs, deserts.

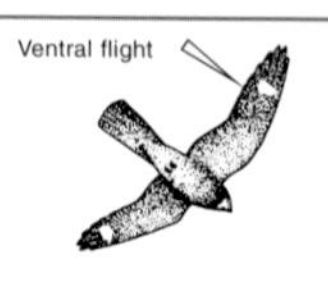
Ventral flight

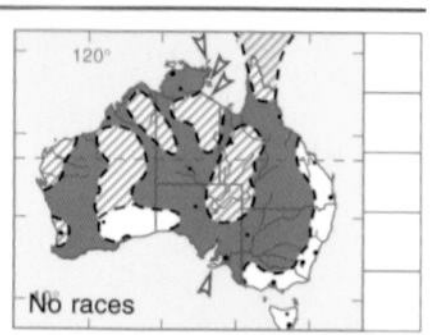

Large-tailed Nightjar *Caprimulgus macrurus* **MC** ⁂–?◎

Smaller, greyer nightjar with large white wing and tail-tip spots. Rounded wings. Throat as Spotted. **Size** 27 cm. **Voice** Echoing, monotonous 'chrop, chrop, chrop'. **Hab.** Tropical woodland margins; coastal and sub-coastal areas.

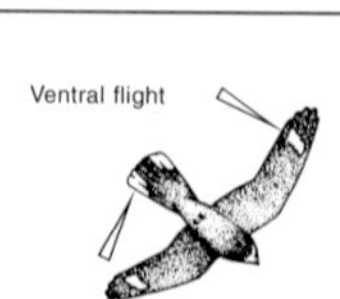
Ventral flight

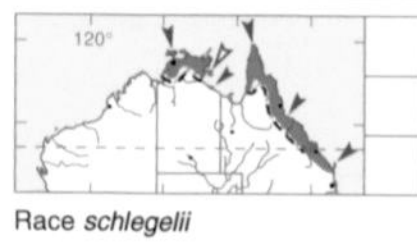

Race *schlegelii*

Australian Owlet-nightjar *Aegotheles cristatus* **C** ◎

Delicate, nocturnal. Large non-reflective brown eye. Small, broad bill, 'whiskery'. Head 'possum-like'; three dark stripes on crown meet dark collar. Grey to rufous, finely barred blackish above; pale below. **Four morphs** Light grey, rufous grey on mainland; rufous arid inland; dark grey coastal. **Size** 21–24 cm. **Voice** Strident churring; softer yelps, squeaks. **Hab.** Trees with hollows.

Dorsal flight

A = Race *cristatus*
B = Race *tasmanicus* **E**
Vulnerable

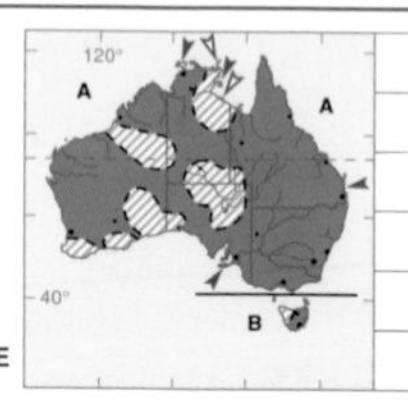

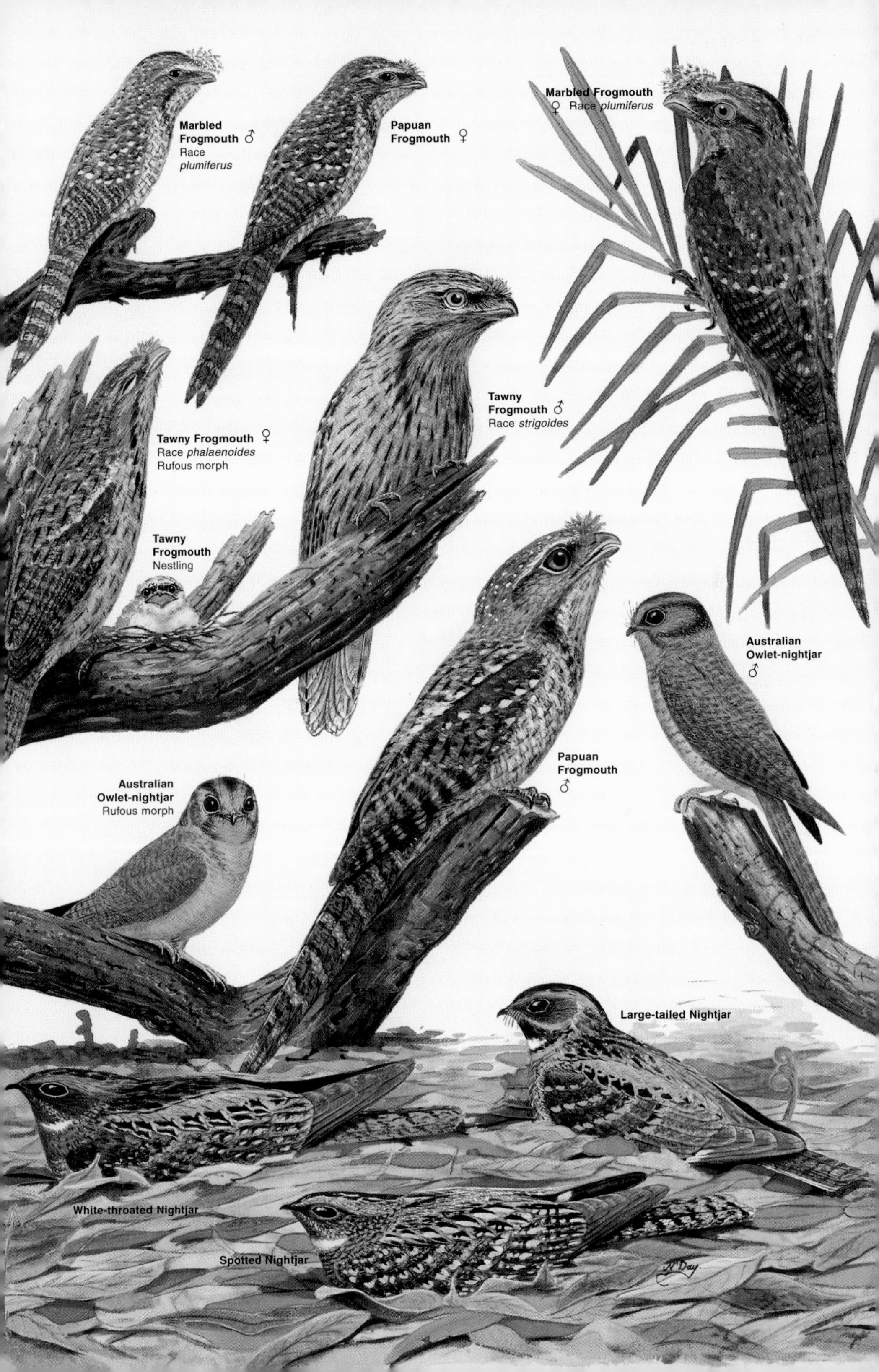
Marbled Frogmouth ♂
Race plumiferus
Papuan Frogmouth ♀
Marbled Frogmouth
♀ Race plumiferus
Tawny Frogmouth ♂
Race strigoides
Tawny Frogmouth ♀
Race phalaenoides
Rufous morph
Tawny Frogmouth
Nestling
Australian Owlet-nightjar
♂
Papuan Frogmouth
♂
Australian Owlet-nightjar
Rufous morph
Large-tailed Nightjar
White-throated Nightjar
Spotted Nightjar

Glossy Swiftlet *Aerodramus (Collocalia) esculenta* UC ?

Note Sexes of swiftlets, swifts, indistinguishable in the field. Aerial foragers.

Smallest swiftlet. View both surfaces to identify from White-rumped. Shiny black-blue above, to rump; may look black, hooded. Wing tips rounded. Tail rounded with shallow notch. Tiny pale tail panels. Chest black. Belly to flanks white, fine black speckles at edges. Underwing black. **Size** 9–11 cm. **Voice** Soft twittering. **Hab.** Feeds over northern coastal ranges, islands.

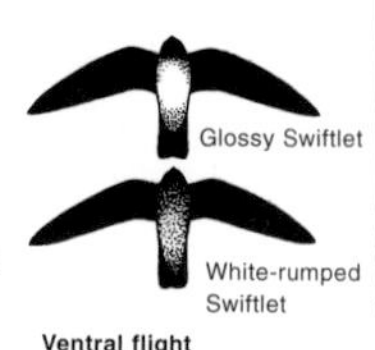

Ventral flight

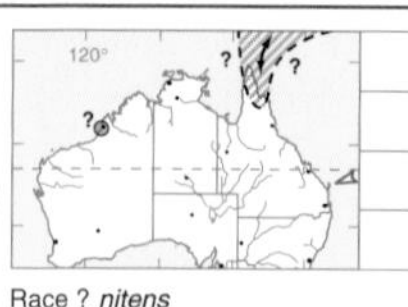

Race ? *nitens*
Racial identity of these swiftlets is uncertain.

White-rumped Swiftlet *Aerodramus (Collocalia) spodiopygius* LC

Small. Often about squalls, fast-rising clouds. Dark grey-brown above. Long black wings slightly glossy. Looks black, stiff-winged in flight. Wings in anhedral posture when gliding. Shallow fork in tail. Rump pale grey. Tail black. Grey chin, throat, breast; belly, vent paler. In sunlight, underside may look whitish. Race *chillagoensis* (B) Breeds at Chillagoe (NE Qld). Darker above; paler belly. **Size** 10–12 cm. **Voice** Chips, twitters. **Hab.** Forages over tropical coastal ranges, cliffs, grassland, islands. Echo-locates in totally dark breeding caves.

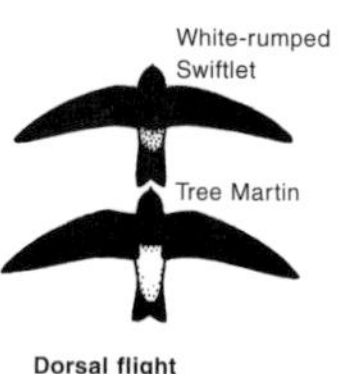

Dorsal flight

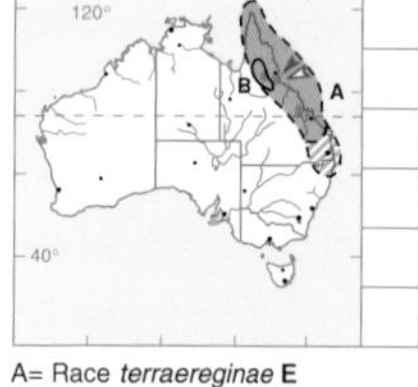

A= Race *terraereginae* **E**
B= Race *chillagoensis* **E**

Uniform Swiftlet *Aerodramus (Collocalia) vanikorensis* R–UC ?

Inseparable in field from similar New Guinea, Asian swiftlets. All grey-brown; upperparts darker with faint metallic sheen; rump slightly paler. Tail has very shallow fork. Throat, undertail paler than belly. **Size** 13 cm. **Voice** Soft twittering. **Hab.** Over coastal ranges and islands. Only one specimen reliably recorded in Aust.

Ventral flight

When unidentified, completely dark swiftlets are seen, take data on subtle body colour changes, shape, flight actions, calls, and size comparisons with other swiftlets; locality and date.

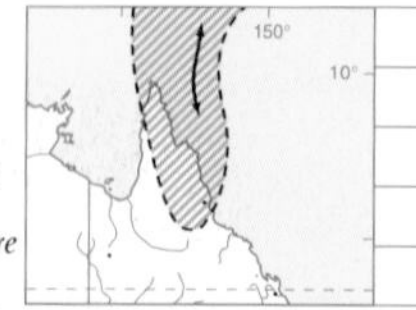

Race *yorki*

White-throated Needletail *Hirundapus caudacutus* C

Largest swift in Aust. Flies with flickering wing strokes, then long raking glides; slow turns with tail fanned wide. Frons pale grey. Body dark with white throat, vent, flanks. Tertiary feather edges white. Back, rump brown. Rest of upperparts have glossy green sheen. Wings swept back (curved, anchor-shaped); tips pointed. Tail black, rounded tip. **Size** 20 cm. **Juv.** Brown frons; fine brown tips to lateral undertail coverts (visible in hand only). **Voice** Strident high chatter. **Hab.** Usually over forested coastal and mountain regions; also farmland, orchards.

Perched
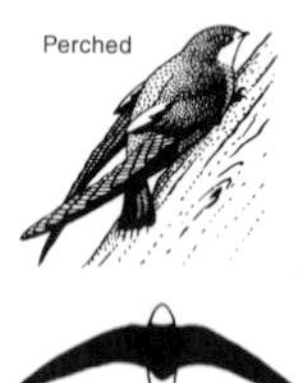

Ventral flight

Race *caudacutus*

Prior name 'Spine-tailed Swift'. This species, and Fork-tailed Swift, breed in North Asia during our winter.

Fork-tailed Swift *Apus pacificus* C

Singles or flocks. Sometimes travels, feeds, with Needletails. Flight less powerful, 'drifting'. Body slimmer than White-throated Needletail; appears dappled if seen closely. Dark, sooty-coloured; pale throat; white rump. Wing-tips pointed. Tail long, thin; deeply forked when fanned; fork invisible when tail closed. **Size** 18–?21 cm. **Voice** Not often heard. Twittering, buzzing. **Hab.** Varied; possible tendency to more arid areas. Rarely, under conditions of heat and strong winds, observed in long straggling flocks numbering thousands. Also over coasts, urban areas.

Ventral flight

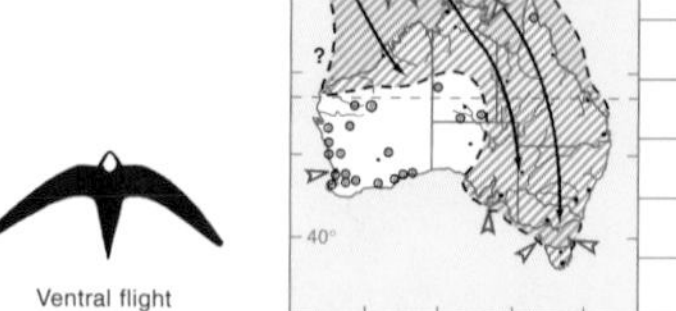
Race *pacificus*

House Swift *Apus affinis* R

Aerial. Smaller, stockier; proportionately broader-winged than Fork-tailed Swift. Identify from martins. Dark grey; appears black. Like Fork-tailed Swift with white rump and throat, but tail shorter, very shallowly forked, becoming square when fanned. **Size** 15 cm. **Voice** Shrill rattling trill. **Hab.** Over open areas. Increasingly reported and almost certainly a more regular visitor than the single specimen and six confirmed sight records suggest.

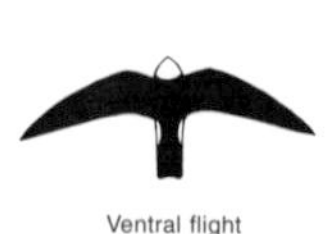
Ventral flight

Race *nipalensis*

Glossy Swiftlet
Glossy Swiftlet
White-rumped Swiftlet
Race *chillagoensis*
Uniform Swiftlet
White-rumped Swiftlet
Race *terraereginae*
White-rumped Swiftlet
Race *terraereginae*
Uniform Swiftlet
White-throated Needletail
White-throated Needletail
White-throated Needletail
White-throated Needletail
White-throated Needletail
Fork-tailed Swift
Fork-tailed Swift
Fork-tailed Swift
Fork-tailed Swift
House Swift
House Swift
N. DAY.

Azure Kingfisher *Alcedo azurea* **MC** ◎–↻

Swift flight, low over water. Long black bill. Rufous spot before eyes. Buff-white plume on sides of neck, become 'eyespots' when seen from rear. Upperparts, sides of chest, dark blue. Pale throat. Underparts orange/rufous (variable). Legs bright orange. **Size** 16–19 cm. **Juv.** Duller. **Voice** High insect-like trill. **Hab.** Rivers, creeks, mangroves.

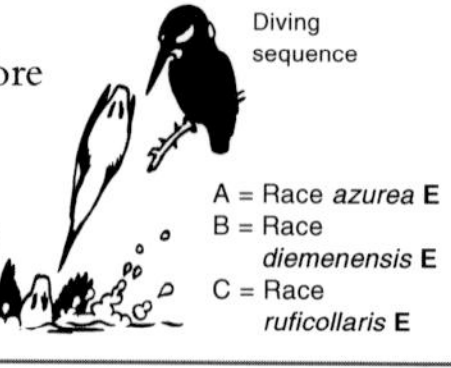

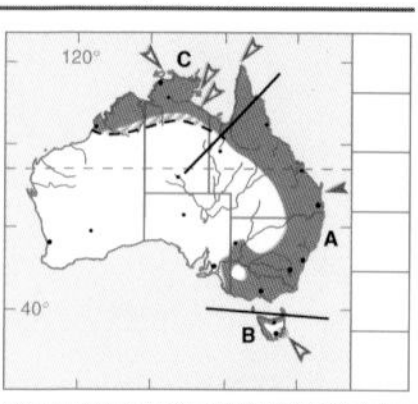

Little Kingfisher *Alcedo pusilla* **UC** ◎

Smallest in Aust. Flies slower, lower, than Azure, usually in dense cover. Long black bill. White spot before eyes, white plume on sides of neck. Upperparts violet-blue. Underparts white. Legs black. Race *halli* (B) Larger, darker violet-blue. Race *ramsayi* (C) Upperparts less violet; half to full blue breast band. **Size** 11–13 cm. **Juv.** Duller; legs pink. **Voice** Calls in flight; shriller than Azure. **Hab.** Well-vegetated creeks, swamps, mangroves.

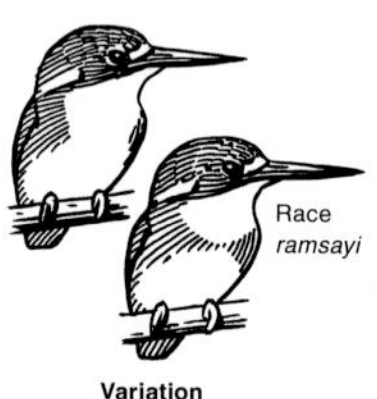

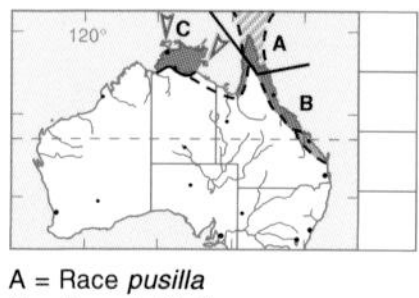

A = Race *pusilla*
B = Race *halli* E
C = Race *ramsayi* E

Laughing Kookaburra *Dacelo novaeguineae* **C** ◎–?↻ E

Largest kingfisher. Families 4–8 birds. White wing patches in heavy direct flight. Tail up on alighting, slowly lowered. Massive bill, black above, horn below. Dark eye-stripe. Large pale head; brown spots, crown patch. Back, wings, brown; wings mottled pale blue. Often blue rump. Tail barred rufous-brown and black; edged white. Plain white below. **M br.** Centre rump bright blue. Race *minor* (B) Smaller. **F** Brown or pale blue rump; head more buff. **Size** 40–48 cm. **Juv.** More barred, washed warm brown. All black bill. **Imm.** As female. **Voice** Raucous 'koo-koo-ka-ka-kook' chorus, warning 'kooaa'. **Hab.** Open forest, woodland.

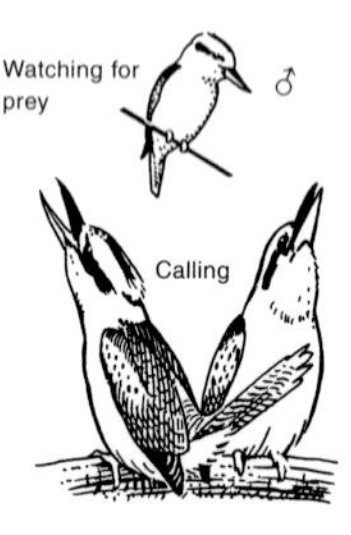

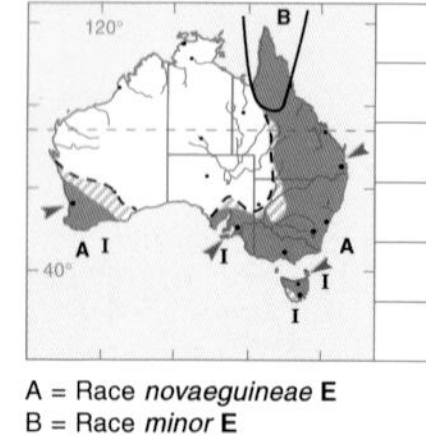

A = Race *novaeguineae* E
B = Race *minor* E

Blue-winged Kookaburra *Dacelo leachii* **C** ◎–⚘

White wing patches in flight. Massive bill. Large creamy head, streaked brown (some look brown-headed). Pale eye, no dark eye stripe. Back brown, lower back light blue. Light blue shoulders, rump. Wings mostly blue. Tail deep blue, white tip. Fine barring on neck, underparts. **F/Imm.** Larger. Tail rufous-brown, barred dark blue. Race *occidentalis* (B) Larger. Thinner streaks, whiter head. **Size** 39 cm. **Juv.** Head buffy; underparts more scalloped. **Voice** Harsh, cackling scream with twittering. Female deeper than male. **Hab.** Woodland, open forest, paperbark swamps.

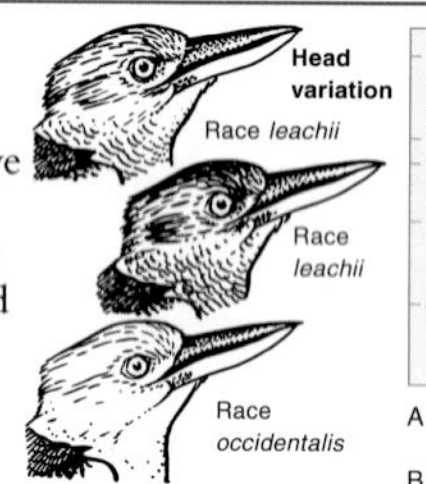

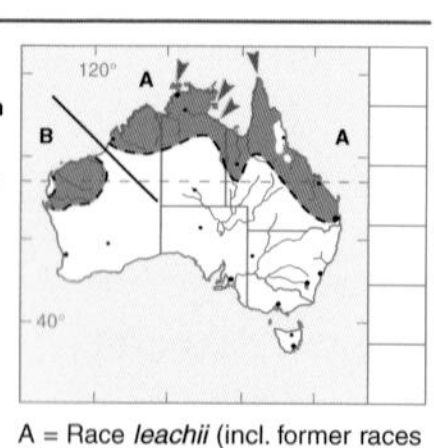

A = Race *leachii* (incl. former races *cervina, kempi*)
B = Race *occidentalis* (prior *cliftoni*)

Rainbow Bee-eater *Merops ornatus* **C** ↻

Bright green and rufous. Hawks insects. Rufous wings in flight. Bill black. Red eye. Black eye-stripe, edged blue. Rufous crown. Black band on yellow throat. Back light green, rump blue. Black tail; extended thin central feathers. **F** Some plumaged like males. Shorter tail, blue centre. Broader throat-band, blue below. **Size** 22–25 cm incl. streamers. **Juv.** Throat band absent or dusky. Lacks streamers. **Voice** Melodious trilling 'prrrt-prrrit' in flight. **Hab.** Open country, most vegetation types; sand dunes, banks.

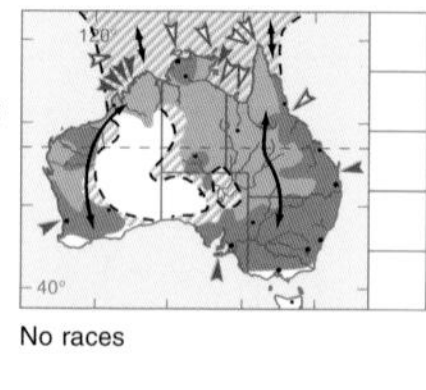

No races

Dollarbird *Eurystomus orientalis* **MC** ↻

Perches high on dead branches, hawks insects. Chunky body, stout bill, square tail. Tumbling, rolling flight shows pale blue 'dollars' on wings. Brown head grades to blue-green body, dull on saddle, brighter on wings, rump. Blue-violet on throat, wings, tail. Red bill, eye-ring, legs. **Non-br.** Bill less red. **Size** 26–29 cm. **Juv.** Duller. Lacks violet throat. Dark bill, legs. **Voice** Harsh accelerating nasal yap; churring. **Hab.** Woodland, watercourses.

Perches prominently

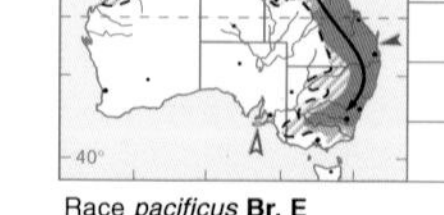

Race *pacificus* **Br. E**

Laughing
Kookaburra
Juv.
Laughing
Kookaburra
Ad.
Laughing
Kookaburra
♂
Blue-winged
Kookaburra ♂
Race accidentalis
Blue-winged
Kookaburra ♂
Race leachii
Blue-winged
Kookaburra
♀
Little Kingfisher
Juv.
Race halli
Azure Kingfisher
Juv.
zure Kingfisher
Ad.
Little
Kingfisher
♂ Race halli
Little Kingfisher
♂ Race ramsayi
Dollarbird
Juv.
Dollarbird
Rainbow
Bee-eater
Juv.
Rainbow
Bee-eater
♂
Rainbow
Bee-eater
♂
Dollarbird
Ad. Breeding

Red-backed Kingfisher *Todiramphus pyrrhopygia* **C** ♁ E

Bill black, pale lower base. Erectile crown feathers olive-green streaked white. Black eye-stripe to nape. Collar, underparts white. Dull green back. Wings, tail blue-green. Lower back, rump, uppertail coverts rufous. **F** Shorter 'crest'. Crown darker, heavily streaked; collar, flanks, tinged buff. **Size** 23 cm. **Juv.** More buff; dark mottled breast. **Voice** Repeated mournful whistle; harsh chatter. **Hab.** Dry open woodland.

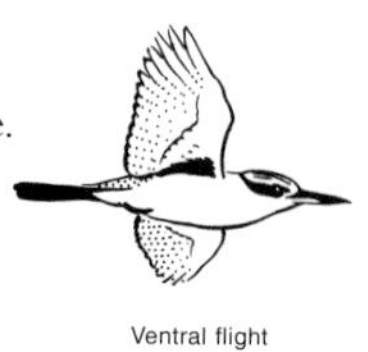
Ventral flight

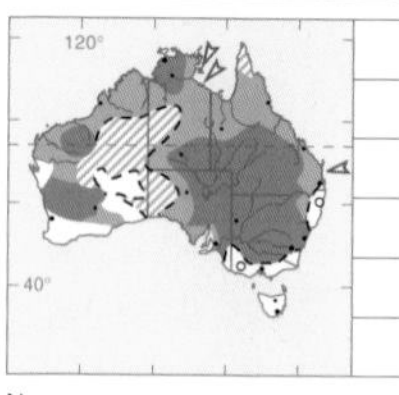

No races

Forest Kingfisher *Todiramphus macleayii* **C** ⟲

Often in pairs. White wing spot in flight. Bill black, pale lower base. White spot before eye. Broad black stripe, bill to ear coverts. Head, wings, tail, rich blue. Back, rump, blue. Throat, collar, underparts white. Belly, flanks, may be washed buff. **F** White collar incomplete. Race *incinctus* (B) Turquoise back. Smaller wing spot. **Size** 18–21 cm. **Juv.** Forehead, shoulders, fine buff scallops. Head, wing spot, underparts, buff. Sides of breast scalloped grey. **Voice** Rapid high whistles, strident chatter. **Hab.** Coastal open forest, wooded swamps, mangrove, woodland.

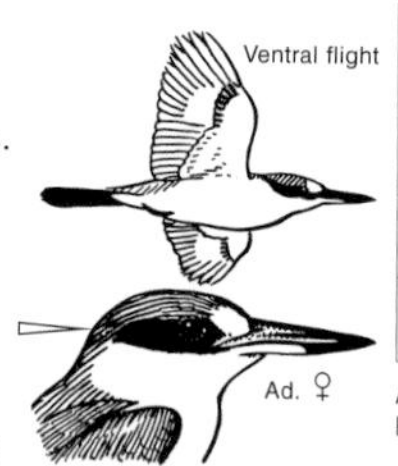

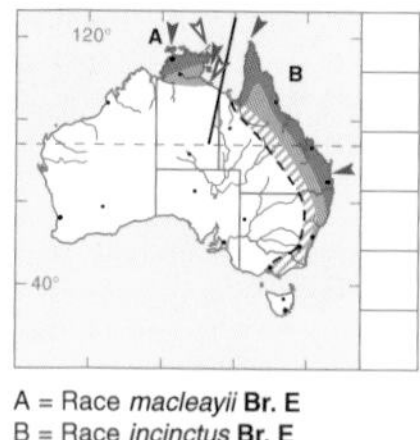

A = Race *macleayii* **Br. E**
B = Race *incinctus* **Br. E**

Collared Kingfisher *Todiramphus chloris* **C** ?⟲

Strongly marked green/black/white; stockier, larger than Sacred; longer, heavier bill. Head, back, green. White spot before eye. Black band through eye to nape. Collar, underparts white. Green, blue on wings; tail blue. **F** Duller. Races *sordidus* (B), *pilbara* (C) Progressively browner, from N Aust to Pilbara coast, WA. **Size** 23–27 cm. **Juv./Imm.** Collar, breast speckled brown. **Voice** As Sacred, slower, more strident. **Hab.** Mangrove, coastal.

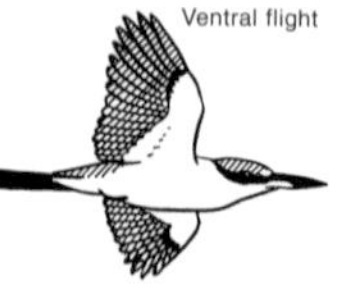

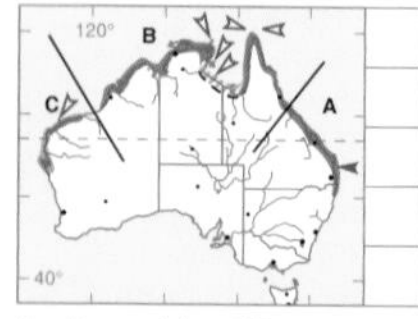

A = Race *colcloughi* **E**
B = Race *sordidus*
C = Race *pilbara* **E**

Sacred Kingfisher *Todiramphus sanctus* **C** ⟲

Buff spot before eye. Black band through eye to nape. White collar has buff tinge. Crown, back green. Wings, rump, tail blue. In new plumage, underparts scalloped buff, becomes whiter. **F** Greener above. **Size** 21 cm. **Juv./Imm.** Fine buff scallops. **Voice** Loud repeated 'kek-kek-kek'. Rising 'kee-kee-kee' duets near nest. **Hab.** Eucalypt, paperbark forest; woodland; mangrove.

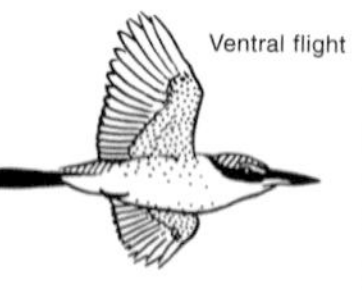

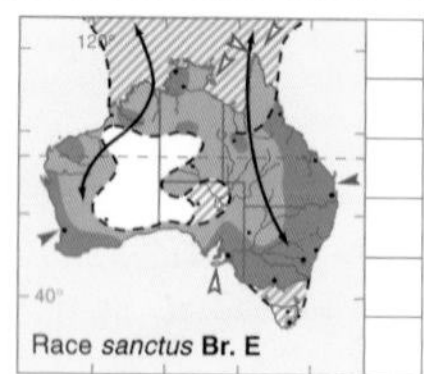

Race *sanctus* **Br. E**

Yellow-billed Kingfisher *Syma torotoro* **UC** ◎

Bright orange and green bird. Rusty head. Black eye-ring, nape mark. Yellow bill, legs. Back, wings, green. Rump, tail blue. Underparts orange. **F** Black patches on crown and nape. Belly paler. **Size** 19–21 cm. **Juv.** Eye-ring skin pale blue. Dark bill; dusky black nape patch. **Voice** Loud, descending trill, like Fan-tailed Cuckoo. Brief chirrp. **Hab.** Rainforest edges.

May cock tail up when calling

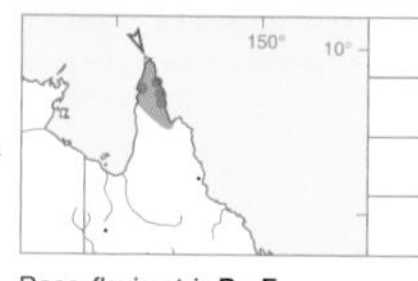

Race *flavirostris* **Br. E**

Buff-breasted Paradise-Kingfisher *Tanysiptera sylvia* **UC** ⟲

Look near terrestrial termite nests. Fly low through canopy. Spectacular blue/black/rufous, with long tail. Bill orange-red. Black eye band to nape. Crown, wings, purple-blue. Shoulders blue-black; white back shows as 'triangle'. Rump white. Tail dark blue, white streamers. Rich rufous underwing coverts and underparts. Legs orange-red. **F** Slightly duller; pale buff 'triangle'; shorter streamers. **Size** M 36 cm with tail streamers; F 30 cm. **Juv.** Face mask indistinct. Dark bill; body brown, blackish striated breast. Very short tail. **Imm.** Dark bill; crown, wings dull blue; short grey tail. **Voice** Repeated rising piping. Descending alarm trills near nest. **Hab.** Lowland rainforest.

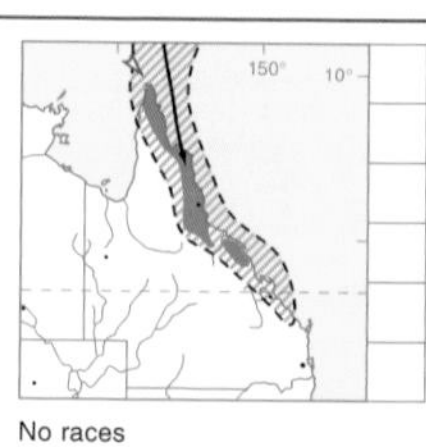

No races

Buff-breasted Paradise-Kingfisher ♂
Buff-breasted Paradise-Kingfisher Juv.
Buff-breasted Paradise-Kingfisher
Yellow-billed Kingfisher ♂
Yellow-billed Kingfisher ♀
Forest Kingfisher ♂ Race *incinctus*
Red-backed Kingfisher ♂
Red-backed Kingfisher ♂
Red-backed Kingfisher Juv.
Forest Kingfisher Juv.
Forest Kingfisher
Sacred Kingfisher ♂
Collared Kingfisher ♂ Race *colcloughi*
Sacred Kingfisher Juv.
Collared Kingfisher Juv.
N. DAY.

Red-bellied Pitta *Pitta erythrogaster* **UC** ○

Frons, crown, mid-brown. Bright rufous nape. Shoulders, rump, chest, bright blue. Black chest band, red belly. Back, wings, tail blue-green. Legs dark grey. **Size** 17–19.5 cm. **Juv.** Olive-brown above; tail bluish-grey. White throat band; scalloped pale brown below. Colours appear with increasing age. **Voice** Slow 'kuraah-kraah-raah' rising, falling. **Hab.** Tropical closed forest, scrubs.

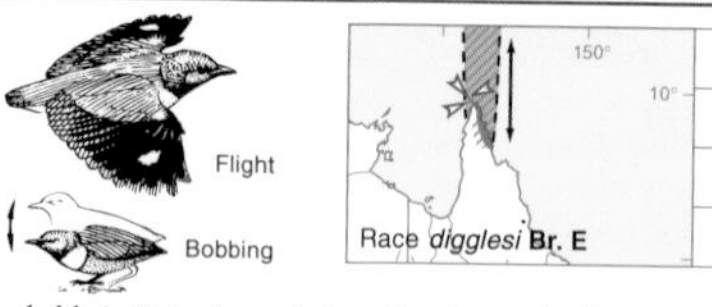

'Thrush-like', Pittas have dark underwing with white patch conspicuous in swift, direct flight. Forage, breed, close to ground.

Noisy Pitta *Pitta versicolor* **MC** ◎

Black face, throat. Crown chestnut, black central stripe. Green above; shoulders, rump, iridescent turquoise. Buff below; black central stripe extends to red vent. Short green tail. Long flesh-pink legs. **Size** 18–26 cm. Clinal, N Aust. birds smaller. **Juv.** Black and olive-green; duller. **Voice** Loud whistle 'walk-to-work'; high alarm 'keow'. **Hab.** Rainforest, scrubs.

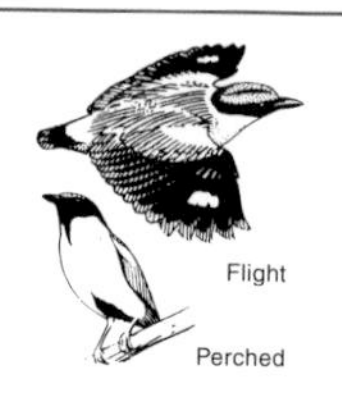

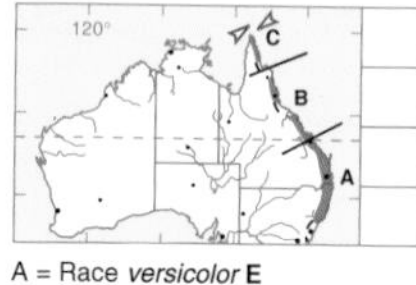

A = Race *versicolor* E
B = Race *intermedia* E
C = Race *simillima*

Rainbow Pitta *Pitta iris* **MC** ◎ E

Like Noisy Pitta; black underparts. **Size** 16–18 cm. **Juv.** Orange gape; duller. **Voice** Shriller than Noisy. **Hab.** Closed forests, thick vine-scrub, mangrove edges; remnant, wet vegetation.

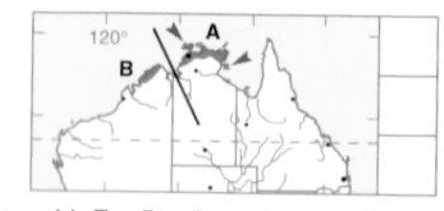

A = Race *iris* E B = Race *johnstoneiana* E

Albert's Lyrebird *Menura alberti* **LC** ◎ E Vulnerable

Extremely wary. Smaller than Superb Lyrebird. Rich rufous-brown above; rufous throat. Buff-grey below. Male displays on vine-stem platforms. Tail filamentaries blackish-brown above, silver below. Outer 'lyre' dark, broad, plain. **F/Juv./Imm.** Tail without filamentous feathers. **Size** (incl. tail) M 86–90, F 65–75 cm. **Voice** Not unlike Superb. **Hab.** Rainforests and edges.

No races

Superb Lyrebird *Menura novaehollandiae* **MC** ◎–?♧ E

Ground foragers. Male performs spectacular courtship displays on earthen 'dancing' mounds. Dark brown above; grey-brown below. Long silver filamentous tail feathers; two outer 'lyre' feathers banded chestnut, white and black. Long grey legs; powerful feet. **F/Juv./Imm.** Smaller; shorter plain grey-brown tail without filamentous plumes. **Size** (incl. tail) M 85–103, F 76–80 cm. **Voice** Own voice: 'ch-wik, ch-wik'; metallic whirring with deep thudding; clear whistle. Also loud, protracted, complex song with expert mimicry. **Hab.** Prefer wetter forest areas.

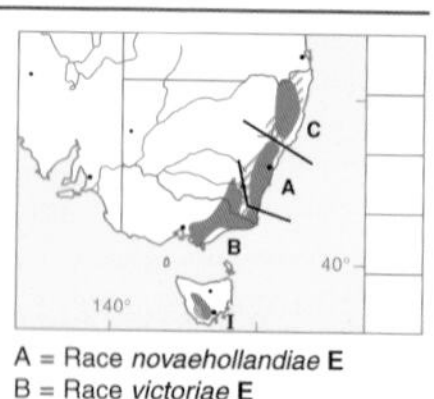

A = Race *novaehollandiae* E
B = Race *victoriae* E
C = Race *edwardi* E
Introduced to southern Tasmania

Rufous Scrub-bird *Atrichornis rufescens* **R** ◎ E

Elusive. Appears soft-plumaged. Rufous-brown with fine black bars (vermiculation). Soft black and white throat mark; chest blackish to sides of abdomen. Tail often 'cocked'. **F** No black markings; throat whitish. **Size** 17–18.5 cm. **Juv.** Plainer; greyish throat. **Voice** Loud territorial calls; low chatter; mimicry. **Hab.** Dense, often secondary undergrowth in forest.

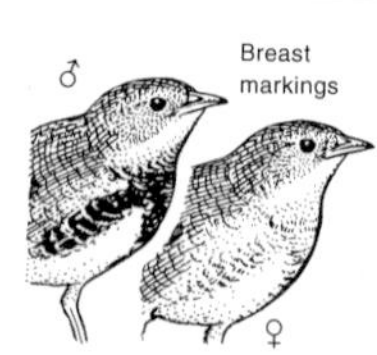

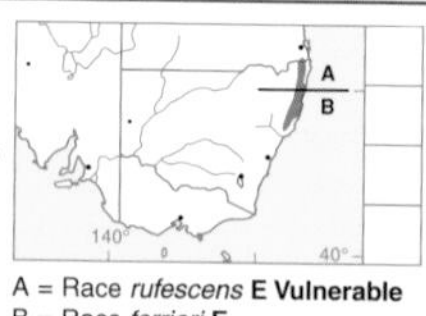

A = Race *rufescens* E **Vulnerable**
B = Race *ferrieri* E

Noisy Scrub-bird *Atrichornis clamosus* **R** ◎ E Endangered

Elusive. Dark brown above; fine black dorsal bars. Upper chest blackish, paler below. Strong black and white throat mark. Tail often 'cocked'. **F** Pale throat; brown below. **Size** (approx.) M 23, F 19.5 cm. **Juv.** Reddish throat; no barring. **Voice** Complex, strong; male most vocal. **Hab.** Low, thick, coastal vegetation.

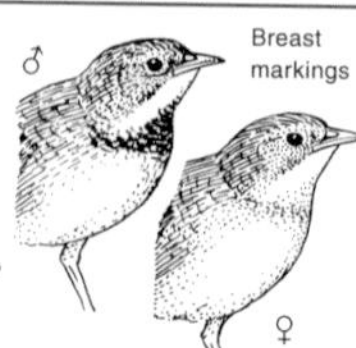

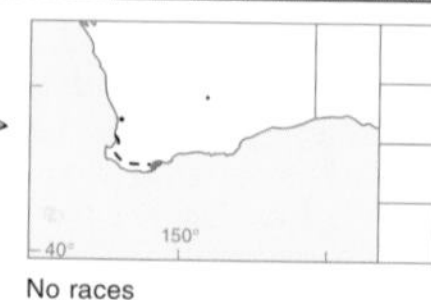

No races

Blue-winged Pitta *Pitta moluccensis* see **Vagrant Bird Bulletin** p. 298.

Note A *related* species Fairy Pitta *P. nympha* is on plate opposite.

Rufous Scrub-bird
♂
Noisy Scrub-bird
Juv.
Red-bellied Pitta
Fairy Pitta
Noisy Scrub-bird ♂
Noisy Pitta
Albert's Lyrebird
♂
Rainbow Pitta
Albert's Lyrebird
♀
Superb Lyrebird
♀
Superb Lyrebird ♂

Varied Sittella *Daphoenositta chrysoptera* **MC** ?◎–⚘

Groups actively forage head down: longer-billed males on trunks, main stems; females on finer branches, foliage. Bill, eye-ring, feet, all yellow. Crown sooty-grey; back dusky. Orange wing bar. Streaked below. Race *leucocephala* (B) White head. Race *striata* (C) Boldest streaks. Race *leucoptera* (D) Darkest back, white wing bar, white below. Race *pileata* (E) Grey-brown back, white below. **F** Races (C), (D), (E), Black-headed. **Size** 10–11 cm. **Juv.** Paler crown, back. Buff on wing coverts. **Voice** Incessant 'chip'; upward inflected whistles. **Hab.** Sclerophyll forest, woodland.

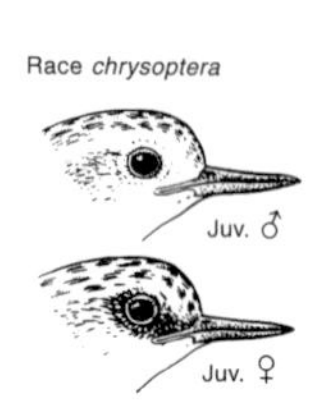

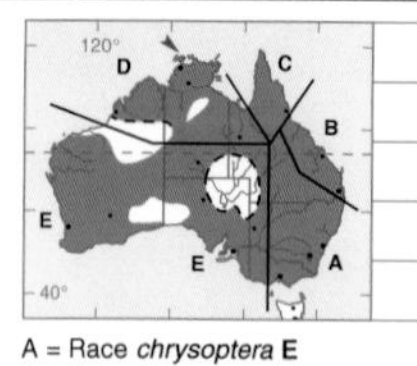

A = Race *chrysoptera* **E**
B = Race *leucocephala* **E**
C = Race *striata* **E**
D = Race *leucoptera* **E**
E = Race *pileata* **E**

White-throated Treecreeper *Cormobates leucophaeus* **C** ◎ E

Forage upwards on trunks, lower branches. Dark back contrasts with grey rump. White throat, breast. Striped belly, flanks; barred undertail. Northern races more olive, darker, greyish throat. **F** Orange mark on cheek. **Size** 14–16.5 cm. **Juv.** Pale white streaks on scapulars; females orange-chestnut rump. **Voice** Repeated drawn-out piping; strong or tremulous calls. Some 'whistler-like'. **Hab.** Rainforest, open forest, woodland.

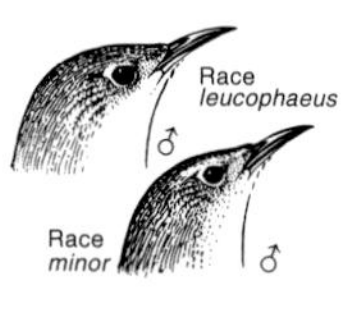

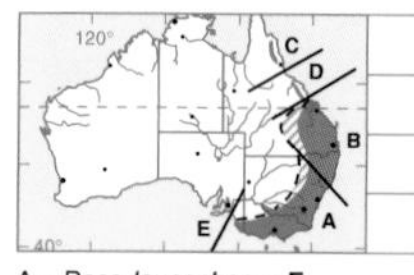

A = Race *leucophaeus* **E**
B= Race *metastasis* **E**
C = Race *minor* **E**
D= Race *intermedius* **E**
E= Race *grisescens* **E**

Red-browed Treecreeper *Climacteris erythrops* **LMC–UC** ◎ E

Tends to forage in upper storey. Reddish eyebrow. Face brownish-orange. Boldly striped belly. **F** Chestnut face and stripes on chest. **Size** 14.5–16 cm. **Juv.** Grey face; buffish-grey underparts. **Voice** Descending chatter, often answered by two sharp notes. **Hab.** Tall eucalypt forest, sub-alpine woodland.

In poor light among trees, may appear very dark and plain, with little contrast between eyebrow and head.

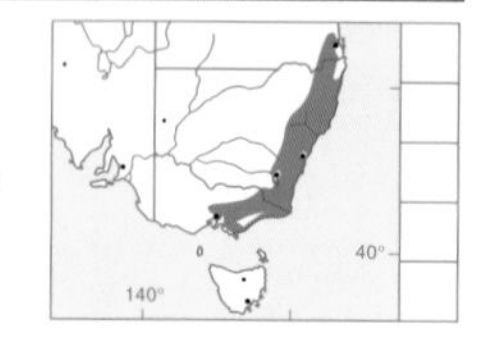

White-browed Treecreeper *Climacteris affinis* **UC** ◎ E

Appears 'grey-plumaged'. White eyebrow. Bolder black and white striped ear coverts and belly striations than Brown Treecreeper. **F** Chestnut line over brow; faint stripes on chest. **Size** 14–16 cm. **Juv.** Brow indistinct. **Voice** Weak, insect-like notes and song. **Hab.** Acacia woodland, belah, *Callitris*.

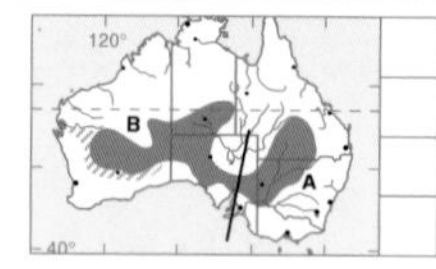

A = Race *affinis* (larger) **E**
B = Race *superciliosa* (smaller) **E**

Brown Treecreeper *Climacteris picumnus* **C** ◎ E

Often on ground, fallen timber. Bobs tail when resting. Broad buff eyebrow, pale cheeks. Upperparts brown. Rufous wing bar. Dark striped breast, belly. Lower flanks washed rufous. Race *melanotus* (B) Darker. White eyebrow, throat, cheeks. Race *victoriae* (C) More rufous throughout. **F** Rufous chest marks (often hidden). **Size** 14–18 cm. **Juv.** Darker, more colourful. **Voice** Staccato 'spink spink', harsh rattle; chuckling songs. **Hab.** Drier woodlands, forest clearings, edges; eucalypts along streams.

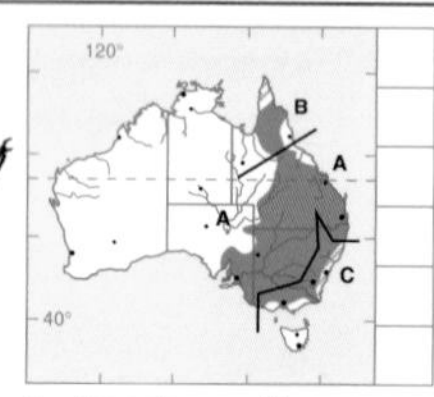

A = Race *picumnus* **E**
B = Race *melanotus* **E**
C = Race *victoriae* **E**

Rufous Treecreeper *Climacteris rufa* **C** ◎ E

Behaviour generally like Brown, Black-tailed Treecreepers. Birds brighter, larger in east of range. Grey-brown crown, back, side of neck. Cinnamon-rufous face, underparts. Fine black, buff streaks on chest. **F** Buff chest streaks. **Size** 16.5–18 cm. **Voice** Higher-pitched than Brown. **Hab.** Forest, woodland, mallee.

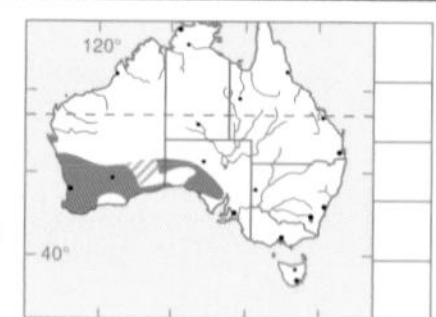

Black-tailed Treecreeper *Climacteris melanura* **C** ◎ E

Feeds from fallen timber. Brownish-black head, upperparts. No eyebrow. Dull rufous belly. Black-streaked white chin to upper breast. **F** White throat; chestnut breast stripes. **Size** 16–19 cm. **Voice** Piping notes like White-throated Treecreeper; other calls like Brown Treecreeper. **Hab.** Eucalypt forest, woodland.

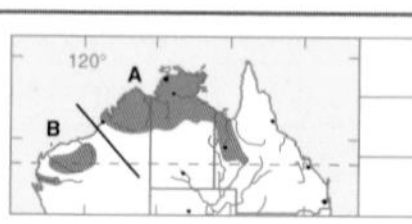

A = Race *melanura* **E**
B = Race *wellsi* **E**

Varied Sittella ♀
Race chrysoptera
♂
Varied Sittella ♂
Race striata
Varied Sittella ♂
Race pileata
Varied Sittella ♀
Race striata
Red-browed
Treecreeper
♂
Varied Sittella ♀
Race pileata
Varied Sittella
Race chrysoptera
Red-
browed
Treecreeper
Juv.
Varied Sittella
Race leucocephala
Red-browed
Treecreeper
♀
♀
White-browed
Treecreeper
♂
Black-tailed
Treecreeper
♀
Brown Treecreeper ♀
Race picumnus
White-throated
Treecreeper
♂
White-throated
Treecreeper
♀ Juv.
Brown Treecreeper ♂
Race picumnus
Rufous
Treecreeper
♀

Purple-crowned Fairy-wren *Malurus coronatus* **UC** ◎ E

Note In many Maluridae species, hybrid zones exist between races.

Crown, most of frons, purple. Black central crown patch. Face, lores to nape, black. Cinnamon brown back. Tail intense blue. Buffy cream-white underparts. **M eclipse** Brown head, black eye patch; otherwise resembles female. **F** Smaller. Mainly buff. Chestnut face and ear coverts are diagnostic. Tail deep greenish-blue. Race *macgillivrayi* (B) Smaller. Darker grey-brown above; plain cream-white below. Tail deep greenish-blue. **F** Blue-grey crown, nape; chestnut ear coverts. Plain cream-white below. Tail mid greenish-blue. **Juv.** Broadly resembles female. **Size** 13.5–14.7 cm. **Voice** High-pitched, very varied. Loud songs, contact calls. **Hab.** Thickets of cane grass and/or pandanus very close (5–10 m) to the water's edge. Strictly riparian.

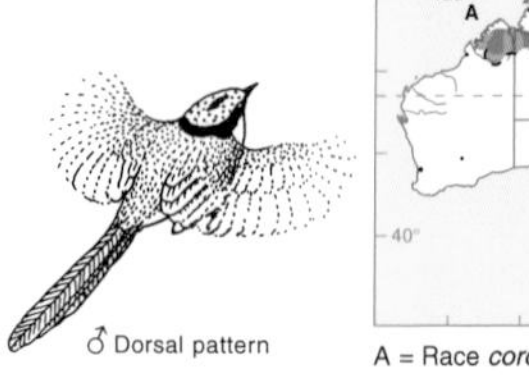

♂ Dorsal pattern

A = Race *coronatus* **E Vulnerable**
B = Race *macgillivrayi* **E**
Due to habitat damage, distribution is badly fragmented within each section of its range.

Superb Fairy-wren *Malurus cyaneus* **C** ◎ E

Family groups; often on ground. Black bill. Bright blue crown, upper back, ear coverts. Black nape, breast, lower back. Tail dark blue. Buffy-white underparts. **M eclipse** Like female; bill black, blue tail shorter. Variations between races include size, plumage colour, tail and leg lengths. Tas. birds (both sexes) slightly larger, brighter, longer-tailed. **F** Brown. Reddish-brown bill, lores, eyebrows. Tail brownish. Females 'bluer-tailed' in SE of SA; 'browner-tailed' in the four easternmost states. **Size** 11–14 cm. **Juv.** As female, whitish underparts. Tail usually shorter. **Voice** Thin zizzing musical trills. **Hab.** Open forest, swamps, coastal areas, rainforest; gardens.

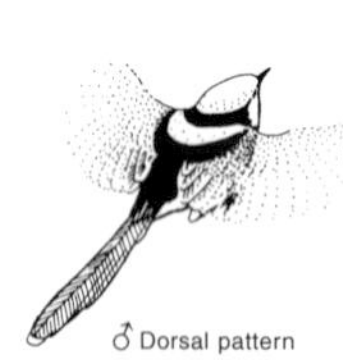

♂ Dorsal pattern

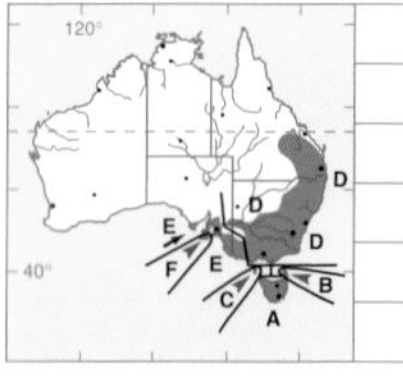

A = Race *cyaneus* **E**
B = Race *samueli* **E**
C = Race *elizabethae* **E**
D = Race *cyanochlamys* **E**
E = Race *leggei* **E**
F = Race *ashbyi* **E**

Splendid Fairy-wren *Malurus splendens* **C** ◎ E

Often feeds higher in trees, shrubs, than other fairy-wrens. Black bill. Rich violet-blue crown, mantle, rump, underparts. Contrasting ear coverts sky-blue. Long, slender tail dark cobalt. Broad black chest band. No black band on back or scapulars. **M eclipse** Like female but black bill; blue-grey wings, dark blue tail. **F** Brown like Superb Fairy-wren but dark bluish tail. Nominate race has slightly longer, narrower tail than other races. Race *musgravi* (B, formerly *callainus*) 'Turquoise Fairy-wren' Sky-blue upperparts and ear coverts. Wide black band over back to scapulars. Deep violet-blue throat above black chest band; azure belly. Wings, tail, dusky turquoise. **M eclipse** Bill black. Blue-grey wings. Tail blue, shorter, broader. **F** Tail mid turquoise-blue. Race *melanotus* (C) 'Black-backed Fairy-wren' Violet-blue crown, mantle. Light blue ear coverts. Throat rich blue with violet tinge. Narrower black breast band; less black on scapulars than *musgravi*. Broader black back to rump. Tail mid turquoise-blue. **M eclipse** Like females but bill black. **F** As *musgravi* female. Race *emmottorum* (D) Resembles *melanotus* but generally more sky-blue than all other races. Slightly wider black band to scapulars from breast than *melanotus*; less black on scapulars. Tail pale turquoise. **M eclipse** Like female but black bill; tail dull blue. **F** Brown like Superb Fairy-wren female; tail dull blue. **Size** 11–13.5 cm. **Juv.** As their respective females. **Voice** Resembles Superb Fairy-wren. **Hab.** Race *splendens* Many vegetation types including forest margins, dry woodland, inland heath; *musgravi* Dense mulga, mallee, saltbush; *melanotus* mallee, *Triodia*, saltbush; *emmottorum* Mulga, brigalow, *Callitris* woodland.

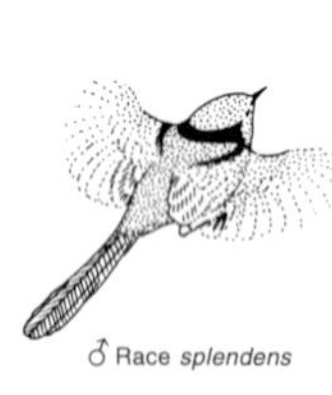

♂ Race *splendens*

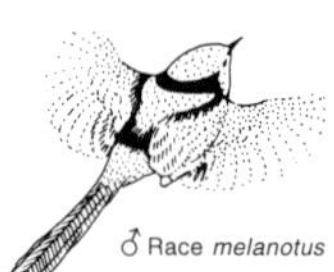

♂ Race *melanotus*

Dorsal patterns

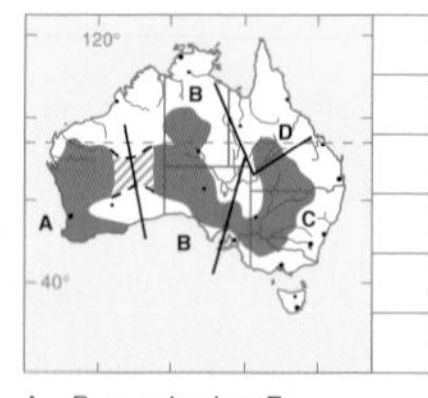

A = Race *splendens* **E**
B = Race *musgravi* **E**
C = Race *melanotus* **E**
D = Race *emmottorum* **E**
There are several well-defined races with hybrid zones between them. Race *musgravi* (B) supersedes prior race *callainus*, because original specimen came from a hybrid zone (based on Schodde & Mason, 1999).

Superb Fairy-wren
♂ Breeding
Purple-crowned Fairy-wren
♂ Moult
Purple-crowned Fairy-wren
♀
Purple-crowned Fairy-wren
♂ Non-breeding
Superb Fairy-wren
♂ Non-breeding
Purple-crowned Fairy-wren
♂ Breeding
Superb Fairy-wren
♂ Moult
Superb Fairy-wren
♀
Splendid Fairy-wren
♂ Breeding
Race splendens
Splendid Fairy-wren
♂ Breeding
Race musgravi
Splendid Fairy-wren
♀ All races
Splendid Fairy-wren
♂ Moult
Splendid Fairy-wren
♂ Non-breeding
Race melanotus
Splendid Fairy-wren
♂ Breeding
Race melanotus
N. DAY

Variegated Fairy-wren *Malurus lamberti* **C** ◎ E

Black bill. Dark brown iris. Mid-blue crown and mantle. Paler blue ear coverts. Frons, chest, neck, black. Sides of chest dark blue. Wings brownish; scapulars chestnut. Black rump. Tail very long; blue with white tips. Whitish underparts. Dark brown legs. **M eclipse** Grey upperparts; white underparts. Black bill, pale eye-ring. Tail blue. **F/Juv.** Grey head with reddish bill, lores, eye-ring. Grey-brown upperparts, whitish underparts. Tail dull blue. Legs reddish. Race *assimilis* (B) 'Purple-backed Fairy-wren' Darker blue cap and mantle. Race *dulcis* (C) 'Lavender-flanked Fairy-wren' Like *assimilis* but has purplish flanks. **F** Grey-blue with white lores, eye-ring. Race *rogersi* (D), also called 'Lavender-flanked Fairy-wren' Like *dulcis* but **F** has reddish bill, lores, eye-ring. Race *bernieri* (E) Dark violet-blue cap. **Size** 11–15 cm. **Voice** Like Superb Fairy-wren but faster, far more metallic. **Hab.** Race *lamberti* Heathland, open forest of coastal ranges in E Australia; *assimilis* Across inland Australia; *dulcis* Rocky escarpments, Arnhem Land (NT); *rogersi* Rocky escarpments, of Kimberley (northern WA); *bernieri* Bernier Is. WA.

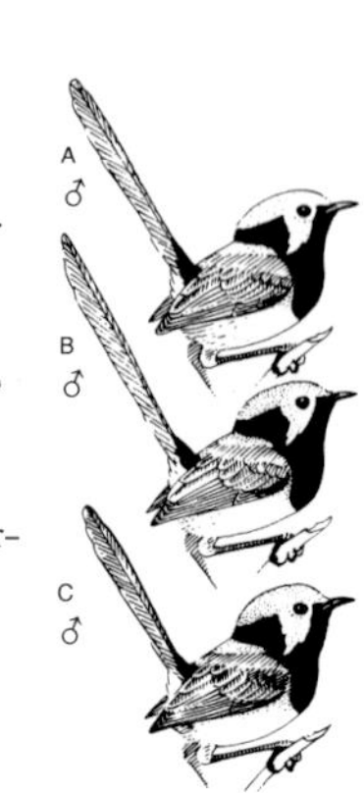

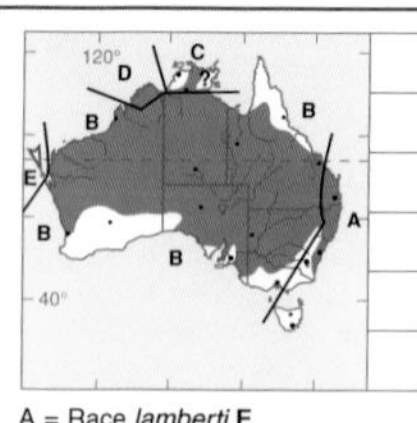

A = Race *lamberti* **E**
B = Race *assimilis* **E**
C = Race *dulcis* **E**
D = Race *rogersi* **E**
E = Race *bernieri* **E Vulnerable**

Lovely Fairy-wren *Malurus amabilis* **MC** ◎ E

Resembles Variegated Fairy-wren race *lamberti* (A) but all blue areas are lighter. Ear coverts rounder, broader. Wings dark with chestnut-edged scapulars. Tail dark blue, shorter, with broad white tips. **F** Bill black. Bright blue upperparts. Prominent blue ear coverts. White lores, eye-ring, underparts. Tail hazy-blue, also tipped white. **Size** 12–13 cm. **Voice** A variety of single and whistling, trilling calls. **Hab.** Rainforest edges of NE Qld. Frequently in trees, above ground level.

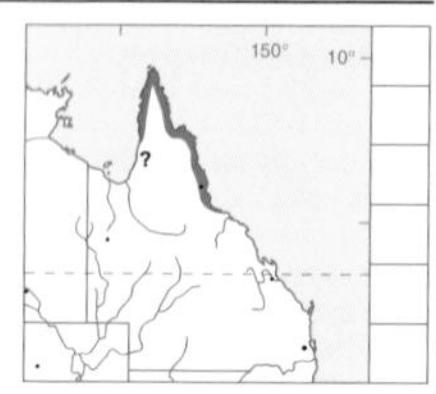

No races
Formerly race *amabilis* of Variegated Fairy-wren; now considered a full species.

Blue-breasted Fairy-wren *Malurus pulcherrimus* **MC** ◎ E

Resembles Variegated Fairy-wren, race *assimilis* (B). Dark blue crown, mantle, with a purplish sheen; slightly paler ear coverts. Dark slate breast, with a blue to navy-blue sheen merging into bluer sides of breast and soft black lower breast band. SA (Eyre Penin.) birds slightly paler than WA birds. **F/Juv.** Like Variegated. **Size** 12.5–14.5 cm. **Voice** Like Variegated. **Hab.** Sand plains, heath, mallee, mulga-eucalypt and jarrah forests.

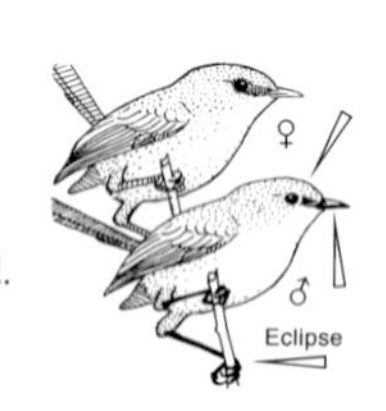

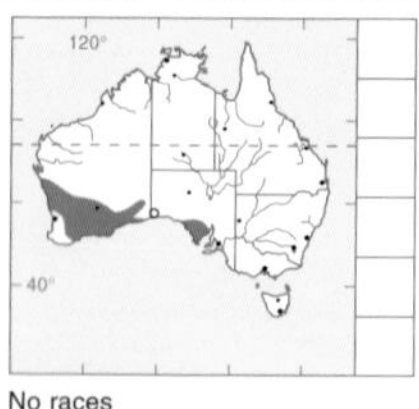

No races

Red-winged Fairy-wren *Malurus elegans* **LMC–LUC** ◎ E

Identify eclipse males, females, from those of Splendid Fairy-wren, race *splendens*. Like Blue-breasted Fairy-wren except pale blue crown and mantle; ear coverts even paler. Broader red scapulars (richer than illustrated). **M non-br.** Black lores; dark legs, feet. **F** Dull black bill. **Voice** Like Variegated Fairy-wren. **Size** 13.5–15 cm. **Juv.** Bill brown on fledging. **Hab.** Near water; swamps in Darling and Stirling Ranges, SW of WA. Also dense to open vegetation fringes.

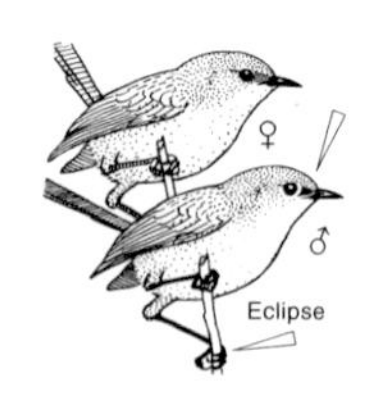

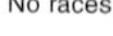

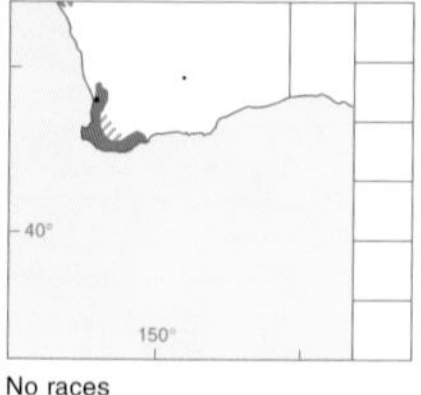

No races

Superb Fairy-wren ♂

Splendid Fairy-wren Race A ♂

Variegated Fairy-wren ♂

Variegated Fairy-wren ♀
Race rogersi
Lovely Fairy-wren ♀
Lovely Fairy-wren ♂
Breeding
Variegated Fairy-wren ♀
Race lamberti
Variegated Fairy-wren ♂
Breeding
Race lamberti
Variegated Fairy-wren ♂
Non-breeding
Race lamberti
Red-winged Fairy-wren ♂
Breeding
Red-winged Fairy-wren ♀
Blue-breasted Fairy-wren ♀
Blue-breasted Fairy-wren ♂
Breeding
N. Day

White-winged Fairy-wren *Malurus leucopterus* LC–UC ◎ E

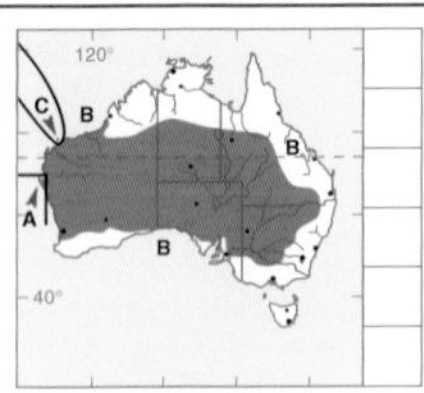

A = Race *leucopterus* **E Vulnerable**
B = Race *leuconotus* **E**
C = Race *edouardi* **E Vulnerable**
Rarely, 'black' males reported on coast of WA, opposite Dirk Hartog and Barrow islands. Other occasional reports are scattered across mainland range of race *leuconotus*.

Good light needed for all malurid observations – reflectivity off pigment melanin varies.

Race *leucopterus* (A) 'Black and White Fairy-wren' Velvety black plumage with bluish sheen. White wings; tail deep violet-blue. **M eclipse** Patchy black or brown above. Race *leuconotus* (B) 'White-winged Fairy-wren' Distinctive bright to deep cobalt blue; wings white; tail deep blue. **M eclipse** Like female; bill dark horn. Tail dusky-blue. Race *edouardi* (C) Satin black, wings dusky, tail dark blue-grey. **F/Juv.** Dull grey-brown above; whitish below, dull brown wash on flanks; lacks reddish eye-ring. **Size** 11–13 cm. **Voice** Distinctive thin musical trilling, higher than Superb Fairy-wren. **Hab.** Races *leucopterus* Dirk Hartog Is. and *edouardi* Barrow Is. Heathland, saltbush. Race *leuconotus* Arid to semi-arid saltbush, *Triodia*, cane-grass areas.

Red-backed Fairy-wren *Malurus melanocephalus* C ◎ E

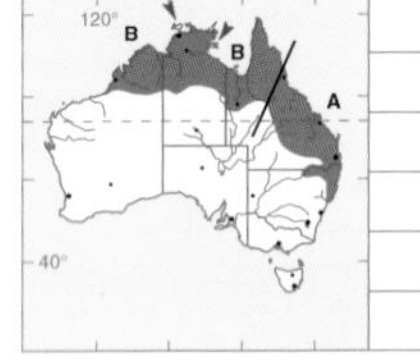

A = Race *melanocephalus* **E**
B = Race *cruentatus* **E**

Check female Variegated Fairy-wren. Black with bright orange-red back, rump. These feathers are puffed out in display. Long tapered tail. **M eclipse** Like female; traces of red may appear on back. Legs pale pink to fawny-brown. **F** Greyish-brown upperparts; no reddish eye-ring; fawnish-white below; tail brown Race *cruentatus* (B) Black with crimson back and rump. Shorter square-tipped blackish tail. **F** Warmer brown upperparts. **Size** 9–13 cm. **Voice** Drawn out, reedy or chattering songs and notes, similar to White-winged Fairy-wren. **Hab.** Spinifex, tropical swamps, samphire, tidal flats, dense undergrowth.

Southern Emu-wren *Stipiturus malachurus* C–MC ◎ E

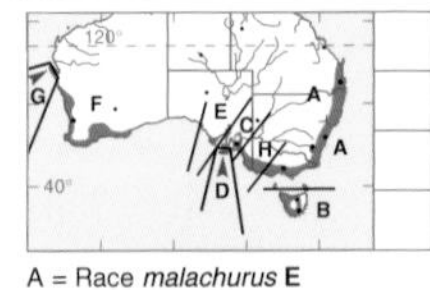

A = Race *malachurus* **E**
B = Race *littleri* **E**
C = Race *intermedius* **E Endangered**
D = Race *halmaturinus* **E**
E = Race *parimeda* **E Vulnerable**
F = Race *westernensis* **E**
G = Race *hartogi* **E Vulnerable**
H = Race *polionotum* **E**

Flight feeble. Crown dark rufous, streaked black. Sky-blue eyebrow, bib. Olive-brown back, streaked darker. Orange-brown underparts. Six dark brown filamentous tail feathers, very long (10 cm). Race *westernensis* (F) Heavily streaked head, rich blue bib. Race *polionotum* (H) Paler, greyer, finer streaking, pale blue bib. **F** Lacks blue colouring; buff below. **Size** 13.5–19 cm. **Juv.** Like duller adults; young males have pale blue bibs. **Voice** As fairy-wrens, faint or thin, trilling, descending; soft chirps; short harsh alarm calls. **Hab.** Coastal heath, swamps, dense cover.

Mallee Emu-wren *Stipiturus mallee* MC–UC ◎ E Vulnerable

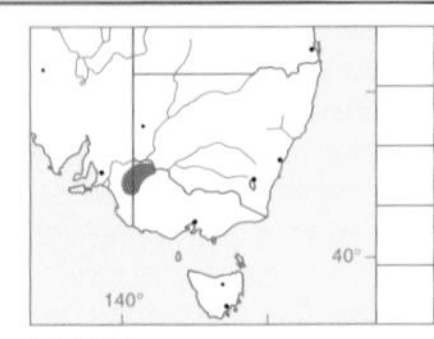

No races

Chestnut crown; nape darker. Blue face, ear coverts, bib. Back, wings, brown with black streaks. Rich buff below. Dark tail filamentous; shortest of all emu-wrens. **F** Streaked crown. Lacks blue face, throat. **Size** 12.5–14.5 cm. **Juv.** Plainer, browner; pale bill pale, shorter tail. Ear coverts streaked white; greyish-white bib. **Voice** High, trilling, rapid; often softer than fairy-wrens. **Hab.** *Triodia* grass in mallee scrub; sandplain heath.

Rufous-crowned Emu-wren *Stipiturus ruficeps* C–MC ◎ E

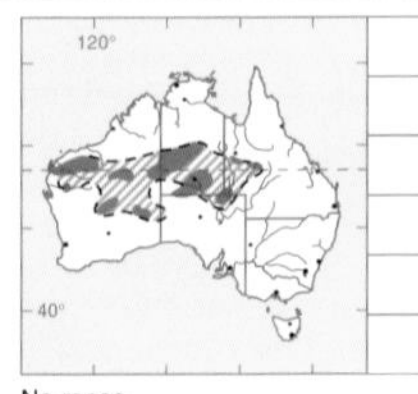

No races

Bright rufous, unstreaked crown. Rich blue face, bib. Ear coverts a little paler than our plate shows. Grey-brown to rufous-brown above, feathers streaked black. Six dark filamentous tail feathers. **F** No blue bib; paler buff below. **Size** 10–15 cm. **Juv.** Off-white face, duller brown above. Bibs in males greyish; in females off-white. **Voice** High, trilling, rapid; often softer than fairy-wrens. **Hab.** *Triodia*; sometimes in adjacent or associated mallee scrub.

White-winged Fairy-wren ♀
White-winged Fairy-wren ♂
Br. Race *leucopterus*
White-winged
Fairy-wren ♂
Br. Race *leuconotus*
Red-backed Fairy-wren ♀
Red-backed Fairy-wren ♂
Br. Race *cruentatus*
Southern Emu-wren ♀
Mallee Emu-wren ♂
Southern Emu-wren ♂
Rufous-crowned
Emu-wren ♂
Rufous-crowned
Emu-wren ♀
N. Day

Black Grasswren *Amytornis housei* **MC** ◎ E

Black with chestnut back, wings, rump. Bold white streaks on head, back, breast. **F** Light chestnut below. **Size** 18–20.5 cm. **Juv.** Duller; finer streaks. **Voice** Wren-like; ticking, grating. **Hab.** *Triodia* in sandstone gullies, King Leopold area of WA.

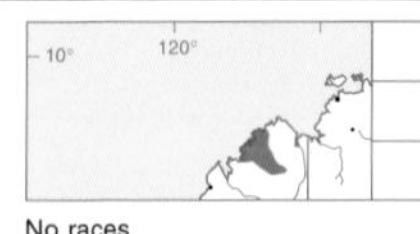

No races

White-throated Grasswren *Amytornis woodwardi* **UC** ◎ E Vulnerable

Stocky, black and chestnut. White-streaked black head, mantle. **F** Chestnut belly. **Size** 20–22 cm. **Juv.** Pale bill; duller, streaks fainter. **Voice** Rising, falling trills. **Hab.** *Triodia* on escarpments.

Geographic separation identifies 3 Top End species.

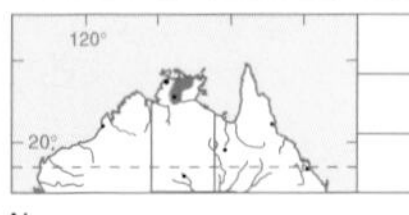

No races

Carpentarian Grasswren *Amytornis dorotheae* **UC** ◎ E

Black face, frons, streaked white. Rufous lores, black whisker-mark. Rufous lower back, tail, flanks. **F** Chestnut flanks, lower belly. **Size** 16–17.5 cm. **Juv.** Paler markings. **Voice** Cricket-like buzz. **Hab.** Sandstone escarpments, SE to stony *Triodia* areas.

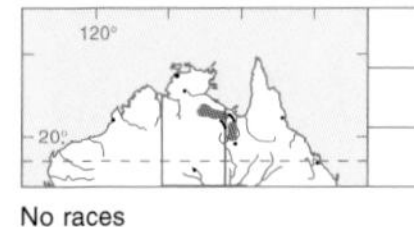

No races

Striated Grasswren *Amytornis striatus* **LC–UC** ◎ E

Great variation. Bold chestnut above (inland WA) to brownish above (SE Aust.); streaked white. Orange-buff eyebrow. Black whisker-mark. White throat. Buff below, variably streaked white. **F** Chestnut flanks. **Size** 14.5–18.5 cm. **Juv.** Dull; softer streaks. **Voice** Melodious song; thin squeak. **Hab.** *Triodia*, mallee.

Short-tailed Grasswren *A. merrotsyi* **LC–UC** ◎ E

As Striated; plainer face, streaked throat, shorter tail. **Size** 15–16 cm. **Hab.** *Triodia*, mallee. Only Flinders, Gawler Ranges, SA.

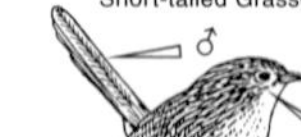

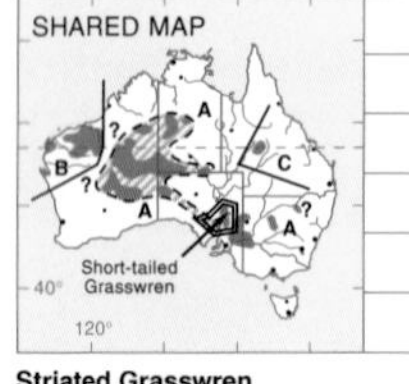

Striated Grasswren
A = Race *striatus* **E**
B = Race *whitei* **E**
C = Race *rowleyi* **E**
Short-tailed Grasswren E

Eyrean Grasswren *Amytornis goyderi* **MC–UC** ◎ E

Small groups. Stout bluish bill. Pale rufous above, streaked white. Grey ear coverts. White throat, breast. Flanks washed brown. **F** Flanks rufous, match upperparts. **Size** 15–16.5 cm. **Voice** Faint 2-note whistle. **Hab.** Cane grass on high sand dunes.

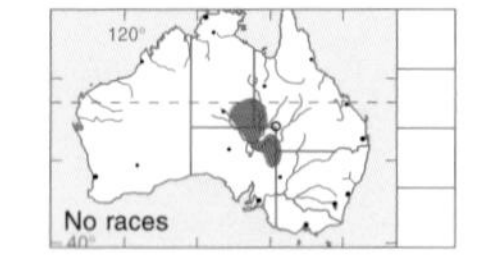

No races

Grey Grasswren *Amytornis barbatus* **MC** ◎ E

Ginger-brown, white streaks, above. Black streaked crown. White face. Black eye-line, 'beard' lines on cheek, throat. White breast, sides scalloped. Flanks pale buff. **F** Face, breast, finely patterned. **Size** 18–20 cm. **Juv.** Plainer. **Voice** High, twittering; 2 notes. **Hab.** Flood-zone cane grass, lignum, tall saltbush clumps.

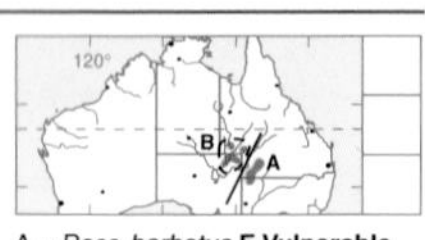

A = Race *barbatus* **E Vulnerable**
B = Race *diamantina* **E**

Thick-billed Grasswren *Amytornis textilis* **MC–LC** ◎ E

Races *textilis* (A), *myall* (B). Stout bill. Dull rufous, streaked boldly above, finely below. **F** Rufous flank patch. Race *modestus* (C) Plainer below. **F** Chestnut flanks. **Size** 13.5–19.5 cm. **Juv.** Duller. **Voice** Soft songs; squeaks. **Hab.** Saltbush, cane grass.

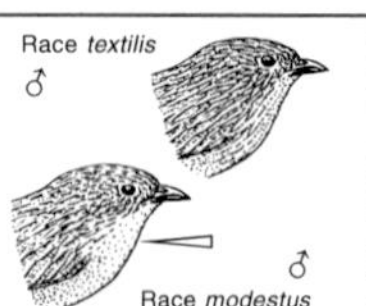

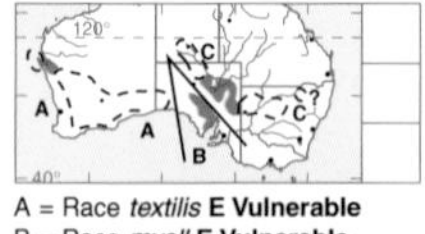

A = Race *textilis* **E Vulnerable**
B = Race *myall* **E Vulnerable**
C = Race *modestus* **E Vulnerable**

Dusky Grasswren *Amytornis purnelli* **MC–UC** ◎ E

'Brownest' grasswren; streaked. Slender bill. Rufous lores, dark head. Warm brown breast, white-streaked; grey-brown flanks. **F** Rufous flank patch. **Size** 14.5–17.5 cm. **Juv.** Duller. **Voice** High sibilant reels. **Hab.** Spinifex slopes, rocky ridges.

Kalkadoon Grasswren *A. ballarae* **UC** ◎ E Vulnerable?

As Dusky, brighter. Grey breast, belly, flanks. **F** Rufous flanks. **Size** 16–17.5 cm. **Voice** Higher than Dusky. **Hab.** Rocky ridges.

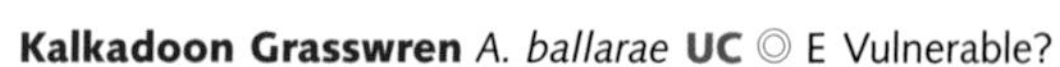

SHARED MAP
Kalkadoon Grasswren
Dusky Grasswren
40°

Dusky Grasswren E
Kalkadoon Grasswren E

Black Grasswren ♂
Black Grasswren ♀
White-throated Grasswren ♀
White-throated Grasswren ♂
Carpentarian Grasswren ♂
Eyrean Grasswren ♀
Eyrean Grasswren ♂
Carpentarian Grasswren ♀
Striated Grasswren ♂
Race striatus
Striated Grasswren ♂
Race whitei
Grey Grasswren ♂
Race barbatus
Striated Grasswren ♀
Race striatus
Dusky Grasswren ♂
Thick-billed Grasswren ♀
Dusky Grasswren ♀
Thick-billed Grasswren ♂

Spotted Pardalote *Pardalotus punctatus* **C–MC** ◎–♧ E

Note Pardalotes are tiny foliage-foragers that breed in small burrows or tree-hollows.

Stout black bill. Eyebrow white. Grey cheeks. Crown, wings black with rows of white spots. Tail black, white spots. Back blackish, patterned with buff spots. Underparts pale buff. Rump chestnut; uppertail coverts red, fading to tan in upper centre. Throat, undertail coverts bright yellow. Race *xanthopyge* (B) 'Yellow-rumped Pardalote' Rump bright yellow. Back greyer. **F** (both races) Brow buffy, crown spots yellow. Throat cream. Isolated NE Qld race *millitaris* (C) Smaller. **Size** *punctatus* 8–9.5 cm; *xanthopyge* 9–10 cm. **Juv.** As female; crown paler, not spotted. **Voice** Three separate notes in a chime; loud single note. Race *xanthopyge* has higher-pitched call. **Hab.** Eucalypt forests; race *xanthopyge* dry eucalypt woodland, especially mallee.

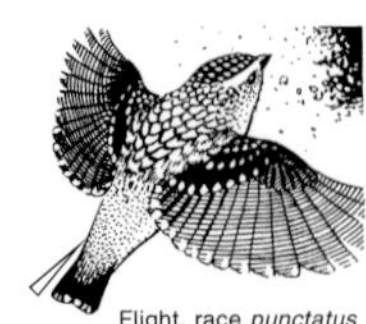
Flight, race *punctatus*

Flight, race *xanthopyge*

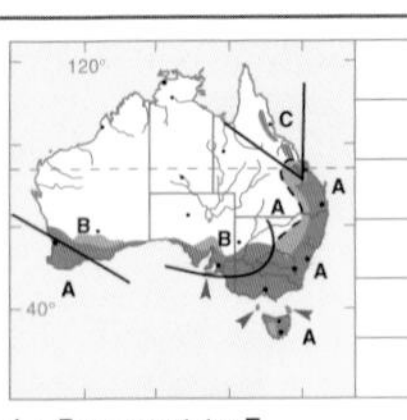

A = Race *punctatus* **E**
B = Race *xanthopyge* **E**
C = Race *millitaris* **E**

Forty-spotted Pardalote *Pardalotus quadragintus* **R** ◎ E Endangered

Small colonies. Check juv. Spotted, Striated Pardalotes. Very short bill. Cheeks, ear coverts, olive to lemon-yellow. Uniform dull olive-green above. Small white spots (20 per side) on dark (brown-black) wings. Tail dark with tiny white tips. Undertail coverts olive. Pale grey chest, belly. **Size** 9–10 cm. **Voice** Soft double note; also repeated single note (hollow, faint). **Hab.** Dry Tas. coastal forest; main food source White (Manna) Gum.

No races

Red-browed Pardalote *Pardalotus rubricatus* **C–MC** ?◎ E

Palest, largest pardalote. Large bicoloured bill. Iris pale fawn. Eyebrow spot at front is red or orange; orange-buff over, behind eye. Crown black, spotted white. Body pale fawn-grey; not spotted, some finely streaked. Orange-buff wing patch prominent. Some yellow on breast. Race *yorki* (B) smaller, brighter. **Size** 11–12 cm. **Juv.** Plain crown; yellow underparts. **Voice** Strong 5-note call, pitch, speed increasing; may be 'parrot-like'. **Hab.** Inland watercourses and woodland, mulga semi-desert.

Dorsal variation

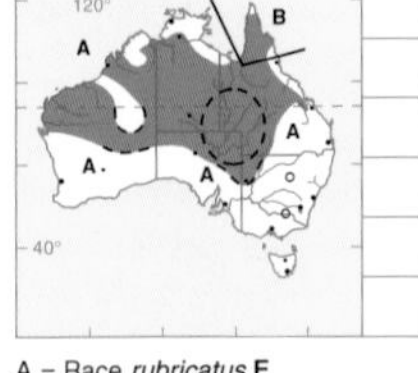

A = Race *rubricatus* **E**
B = Race *yorki* **E**
Birds paler in Lower Lake Eyre Basin (dotted circle on map).

Striated Pardalote *Pardalotus striatus* **C** ○–♧–?◎ E

Note Consider as 'Stripe-crowned Pardalote complex' with six races.

Autumn, winter flocks, and often with thornbills. Displays on bare twigs. Check Weebill. Sexes almost alike. Mostly olive-grey. Yellow lores. Broad white eyebrow. Crown black; white-streaked in some races. White stripe (is wing bar in flight), plus red or yellow spot on dark wings. Back brown; rump paler. Tail black, tipped white. Yellow throat. Underparts pale; flanks yellow. Race *striatus* (A) 'Yellow-tipped Pardalote' Yellow wing spot, narrow white wing stripe, secondary wing feathers buff-edged. Winter migrant to SE Aust. (see lower map). Race *substriatus* (B) 'Striated Pardalote' Red or orange wing spot, wide white wing stripe, secondaries buff-edged. Race *ornatus* (C) 'Eastern Striated Pardalote' Red or orange wing spot, narrow white wing stripe, secondaries buff-edged. Race *melanocephalus* (D) 'Black-headed Pardalote' Plain black crown, wide black eye-line to nape, no facial streaks, red or orange wing spot, wide white wing stripe, secondaries white-edged, tan rump. SE to mid-N Qld ranges. Race *uropygialis* (E) Tropical northern Aust. Mid-yellow rump. Race *melvillensis* (F) Melville Is. Tan rump. **F** Races *uropygialis*, *melvillensis* Crown scalloped grey. **Size** 9–11.5 cm. **Juv.** Dull, olive unstreaked crown (all races). **Voice** Loud, repetitive, double or triple note 'witchi-chew'. **Hab.** Eucalypt forest, woodland; in tree crowns.

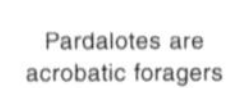
Pardalotes are acrobatic foragers

Striated Pardalote is variable across Aust. in crown-streaking, number of primaries edged white, and width of white showing in wing ('wing stripe'), wing spot colour, and rump colour. Sexes very similar. Races striatus, substriatus, ornatus *are winter migrants or nomads; others sedentary.*

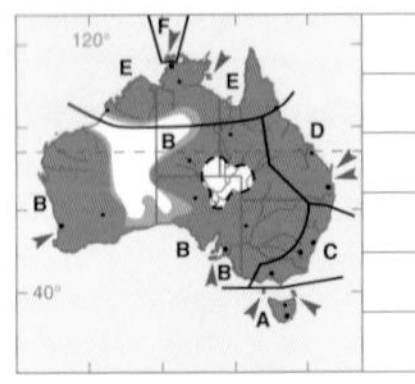

A = Race *striatus* **E**
B = Race *substriatus* **E**
C = Race *ornatus* **E**
D = Race *melanocephalus* **E**
E = Race *uropygialis* **E**
F = Race *melvillensis* **E**

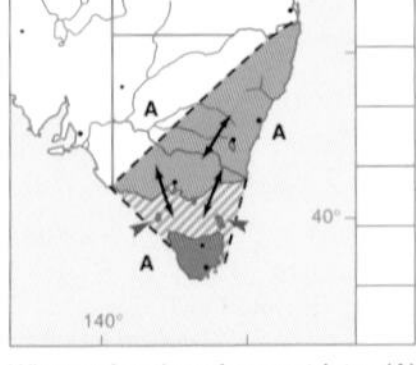

Winter migration of race *striatus* (A) overlaps that of races (B), (C) and (D) in part. Modified from Schodde & Mason (1999).

Spotted Pardalote ♀
Race punctatus
Spotted ('Yellow-rumped') Pardalote ♂
Race xanthopyge
Spotted Pardalote
Juv.
Race punctatus
d Pardalote ♂
Race punctatus
Forty-spotted
Pardalote
Weebill
Race flavescens
Red-browed
Pardalote
Juv.
Red-browed
Pardalote
Striated
Pardalote
Juv.
Race striatus
Striated
-tipped')
Pardalote
e striatus
Striated ('Black-headed')
Pardalote
Race melanocephalus
Striated
Pardalote
ce ornatus
Striated Pardalote
Race substriatus
Striated Pardalote ♂
Race uropygialis
N.DAY.

Eastern Bristlebird *Dasyornis brachypterus* **UC** ◎ E Endangered

Check Pilotbird, also female Common Blackbird (25 cm). Pale eyebrow, throat. Upperparts rich to soft browns and grey-browns, tinted olive. Light scaly breast pattern. Belly greyish-white. Race *monoides* (B) Darker back, plain breast, flanks. Breast, belly washed olive-brown. **Size** 20–22 cm. **Juv./Imm.** No reliable data. **Voice** Penetrating 4-part call; harsh, short notes. **Hab.** Dense coastal, mountain heath; taller swamps, stream thickets.

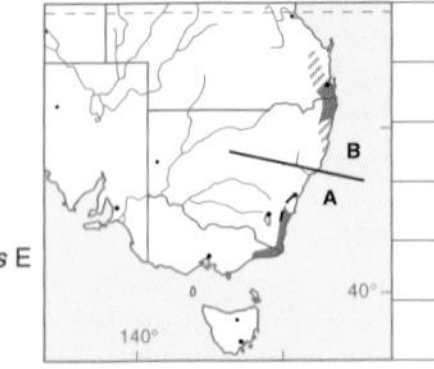

A = Race *brachypterus* E **Endangered**
B = Race *monoides* E **Endangered**

Western Bristlebird *Dasyornis longirostris* **UC** ◎ E Endangered

Smaller, greyer than Eastern. Bill longer, tail shorter than other bristlebirds. Crown, nape brownish-black, dappled grey. Pale lores, eye-ring. Upper- and underparts subtle browns and greys tinted olive and rufous. Faint scaly breast pattern. **Size** 17–20 cm. **Juv./Imm.** Not well known. **Voice** 5-part call, probably male only; 3-part call, probably female only. Also 'tink'; other short harsh notes. **Hab.** Dense coastal heath; taller swamp/stream thickets.

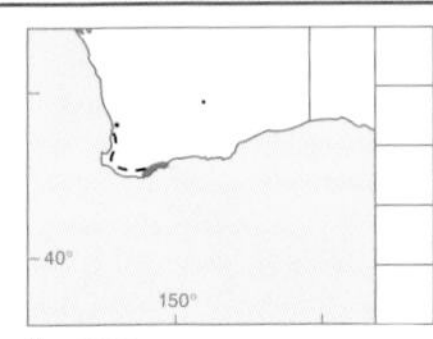

No races

Rufous Bristlebird *Dasyornis broadbenti* **LMC–UC** ◎ E

Largest bristlebird. Check female Common Blackbird (25 cm). Pale lores, eye-ring. Rich rufous crown, nape, ear coverts. Back, flanks greyish or brown tinted olive. Wing, rump, tail, cinnamon-brown. Tail dark brown. Throat, breast, pale grey, with dark scaly pattern. Race *litoralis* (B) Brighter rufous (extinct?). Race *caryochrous* (C) Darker, browner. **F** Smaller. **Size** 23–27 cm. **Juv./Imm.** Little reliable data. **Voice** Penetrating, repetitive call; squeaking variations; short, sharp 'tik'. **Hab.** Dense coastal heath, tall thickets; wet forest (Otway Ranges, Vic.).

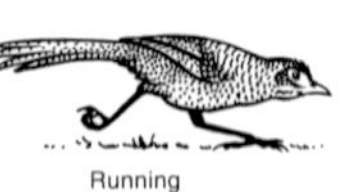

Running

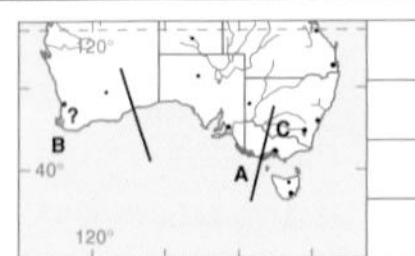

A = Race *broadbenti* **E**
B = Race *litoralis* **E Extinct?**
C = Race *caryochrous* **E Vulnerable**

Bristlebirds are the largest of the scrubwren complex. Approx. size comparisons between rare bristlebirds and some common birds are: Eastern cf. Common Starling; Western cf. Rufous Treecreeper; Rufous cf. Common Myna.

Pilotbird *Pycnoptilus floccosus* **MC–UC** ◎ E

Sturdy; terrestrial. Identify from Rockwarbler which flicks tail sideways. Eastern Bristlebird (20–22 cm) is larger. Eye red. Upperparts chocolate-brown; rufous-washed rump. Rich reddish-buff from frons to throat; breast darker, scaly pattern. Underparts rufous-brown; centre belly whitish. Rather broad, semi-erect tail is flicked up and down. Race *sandlandi* Lighter brown, plainer, smaller. **Size** 16.5–17 cm. **Juv.** As adult. **Voice** Sweet, powerful whistle, (traditionally) 'a-guinea-a-week' (male); short reply (female). Alarm call is harsh 'chack'. **Hab.** Dense, wet-damp forest gullies.

Associates with foraging Superb Lyrebird

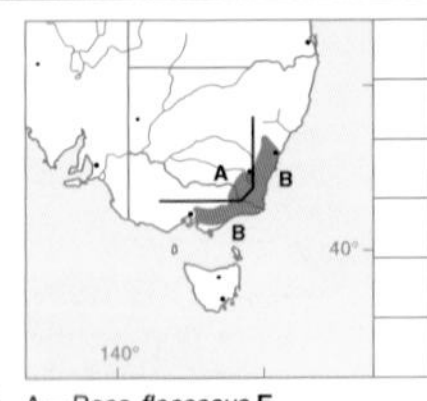

A = Race *floccosus* **E**
B = Race *sandlandi* **E**

Rockwarbler (Origma) *Origma solitaria* **MC** ◎ E

Tail flicked sideways. Frons, front cinnamon-brown. Upperparts dark brown. Rich rufous underparts, contrast with greyish-white throat. Rump washed rufous. Tail blackish. **Size** 14 cm. **Juv.** As adult; duller. **Voice** Shrill, melancholy, repeated 'goodbye'; staccato, softer and rasping notes. **Hab.** Floors of rocky gullies; caves in sandstone, limestone. Endemic to Hawkesbury Sandstone area of SE NSW.

Rockwarbler

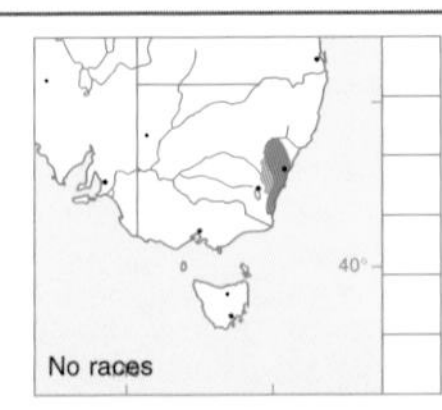

No races

Fernwren *Oreoscopus (Crateroscelis) gutturalis* **UC** ◎ E

Often forages under litter. Bows head; flicks short tail. Not well-known. Sexes virtually alike. Long slender bill. Upperparts dark olive-brown, crown darker. Contrasting white eyebrow and throat. Underparts paler. **Size** 12–14 cm. **Juv.** Dark brown without white facial markings. **Voice** A scolding note; high-pitched squeaks; strong whistling; chattering. **Hab.** Rainforest floors above 650 m.

Flight, dorsal pattern

Previously called 'Australian Fernwren'.

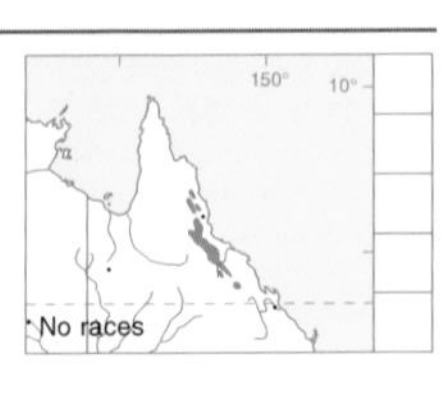

No races

Eastern Bristlebird
Western Bristlebird
Rufous Bristlebird
Pilotbird
Rockwarbler
Fernwren
Juv.
Fernwren
♂

Scrubtit *Acanthornis (Sericornis) magnus* **C** ◎ E

Shy. Brown eye. Whitish eye-ring, eyebrows, lores and throat. Ear coverts grey. White spots near shoulder. White edges to wing-tips. Black subterminal tail band. King Is. birds smaller; narrower subterminal tail band. **Size** 11–11.5 cm. **Voice** 'too-whe-too', like White-browed ('Tasmanian') Scrubwren, Brown Thornbill. Also whistling. **Hab.** Dense, ferny, wet forest undergrowth.

Scrubtits move into trees, where they forage in 'treecreeper-like' manner.

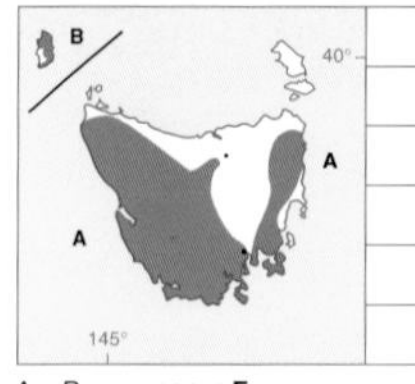

A = Race *magnus* **E**
B = Race *greenianus* **E**
Endangered

Atherton Scrubwren *Sericornis keri* **MC** ◎ E

Dark olive-brown with rufous rump. Bill black. Eye, face, dark. Slightly larger, longer-legged, shorter-winged, more terrestrial than Large-billed Scrubwren. **Size** 13.5 cm. **Juv.** Underparts yellower. **Voice** Scolding call. **Hab.** Rainforest floor above 650 m.

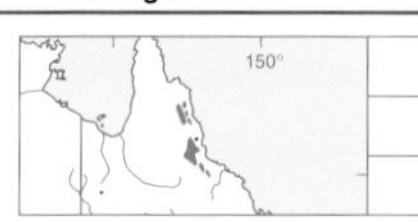

No races

Large-billed Scrubwren *Sericornis magnirostris* **C–MC** ◎ E

Sunlight through vegetation can 'alter' colour of this species. Longish black bill. Dark eye. Face, lores sandy-buff. Upperparts brown to olive-brown, quite variable. Underparts paler. **Size** 12–13 cm. Race *minimus* (prior *beccarii*) (B) 'Tropical Scrubwren' Eye reddish; thin interrupted white eye-ring. Frons, lores blackish. Whitish above lores. Small double white wing bar on dark shoulders. **F** Olive-brown forehead, lores. **Size** 11–11.5 cm. **Voice** Soft twittering, scolding notes, repeated 's-cheer'. Race *minimus* Soft musical warble. **Hab.** Dense, wet forests. Rarely on ground; on tree trunks, vines; very active to middle storey. Race *minimus* Rainforest, monsoon forest, dense riverine scrubs.

'Tropical Scrubwren', S. beccarii, has been returned as a race of Large-billed Scrubwren because DNA work finds extremely close affinities. It is now race minimus (B) here.

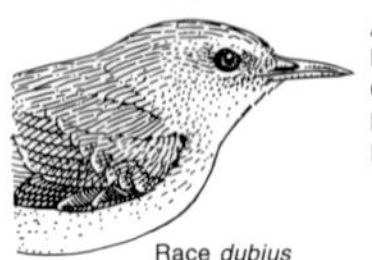
Race *dubius*

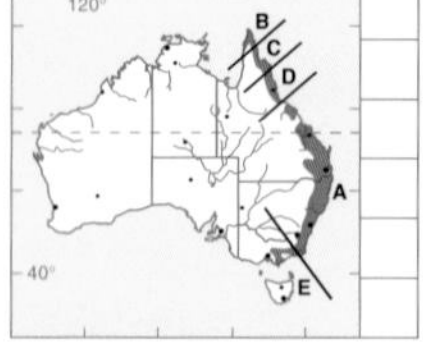

A = Race *magnirostris* **E**
B = Race *minimus* (prior *beccarii*)
C = Race *dubius* **E**
D = Race *viridior* **E**
E = Race *howei* **E**

White-browed Scrubwren *Sericornis frontalis* **C** ◎ E

Twelve races; four best-known described here. Pale eye; blackish lores, grey ear coverts. White eyebrow, cheek stripe. Throat whitish with faint dark streaks. Small white marks on black 'shoulders'. Upperparts dark olive-brown; rump rufous. Underparts dirty yellow, darker at sides. **F** Greyer. Race *laevigaster* (B) Black ear coverts; underparts yellowish, brighter. Race *maculatus* (C) 'Spotted Scrubwren', Black throat, breast heavily 'spotted'; tail tipped white. **Size** 11–14 cm. Race *humilis* (J) 'Tasmanian Scrubwren' Check Scrubtit. Larger, darker than mainland White-browed Scrubwrens. Plainer, almost chocolate-brown body; dull face, wing marks. Eyebrow paler. Tail plain. **Size** 12–15 cm. **Juv.** (all races) Always duller than female, browner; eyebrow undeveloped **Voice** Repeated 'ts-cheer'; harsh scolding notes. **Hab.** (all races) Dense undergrowth all altitudes, saltmarshes, heath, some urban areas.

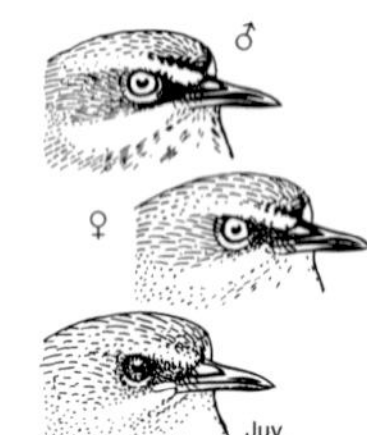

Race *frontalis*

'Tasmanian Scrubwren' has been returned as a race (humilis) of White-browed Scrubwren because DNA work finds close affinities.

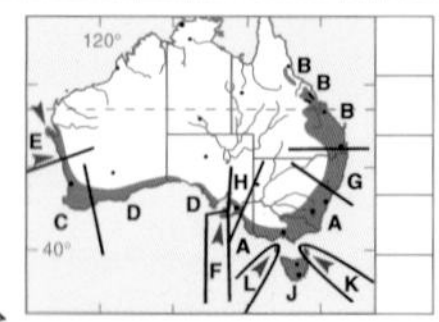

A = Race *frontalis* **E**
B = Race *laevigaster* **E**
C = Race *maculatus* **E**
D = Race *mellori* **E**
E = Race *balstoni* **E**
F = Race *ashbyi* **E**
G = Race *tweedi* **E**
H = Race *rosinae* **E**
I = Race *harterti* **E** (Otway Ranges, Wilsons Promontary areas, Vic., only. Too small to show on this map.)
J = Race *humilis* **E ('Tasmanian')**
K = Race *flindersi* **E**
L = Race *tregallisi* **E**

Yellow-throated Scrubwren *Sericornis citreogularis* **C** ◎ E

Largely terrestrial. Pairs hop ('bounce') along forest floors. Striking appearance. Black face, forehead, ear coverts. White and yellow eyebrow. Bright yellowish throat. Outer primary edges yellowish. Legs longish; cream or pinkish-brown; very noticeable in field. **F** Facial area brownish. **Size** 12.5–15 cm. **Juv.** Duller; underparts washed fawn. **Voice** Clear, melodious and with mimicry; harsh chatter. **Hab.** Dense wet forest gullies.

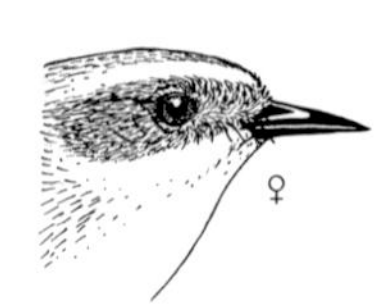

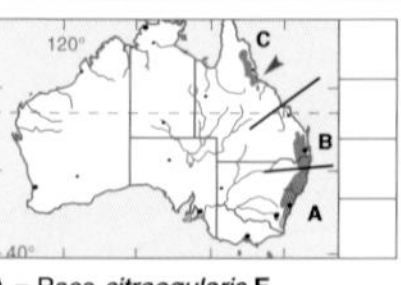

A = Race *citreogularis* **E**
B = Race *intermedius* **E**
C = Race *cairnsi* **E**

Large-billed Scrubwren
Race magnirostris
Scrubtit
White-browed
('Tasmanian')
Scrubwren ♂
Race humilis
White-browed
Scrubwren
Race frontalis
White-browed
Scrubwren ♂
Race frontalis
White-browed
('Spotted')
Scrubwren ♂
Race maculatus
White-browed
Scrubwren ♂
Race laevigaster
Atherton Scrubwren
Yellow-throated Scrubwren
♂
Large-billed
('Tropical')
Scrubwren
♀
Large-billed
('Tropical')
Scrubwren ♂
Race minimus

Chestnut-rumped Heathwren (Hylacola) *Hylacola (Sericornis) pyrrhopygius* LMC–UC ◎ E

In flight, chestnut rump. Cocks tail; dark subterminal band, pale tip. Dull white eyebrow. Greyish crown, nape. Dark olive-brown above. Greyish-white below, streaked darker. Plain olive flanks. Race *parkeri* (B) Lighter. Upperparts more rufous. Race *pedleri* (C) Clear white eyebrow. Paler; brown rump; plainer below. **F** More buff, less streaking below. **Size** 13–14 cm. **Juv.** As female, buffer, unstreaked below. **Voice** Varied, lengthy, canary-like with mimicry; harsh 'chip'. **Hab.** Heath; dense undergrowth.

Tail cocked

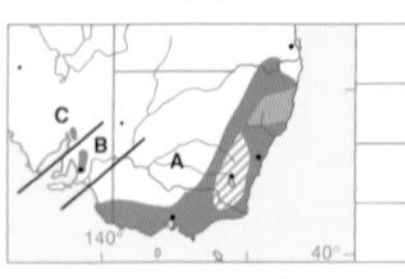

A = Race *pyrrhopygius* E
B = Race *parkeri* E **Endangered**
C = Race *pedleri* E **Vulnerable**

Shy Heathwren (Hylacola) *Hylacola (Sericornis) cautus* MC ◎ E

Stays low. Bold white eyebrow. Grey-brown above, tinged rufous on back. White wing spot. Bright rufous rump, undertail. Long cocked dark tail, white tip. White below, boldly streaked black. Race *whitlocki* (B) Wing feathers edged greyish. Other races darker. **F** Less streaks, throat buffy. **Size** 12–14 cm. **Juv.** As female, paler. **Voice** Strong song, less vocal range than Chestnut-rumped. Sharp, harsh notes. **Hab.** Dense mallee; coastal thickets; *whitlocki* sandplains.

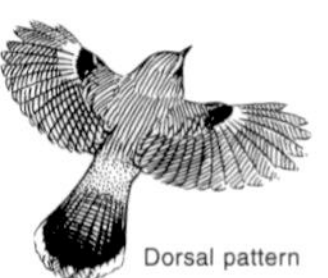
Dorsal pattern

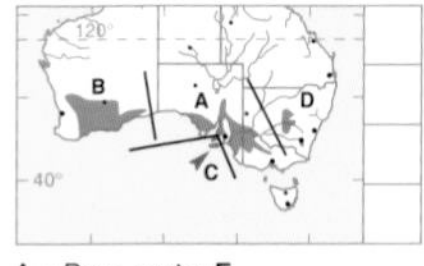

A = Race *cautus* E
B = Race *whitlocki* E
C = Race *halmaturinus* E
D = Race *macrorhynchus* E

Rufous Fieldwren (Calamanthus) *Calamanthus (Sericornis) campestris* UC–MC ◎ E

Sings above cover. Grey-brown above, boldly striated; inland birds more rufous, finer streaking. Pale eyebrow. Erect tail, dark band before white tip. Pale underparts, streaked black. **Size** 12–13 cm. **Voice** Musical, twittering. **Hab.** Scrubby heath, saltbush.

Western Fieldwren (Calamanthus) *Calamanthus (Sericornis) montanellus* UC–MC ◎ E

Sings above cover. Check Little Grassbird. Like Striated Fieldwren but olive-grey above; wing feathers edged pale olive-grey. Less rufous than Shy Heathwren. Pale eyebrow, underparts whitish. **Size** 11–14 cm. **Voice** Like Rufous. **Hab.** Sparse cover.

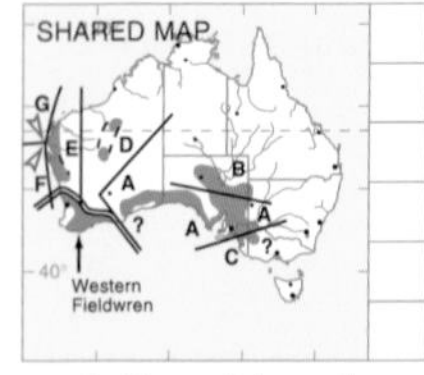

Rufous Fieldwren
A = Race *campestris* E
B = Race *isabellinus* E
C = Race *winiam* E
D = Race *wayensis* E
E = Race *rubiginosus* E
F = Race *hartogi* E **Vulnerable**
G = Race *dorrie* E **Vulnerable**

Western Fieldwren E

Striated Fieldwren (Calamanthus) *Calamanthus (Sericornis) fuliginosus* UC–MC ◎ E

Sings above cover. Check Little Grassbird. Olive above, buff below; all streaked black. White eyebrow, throat. Rufous frons, ear coverts. Dark tail band, white-tipped. Race *diemenensis* (B) Darker. Race *albiloris* (C) Bold streaks. Race *bourneorum* (D) 'Greener'. **F** Buff eyebrow, throat. **Size** 12–14 cm. **Voice** Musical twittering. **Hab.** Damp coastal, alpine heaths; saltmarsh.

Sings above cover

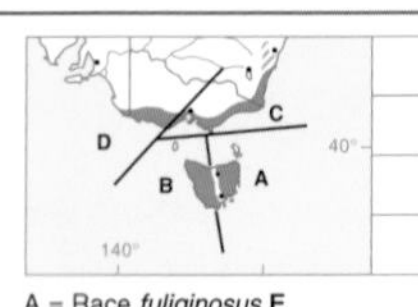

A = Race *fuliginosus* E
B = Race *diemenensis* E
C = Race *albiloris* E
D = Race *bourneorum* E

Redthroat *Pyrrholaemus brunneus* MC ◎ E

Pale eyebrow, lores. Chin, throat, chestnut-red centre. Upperparts grey-brown, washed olive on back, rump. Tail darker; white outer tail feathers, tip. Greyish below. Northern inland birds paler. **F** Chin white, throat grey. **Size** 11.5–12 cm. **Voice** Rich, varied like Reed-Warbler but softer. Accomplished mimic; female less so. **Hab.** Mallee, mulga, saltbush, bluebush, lignum, spinifex.

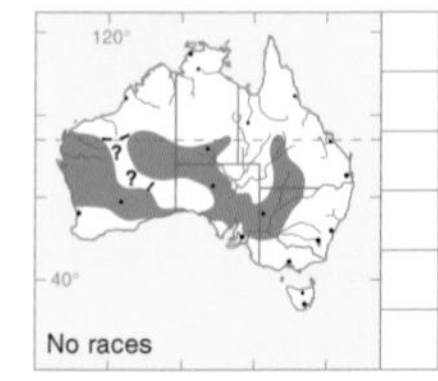

No races

Speckled Warbler *Pyrrholaemus (Chthonicola) sagittatus* MC–UC ◎ E

Often with thornbills. Crown brown, finely streaked white. Black line above long eyebrow. Whitish eyebrow, lores, behind ear coverts. Back, wings grey-brown, broadly streaked darker. Cream below, yellower flanks, boldly streaked blackish. Tail black subterminal band, white tip. **F** Chestnut stripe over eyebrow. **Size** 11.5–12.5 cm. **Juv.** Brow as female; underparts speckled. **Voice** Soft, musical, song; harsh grating twitters; mimicry. **Hab.** Open woodland. Nests, forages in ground litter.

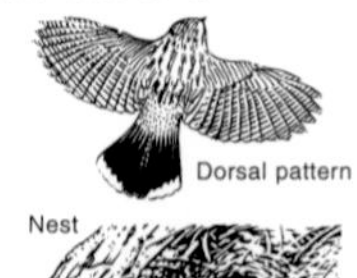
Dorsal pattern

Nest

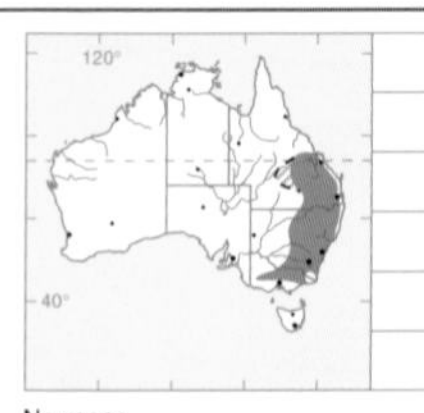

No races

Juv.
Chestnut-rumped
Heathwren
♀
♂
Shy Heathwren
Juv.
♂
Rufous
Fieldwren ♂
Striated
Fieldwren ♂
Western
Fieldwren ♂
Little
Grassbird
Redthroat
♂
♀
♀
Speckled
Warbler
♂

Weebill *Smicrornis brevirostris* **C** ◎ E

Check pardalotes, Yellow Thornbill. Pale eyebrow. Bill short, pale. Face pale; ear streaked. Back olive; abdomen yellow. Races *flavescens* (B) Brighter, yellower; *occidentalis* (C) Greyer; crown deep grey; *ochrogaster* (D) Paler birds. **Size** 8–9 cm. **Voice** Loud for small bird: repeated 'wheet-will'; 'whit-a-whit'. Lower 'tizit'. **Hab.** Foliage of drier forest, woodland.

Yellow Thornbill

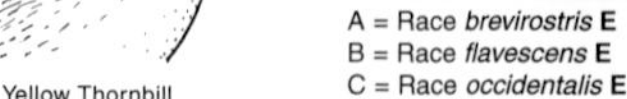
A = Race *brevirostris* **E**
B = Race *flavescens* **E**
C = Race *occidentalis* **E**
D = Race *ochrogaster* **E**

White-throated Gerygone *Gerygone olivacea* **LMC** ↻

Eye red. White forehead spot. Upperparts grey-brown. Tail dark, white tips. Throat white. Bright yellow below. Race *cinerascens* (B) Smaller, paler. **Size** 10 cm. **Juv.** All yellow below. **Voice** Distinctive falling, tinkling song. **Hab.** Open forest, woodland.

Gerygones previously called 'warblers', 'fairy-warblers', 'fly-eaters'.

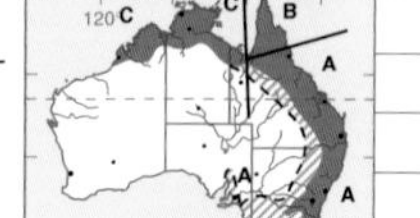
A = Race *olivacea* **E**
B = Race *cinerascens*
C = Race *rogersi* **E**

Fairy Gerygone *Gerygone palpebrosa* **C–MC** ◎

Check Green-backed Honeyeater. Race *personata* (A) 'Black-throated Warbler'. Deep olive-black face, throat. White frons, cheek stripe. Brown-green above; lemon below. Race *flavida* (B) Greener. Chin blackish, throat yellow-grey. White tail marks. **F** Whitish throat (both races). **Size** 10–11.5 cm. **Juv.** Pale yellow throat. **Voice** Long warble. **Hab.** Rainforest, mangroves.

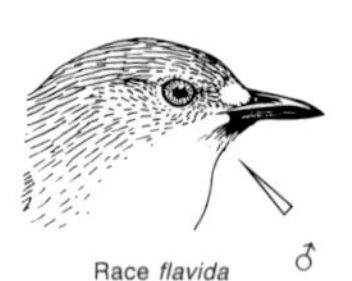
Race *flavida* ♂

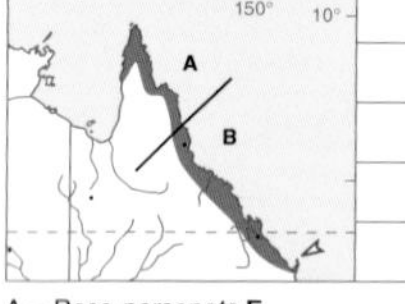
A = Race *personata* **E**
B = Race *flavida* **E**

Green-backed Gerygone *Gerygone chloronotus* **MC** ◎

Black bill. Red eye. Grey head. 'Silvereye'-green above. Greyish-white below; yellow flanks, undertail. Tail brown. **Size** 10 cm. **Voice** Repeated musical reel. **Hab.** Dense edges of paperbark swamps, mangroves, nearby open forest.

Gerygone undertail patterns

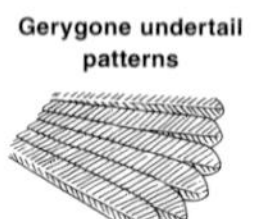

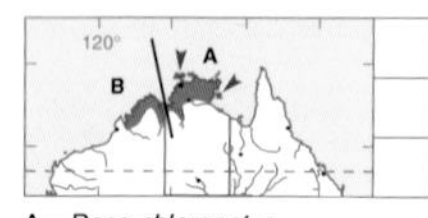
A = Race *chloronotus*
B = Race *darwini* **E**

Brown Gerygone *Gerygone mouki* **MC** ◎ E

Bold white eyebrow. Eye red-brown in grey face. Olive-grey above, whitish below. Dark tail band; spotted white. Race *richmondi* (B) Warmer brown. **Size** 9.5–10 cm. **Voice** Busy soft calls, insect-like. **Hab.** Rainforest, mangroves, dense gullies.

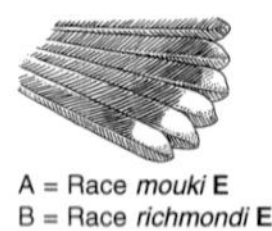
A = Race *mouki* **E**
B = Race *richmondi* **E**
C = Race *amalia* **E**

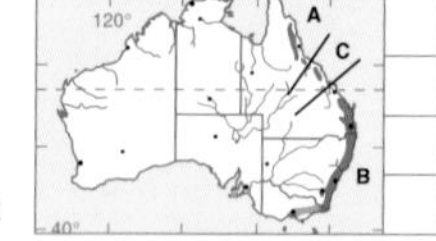

Western Gerygone *Gerygone fusca* **C** ◎ E

Faint eyebrow; red eye. Greyish-brown above, whitish below. Tail dark, bold white spots. **Size** 11–11.5 cm. **Juv.** Yellowish. **Voice** Sweet rising, falling, fading. **Hab.** Open woodland, mallee.

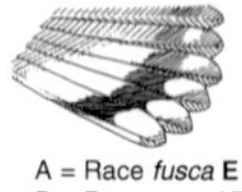
A = Race *fusca* **E**
B = Race *mungi* **E**
C = Race *exsul* **E**

Mangrove Gerygone *Gerygone levigaster* **C** ◎

Bold white eyebrow; reddish eye. Warm brown above, buff-white below. Dark tail, tip white. Race *cantator* (B) Deep brown above; grey-white below. **Size** 11 cm. **Juv.** Yellow throat, breast. **Voice** Plaintive warble. **Hab.** Mangroves and their edges; gardens.

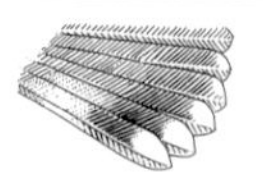
A = Race *levigaster*
B = Race *cantator* **E**

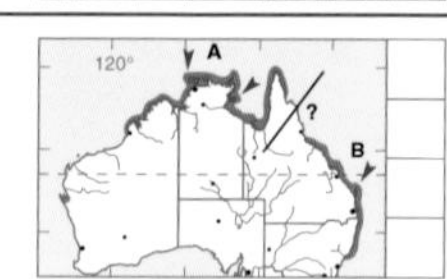

Large-billed Gerygone *Gerygone magnirostris* **C** ◎

Check Large-billed Scrubwren. No eyebrow. Thin white eye-ring. Olive-brown back. White chin, throat; greyish flanks. Race *cairnsensis* (B) Smaller. Warmer brown. Pale tail tips. **Size** 10.5–11.5 cm. **Voice** Jerky, falling reels. **Hab.** Mangroves, streams.

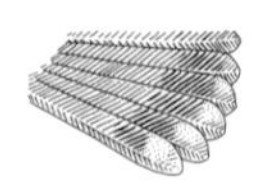

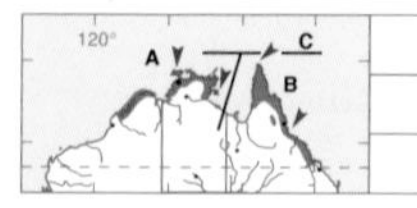
A = Race *magnirostris*
B = Race *cairnsensis* **E**
C = Race *brunneipectus* **E**

Dusky Gerygone *Gerygone tenebrosa* **C** ◎ E

White eye, long eyebrow. Plain olive-grey above; dusky below. Plain tail. Race *christophori* (B) Larger, paler. **Size** 11.5 cm. **Voice** Plaintive, slow, whistler-like. **Hab.** Mangroves.

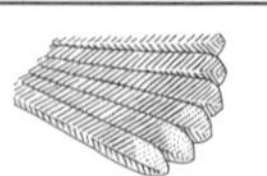
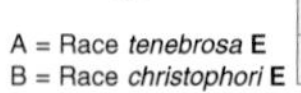
A = Race *tenebrosa* **E**
B = Race *christophori* **E**

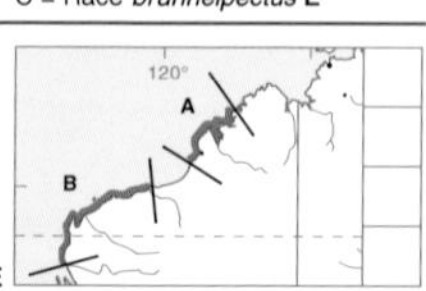

Weebill
Race flavescens
White-throated
Gerygone
White-throated
Gerygone
Juv.
Weebill
Race brevirostris
Fairy Gerygone
♀
Fairy Gerygone ♂
Race personata
Green-backed
Gerygone
Fairy Gerygone
Juv.
Western
Gerygone
Brown
Gerygone
Mangrove Gerygone
Race cantator
Mangrove
Gerygone
Juv.
Large-billed
Gerygone
Race magnirostris
Dusky Gerygone

Mountain Thornbill *Acanthiza katherina* **LC** ◎ E

Note Reflected light often 'greens' the plumage of birds in dense forest.
Eye obviously whitish. Frons buff-olive with pale crescents. Greenish-brown to grey-brown upperparts. Dull rufous rump. Pale to greenish-yellow underparts. **Size** 10 cm. **Voice** Resembles Brown Thornbill, sweeter, louder. **Hab.** Rainforest.

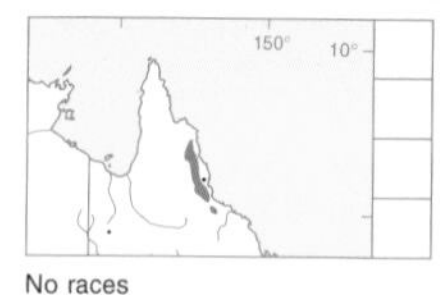
No races

Slaty-backed Thornbill *Acanthiza robustirostris* **C** ◎ E

Identify from Inland Thornbill. Eye red-brown. Frons, crown grey with dark streaks. Slaty-grey upperparts contrast with cinnamon rump. Black tail, tipped dull white. Underparts greyish-white. **Size** 9–9.5 cm. **Voice** Distinctive 'tiz-tiz'; also harsh 'trrit, trrit' alarm. **Hab.** Inland scrub-covered plains, mulga.

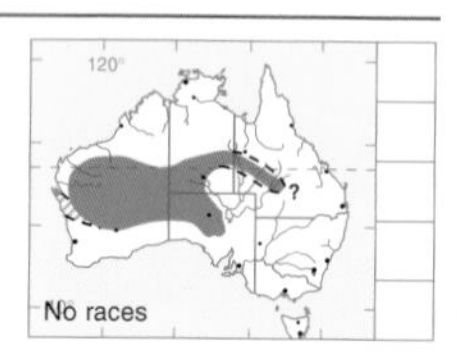
No races

Brown Thornbill *Acanthiza pusilla* **C–LUC** ◎–♣ E

Often in lower vegetation. Identify from Scrubtit, Weebill, Brown Gerygone, Striated Thornbill, juv. White-browed Scrubwren. Dark red eye. Frons rufous with pale buff crescents. Olive-brown above. Cinnamon-brown rump. Light grey, streaked black, below. Brownish flanks. Vary slightly across range: northern birds lighter above, creamy white below. **Size** 10 cm. **Voice** Deep, pleasant 2-note warble; harsh alarm call, rather similar to White-browed Scrubwren's. **Hab.** Understorey in forest; wooded areas with undergrowth; gardens.

Juv.

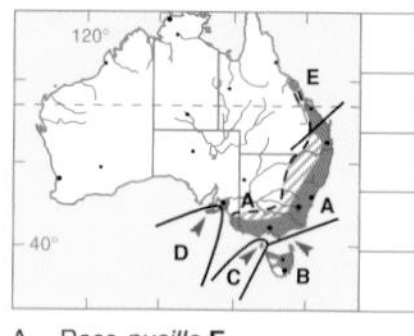
A = Race *pusilla* **E**
B = Race *diemenensis* **E**
C = Race *archibaldi* **E Endangered**
D = Race *zeitzi* **E**
E = Race *dawsonensis* **E**

Inland (Broad-tailed) Thornbill *Acanthiza apicalis* **C** ◎ E

Carries tail cocked. Eye red. Frons finely scalloped, whitish. Black striations on face, throat, breast. Back mid grey-brown. Red-brown rump. Flanks washed rufous. Race *albiventris* (B) Darker, richer rump. Race *whitlocki* (C) Pale grey-brown back, duller rump, white belly. Extreme northern population of *whitlocki* (former race *tanami*) Sandy coloured; dull-rumped. Race *cinerascens* (D) Light grey above, paler below. **Size** 10 cm. **Voice** Similar to Brown, harsher. **Hab.** Dry scrub, mallee, heath.

Tail cocked

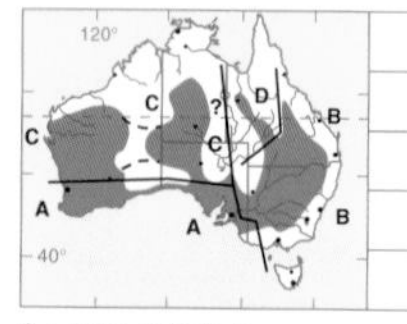
A = Race *apicalis* **E**
B = Race *albiventris* **E**
C = Race *whitlocki* **E**
D = Race *cinerascens* **E**

Tasmanian Thornbill *Acanthiza ewingii* **C** ◎ E

Identify from Brown Thornbill, Scrubtit and larger, darker White-browed ('Tasmanian') Scrubwren. Fluffy white feathers at side of tail very prominent, diagnostic. Eye red. Frons faintly tawny. Deep olive-brown back. Rufous wash on edges of wing feathers, rump. Pale throat, breast, dappled grey. Race *rufifrons* (B) More rufous above. **Size** 10 cm. **Juv.** Smaller. **Voice** Like Brown Thornbill, except when breeding. **Hab.** Tas. woodland, scrub.

Pale coverts

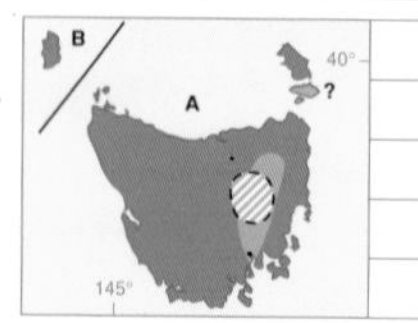
A = Race *ewingii* **E**
B = Race *rufifrons* **E**

Chestnut-rumped Thornbill *Acanthiza uropygialis* **C** ◎ E

Identify from Inland Thornbill. Eye white. Frons light brown, speckled white. Face pale, freckled. Upperparts dull brown. Chestnut rump. Tail black, tipped white. Underparts white. **Size** 10 cm. **Voice** Short, melodious song; also penetrating 'see-tzit-tzit-see'. **Hab.** Dry woodland, mallee, mulga.

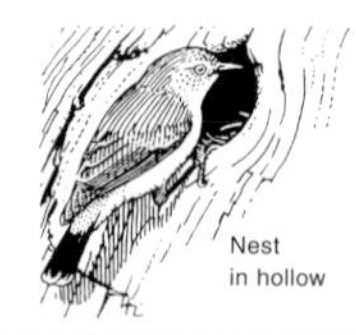
Nest in hollow

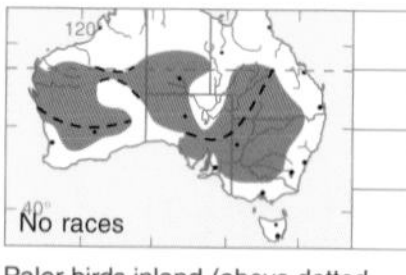
No races
Paler birds inland (above dotted line); darker, greyer birds (below).

Western Thornbill *Acanthiza inornata* **C** ◎ E

Identify from Chestnut-rumped, Inland Thornbills. Does not cock tail. Frons light, freckled brown. Whitish eye. Upperparts grey-brown. Pale olive rump. Tail brown. Underparts pale buff, no streaks. Greyer-backed birds, richer buff below, in northern part of range. **Size** 10 cm. **Voice** Soft twittering; good mimic. **Hab.** Open woodland, karri and jarrah forest, gardens, coastal scrub.

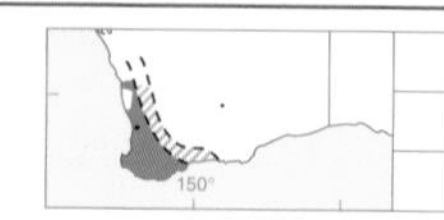
No races

Mountain Thornbill
Slaty-backed Thornbill
Brown Thornbill
Slaty-backed Thornbill
White-browed Scrubwren
Race *frontalis*
Tasmanian Thornbill
Inland Thornbill
Chestnut-rumped Thornbill
Inland Thornbill
Race *albiventris*
Brown Thornbill
Tasmanian Thornbill
Western Thornbill
Chestnut-rumped Thornbill
Western Thornbill

Yellow (Little) Thornbill *Acanthiza nana* **C** ◎–♧ E

Check Weebill (strong pale bill), Striated Thornbill. Paler birds inland. Bill black. Eye dark; no eyebrow. Streaked ear coverts. Plain brown crown. Dull olive-green above. Yellow below, washed rufous on throat. Tail brown. **Size** 10 cm. **Voice** Persistent 'tizz tizz'. **Hab.** Dry forest; acacias, box eucalypts.

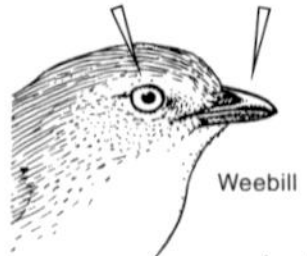

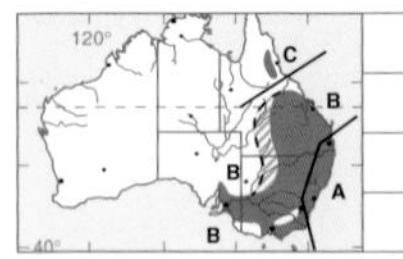

A = Race *nana* **E** C = Race *flava* **E**
B = Race *modesta* **E**

Striated Thornbill *Acanthiza lineata* **C** ◎ E

Check Weebill. Feeds 'higher' than Brown Thornbills; hovers at foliage. Copper crown, streaked white. White brow; pale eye in striated face. Olive back. Dark striations on cream breast. Flanks grey-olive. Race *alberti* (B) Greener. Race *clelandi* (C) Yellower. **Size** 10 cm. **Voice** Staccato 'tzizz, tzizz'. **Hab.** Dry to wet forest.

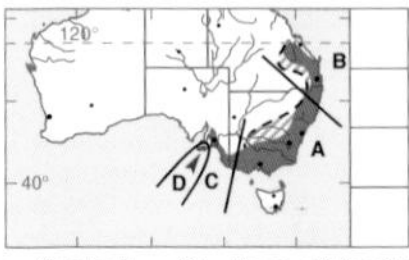

A = Race *lineata* **E** C = Race *clelandi* **E**
B = Race *alberti* **E** D = Race *whitei* **E**

Buff-rumped Thornbill *Acanthiza reguloides* **C–MC** ◎ E

Ground forager. Check Yellow-rumped. Frons, face, scalloped buff. White eye, throat speckled grey. Grey-brown above, creamy buff below. Broad black tail band; white tip. Pale buff rump. Races (B), (C), more yellow; (D) dull buff, darker. **Size** 11 cm. **Voice** Tinkling reel. **Hab.** Open forest, lightly timbered ranges.

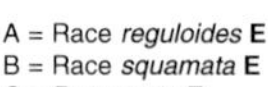
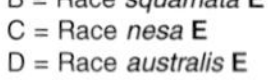

A = Race *reguloides* **E**
B = Race *squamata* **E**
C = Race *nesa* **E**
D = Race *australis* **E**

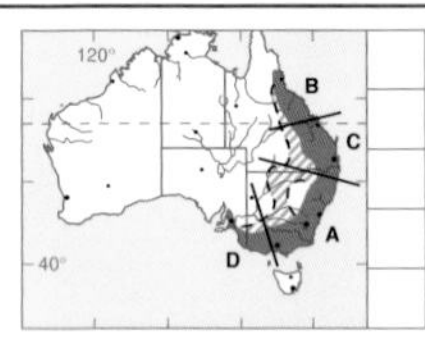

Slender-billed Thornbill *Acanthiza iredalei* **UC** ◎ E

Pale eye. Pale speckled forehead, face. Olive-grey above; pale buff rump. Creamy underparts. Tail dark brown, tipped white. Eastern races darker. **Size** 9 cm. **Voice** Musical twitter in flight. **Hab.** Samphire near salt pans; semi-desert, sandplain heath.

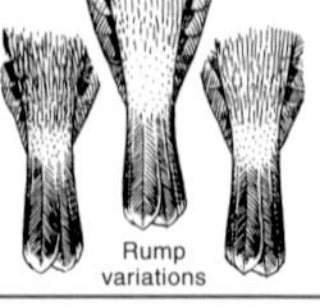
Rump variations

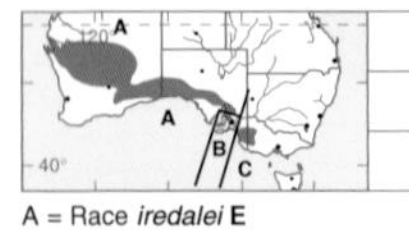

A = Race *iredalei* **E**
B = Race *rosinae* **E Vulnerable**
C = Race *hedleyi* **E**

Yellow-rumped Thornbill *Acanthiza chrysorrhoa* **C** ◎–♧ E

Small flocks on ground. Forecrown black, spotted white. White eyebrow, dark eye-line. Spotted cheek. Olive-brown above, creamy below; flanks buff washed. Rump dull yellow. Dark tail, tipped white. Race *leighi* (B) More olive; deep yellow rump, more buff below. Race *normantoni* (C) Paler. Bright yellow rump. Race *leachi* (D) Duller. **Size** 10–12 cm. **Voice** Repetitive tinkling song. **Hab.** Open woodland, farms, pine forest margins.

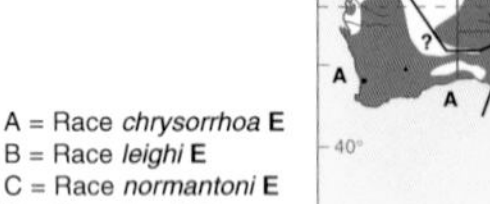

A = Race *chrysorrhoa* **E**
B = Race *leighi* **E**
C = Race *normantoni* **E**
D = Race *leachi* **E**

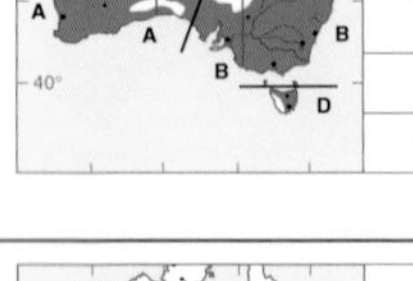

Southern Whiteface *Aphelocephala leucopsis* **C–MC** ◎ E

Note Face pattern diagnostic in whitefaces: all species look 'unhappy'. Ground forager. Check thornbills, Weebill, juv. Zebra Finch. Eye white. Black border through eye above white face. Grey-brown upperparts. Underparts off-white, flanks mottled grey-buff. Dull brown tail, white tip. Race *castaneiventris* (B) Chestnut flanks. Birds paler inland (both races). **Size** 10 cm. **Voice** Tinkling, wistful. **Hab.** Open arid country, esp. near dead trees.

Foraging with Yellow-rumped Thornbills

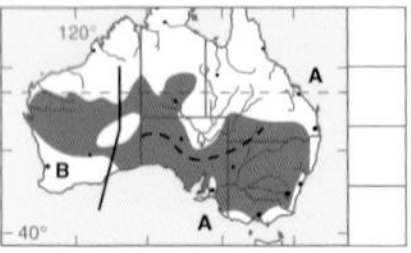

A = Race *leucopsis* **E**
B = Race *castaneiventris* **E**

Chestnut-breasted Whiteface *Aphelocephala pectoralis* **UC** ◎ E

Eye white. Face white, bordered black before grey crown. Back rusty-brown. Chestnut band across chest. Rufous flank marks. **Size** 10 cm. **Juv.** Paler breasted. **Voice** Plaintive bell-like tinkle. **Hab.** Gibber plains, semi-desert.

Breast marking

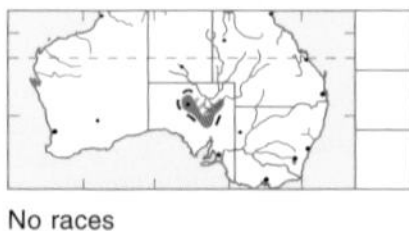
No races

Banded Whiteface *Aphelocephala nigricincta* **MC** ◎ E

Accompanies thornbills, other whitefaces. Eye white. White face, bordered black on forehead. Chestnut-brown back, rich rump. Whitish below; narrow black breast band. Rufous flank marks. **Size** 10 cm. **Voice** Musical trill, weaker than Southern Whiteface. **Hab.** Gibber plains; sandhills with scattered plants, saltbush.

Breast marking

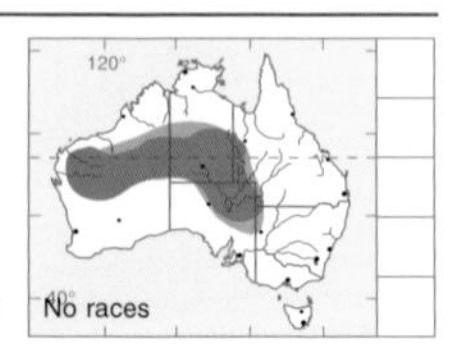

No races

Yellow Thornbill
Striated Thornbill
Slender-billed Thornbill
Slender-billed Thornbill
Yellow-rumped Thornbill
Yellow-rumped Thornbill
Buff-rumped Thornbill
Race reguloides
Buff-rumped Thornbill
Race reguloides
Buff-rumped Thornbill
Race squamata
Southern Whiteface
Race castaneiventris
Chestnut-breasted Whiteface
Banded Whiteface
Southern Whiteface
Race leucopsis
N. Day

Red Wattlebird *Anthochaera carunculata* **C** E

Flocks follow flowering in autumn, winter. Domineering behaviour to other birds. Large, slender grey-brown honeyeater, white streaks (smaller, more streaked in WA). Iris dark red. Wattle at ear dark pink. Crown blackish; silvery-white face. Belly yellow. Legs pink. **F** Smaller. Race *clelandi* (B) Notably darker. **Size** 33–37 cm. **Juv.** Iris red-brown. Browner, smaller wattles; very white wing feather edges. **Voice** Raucous 'tobacco box', 'chokk'; 'growling' sounds when in flocks. **Hab.** Forests, woods, suburbs.

Calling

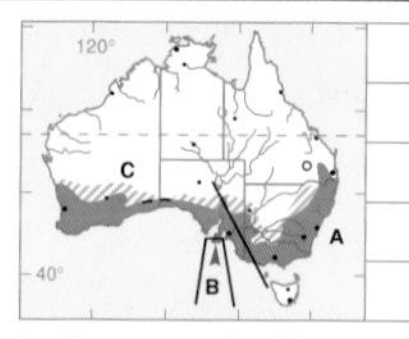

A = Race *carunculata* **E**
B = Race *clelandi* **E**
C = Race *woodwardi*

Yellow Wattlebird *Anthochaera paradoxa* **C** ◎ E

Largest honeyeater. White face contrasts with black-streaked crown, nape. Long, pendulous, yellow-orange wattle. Grey-brown upper body, streaked white; dark wings. Whiter below; yellow belly. Long tail. **F** Much smaller. **Size** M 44–50; F 37–43 cm. **Juv.** Crown paler; smaller wattles; belly brownish. **Voice** Raucous 'kuk', 'kukuk'. **Hab.** Tas. coastal heaths with emergent eucalypts; forests, gardens.

Ventral flight

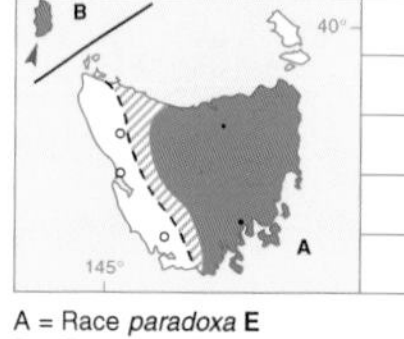

A = Race *paradoxa* **E**
B = Race *kingi* **E**

Western Wattlebird *Anthochaera lunulata* **C** E

Rufous wing patch conspicuous in flight. Long slender black bill. Iris red-brown. Face, cheek, side of neck strongly streaked silver-white. No wattles. Dark olive-brown, finely streaked and spotted with white. White margins to all wing coverts. Belly streaked grey-white. **F** Smaller. **Size** M 29–33; F 27–31 cm. **Juv.** Plumage less striated. **Voice** Prominent in 'dawn chorus'. Loud drawn-out complex, chattering song with many 'chock' sounds; high rapid twittering. **Hab.** Coastal woodlands, heaths, scrubs, gardens.

Face patterns

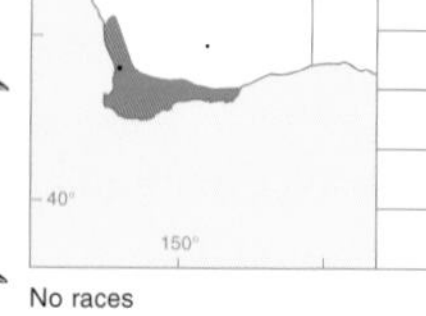

No races

Little ('Brush') Wattlebird *Anthochaera chrysoptera* **C** E

Aggressive to other h'eaters. Rufous wing patch in flight. Iris pale khaki. Brown face, cheek, side of neck. No wattles. Grey-brown bird, finely streaked. Some southern Vic. and NSW birds have pale yellow belly flush. **F** Smaller. Race *tasmanica* (B) Darker. Race *halmaturina* (C) Kangaroo Is. Very dark (melanistic). **Size** 27–35 cm. **Juv./Imm.** Eye dark. Fluffier plumage, less striated. **Voice** Harsh cackles at dawn, 'cockay cock', 'quok'. **Hab.** Woodland, heath, scrub; favours *Banksia*; coastal parks, gardens.

Calling

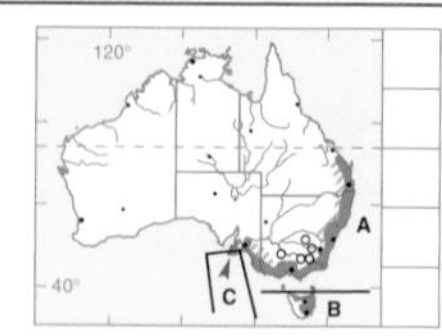

A = Race *chrysoptera* **E**
B = Race *tasmanica* **E**
C = Race *halmaturina* **E**

Spiny-cheeked Honeyeater *Acanthagenys rufogularis* **C** E

Large cinnamon-breasted honeyeater with dark-tipped pink bill. Iris pale blue. Pink skin under eye, about gape, above white cheek spines. Crown grey-brown, finely scalloped. Back mottled grey-brown. Wing feathers white-edged. Rump pale grey. Cinnamon throat, breast; creamy-white below, brownish streaks. Tail black-brown, white tip. Some darker-bellied on Mornington Penin., Vic. **Size** 22–27 cm. **Juv.** Iris brown. Facial skin paler. Yellow spines. **Voice** Slow 'butcherbird' warble when perched; sharp 'tock'. **Hab.** Desert, mallee, woodland, coastal scrub; orchards.

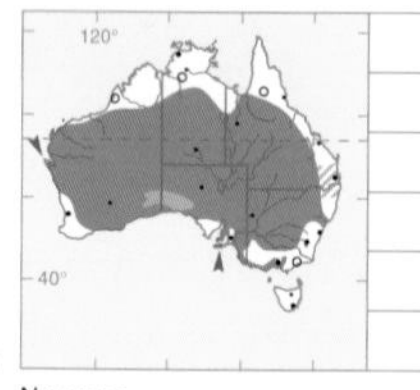

No races

Striped Honeyeater *Plectorhyncha lanceolata* **MC** ? E

Whitish head, nape, boldly streaked black. White eyebrow. Chin, throat off-white. Throat, upper sides of breast feathers lanceolate, white centres. Mantle grey-brown, heavily streaked brown. Wings, tail brown. Whitish below, finely streaked. Bill, legs, grey-blue. **F** Browner back; faint buff-grey underparts. **Size** 21.5–23.5 cm. **Juv.** As female, paler; less streaked. Can appear 'fluffy' when perched. **Voice** Melodious 'cherr-cherr-cherry-cherry'. **Hab.** Mallee, woodland, open forests.

Calling

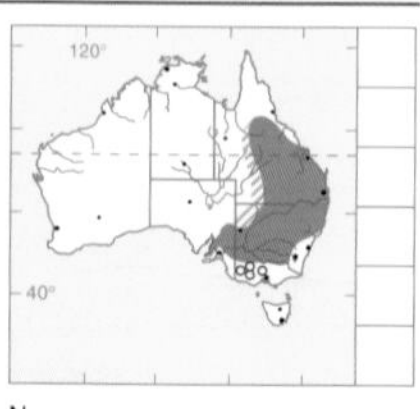

No races

Red Wattlebird
Little Wattlebird
Little Wattlebird
Red Wattlebird
Red Wattlebird ♂
Red Wattlebird Juv.
Yellow Wattlebird Juv.
Yellow Wattlebird
Little Wattlebird Juv. Race chrysoptera
Little Wattlebird Race chrysoptera
Western Wattlebird
Spiny-cheeked Honeyeater
Striped Honeyeater Juv.
Spiny-cheeked Honeyeater Juv.
Striped Honeyeater
N. DAY.

Helmeted Friarbird *Philemon buceroides* **LC**

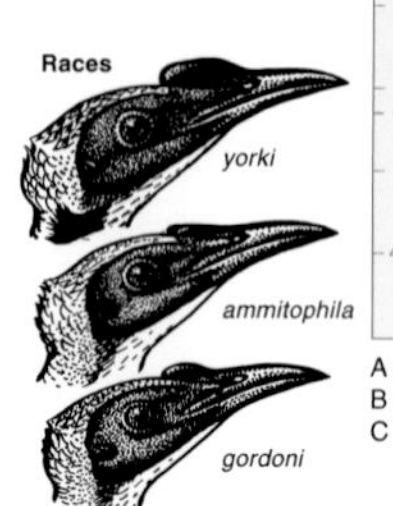

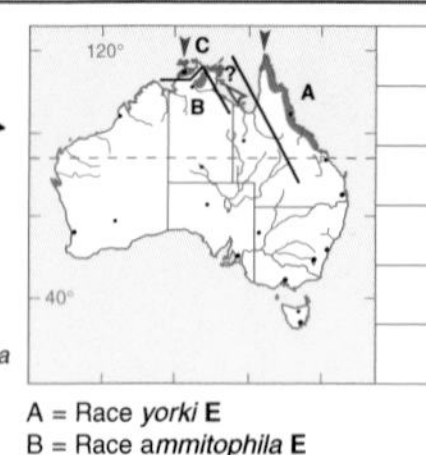

A = Race *yorki* **E**
B = Race *ammitophila* **E**
C = Race *gordoni* **E**

Largest mainland honeyeater; largest Aust. friarbird. Silver crown, frilled whitish nape. Large, gently sloping knob (casque) on bill base. Iris red-brown. Face bare, skin dark leaden-grey. Back, rump, tail grey-brown. Underparts paler, silvery-brown and lightly streaked. Race *ammitophila* (B) 'Sandstone Friarbird' Larger; no knob. Race *gordoni* (C) 'Melville Island Friarbird' Smaller. **Size** 32–36 cm. **Juv.** Eye brown. Smaller knob. Throat, breast less streaked. **Imm.** Back, rump, sides of neck, scalloped white. **Voice** Harsh, repetitive squawks, yaps; 'poor devil, poor devil'; 'watch-out'; *ammitophila* metallic 'chank'. **Hab.** Race *yorki* (A) Closed forest, gardens; woodland; *ammitophila* (B) Sandstone areas; *gordoni* (C) Mangroves.

Silver-crowned Friarbird *Philemon argenticeps* **LC** E

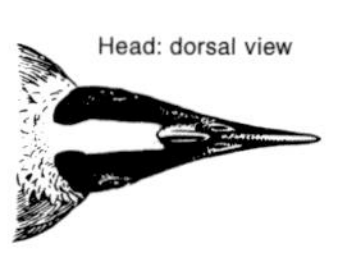

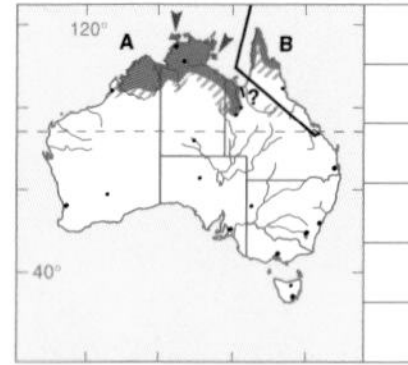

A = Race *argenticeps* **E**
B = Race *kempi* **E**

Like Helmeted Friarbird, smaller. Iris red-brown. Face bare; skin blackish. Forehead, crown, nape silvery-grey (nape tufted). Conspicuous small, erect knob on bill base. Dull grey-brown back, rump, tail. Silvery-grey gorget ('breastplate'); rest of underparts paler. **Size** 25–32 cm. **Juv.** Eye brown; smaller knob. Yellow wash on throat. **Imm.** Back, rump, sides of neck scalloped white. **Voice** Harsh 'more tobacco, uh-more tobacco-uh'; warning 'plik'. **Hab.** Open forests, woodland, mangroves.

Noisy Friarbird *Philemon corniculatus* **C–LA** –?

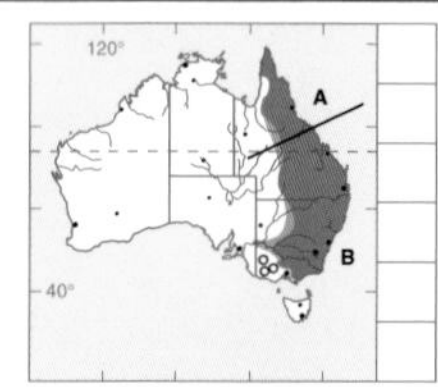

A = Race *corniculatus* **Br. E**
B = Race *monachus* **E**

Gregarious, noisy; often in large flocks. Eye red; narrow buffy eyebrow; silvery chin feathers. Small knob (casque) on bill bas Head has bare black skin. Plumed gorget of long dark-shafted silvery feathers. Plain dull brown back, rump, tail. Pale grey below. Race *monachus* (B) Larger, greyer. **Size** 30–35 cm. **Juv.** Eye brown. Neck, back of head, feathered. No knob or gorget. **Imm.** Small casque. **Voice** Loud, raucous 'four-o-cloc 'chokk chokk'. **Hab.** Open forests, woodland, gardens.

Little Friarbird *Philemon citreogularis* **C–LA** –?

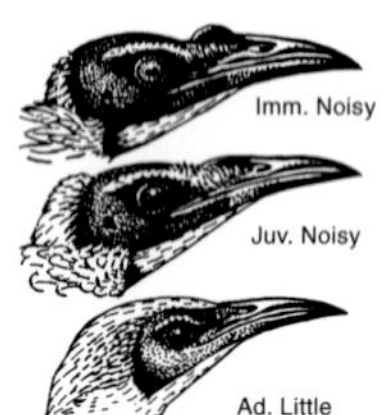

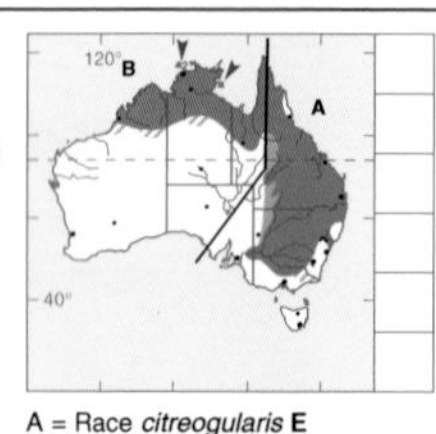

A = Race *citreogularis* **E**
B = Race *sordidus* **E**

No knob on bill. Head grey-brown. Eye dark. Dark feathers above and below prominent bare, bluish-black facial skin. Whitish nape. Back dark grey-brown. Fine silky white chin feathers. Silvery-white streaks on breast. Underparts pale grey. **Size** 25–29 cm. **Juv.** Browner; yellowish wash over throat. **Imm.** Face duller. Back, rump, edged white. Tiny yellow spots on side of breast. **Voice** Musical series of double notes; harsh chatter; 'arr-koo'. **Hab.** Open forest, woodland, orchards.

Regent Honeyeater *Xanthomyza phrygia* **R** E Endangered

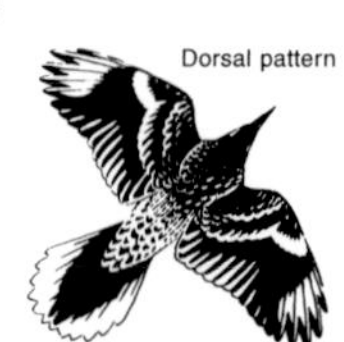

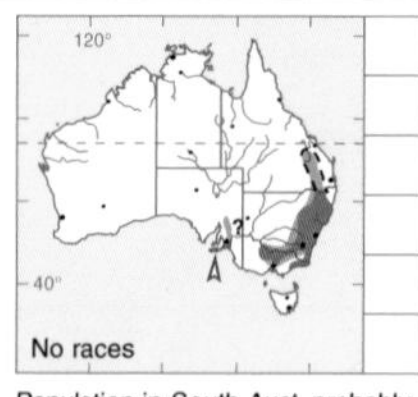

Population in South Aust. probably extinct.

Now known to be related to the wattlebirds.

Striking black and yellow honeyeater. Follows blossoming eucalypts, mistletoe; fruits. Bobs head when calling. Variable yellowish or pinkish bare warty facial skin encloses eye. Bill, head, neck, throat, upper breast, black. Pale lemon back, breast, scaled black. Wings mainly black, conspicuous yellow patches. Belly feathers pale lemon, black margins. White to pale yellow undertail coverts. Tail feathers black, yellow outer-web. **F** Shorter bill; facial skin less extensive; less black on throat. **Size** 20–24 cm. **Juv.** Bill yellow. Sooty brown. Paler, less extensive yellow pattern of wings, tail. Whitish underparts. **Imm.** Brown; new plumage contrasts strongly during first moult. **Voice** Quiet, melodious flute-like chiming. Call resembles wattlebirds, friarbirds, in feeding flocks. **Hab.** Open forest, box-ironbark woodland.

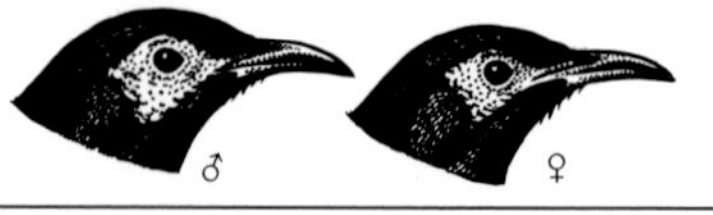

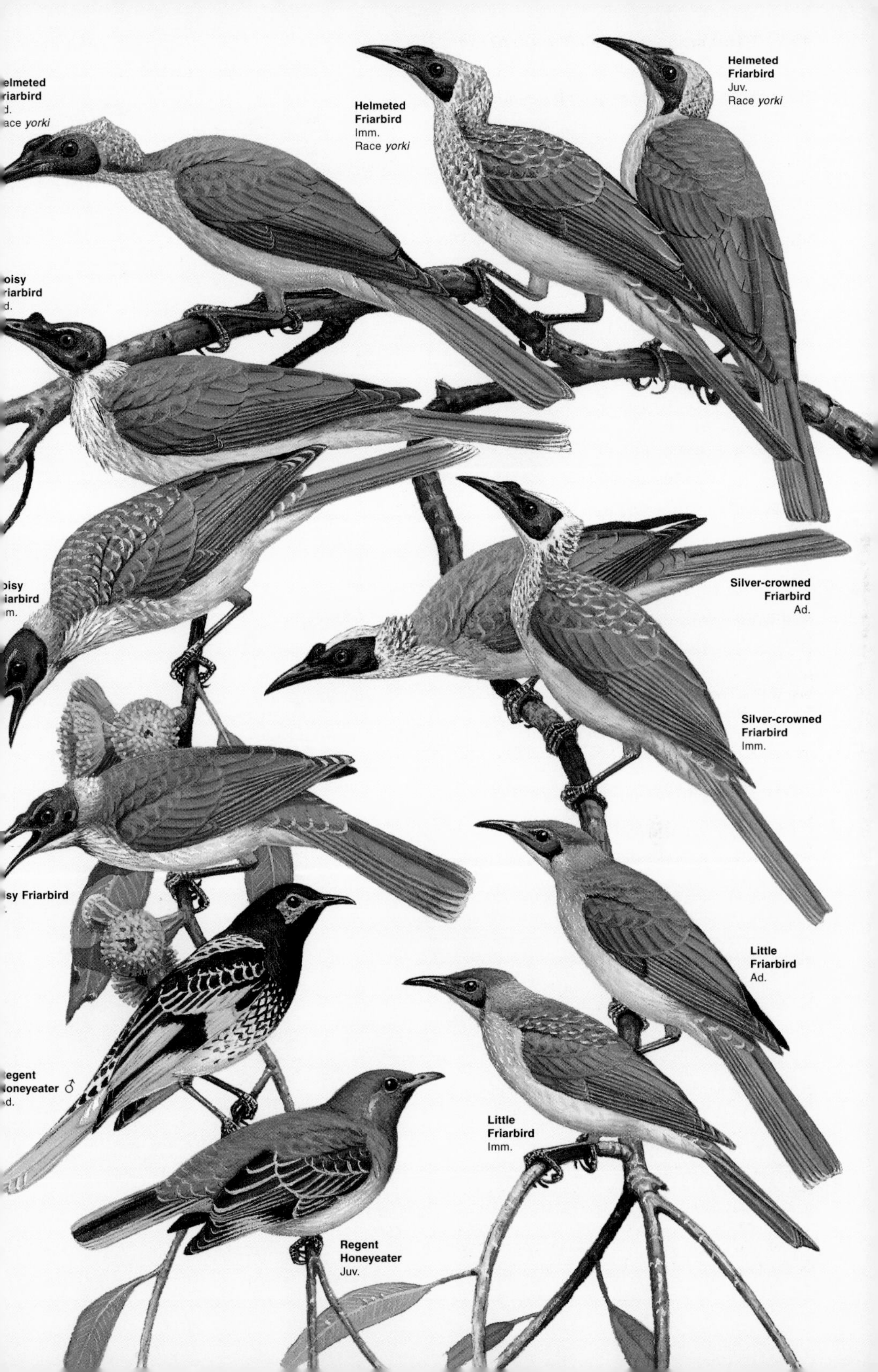

elmeted
riarbird
d.
ace yorki
Helmeted
Friarbird
Imm.
Race yorki
Helmeted
Friarbird
Juv.
Race yorki
oisy
riarbird
d.
oisy
iarbird
m.
Silver-crowned
Friarbird
Ad.
Silver-crowned
Friarbird
Imm.
isy Friarbird
Little
Friarbird
Ad.
egent
oneyeater ♂
d.
Little
Friarbird
Imm.
Regent
Honeyeater
Juv.

Blue-faced Honeyeater *Entomyzon cyanotis* **C–LC**

Head black, white line at nape. Yellow eye. Blue bare facial skin. White malar stripe. Bib dark grey. Back olive-yellow; white below. Buff wing patch in flight. Race *griseigularis* (B) Smaller. Larger facial skin area, wing patches. Race *albipennis* (C) Face patch greener; wing patch white. **Size** 26–32.3 cm. **Juv./Imm.** Head, throat, grey. Facial skin olive-yellow, turns blue by 16 months. **Voice** Penetrating 'ki-owt'. **Hab.** Open/riparian forest, gardens.

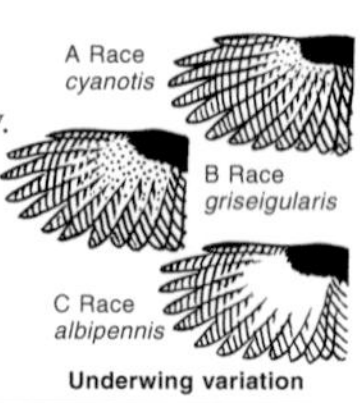

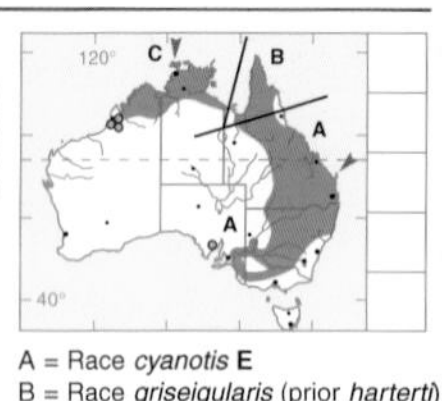

A = Race *cyanotis* **E**
B = Race *griseigularis* (prior *harterti*)
C = Race *albipennis* **E**

Macleay's Honeyeater *Xanthotis macleayana* **MC** E

Distinctive, dark honeyeater. Head and neck brown-black; nape speckled white. Naked skin below eye orange. Golden ear tufts. Back brown, heavily streaked buff-yellow and white. Chin grey. Breast darker, streaked olive and white. **Size** 17–21.5 cm. **Juv./Imm.** Duller, greyer. **Voice** Musical 'to wit, too weeee twit'. **Hab.** Rainforest, mangroves, gardens, banana plantations.

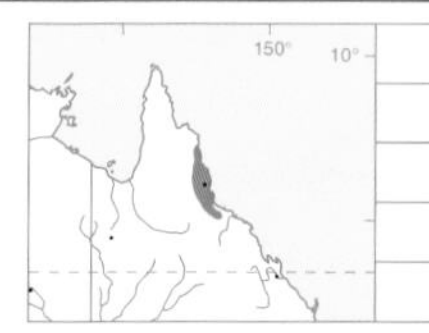

No races

Tawny-breasted Honeyeater *Xanthotis flaviventer* **MC**

Upperparts dark olive-brown, nape speckled grey. White streak under eye from gape to nape. Small yellow ear tuft. Throat, sides of neck, ear coverts grey. Breast tawny, faint streaks. Race *saturatior* (B) Northern Torres Strait islands, darker, plainer. **Size** 18–21 cm. **Juv.** Duller face, buff wing edges **Voice** Varied series of whistles. **Hab.** Mangroves, rainforest understorey, edges.

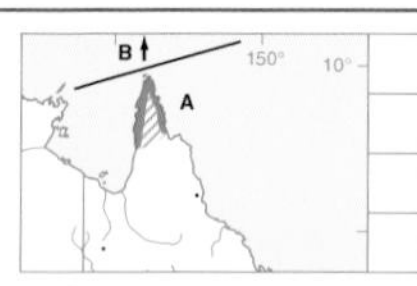

A = Race *filigera* **E**
B = Race *saturatior*

Bell Miner *Manorina melanophrys* **C** ◎ E

'Bellbird'. Aggressive, colonial. Olive-green head and back. Bill orange-yellow. Bare skin behind eye bright orange. Lores bright yellow; frons, cheek black. Legs orange. Underparts paler olive-green. **Size** 17.5–20 cm. **Juv./Imm.** Skin around eye paler. **Voice** Carrying bell-like 'tink'. **Hab.** Dense understorey of riparian forest with psyllid infestation, usually with dieback.

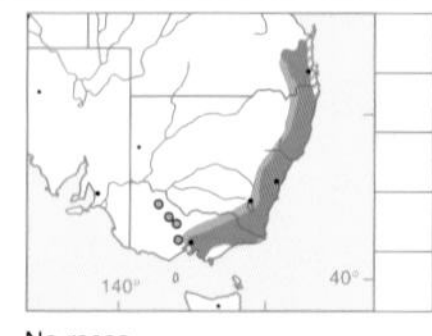

No races

Noisy Miner *Manorina melanocephala* **C** ◎ E

Colonial, aggressive. Black mask from crown to chin; rest of head grey. Bill, bare skin behind eye, feet, yellow. Back, rump grey. Underparts pale grey with darker scallops on breast. Tail tip white. **Size** 24–28 cm. **Juv.** Less distinctly marked. **Voice** 'A garrulous honeyeater'; harsh calls; 'pwee-pwee-pwe'. **Hab.** Open woodland; dominates cleared remnants, gardens.

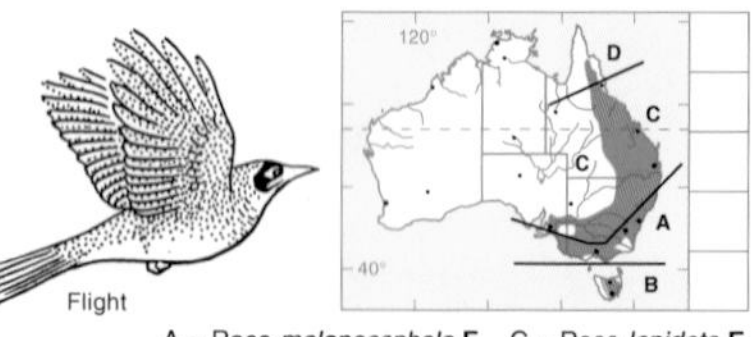

A = Race *melanocephala* **E**
B = Race *leachi* **E**
C = Race *lepidota* **E**
D = Race *titaniota* **E**

Yellow-throated Miner *Manorina flavigula* **C** ◎ E

Large flocks. Like a pale Noisy Miner. Black face mask, grey head, side of neck washed yellow. Two yellow streaks of bare skin from bill. Rump white. Race *obscura* (B) 'Dusky Miner' Narrow mask. Race *lutea* (C) Smaller, whiter. Race *wayensis* (D) Paler. Race *melvillensis* (E) Darkest. **Size** 22–28 cm. **Juv.** Throat yellower. Less scaling. **Voice** Sharper, higher than Noisy. **Hab.** Dry open woodland; part-cleared mallee and fringes, farms.

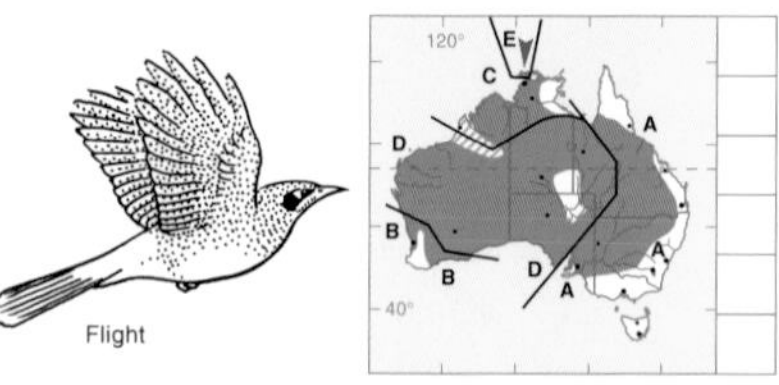

A = Race *flavigula* **E**
B = Race *obscura* **E**
C = Race *lutea* **E**
D = Race *wayensis* **E**
E = Race *melvillensis* **E**

Black-eared Miner *Manorina melanotis* **R** ◎ E Endangered

Cannot be reliably identified in field: intergrades with Yellow-throated Miner *flavigula* (A). Variably darker-bodied; black ear patch; less yellow forehead, cheeks, neck. Crown, throat, breast, back, rump, dark grey. Tail tips not white. **Size** 23–26 cm. **Voice** Like Noisy Miner. **Hab.** Totally undisturbed dense mallee.

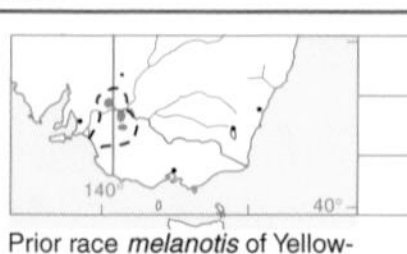

Prior race *melanotis* of Yellow-throated Miner

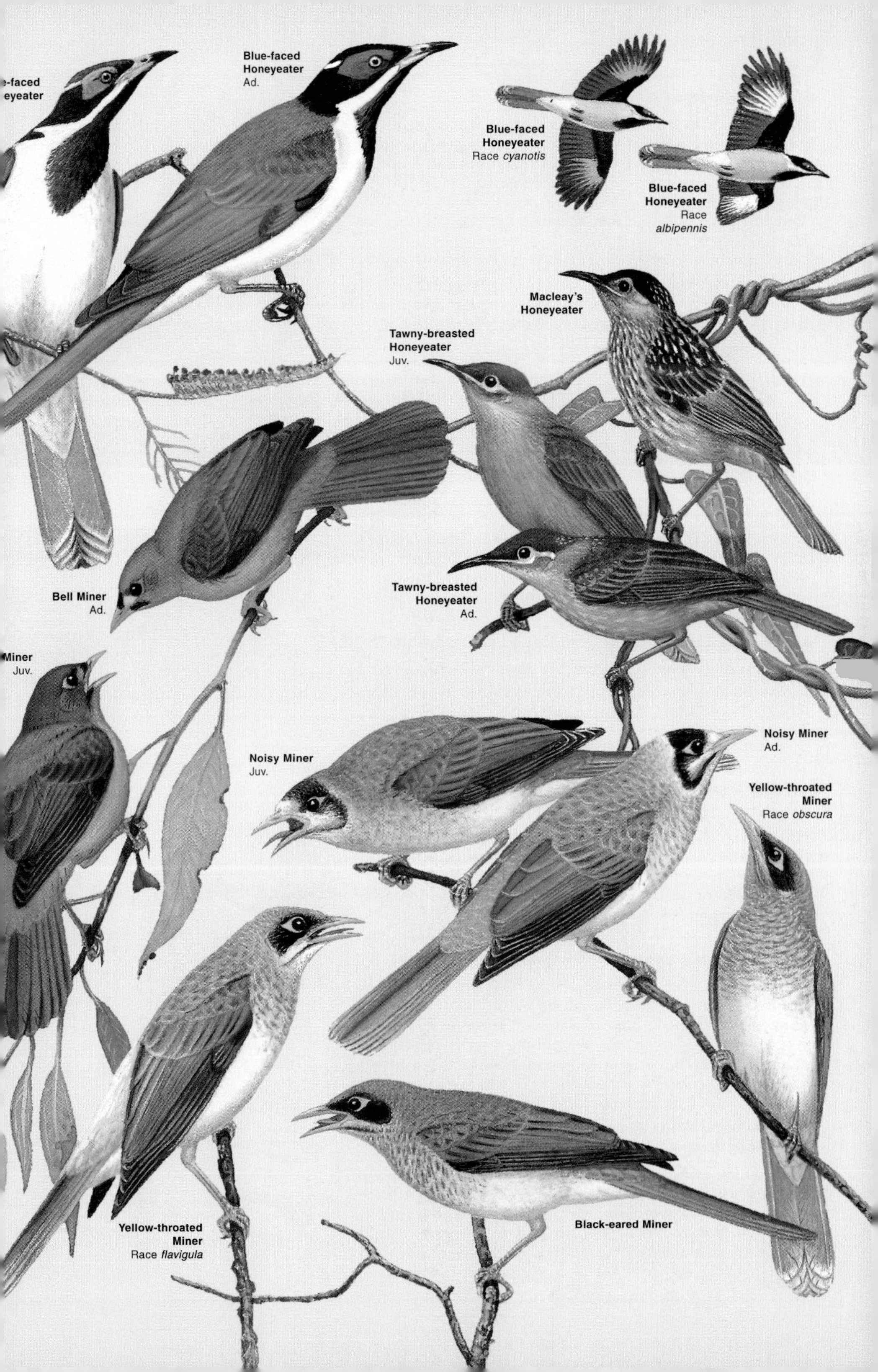

-faced
eyeater
Blue-faced
Honeyeater
Ad.
Blue-faced
Honeyeater
Race cyanotis
Blue-faced
Honeyeater
Race
albipennis
Macleay's
Honeyeater
Tawny-breasted
Honeyeater
Juv.
Bell Miner
Ad.
Tawny-breasted
Honeyeater
Ad.
Miner
Juv.
Noisy Miner
Juv.
Noisy Miner
Ad.
Yellow-throated
Miner
Race obscura
Yellow-throated
Miner
Race flavigula
Black-eared Miner

Lewin's Honeyeater *Meliphaga lewinii* **LC** E

Dark olive-green. Stout bill. Eye bluish. Dark head; crown tinged grey, squarish to crescentic yellow ear tufts. Cream gape extends under eye. Faint breast streaks. Race *mab* (B) Smaller, lighter. Race *amphochlora* (C) Longer-billed; pale yellowish-olive. **Size** 19–21.5 cm. **Juv.** Browner frons, dark iris. **Voice** Distinctive, 1-note, long vibrating 'brrrrrrrrrrp'. **Hab.** Wet forest, dense vegetation; tropical gardens. Race *amphochlora* isolated on mountain summit rainforests of eastern Cape York Peninsula.

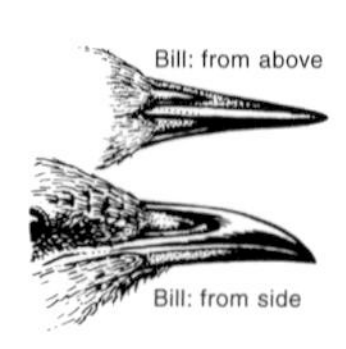

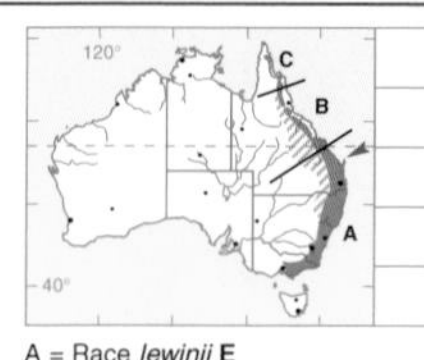

A = Race *lewinii* **E**
B = Race *mab* **E**
C = Race *amphochlora* **E**

Yellow-spotted Honeyeater *Meliphaga notata* **C** E

Identify from smaller Graceful Honeyeater. Like smaller Lewin's Honeyeater but paler; bright yellow gape and rounder ear patch. Eye brown. **Size** 16.5–20 cm. **Voice** 'Little Lewin': 'ee-yeu' repeated 4 or 5 times; 'tchu-chua' with 5–7 downward repetitions. **Hab.** Lowland wet forest; tropical gardens.

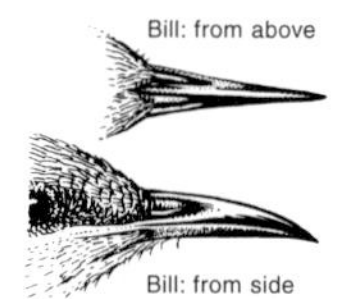

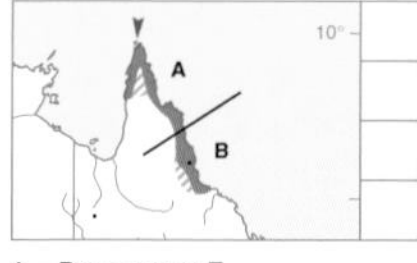

A = Race *notata* **E**
B = Race *mixta* **E**

Graceful Honeyeater *Meliphaga gracilis* **C**

Like Yellow-spotted but slightly smaller. Longer, thinner bill; acrobatic forager. Both occur in same habitats, overlap part of Lewin's range. Crown olive-green. Eye brown. Uniform olive above, pale green-grey below. Race *imitatrix* (B) Dark olive above; deeper grey-olive below. **Size** 15–17 cm. **Voice** Distinctive 'plik'; also 'chik' (several repeats). **Hab.** Wet forest.

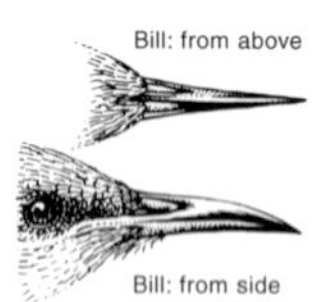

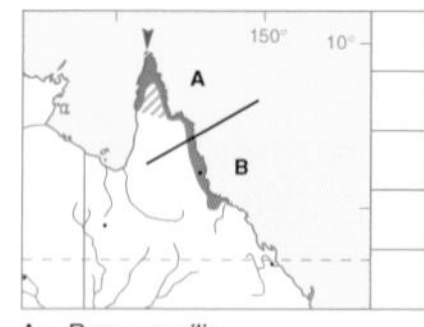

A = Race *gracilis*
B = Race *imitatrix* **E**

White-lined Honeyeater *Meliphaga albilineata* **LUC** E

Dark grey head. Whitish gape-line passes under bluish eye to small white ear tuft. Race *fordiana* (B) Greyer tail; cream-buff underwing coverts. **Size** 17–20.5 cm. **Juv.** As adult, greyer. No face stripe. **Voice** Loud, echoing 'tu-wheer, tuwhit'. **Hab.** Dense upper canopy of sandstone gorges; floodplains near escarpments.

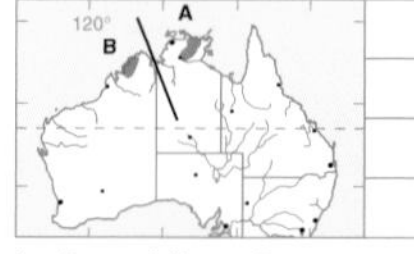

A = Race *albilineata* **E**
B = Race *fordiana* **E**

Bridled Honeyeater *Lichenostomus frenatus* **MC** E

Conspicuous. Dark brown with blackish head. Bill black, yellow base. Iris blue. Small whitish spot above eye. Thin yellow ear tuft. Yellowish-white streak ('bridle') from gape to nape. Silver-buff patch on side of neck. **Size** 20–22 cm. **Juv.** Similar, browner. **Voice** Loud 'we-arr', 'wachita'. **Hab.** Rainforest; mid to upper canopy. Many disperse to drier forests in winter.

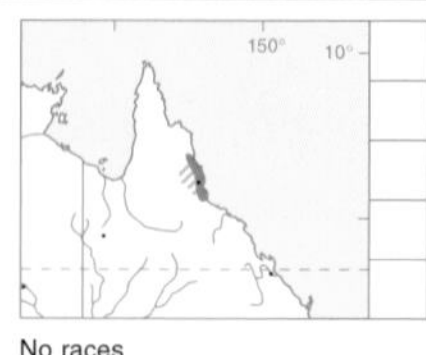

No races

Eungella Honeyeater *Lichenostomus hindwoodi* **LUC** E

Smaller than Bridled Honeyeater. Short black bill. Stripe below eye whitish. Greyer with white streaks on breast; narrow white plume on side of neck. **Size** 17–19.5 cm. **Voice** Laughing whistle; a recorded call is 'pee-pee-pip-pip-pip-pip-pip-pip', slower at end. **Hab.** Eungella rainforest, Qld. Some non-breeding movements to coastal lowlands.

Facial, breast pattern

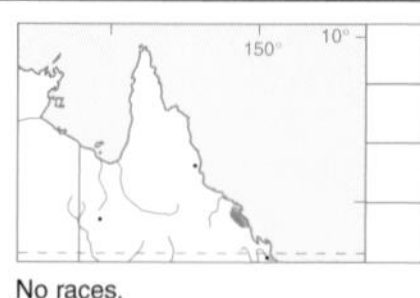

No races.
First located 1961; described 1983.

Yellow-faced Honeyeater
Lichenostomus chrysops **C** E

Often travels, feeds, with White-naped Honeyeaters. Grey-brown above, paler below. Black-bordered yellow facial stripe. Small yellow post-orbital spot. **Size** 15–17.5 cm. **Voice** Cheerful 'chick-up'. Liquid repeated 'chir rup, chir-rup' in falling sequence, loud for size of bird. **Hab.** Open forest, gardens.

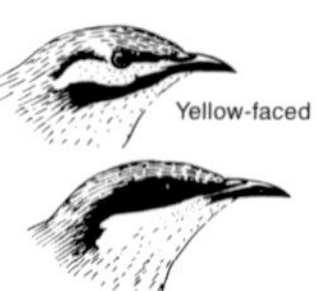

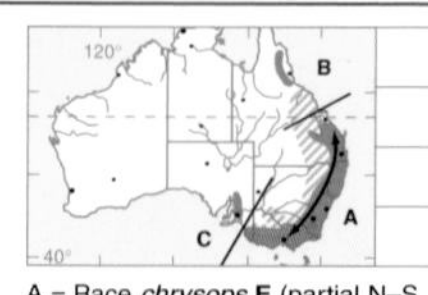

A = Race *chrysops* **E** (partial N–S migrant in SE Aust.)
B = Race *barroni* **E**
C = Race *samueli* **E**

White-lined Honeyeater
Graceful Honeyeater
Eungella
Honeyeater
Yellow-spotted
Honeyeater
Bridled
Honeyeater
Lewin's
Honeyeater
Yellow-faced Honeyeater

Singing Honeyeater *Lichenostomus virescens* **C–LC** ⚘ E

Check Purple-gaped in south, Grey-headed Honeyeater in north of range. Grey-brown above. Broad black band from bill through eye to neck. Yellow streak from bill to ear coverts. Ear tuft white. Cream throat. Breast pale, streaked dark grey. **Size** 16–24 cm. **Voice** Strong whistling calls; pairs may sing together. **Hab.** Forage low in arid and coastal shrubland, woodland; suburbs.

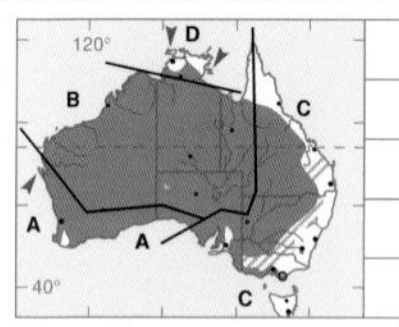

A = Race *virescens* **E** B = Race *forresti* **E** C = Race *sonorus* **E** D = Race *cooperi* **E**

Varied Honeyeater *Lichenostomus versicolor* **MC** ?◎

Larger than Singing. Iris red-brown. Chin, throat, underparts yellow, streaked olive. **Size** 19-24 cm. **Hab.** Mangroves.

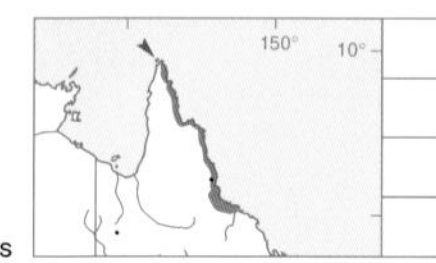

No races

Mangrove Honeyeater *Lichenostomus fasciogularis* **MC** ?◎ E

Like Singing, Varied, but much darker. Iris blue-grey. Diagnostic dull yellow throat, scalloped brown, above dark grey-brown breast band. Underparts heavily streaked grey-brown. **Size** About 19.5 cm. **Hab.** Mangroves; adjacent vegetation, gardens.

Although hybridises with Varied Honeyeater, has again been separated as a distinct species.

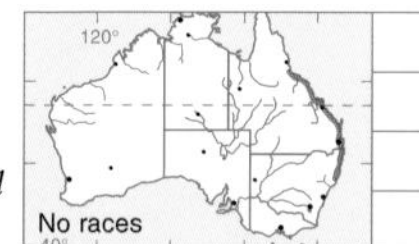

White-gaped Honeyeater *Lichenostomus unicolor* **MC–LC** ⚘ E

Plumage browner with wear. Conspicuous white gape. Dark olive-grey upperparts; greenish wash on wings. Underparts mid-grey. **Size** 17–22 cm. **Juv.** Similar, yellow gape. **Voice** Br. pair in duet 'whit-o-weee'. **Hab.** Mangroves, riverine forest, gardens.

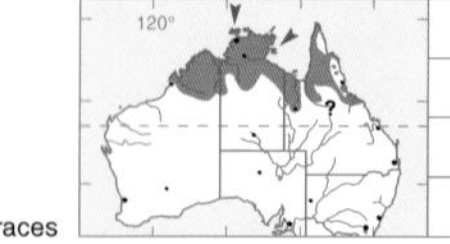

No races

Yellow Honeyeater *Lichenostomus flavus* **MC** ?◎ E

Uniformly olive-yellow above, lemon below. Subtle olive eye-stripe. Race *addendus* (B) Slightly larger, greener. **Size** 16–18.5 cm. **Juv.** Duller. **Voice** Varied loud whistles 'wheee-a'. **Hab.** Forest, mangroves, gardens.

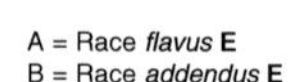
A = Race *flavus* **E**
B = Race *addendus* **E**

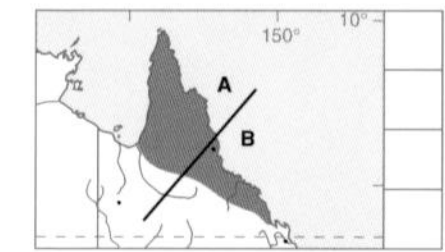

White-eared Honeyeater *Lichenostomus leucotis* **C–LC** ⚘–?◎ E

Conspicuous white ear patch contrasts with black face, chin, throat. Crown grey, fine black striations. Bright olive-green upperparts. Yellowish-green abdomen. Race *novaenorciae* (B) Smaller, duller. Race *thomasi* (C) Greyer. **Size** 16.5–21.5 cm. **Juv.** Duller, with olive-green crown; cream ear patch. **Voice** Loud 'chock up, chock up' and other softer calls. **Hab.** Forest, woodland, mallee.

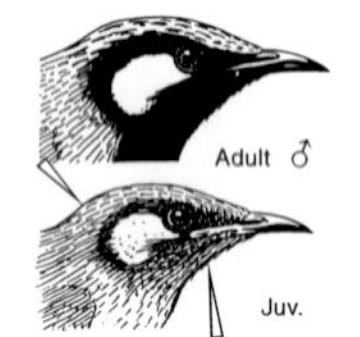

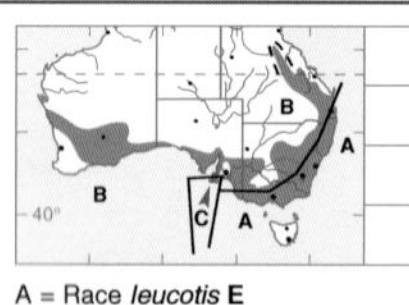

A = Race *leucotis* **E**
B = Race *novaenorciae* **E**
C = Race *thomasi* **E**

Yellow-throated Honeyeater *Lichenostomus flavicollis* **C** ?◎ E

Eye deep red. Dark grey crown, nape, face, upper breast. Silver-grey ear patch, tipped yellowish to cream. Back olive-green. Bright yellow chin, throat. Abdomen grey-yellow. **Size** 20–23 cm. **Juv.** Brownish nape; duller throat. **Voice** Loud 'tonk, tonk' often repeated; also 'pick-em-up'. **Hab.** Most in its range.

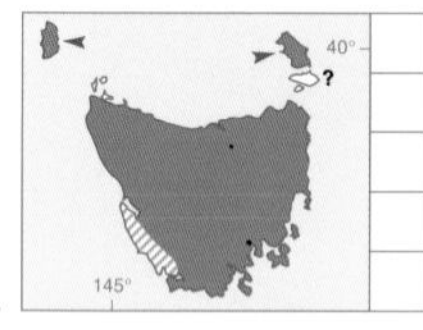

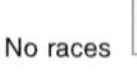
No races

Yellow-tufted Honeyeater *Lichenostomus melanops* **MC–LA** ⚘–?◎ E

Races *melanops* (A), *meltoni* (B) Yellow forehead feathers slightly tufted. Black mask from bill through eye expanding on ear coverts. Bright golden ear tuft, crown, sides of throat. Centre throat blackish. Back olive-green; abdomen olive-yellow. Race *cassidix* (C) 'Helmeted Honeyeater' Larger, darker, brighter; longer 'crest' feathers, broader mask. **Size** 16.5–21 cm. **Juv.** Duller, paler. **Hab.** Eucalypt forest, woodland with shrub layer, often near water. 'Helmeted' has tiny, vulnerable range; constant threats are habitat damage/dieback, with Bell Miner dominance.

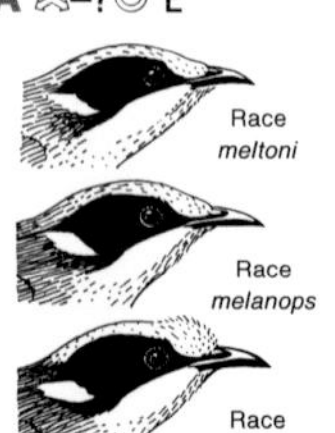

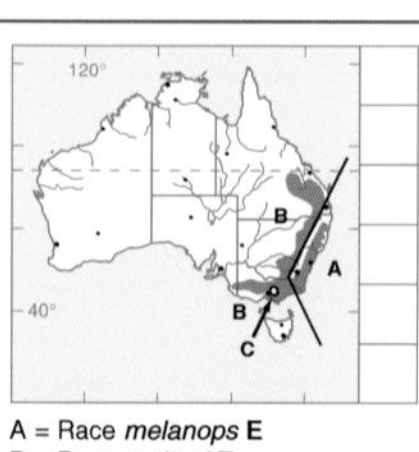

A = Race *melanops* **E**
B = Race *meltoni* **E**
C = Race *cassidix* **E Endangered**

Varied Honeyeater
Singing Honeyeater
Mangrove Honeyeater
Yellow-throated Honeyeater
Yellow Honeyeater
White-gaped Honeyeater
White-eared Honeyeater
Yellow-tufted ('Helmeted') Honeyeater
Race cassidix
Yellow-tufted Honeyeater
Race meltoni
N. Day

Purple-gaped Honeyeater *Lichenostomus cratitius* **MC–LUC** ♧–?◎ E

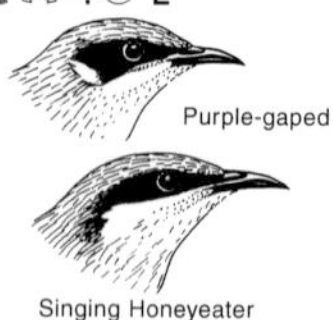

Identify from larger Singing Honeyeater. Prominent, bright yellow side of throat, below purple skin (wattle) from gape to cheek. Blackish mask through eye. Grey head, ear coverts; small yellow ear tuft. Olive-green back; yellow-grey abdomen. **Size** 16–19 cm. **Juv.** Duller with yellow gape. **Voice** Noisy chattering. **Hab.** Mallee, woodland.

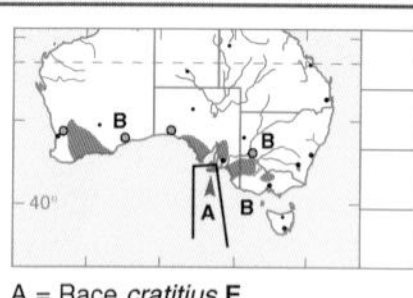

A = Race *cratitius* **E**
B = Race *occidentalis* (prior *halmaturinus*) **E**

Grey-headed Honeyeater *Lichenostomus keartlandi* **MC** ♧ E

Check Singing, Yellow-plumed, Grey-fronted Honeyeaters. Pale grey head. Blackish face, dark grey ear coverts. Crescent-shaped yellow ear tuft. Buff-olive back. Pale yellow breast, faintly darker streaked. **Size** 13–16.5 cm. **Juv.** Duller. **Voice** Loud 'chee toyt' repeated. **Hab.** Mulga, woodland, rocky hillsides, gorges.

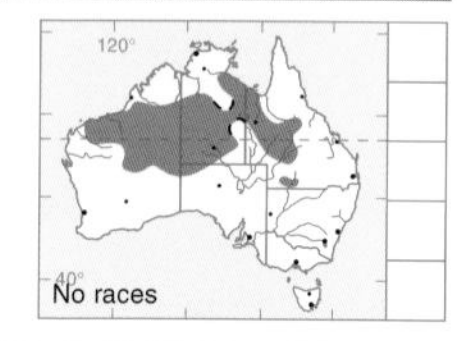

No races

Yellow-tinted Honeyeater *Lichenostomus flavescens* **C** ♧

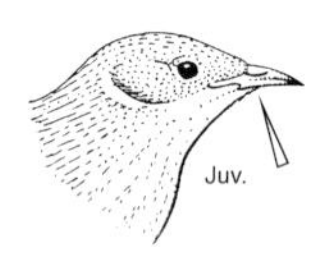

Bill black. Forehead and face yellow. Black, crescent-shaped mark at ear above thin, bright yellow (but inconspicuous) plume. Olive-buff back. Yellow underparts, faint streaks. **Size** 13–15.5 cm. **Juv.** Similar; brownish bill. **Voice** 'chee-uk-ooo-wee'; 'porra-chu-porra-cheu-cheu-cheu'. **Hab.** Woodland.

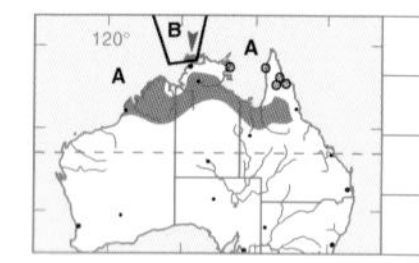

A = Race *flavescens*
B = Race *melvillensis* **E**

Fuscous Honeyeater *Lichenostomus fuscus* **C** ♧ E

Black bill, eye-ring. Dull olive-brown, paler below. Face darker. Dusky ear coverts, tipped yellow. **Non-br./Imm.** Gape, base of bill and eye-ring, yellow. **Size** 13.5–17 cm. **Juv.** Like Imm., bill brownish. **Voice** Loud 'arig rig-a-taw-taw'. **Hab.** Open forest and woodland.

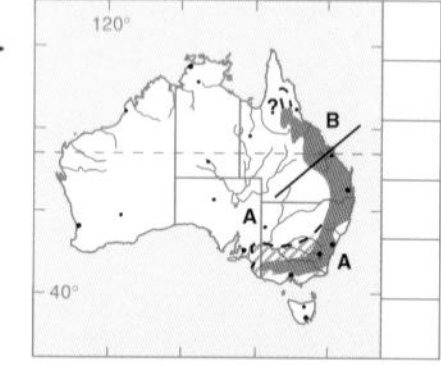

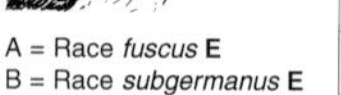
A = Race *fuscus* **E**
B = Race *subgermanus* **E**

Grey-fronted Honeyeater *Lichenostomus plumulus* **MC** ♧–?◎ E

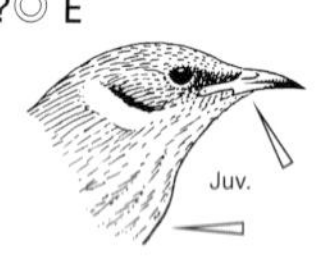

Check Yellow-plumed Honeyeater. Bill black. Black lores. Fine black line from bill to below ear. Grey frons; crown yellowish-olive. Face darker. Thin black plume in front of large yellow neck plume. Back olive-green. Underparts buffish-grey, lightly streaked dark brown. **Size** 14–16.5 cm. **Juv.** Base of bill, gape yellowish. **Hab.** Open woodland, mulga, mallee.

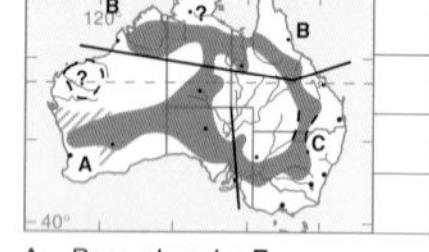

A = Race *plumulus* **E**
B = Race *planasi* **E**
C = Race *graingeri* **E**

Yellow-plumed Honeyeater *Lichenostomus ornatus* **C–MC** ♧ E

Check Grey-fronted, Yellow-faced Honeyeaters. Bill black. Yellow neck plume. Faint yellow line under eye. Ear coverts tipped dark brown. Greenish-olive crown; darker around face. Olive-brown back. Underparts fawn, heavily streaked olive-brown. **Size** 14–18.5 cm. **Juv.** Duller; orange-yellow base of bill, gape. **Voice** Loud 'chick-owee', 'chickwididee'. **Hab.** Mallee, semi-arid eucalypt woodland.

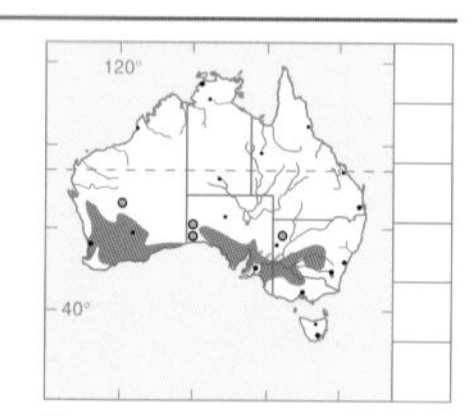

No races

White-plumed Honeyeater *Lichenostomus penicillatus* **C–MC** ♧–◎ E

Bill black. Olive bird with yellow cheeks, ear coverts; white neck plume with fine dark border. Race *carteri* (B) Fawn back; face, underparts, bright yellow. Race *leilavalensis* (C) Paler. Race *calconi* (D) Light yellow face, all parts paler than *carteri*. **Size** 13.5–18 cm. Other races smaller. **Juv.** Base of bill orange. Paler-bodied; indistinct or no plume. **Voice** 'chick-owee'; 'chick-abiddy'. **Hab.** Open forest, woodland; streamside vegetation. Along inland watercourses, especially occurs in red gums. Adaptable; aggressive in urban gardens.

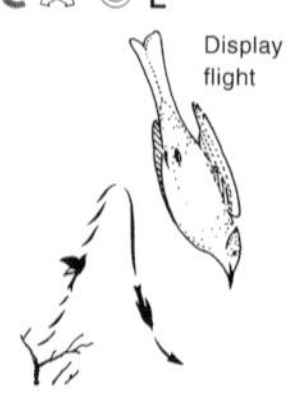

Also called 'Greenie'.

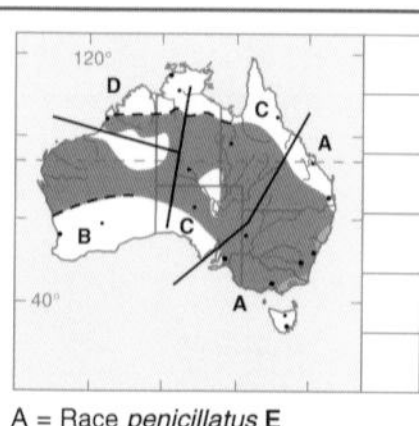

A = Race *penicillatus* **E**
B = Race *carteri* **E**
C = Race *leilavalensis* **E**
D = Race *calconi* **E**

Purple-gaped Honeyeater
Yellow-tinted Honeyeater
Grey-headed Honeyeater
Fuscous Honeyeater
Non-breeding
Grey-fronted Honeyeater
White-plumed Honeyeater
Yellow-plumed Honeyeater
Juv.
White-plumed Honeyeater
Juv.
Yellow-plumed Honeyeater

Black-chinned Honeyeater *Melithreptus gularis* **MC** E

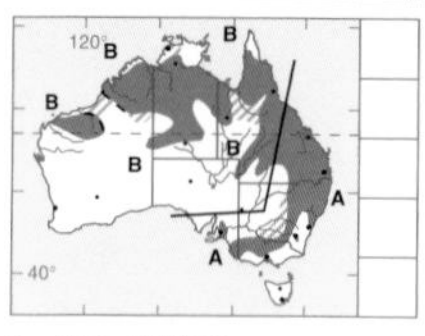
A = Race *gularis* **E**
B = Race *laetior* **E**

Black bill, head. Bold white line around nape to blue eye-skin. Centre of chin, throat, black, often inconspicuous. Sides of throat white. Olive-grey back. Pale grey underparts. Race *laetior* (B) 'Golden-backed Honeyeater' Eye-skin green-yellow, bright golden back. Buffish below. **Size** 14–16.5 cm. **Juv.** Dull brown head, back. Yellow-orange bill. Eye-skin dull blue, *laetior* pale grey. **Voice** Distinctive loud churring calls. **Hab.** Woodland.

Strong-billed Honeyeater *Melithreptus validirostris* **C** –?◎ E

Juv.

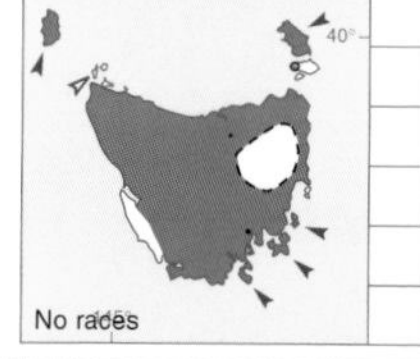
No races

Black bill, head and chin. Broad white band across nape to blue-green eye-skin. Sides of throat white. Back, scapulars, grey-brown; olive wash down centre back to rump. Abdomen grey-brown. **Size** 15 cm. **Juv.** Head sooty. Face stripe, nape, bright lemon. Eye-skin, base of bill, yellow-orange. **Voice** Loud 'cheep'. **Hab.** Tas. and Bass Strait island forests.

Brown-headed Honeyeater *Melithreptus brevirostris* **C** E

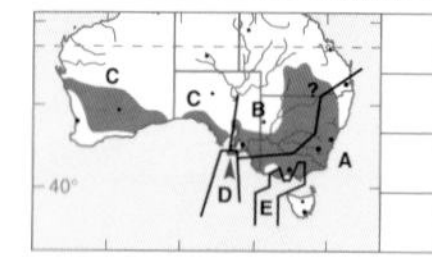
A = Race *brevirostris* **E**
B = Race *pallidiceps* **E**
C = Race *leucogenys* **E**
D = Race *magnirostris* **E**
E = Race *wombeyi* **E**

Small sittella-like flocks, very active in canopies. Eye-skin creamy. Head brown; pale buffish line on nape. Upperparts olive-brown; underparts pale grey-buff. Race *pallidiceps* (B) Smaller; cap scalloped grey-brown. Race *leucogenys* (C) Paler; eye-skin orange-yellow. Race *magnirostris* (D) Longer bill, darker plumage. Race *wombeyi* (E) Largest, darkest; olive upperparts. **Size** 11.5–14 cm. **Juv.** Paler, browner. Eye-skin bluish. **Voice** 'chick'; 'breeet, breeet'. **Hab.** Woodland, mallee.

White-throated Honeyeater *Melithreptus albogularis* **C**

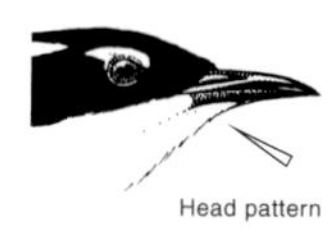
Head pattern

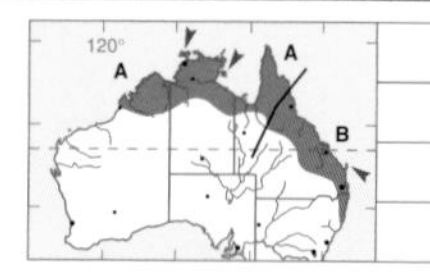
A = Race *albogularis*
B = Race *inopinatus* **E**

Resembles White-naped. Slender, down-curved black bill. Black head, extending to sides of breast. White nape line extends almost to bluish-white eye-skin. Back olive-yellow. Chin, underparts, white. Race *inopinatus* (B) Larger; duller. **Size** 11.5-14.5 cm. **Juv.** Brownish crown, back. Nape stripe incomplete. **Voice** 'tserp-tserp'; 'pi-pi-pi'. **Hab.** Woodland.

White-naped Honeyeater *Melithreptus lunatus* **C** E

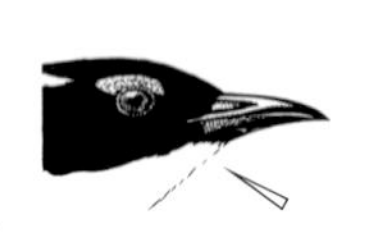
Head pattern

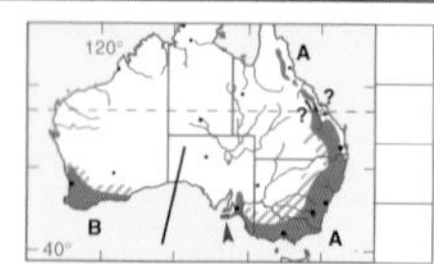
A = Race *lunatus* **E**
B = Race *chloropsis* **E**

Flocks. Migrates with Yellow-faced Honeyeater. Like White-throated but black on face continues below bill and just on to chin; white nape-line falls short of red eye-skin. Race *chloropsis* (B) Eye-skin white. **Size** 10.5–15.5 cm. **Juv.** Brown crown; eye-skin flesh; nape stripe incomplete. **Voice** Lisping 'mjerp, mjerp'; 'tsip'. **Hab.** Open forest, woodland; often high in canopy.

Black-headed Honeyeater *Melithreptus affinis* **C** –?◎ E

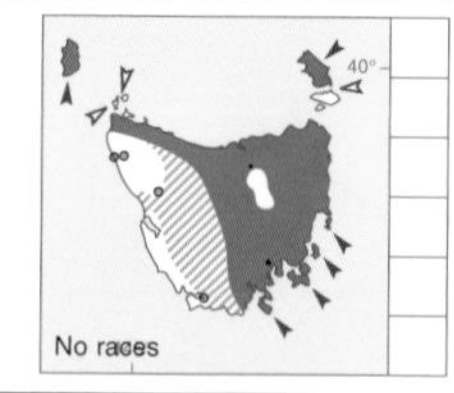
No races

Eye-skin white-cream. Completely black head extends to chin and side of breast. No white across nape. **Size** 14 cm. **Juv.** Less black. Crown, nape, brown. Lemon wash on side neck, throat. Eye-skin blue-tinged. **Voice** Sharp 2-note whistle; 'mjerp, mjerp', as White-naped. **Hab.** Mature forest, dense vegetation.

Green-backed Honeyeater *Timeliopsis (Glycichaera) fallax* **MC** –?◎

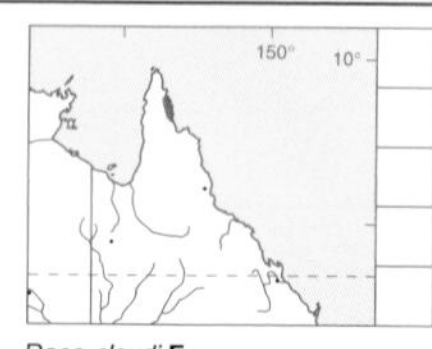
Race *claudi* **E**

Small. Very active. Compare Green-backed and female Fairy Gerygones; Yellow-legged Flycatcher. Grey-brown bill. Eye pale grey; faint, whitish eye-ring. Warm grey-green frons, crown, nape. Dull olive upperparts. Dull lemon throat, breast. Belly, undertail coverts, brighter lemon. Legs blue-grey. **Size** 12 cm. **Juv.** Duller; eye dark. **Voice** Soft twitters. **Hab.** Rainforest.

Black-chinned ('Golden-backed') Honeyeater Race laetior
Black-chinned Honeyeater Race gularis
Black-chinned Honeyeater Juv. Race gularis
Brown-headed Honeyeater
Strong-billed Honeyeater
Brown-headed Honeyeater Juv.
White-naped Honeyeater Race lunatus
White-naped Honeyeater Juv. Race lunatus
White-naped Honeyeater Race chloropsis
White-throated Honeyeater Juv.
White-throated Honeyeater
Black-headed Honeyeater Juv.
Green-backed Honeyeater
Black-headed Honeyeater

White-streaked Honeyeater *Trichodere cockerelli* **MC** –?◎ E

Slim honeyeater, dark brown above, golden wash over wings and tail. Diagnostic dark-edged white feathers on throat, breast. Dark iris. Blue-grey base to black bill. Facial stripe, ear tuft, yellow. Belly whitish. **Size** 14–17 cm. **Juv.** Browner, pale gape, plain throat. **Voice** High whistles. **Hab.** Swamps, woodland.

Juv.

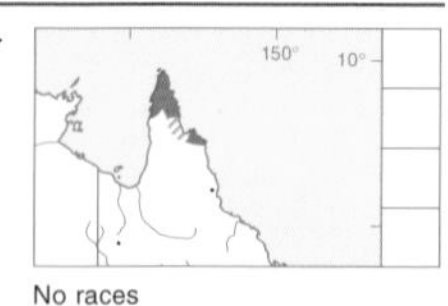

No races

Crescent Honeyeater *Phylidonyris pyrrhoptera* **C–MC** E

Cold grey; bright yellow wing patch. Pale line behind eye. Dark crescent from shoulder to sides of breast, edged white below. White tail shafts in flight. Faint streaks on pale throat. **F** Dull olive-brown. **Size** 14–17 cm. **Juv.** No crescents. **Voice** Varied. Loud, sharp 'e-je-gypt'. **Hab.** Coastal heath to mountain forest.

Tail pattern

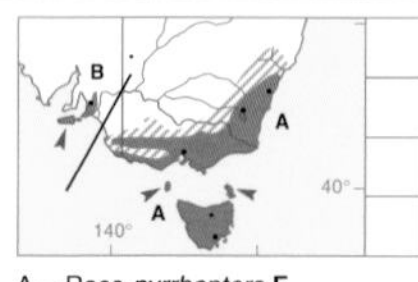

A = Race *pyrrhoptera* **E**
B = Race *halmaturina* **E**

White-fronted Honeyeater *Phylidonyris albifrons* **MC–LC** E

Nomadic/migratory flocks. Black and white bird. Facial markings accentuate long bill. Distinctive white frontal face mask, black-brown bib. White eye-ring; tiny red spot behind eye; ear coverts grey. Crown, back, brown-black. Olive-yellow wing patch. Rump rufous-brown. Tail brown edged olive; flanks white, streaked black. **Size** 13–18.5 cm. **Juv.** Browner, lacks facial contrast. **Voice** Melodic eerie song. **Hab.** Arid shrubland to woodland.

Juv.

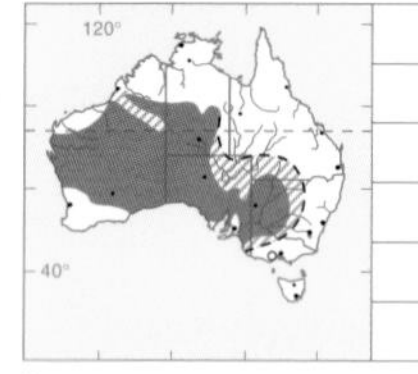

No races

White-cheeked Honeyeater *Phylidonyris nigra* **C** E

Like New Holland but no 'beard'; larger white cheek patch; dark eye; white eyebrow reaches bill. Yellow wing patch. Uppertail black, edged yellow. Race *gouldii* (B) Longer bill, smaller cheek patch. **Size** 16–20 cm. **Juv.** Duller, browner with yellow gape. **Voice** Fast chittering. **Hab.** Moist coastal heath to woodland. Highlands in northern Qld.

Juv.

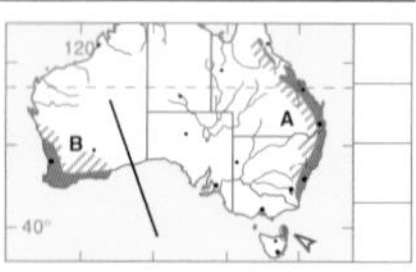

A = Race *nigra* **E**
B = Race *gouldii* **E**

New Holland Honeyeater *Phylidonyris novaehollandiae* **C** E

Streaked black and white with yellow wing patch. Black head. Iris, short eyebrow; small ear patch; malar stripe, 'beard', all white. Yellow tail edges; fine white tail tip. Race *longirostris* (B) Longer bill, malar plume smaller. **Size** 16–20 cm. **Juv.** Brownish; markings less distinct. Iris dark; gape yellow. Rump brown. **Imm.** Eye grey; browner body. **Voice** Strong, high-pitched, sharp. **Hab.** Heath, woodland with dense shrub layer.

Juv.

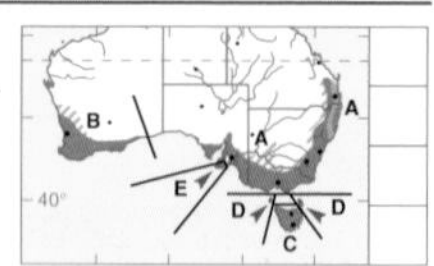

A = Race *novaehollandiae* **E**
B = Race *longirostris* **E**
C = Race *canescens* **E**
D = Race *caudata* **E**
E = Race *campbelli* **E**

Tawny-crowned Honeyeater *Phylidonyris (Gliciphila) melanops* **MC–LC** E

Sings on high perch. Often runs on ground: check Australian Pipit, Horsfield's Bushlark, Skylark. In flight, tawny underwing. Crown tawny. White eyebrow, chin, throat, crescent on ear coverts. Dark crescent from facial stripe to side of breast. Back, flanks grey-brown. Dull white below, lower breast mottled. Race *chelidonia* (B) More rufous. **Size** 14–18 cm. **Juv.** Brownish; pale streaks, crescent. **Voice** Plaintive, flute-like. **Hab.** Heath.

On ground

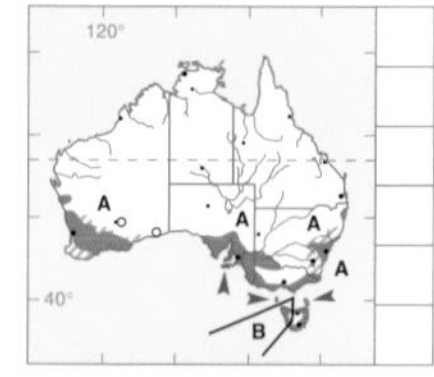

A = Race *melanops* **E**
B = Race *chelidonia* **E**

Brown Honeyeater *Lichmera indistincta* **C**

Check Dusky Honeyeater. Black bill, gape. Plain grey crown, breast; grey-brown back; darker face. Small pale yellow tuft behind eye. Wing patch dull yellow. Pale belly. **M non-br.** Yellowish gape. **F** Pale yellow gape; body tinged olive. **Size** M 12–16; F 11.5–15 cm. **Juv.** Yellower. Yellow at gape; ear tuft small/absent. **Voice** Warbling 'sweetie-sweetie'. **Hab.** Mangroves, streams, forest, heath with emergent trees, suburbs.

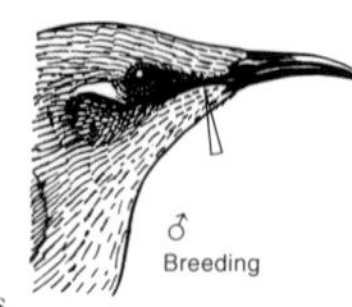
♂ Breeding

Has a black gape when breeding

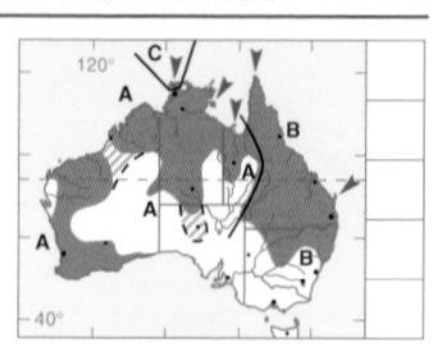

A = Race *indistincta* **E**
B = Race *ocularis*
C = Race *melvillensis* **E**

White-streaked Honeyeater
Crescent Honeyeater ♂
Crescent Honeyeater ♀
White-cheeked
Honeyeater
New Holland
Honeyeater
White-fronted
Honeyeater
Tawny-crowned
Honeyeater
Tawny-crowned
Honeyeater
Juv.
Brown Honeyeater
♀ breeding and non-breeding adult ♂
N. Day.

Painted Honeyeater *Grantiella picta* **C–LUC** ⵔ–⁂ E

Bright pink bill. Black head and back. Bright yellow on wings, upper tail. White underparts; black streaks on flank. **F** Brownish black, underparts plain white. **Size** 14–15 cm. **Juv.** Browner, greyish bill. **Voice** Rising 'georg-ie, georg-ie'. **Hab.** Open forest, box-ironbark woodland, especially with fruiting mistletoe.

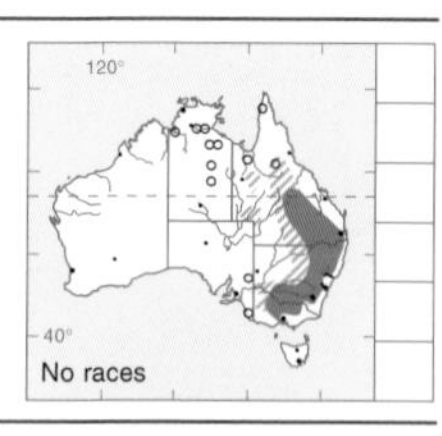

Bar-breasted Honeyeater *Ramsayornis fasciatus* **MC–LC** ⁂ E

Distinctive broken black bars on white breast. Dark brown crown, scalloped white. Black malar stripe; whitish face, chin. Drab brown back with black streaks. Larger, paler at W of range. **Size** 13–14.5 cm. **Juv.** Paler, plainer; breast streaked not barred. **Voice** Chattering song. **Hab.** Paperbarks, mangroves, woodland.

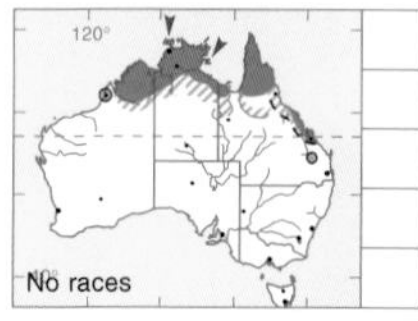

Brown-backed Honeyeater *Ramsayornis modestus* **LC** ?◎

Dusky pink bill, legs, feet. Thin pale line under eye. Drab brown above; dull white below. Breast lightly scalloped pale brown. **Size** 12–13 cm. **Juv.** Breast streaked; not scalloped. **Voice** Sharp 'chit, chit'. **Hab.** Paperbark thickets near swamps; mangroves.

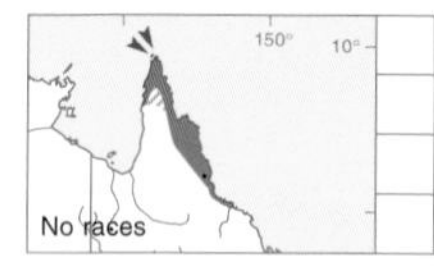

Grey Honeyeater *Conopophila whitei* **LUC–R** ⁂ E

Compact, short-tailed. Hovers like gerygone. Often with Western Gerygone, thornbills. Check female Redthroat. Plain head, pale eye-ring, dark eye. Dull grey-brown above; olive wash on wings. Dull white underparts; darker breast. **Size** 10–13 cm. **Juv.** Pale yellow throat. **Voice** 2-note 'cri-seek'. **Hab.** Arid acacia scrub.

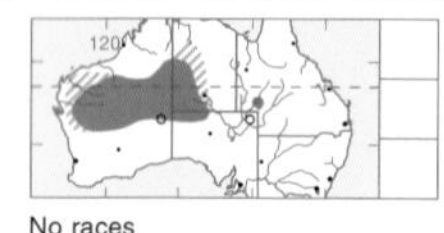

Rufous-banded Honeyeater *Conopophila albogularis* **LC** ⁂

Broad rufous breast band. White chin, throat. Grey head; brown back; yellow wing patch. Grey-brown flanks; white abdomen. **Size** 12–14.5 cm. **Juv.** Browner head. No breast band. **Voice** Musical twitter. **Hab.** Riparian forest, swamps, mangroves.

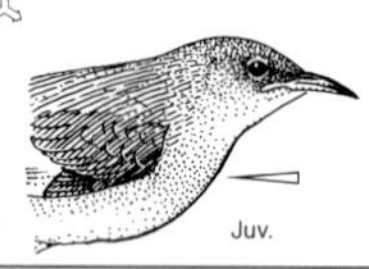

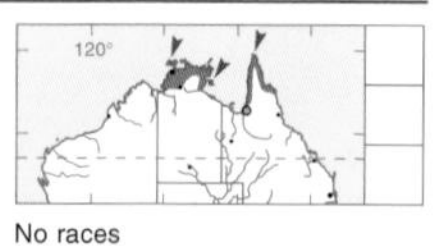

Rufous-throated Honeyeater *Conopophila rufogularis* **C** ⁂ E

Paler head than Rufous-banded. Rich rufous patch below chin. Lemon-yellow wing patch. Pale grey-buff underparts. **F** Dull rufous throat. **Size** 11–14 cm. **Juv.** White throat. **Voice** Rasping chatter. **Hab.** Riverine forest, paperbark, inland watercourses.

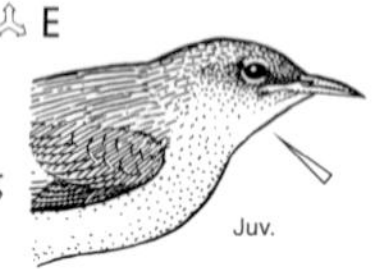

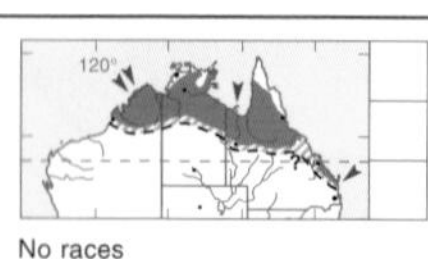

Eastern Spinebill *Acanthorhynchus tenuirostris* **C** ⁂–?◎ E

Long thin black bill. Glossy black head. Red iris. Chin, throat white, rufous centre, edged dark grey. Black shoulder crescents almost meet on breast. Back grey-brown; rufous nape. Wide white outer tail tips. Underparts cinnamon. **F** Dark grey crown. Race *dubius* (B) Browner. Races *halmaturinus* (C), *cairnsensis* (D) Paler. **Size** 13–16 cm. **Juv.** Plain cinnamon. Bill base orange. Brown-red iris. **Voice** Rapid piping. **Hab.** Heath, forest with heath; shrubby gardens. Wings make sharp 'prrrrp' in flight.

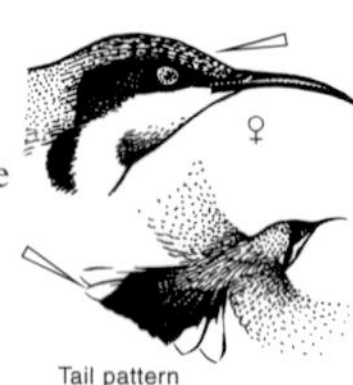

Tail pattern

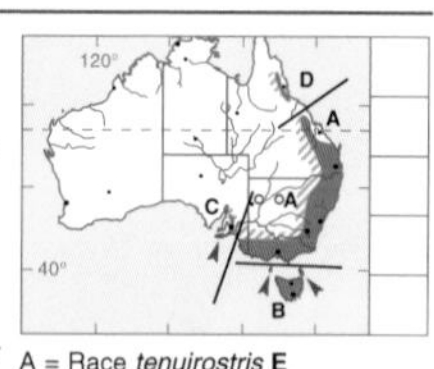

A = Race *tenuirostris* **E**
B = Race *dubius* **E**
C = Race *halmaturinus* **E**
D = Race *cairnsensis* **E**

Western Spinebill *Acanthorhynchus superciliosus* **C** ⁂–?◎ E

Long thin black bill. Red eye, white eyebrow. Dark olive-grey above. Broad chestnut collar over nape to chestnut throat, breast. White band, then black band, on chest. Buff abdomen. Wide white outer tail tips. **F** No face mask; lacks breast bands; no chestnut on throat. **Size** 12.5–15.5 cm. **Juv.** Duller; dark eye; nape grey-brown. **Voice** Shrill 'klee-klee'. **Hab.** Heath, banksia woodland.

Tail pattern

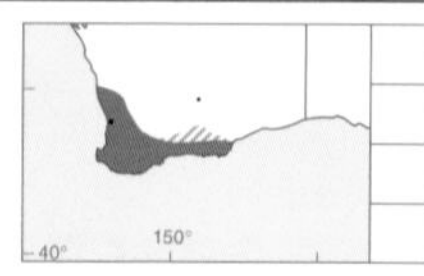

Painted
Honeyeater
♂
Bar-breasted
Honeyeater
Brown-backed
Honeyeater
Grey
Honeyeater
Rufous-throated
Honeyeater
Rufous-banded
Honeyeater
Eastern Spinebill
♂
Eastern Spinebill
Juv.
Western Spinebill
♂
Western Spinebill
♀

Dusky Honeyeater *Myzomela obscura* **C** ♧–?◎

Looks almost black in dull light. Uniform grey-brown, darker on head; paler on belly. Dusky throat patch. **Non-br.** Pale gape. Race *harterti* (B) Darker brown; warmer on crown, face, throat (some tinged crimson). Distinct dark throat patch. Race *fumata* (C) Darker than *obscura*. **Size** 13–15 cm. **Juv.** Warm brown; crimson tinged face; orange-grey lower bill. **Voice** 'chirp-chirp-chirp'; trills and 'tip-tip-eeee-chip'. Continuous twittering in flocks. **Habitat** Dense forest, mangroves, woodland, near swamps.

Juv.

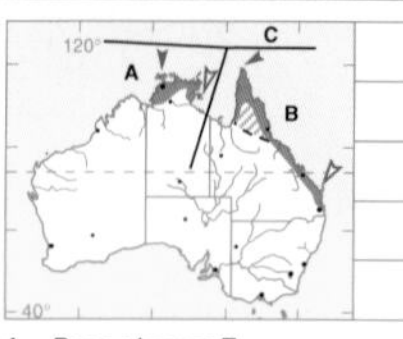

A = Race *obscura* **E**
B = Race *harterti* **E**
C= Race *fumata*

Red-headed Honeyeater *Myzomela erythrocephala* **LC** ◎

Head, neck, chin, throat and rump scarlet. Lores, eye-ring, black. Back, wings, upper breast, sooty-brown; abdomen grey-brown. **F** Forehead, chin, upper throat, tinged crimson. Bill base yellow. Upperparts grey-brown; wings, tail, darker. Paler throat, breast; abdomen whitish. Race *infuscata* (B) Larger, darker; red extends up lower back. **Size** 10–13 cm. **Juv.** As female, warmer brown; less red on face. **M imm.** Patchy red hood, rump. **Voice** Metallic whistle, buzzing. **Hab.** In and near coastal mangroves; gardens.

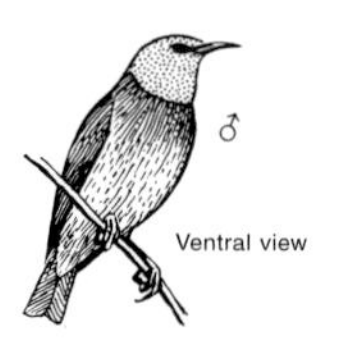

Ventral view

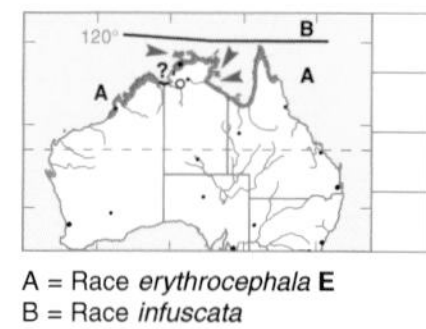

A = Race *erythrocephala* **E**
B = Race *infuscata*

Scarlet Honeyeater *Myzomela sanguinolenta* **C–MC** ♧

Lores black, eye dark. Scarlet head, breast, rump. Scarlet centre to black back. Wings black, white feather edges. Uppertail black. Scarlet breast, creamy-grey flanks. **F** Smaller than Dusky. Very like female Red-headed but more olive-brown. Chin, cheeks, reddish. **Size** 9–11 cm. **Juv.** Warmer brown. **M imm.** Patchy scarlet. **Voice** Sweeter than Red-headed. Males give tinkling song from high branches. **Hab.** Mangroves, coastal forest, woodland.

Singing

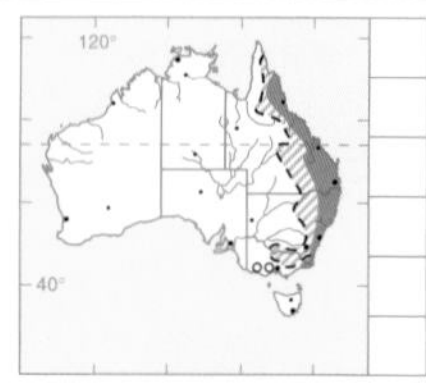

Race *sanguinolenta* **E**

Banded Honeyeater *Certhionyx pectoralis* **MC–LC** ♧ E

Bill, gape black. Black cap over eye, crown, continues down nape to back. Rump greyish-white. White chin, ear coverts, neck, underparts, with black breast band. **Non-br.** Back grey-brown. Pale gape. Dusky ear spot. Wing feathers pale edged. **Size** 11–13.5 cm. **Juv.** Frons, crown, light brown. Yellow ear coverts. Rufous back, wing edges. Underparts creamy-white; dusky breast band. **Voice** Tinkling twitter. **Hab.** Forest, grassy woodland.

Imm.

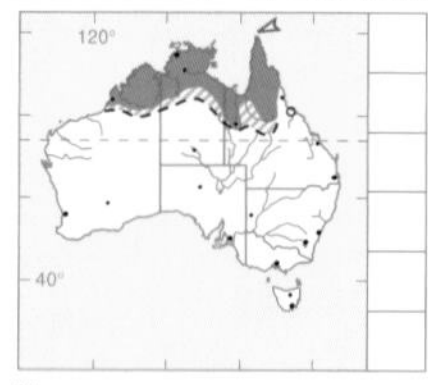

No races

Pied Honeyeater *Certhionyx variegatus* **LC–R** ♧ E

Black hood covering head, throat. Small blue wattle below eye. Bill grey-blue. Breast, rump, abdomen white. Broad white streak on black wings. Tail white but for two black central feathers; broad black tip. **F** Mottled grey-brown above. Throat, breast lightly streaked grey-brown. Mottled shoulder patch, white wing stripe. Streaked breast. **Size** 15–20 cm. **Voice** 'tee-titee-tee-tee'; mournful whistle. **Hab.** Arid savannah, flowering shrubs.

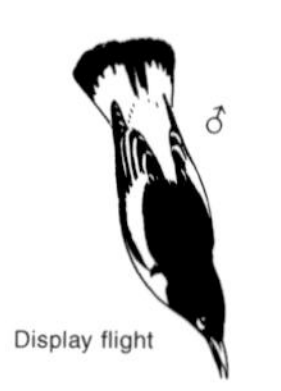

Display flight

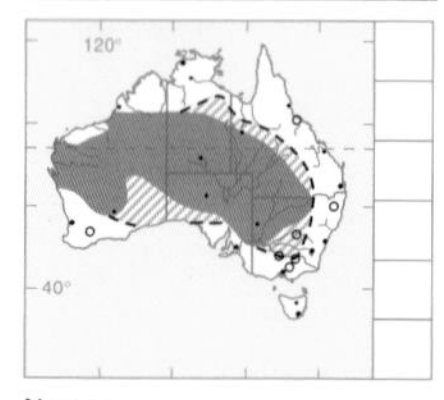

No races

Black Honeyeater *Certhionyx niger* **MC–LC** ♧ E

Smaller than Pied. Long decurved black bill. Head, throat, back, wings, tail and stripe down centre of belly are all sooty black. Underbody white. Legs black. **F** Head, upper surface, ear coverts light brown. Pale-buff stripe behind eye. Breast variably speckled grey-brown. **Size** 10–13 cm. **Juv.** Darker than female. **Voice** Feeble 'peeee'. **Hab.** Arid shrublands, flowering *Eremophila*.

Ventral view

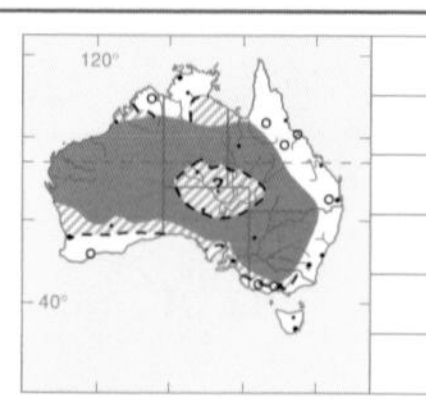

No races

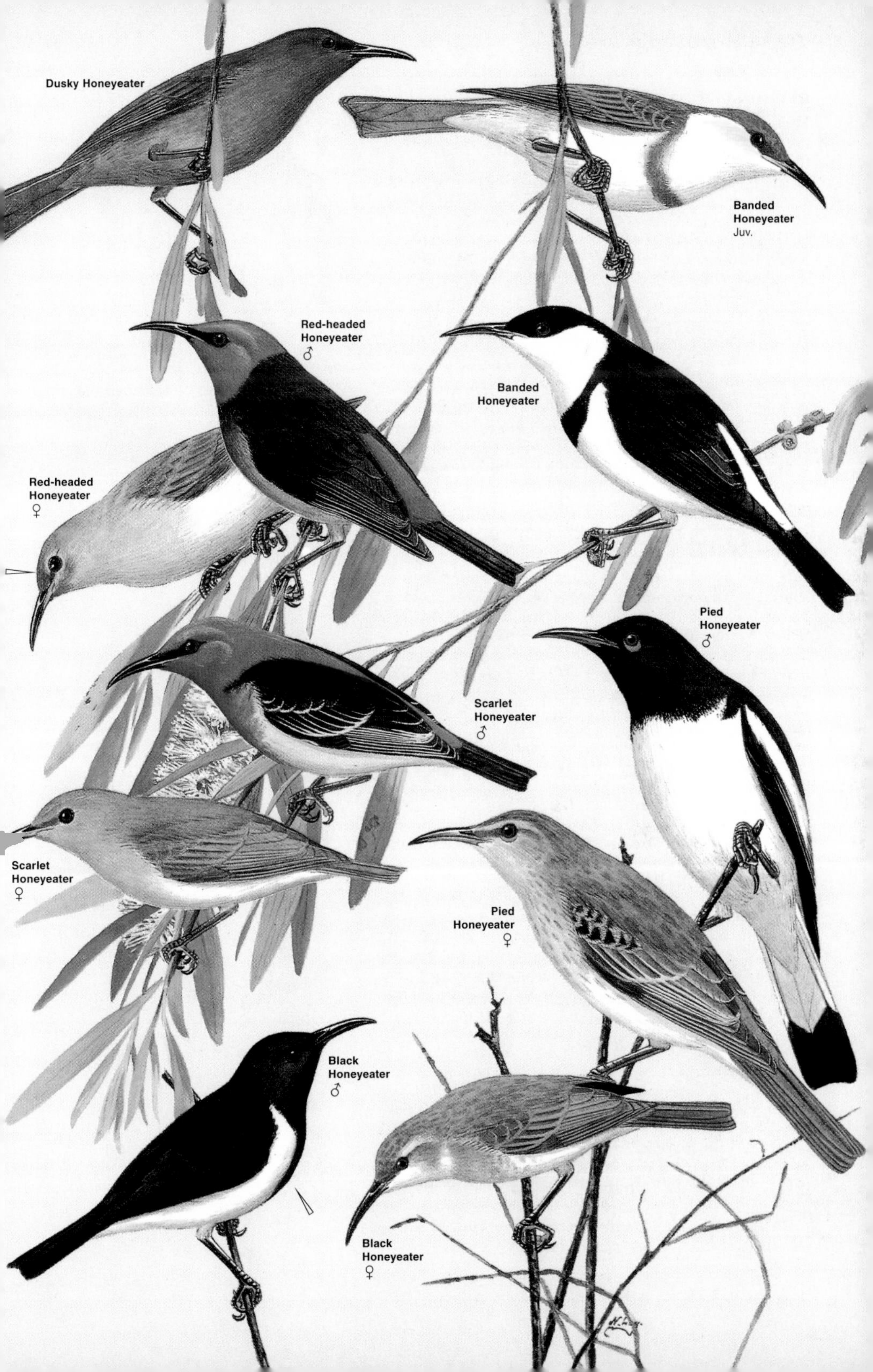
Dusky Honeyeater
Banded Honeyeater Juv.
Red-headed Honeyeater ♂
Banded Honeyeater
Red-headed Honeyeater ♀
Pied Honeyeater ♂
Scarlet Honeyeater ♂
Scarlet Honeyeater ♀
Pied Honeyeater ♀
Black Honeyeater ♂
Black Honeyeater ♀

Crimson Chat *Epthianura tricolor* **C–LUC** ♧ E

Flocks of mixed chat species sometimes occur. Brilliant crimson cap, breast. Eyes creamy-white. Lores, ear coverts, nape, blackish-brown. Back dark brown. Scarlet uppertail coverts. White throat, centre belly, undertail coverts. **Non-br.** Red less vivid. Patchy brown cap, facial mask. Red underbody broken by white patches. **F** Upperparts, head, grey-brown. Throat, belly, white; pale red and buff patches on breast, flanks, rump. **Size** 11–13 cm. **Juv.** As female; no red on breast. **Voice** High melodious 'see-ee-ee'; metallic 'ting'. **Hab.** Salty areas of inland plains, rocky hills, mallee heath.

All chats have black or dark bills and legs, and short blackish-brown tails, tipped white.

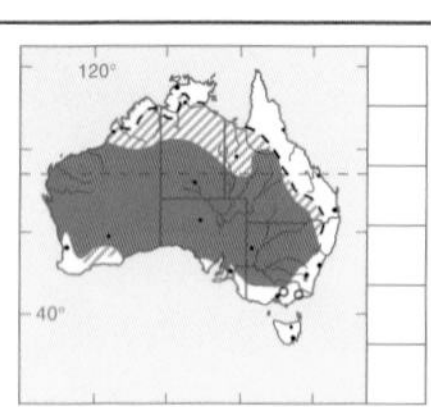

No races

Orange Chat *Epthianura aurifrons* **C–LUC** ♧ E

Eyes reddish-brown. Black lores, chin, throat. Head, rump, underparts, pale orange-yellow, becoming luminous orange on forehead, breast. Back fawny-yellow, mottled darker. **F/Juv.** Whitish lores, yellow eyebrow. Grey to yellowish-brown above. Rump yellowish. Pale yellow below, breast washed grey-brown; belly washed lemon. **Size** 11–12 cm. **Voice** Metallic 'tang'; 'cheep-cheep' in flight. **Hab.** Low shrubs in salty areas, gibber plains where some shrubs; coastal swamps in WA.

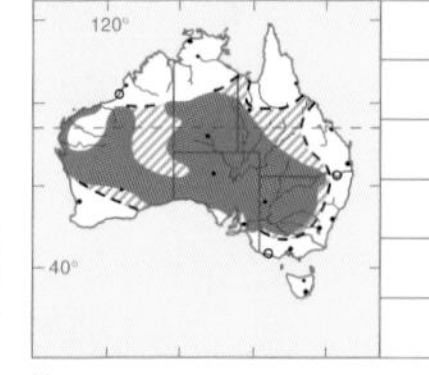

No races

Yellow Chat *Epthianura crocea* **?R–UC** ♧ E

A poorly known species. Eyes creamy. Lores suffused orange. Thin dark eye-line to bill. Crown, back, grey-brown, mottled darker; washed yellow. Forehead, face, rump, underparts, bright yellow. Narrow blackish breast band. Whitish wing bars. **Non-br.** Crown streaked olive; body greyer, paler; narrow breast band. **F** No breast band. **Size** 11–12 cm. **Juv.** Iris dark; bill pale. **Voice** Metallic 'tang'; cricket-like note; musical 'pee-eeep'. **Hab.** Coastal and inland swamps, including vegetated bore-drains. Also shrubby saltbush flats.

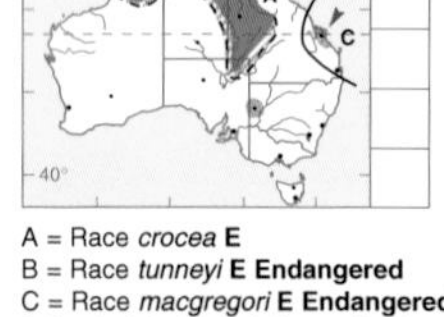

A = Race *crocea* **E**
B = Race *tunneyi* **E Endangered**
C = Race *macgregori* **E Endangered**
A tiny isolated population on Curtis Is., off Rockhampton, Qld. Fragmented occurrence within parts of its total Aust. range.

White-fronted Chat *Epthianura albifrons* **C** ♧–◎ E

Check Chestnut-breasted, Banded, Whitefaces. High, jerky flight; perches prominently. Runs on ground, often continuing to run/fly ahead of observer. Local flocks in winter. Eyes orange to buff or white. White forehead, face, throat and belly. Black band from back of crown and nape across breast. Back grey. Wings blackish-brown. **F** Upperparts, including forehead, grey-brown. Underparts white or pale grey; narrow blackish-brown breast band. **Size** 11–13 cm. **Juv.** As female; browner; breast band absent or indistinct. **Voice** Repeated, soft, finch-like 'tang'. **Hab.** Low vegetation in salty coastal and inland areas; crops.

An early name for this species was 'Tang'.

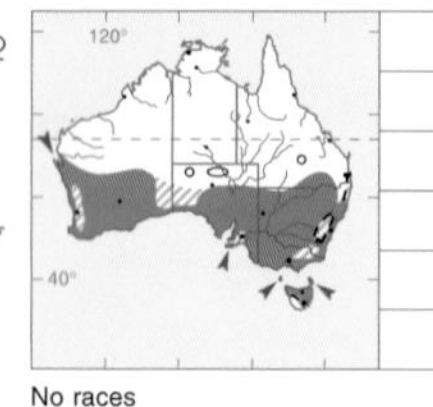

No races

Gibberbird *Ashbyia lovensis* **LC** ?◎ E

Upright posture. Resembles chats but more 'pipit-like'. Stands on rocks; runs, wags tail like Australian (Richard's) Pipit. Could be confused with larger Yellow Wagtail. Eyes white to yellow, grey-fawn crown. Yellow eyebrow, lores, face, underparts. Back, rump, grey-brown to buffy-brown, mottled darker. Yellow breast, flanks, washed grey-brown. **F/Imm.** Browner above; paler below; breast washed buffy-brown. **Size** 11–14 cm. **Juv.** Bill horn. As female, but brown. **Voice** 'wheet-wheet-wheet' in flight; musical chatter; alarm of 5–6 piercing notes. **Hab.** Stony, open inland plains.

Prior name 'Desert Chat'.

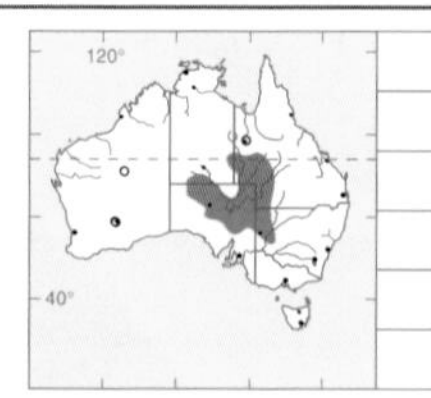

No races

Yellow Chat
♀
Yellow Chat
♂
Orange Chat
♀
Orange Chat
♂
Gibber
bird
♂
Crimson Chat
♀
White-fronted
Chat
♀
Crimson Chat
♂
White-fronted
Chat
♂
White-fronted
Chat
Juv.

Logrunner *Orthonyx temminckii* **MC–UC** ◎

Shy; listen for scratching in, or under, litter. Crown rufous. Face grey. Throat white with broad black edge. Upperparts rufous, mottled black. Rump rufous. Shafts of tail feathers project as spines. **F** Throat orange. **Size** 17–20 cm. **Juv.** Mottled brown. **Voice** Sharp, variable 2-note 'week-week'; rapid, repeated 'kweek' **Hab.** Floors of subtropical rainforest.

Forages by digging

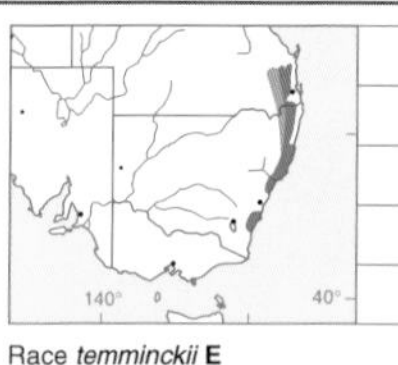

Race *temminckii* **E**

Chowchilla *Orthonyx spaldingii* **MC–UC** ◎ E

May hide under leaves when startled. Eye-ring pale. Head black. Olive-brown upperparts, flanks. White throat, breast white. Tail feathers spine-tipped. Race *melasmenus* (B) Smaller. Sooty wash over mantle, back. **F** Throat, upper breast orange. **Size** 26–28 cm. **Juv.** Browner, cinnamon mottling. **Voice** Very vocal at dawn; groups blend loud 'chow' and 'chilla' with other songs and mimicry. **Hab.** Floors of tropical rainforest.

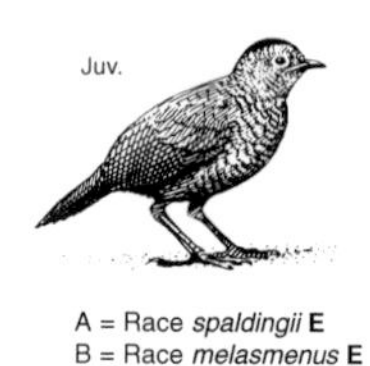

Juv.

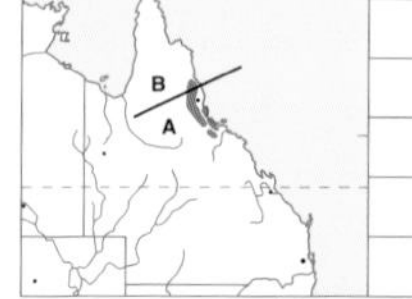

A = Race *spaldingii* **E**
B = Race *melasmenus* **E**

Eastern Whipbird *Psophodes olivaceus* **C–MC** ◎ E

Shy, dark olive-green, black-crested bird with long, broad tail. Black head, throat, breast. Bold white cheek, sides of neck. Sides of tail tipped white. Race *lateralis* (B) Smaller, browner; tail shorter, brown at tip. **Size** 25–30 cm. **Juv.** Olive-brown, lacks head markings. **Imm.** Dull olive, underparts mottled, faint cheek patch. **Voice** Antiphonal. Long, soft, ee-ee-ee before ringing 'whipcrack' (male); softer 'wi-choo' (female response). Harsh alarm; soft chuckles. **Hab.** Dense understorey of rainforest, coastal scrub, wet sclerophyll forest, stream-side forest.

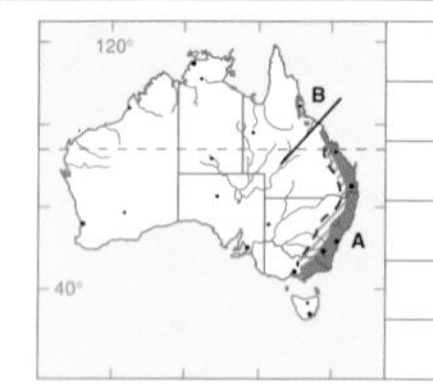

A = Race *olivaceus* **E**
B = Race *lateralis* **E**

Mallee Whipbird *Psophodes leucogaster* **UC** ◎ E Endangered

Paler than Western, whiter below. Upper edge white cheek stripe not black-margined. Race *lashmari* (B) Cheek stripe variably black-margined. Race *oberon* (C) Largest; longest tail. Cheek stripe edged black. **Size** 23–25 cm. **Voice** Antiphonal. Varied; rising more than Western. **Hab.** Dense mallee scrub.

SHARED MAP

Mallee Whipbird
C
A
B
40°
Western Whipbird

Mallee Whipbird
A = Race *leucogaster* **E Vulnerable**
B = Race *lashmari* **E**
C = Race *oberon* **E Endangered**
Western Whipbird E Endangered

Western Whipbird *Psophodes nigrogularis* **UC** ◎ E Vulnerable

Elusive, olive-green. Small crest; long, broad tail. Head, crest olive. Chin, throat, black, bordered by white cheek stripes edged black. Dull grey below. Outer tail feathers tipped white. **Size** 21–25 cm. **Juv./Imm.** Throat rufous to greyish; no cheek stripe. Quick post-fledging moult, possibly male only, to adult plumage. **Voice** Bell-like. Male slow scratchy rising 'eee-choo-chooo'. Female short 3-note response. Chattering alarm. **Hab.** Dense coastal heath.

Mallee
Western

Ventral variation

Chirruping Wedgebill *Psophodes cristatus* **C–UC** ◎ E

Parties glide low like Apostlebird. Crest, upperparts, light brown. Bill black, wedge-shaped. Flight, tail feathers, edged white. Light grey below. **Size** 19–21 cm. **Juv.** Orange-red bill; buff wing marks. **Voice** Antiphonal. Male a rolling 'chirrrp', female responds with falling 'ee cheer'. Sparrow-like, repetitive, **Hab.** Semi-arid areas, low scrub, acacia woodland, savannah.

Often in groups

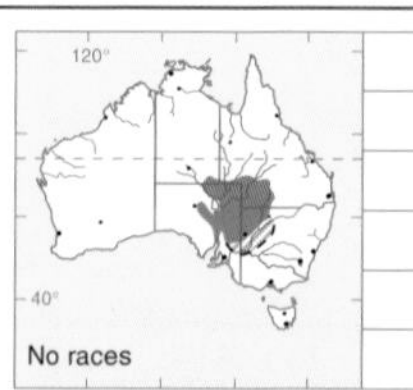

No races

Chiming Wedgebill *Psophodes occidentalis* **C–UC** ◎ E

Except for voice, distribution, almost identical to Chirruping Wedgebill. Shyer. **Size** 19–22 cm. **Juv.** Orange-red bill. **Voice** Falling chime of 4 notes 'chi-da-da-doo' repeated with haunting quality. Also one- and two-note rhythmic chimes. **Hab.** Dense acacia, melaleuca, tea-tree scrub in arid areas.

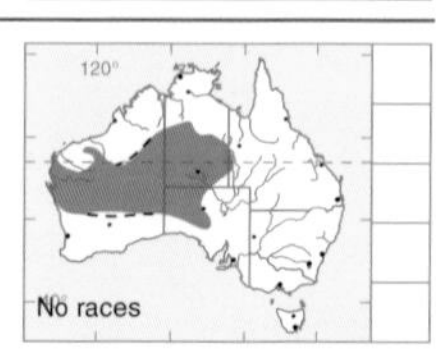

No races

Logrunner
Juv.
Logrunner ♂
Chowchilla
Juv.
Chowchilla
♂
Logrunner ♀
Chowchilla ♀
Eastern
Whipbird
Eastern
Whipbird
Imm.
Eastern
Whipbird
Juv.
Mallee Whipbird
Race *leucogaster*
Mallee Whipbird
Juv.
Western Whipbird
Chirruping
Wedgebill
Juv.
Chirruping
Wedgebill
Chiming Wedgebill
DAY

Spotted Quail-thrush *Cinclosoma punctatum* **UC–R** ◎ E

Shy ground-feeder. White eyebrow. Black face. White patch on sides of black throat. Neck, breast, grey. Back, flanks, streaked white. Shoulder black, small white spots. Tail tipped white. **F/Juv.** No black on head; dull orange neck patch. **Size** 25–28 cm. **Voice** Up to 10 slow liquid notes from high perch; loud repeated 'soo-ee, soo-ee, soo-ee'; repeated thin 'phee', a high contact call (typically difficult to hear). **Hab.** Sclerophyll forest; ideally on leaf-littered rocky ridges with short grass tussocks.

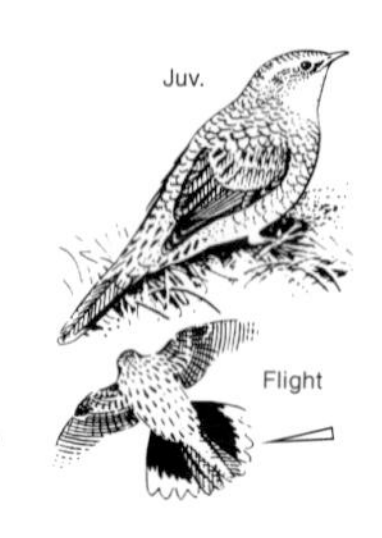

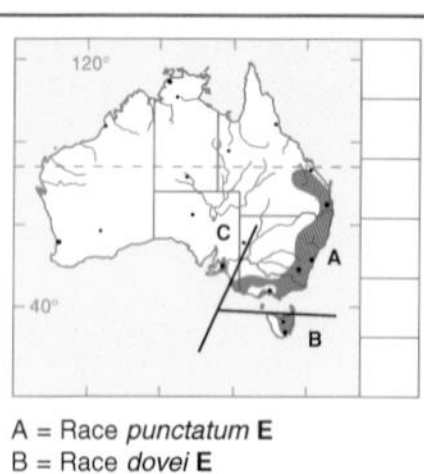

A = Race *punctatum* **E**
B = Race *dovei* **E**
C = Race *anachoreta* **E**
Endangered

Chestnut Quail-thrush *Cinclosoma castanotus* **MC–UC** ◎ E

Face, throat, upper breast, black. White eyebrow. Broad white streak on side of grey throat. Upper back grey-brown. Rich chestnut band across lower back, shoulder. White underparts. Race *clarum* (B) Broader band over mantle, upper wings. Race *fordianum* (C) Deep russet band, lower back. **F/Juv.** Face brown; upper breast grey. **Size** M 22–26, F 17–23 cm. **Voice** Thin, high-pitched; 'rosella-like' piping whistle, faster than Spotted. **Hab.** Mallee, mulga scrub; inland desert heath, woodland.

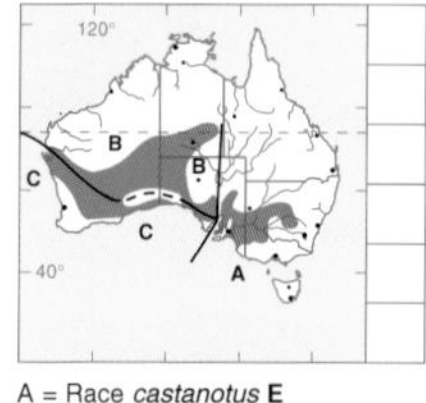

A = Race *castanotus* **E**
B = Race *clarum* **E**
C = Race *fordianum* **E**

Chestnut-breasted Quail-thrush *Cinclosoma castaneothorax* **MC** ◎ E

Upperparts warm olive-brown; breast rich cinnamon-yellow (not chestnut as name suggests). **F** Like female of Cinnamon Quail-thrush race *cinnamomeum*, but has rufous wash on throat and grey breast. Race *marginatum* (B) 'Western Quail-thrush' Larger. Upperparts rich chestnut. Breast reddish-brown, pale-edged. **F** As nominate. **Size** 18–24 cm. **Juv.** Both races generally as female. **Voice** Thin, high-pitched, ventriloquial; tuneful 2-note rhythmic whistle. **Hab.** Races *castaneothorax* and *marginatum* both favour low acacia-covered ridges.

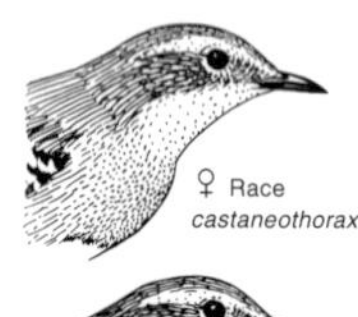
♀ Race *castaneothorax*

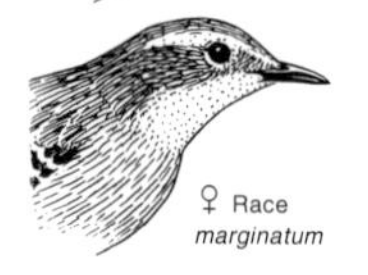
♀ Race *marginatum*

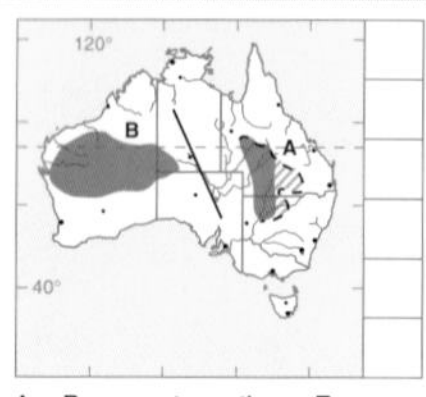

A = Race *castaneothorax* **E**
B = Race *marginatum* **E**

Cinnamon Quail-thrush *Cinclosoma cinnamomeum* **MC–?UC** ◎ E

White eyebrow; black face. Broad white streak down sides of black throat. Upperparts plain cinnamon-rufous. Whitish patch graded to cinnamon on upper breast; broad black band below. Outer tail feathers black, tipped white. Race *alisteri* (B) 'Nullarbor Quail-thrush'. Smallest quail-thrush. Face, throat, upper breast black. White eyebrow. Irregular white streak on sides of throat. Upperparts richer reddish-cinnamon. Outer tail feathers black, tipped white. Race *tirariensis* (C) All cinnamon parts paler than nominate. **F** (all races) Duller; brownish throat, buffy eyebrow. Upper breast grey; no black below. **Size** 18–20 cm. **Juv.** Resembles female but less clearly marked. **M juv.** *cinnamomeum* may have indistinct breast band. **Voice** Insect-like 'seee-si-si-seee'. **Hab.** Races *cinnamomeum*, *tirariensis*, gibber plains, sparse vegetation along usually dry watercourses. Race *alisteri* low vegetation associated with Nullarbor Plain limestone outcroppings. Population declining.

♀ Race *cinnamomeum*

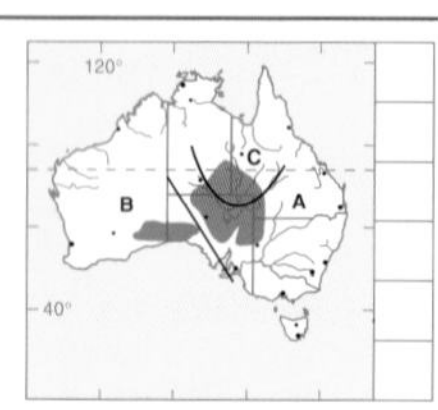

A = Race *cinnamomeum* **E**
B = Race *alisteri* **E**
C = Race *tirariensis* **E**

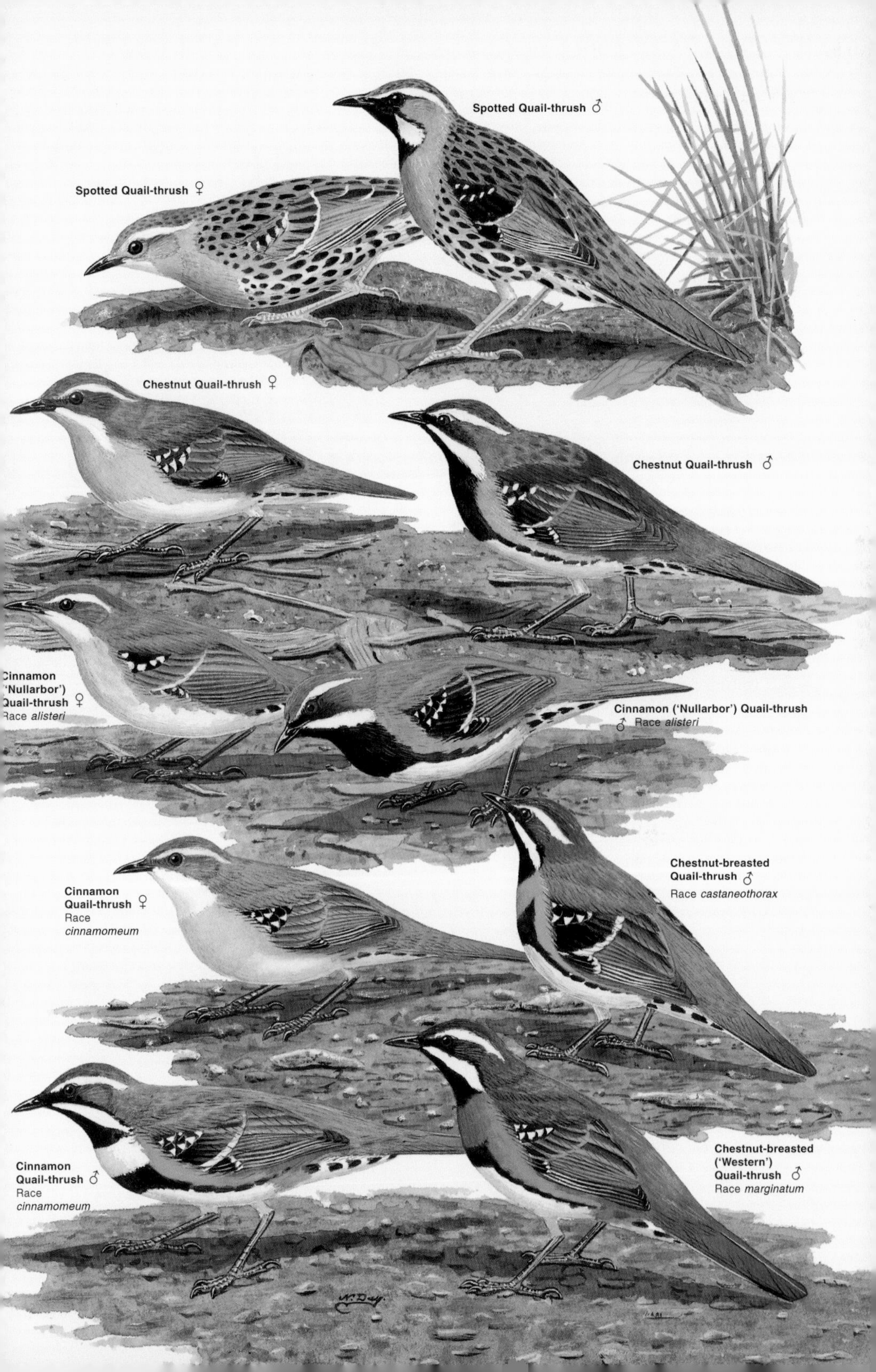

Spotted Quail-thrush ♂
Spotted Quail-thrush ♀
Chestnut Quail-thrush ♀
Chestnut Quail-thrush ♂
Cinnamon ('Nullarbor') Quail-thrush ♀ Race *alisteri*
Cinnamon ('Nullarbor') Quail-thrush ♂ Race *alisteri*
Chestnut-breasted Quail-thrush ♂ Race *castaneothorax*
Cinnamon Quail-thrush ♀ Race *cinnamomeum*
Cinnamon Quail-thrush ♂ Race *cinnamomeum*
Chestnut-breasted ('Western') Quail-thrush ♂ Race *marginatum*

Grey-crowned Babbler *Pomatostomus temporalis* **MC–LUC** ◎

Largest, and only babbler without dark crown. Long, down-curved black bill. Eye pale yellow. Head has narrow grey crown, bordered by broad white eyebrow above dark brown eye-stripe, lores to nape. Upperparts greyish-brown; rump darker. Wings dark brown; chestnut patch in flight. Tail long, blackish-brown, broad white tip. Throat, upper breast, white, merging to grey breast; variably rufous-brown belly. Legs black. Race *rubeculus* (B) Smaller. White eyebrow meets across frons. Reddish-brown breast, darker brown underparts. Short white tail tip. **Size** 25–29 cm. **Juv.** Duller, rufous wash on eyebrow; wing bars buff. Bill shorter; eyes dark. **Voice** Babbling chorus, whistling, mewing. 'Go back, go back', 'Get away! Get away!' **Hab.** Drier, more open forest, scrubby woodland, trees bordering roads along drainage lines, farmland with isolated trees.

Dorsal pattern

In all babblers, a dark ('masked face') eye-stripe, bordered by white eyebrows and white throat, gives a 'band of thieves' appearance to any group of these birds. In Victoria, a few individuals, remnants of colonies, remain on Mornington Peninsula.

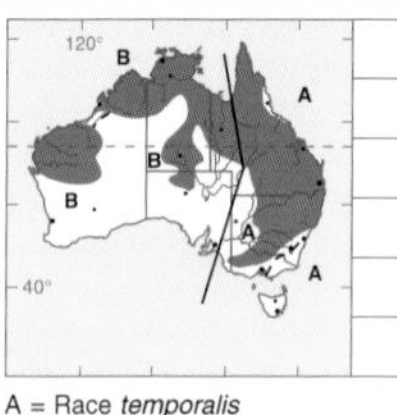

A = Race *temporalis*
B = Race *rubeculus* **E**

White-browed Babbler *Pomatostomus superciliosus* **MC–LC** ◎ E

The plainest babbler. Family parties. Very active, noisy and seemingly 'quarrelsome' bird. Black, down-curved bill. Dark eye in brown eye-stripe. Crown dark brown; prominent long white eyebrow. Upper back, wings, greyish-brown; rump dark brown. Tail blackish-brown, tipped white. Throat, breast, white, merging to grey-brown flanks, belly. Legs dark grey. **Size** 18–22 cm. **Juv.** Duller; brow, throat washed buff. Bill shorter. **Voice** High-pitched chatter; chirring; scratchy scolding. **Hab.** Drier, more open forest with shrubby understorey, mallee, mulga scrubs.

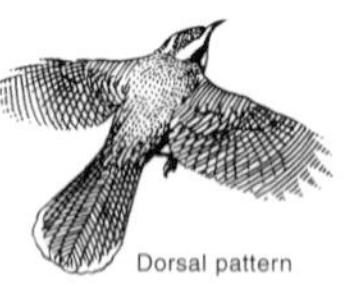

Dorsal pattern

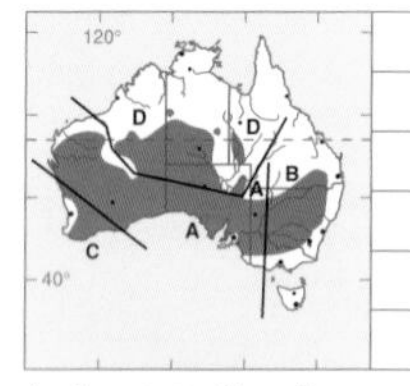

A = Race *superciliosus* **E**
B = Race *gilgandra* **E**
C = Race *ashbyi* **E**
D = Race *centralis* **E**

Hall's Babbler *Pomatostomus halli* **MC** ◎ E

Similar to White-browed Babbler but darker and more definitely marked. Family parties. Black, down-curved bill. Eye dark. Eye-stripe dark, appears black. Narrow, dark brown crown; broad white eyebrow. Tail sooty-brown, tipped white. White throat, upper breast well demarcated from dark brown underparts. Legs black. **Size** 23–25 cm. **Juv.** Duller; brow, throat washed buff. **Voice** High-pitched chatter; more liquid than other babblers. **Hab.** Mainly elevated ridges of dry acacia scrubs; dry eucalypt woodland.

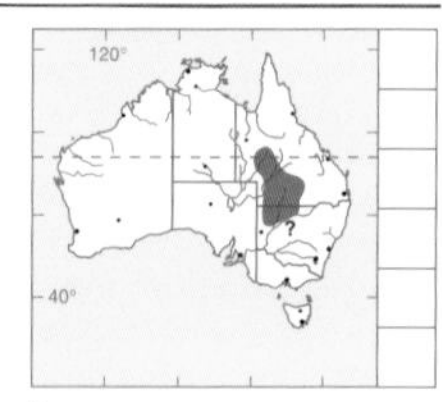

No races

Chestnut-crowned Babbler *Pomatostomus ruficeps* **C–LC** ◎ E

Rather 'dapper' appearance. Family parties. Two white wing bars diagnostic, identifying this from other all other babblers. Eye, eye-stripe brown. Dark, down-curved bill. Crown rich chestnut, highlighted by narrow white eyebrow. Back mottled greyish-brown. Throat, breast, white, grading into grey-brown belly. Flanks dark brown. Tail blackish-brown, tipped white. Legs dark grey. **Size** 20.5–23 cm. **Juv.** Duller; crown browner. Tan face mask. Eyebrow, and also wing bars, washed rufous. **Voice** Harsh chatter, chirring. Contact call 'we-chee-chee-chee'. **Hab.** Dry inland mulga, mallee scrubs, more open arid woodland; she-oaks; acacia trees near edges of salt lakes.

Communal roosting nest

No races

Grey-crowned
Babbler
Race *rubeculus*
Grey-crowned
Babbler
Race *temporalis*
Grey-crowned
Babbler Juv.
Race *temporalis*
White-browed
Babbler
Hall's Babbler
White-browed
Babbler
Chestnut-crowned
Babbler
N. Day

Rose Robin *Petroica rosea* **MC–LC** E

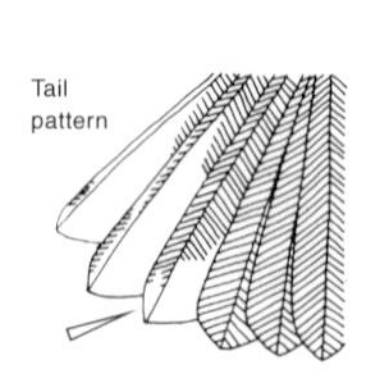

No races

Most acrobatic of *Petroica* robins. Often feeds in high canopy. Cocks tail; droops wings. Breast rose-red. Deep grey head, back, throat. White frons, abdomen, undertail and outer tail feathers. No wing bars. **F/Imm.** Greyish-brown upperparts; throat, breast, greyish-white, sometimes with pale rose wash. Whitish wing bars. Dark brown tail, outer tail feathers white. **Size** 11 cm. **Juv.** Striped; brownish. **Voice** 'tick', like snapping twig. Scratchy contact calls. Male: 'dick-dick-di-di-dzee-dzee'. **Hab.** Breeds in deep gullies of tall open forest, rainforest. Autumn–winter dispersal to more open forest.

Pink Robin *Petroica rodinogaster* **MC–LC** E

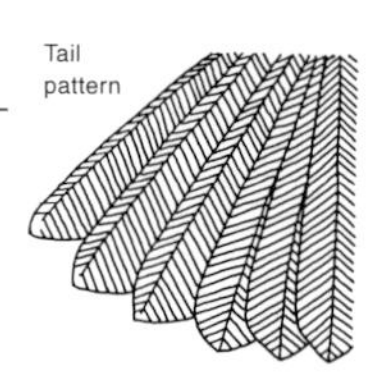

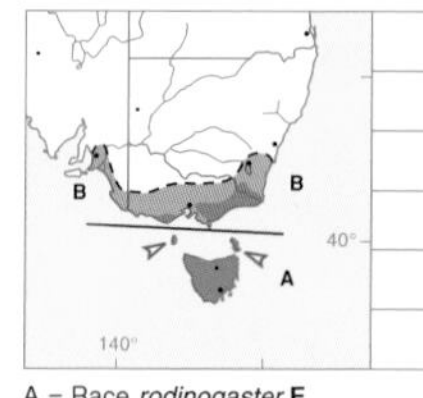

A = Race *rodinogaster* **E**
B = Race *inexpectata* **E**

Perches low in cover, motionless and silent, then darts down for food. Breast, abdomen, rose-pink. Head, back, upper breast sooty-black. White frons (small, indistinct in Tas.). Tail usually all dark (white marks in some). Faint buff wing bars. **F/Imm.** Grey-brown above. Brownish-buff below with occasional pink wash. Two buff wing bars. **Size** 12 cm. **Juv.** Striped; brownish. **Voice** Less tonal variation. Slow single notes, sometimes with warble or soft churr. Sharp 'tick'. **Hab.** Dense gullies of tall open forest. Autumn–winter dispersal to more open forest.

Flame Robin *Petroica phoenicea* **C** E

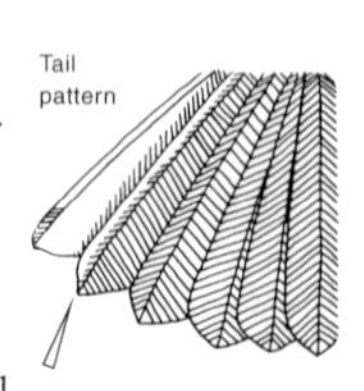

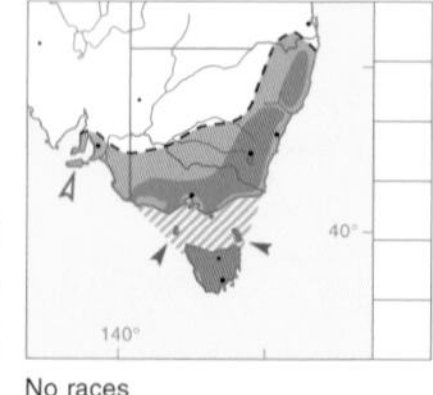

No races

Forages on ground in series of hops, runs, flights. Upright stance; occasional flicks of wings, tail. Flame-red from throat to abdomen. Dark grey upperparts. White frons, wing bar, outer tail shafts. **F/Imm.** Upperparts brown; white to buff wing bars. Brown tail; outer shafts white. Lighter below. Can breed in imm. plumage. **Size** 14 cm. **Juv.** Striped; brownish. **Voice** High, clear staccato 'dee-di-di-di dee-di-di-di dee-do-dee', described as 'You will come, if you will, to the sea'. **Hab.** Nests in low open forest. Small flocks in autumn–winter dispersal. Prefers cropped paddocks, parkland near woodland. Roosts in dense scrub, citrus orchards.

Scarlet Robin *Petroica boodang* **MC**

Note Name *Petroica multicolor* is now confined to Pacific Robin of Norfolk Is. and tropical SW Pacific region, with about 14 races.

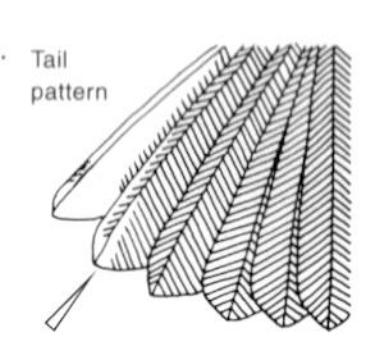

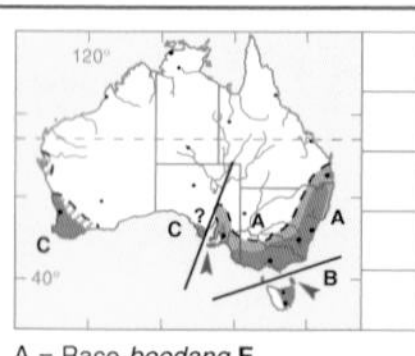

A = Race *boodang* **E**
B = Race *leggii* **E**
C = Race *campbelli* **E**

Single or pairs. Scarlet breast, white lower abdomen. Black head, back, throat. Large white frons; white wing bars, outer tail shafts. **F** Brownish throat; pale scarlet wash on breast. **Size** 13 cm. **Imm.** Resembles duller female, initially lacks red. **Voice** High rippling warble ending in 2 long notes. Scolding chirr. Quiet 'tick'. **Hab.** Breeds in closed and tall open forest. Some autumn–winter altitudinal dispersal to more open localities.

Red-capped Robin *Petroica goodenovii* **MC** E

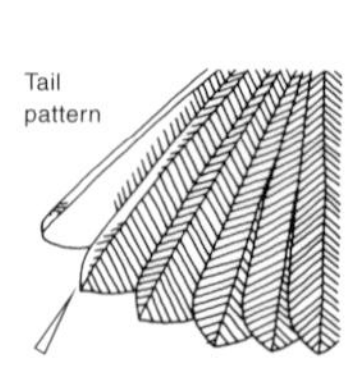

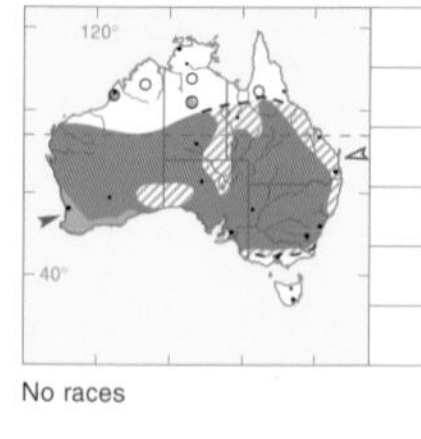

No races

Feeds mainly on ground. Restless; flicks wings and tail while perched. Scarlet cap, breast. Dull black face, back, throat. Bold white wing bar, outer tail shafts. **F** Identify from female Scarlet and Flame Robins. Mature females show red-brown frons. Grey-brown upperparts; darker brown wings, tail. Some have slight red wash on breast (not illustrated). Pale buff wing patch. Outer tail shafts white. **Size** 12 cm. **Juv.** Brownish streaks and blotches. **Imm.** Male may have slightly red-washed breast. Can breed in imm. plumage. Some males have red-brown on frons. **Voice** Falling insect-like 'di-di-dididit drrr'. Warning 'dik!'. **Hab.** Drier scrub, woodland. Autumn–winter dispersal.

Rose Robin Juv.
Rose Robin ♂
Pink Robin ♀
Rose Robin ♀
Pink Robin Juv.
Pink Robin ♂
Flame Robin Juv.
Flame Robin ♀
Flame Robin ♂
Scarlet Robin ♂
Scarlet Robin ♀
Scarlet Robin Juv.
Red-capped Robin Ad. ♀ /Imm.
Red-capped Robin ♂
Red-capped Robin Juv.
Red-capped Robin ♀ Mature Ad.
N.DAY.

Hooded Robin *Melanodryas cucullata* UC ◎ E

Black hood over head, breast. Bill black. Eye dark brown. White bars on black wing. Base of outer tail feathers white. White to grey underparts. **F** Head, back, grey-brown; throat pale grey. Tail, wings, darker with same markings as male. **Size** 16 cm. **Juv.** Striped, mottled dark brown. **Imm.** As female; male darker throat, breast. Upperparts in moult mottled black. **Voice** Often silent. Piping 'bree-yeeuw-yew-yew'. Falling 'chew, chew'. Chatter 'ja-ja-ja'. **Hab.** Dry forest, woodland, mallee, scrubland.

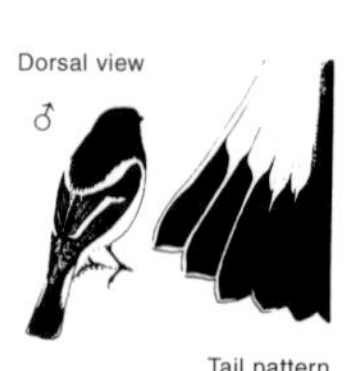

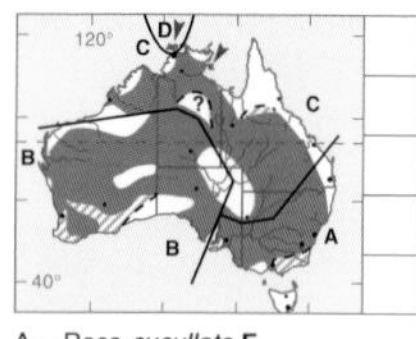

A = Race *cucullata* **E**
B = Race *westralensis* **E**
C = Race *picata* **E**
D = Race *melvillensis* **E Vulnerable**

Dusky Robin *Melanodryas vittata* MC ◎ E

Perches motionless for long periods. Fine dark eye-stripe. Head, upperparts grey-brown, darker on wings, tail. Pale buff edging below bend of wing, on wing stripe and outer tail. Underparts pale brown. Race *kingi* (B) Warm brown above; mid-brown below. **Size** 16.5 cm. **Juv.** Paler streaking above; darker mottling below. **Voice** Sad, meditative 'prree-prree'. **Hab.** Open forest, woodland, scrublands, usually close to cleared land.

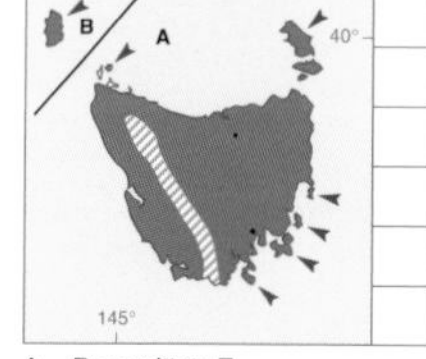

A = Race *vittata* **E**
B = Race *kingi* **E**

Eastern Yellow Robin *Eopsaltria australis* C ◎ E

Dark grey to black bill. Eye dark, pale brow. Head grey, back olive. Pale wing bar; tail brown-grey. Olive rump, uppertail coverts. Whitish throat. Underparts citrus-yellow. Legs brownish-black. Race *chrysorrhoa* (B) Bright yellow rump, uppertail coverts. **Size** 15 cm. **Juv.** Brown; mottled, streaked buff. **Voice** Monotonous piping, slow or fast; loud double 'choop choop'. **Hab.** Wet open forest, woodland, coastal thickets.

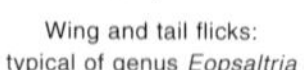

Wing and tail flicks: typical of genus *Eopsaltria*

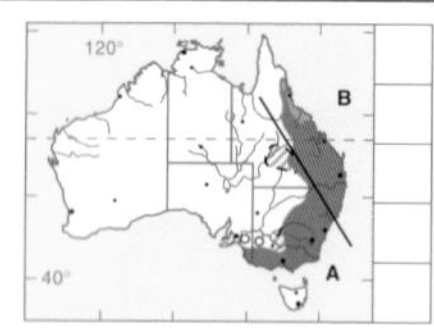

A = Race *australis* **E**
B = Race *chrysorrhoa* **E**

Western Yellow Robin *Eopsaltria griseogularis* C–UC ◎ E

As Eastern Yellow Robin but breast pale grey. Rump yellow, brightest near Perth. Race *rosinae* (B) southern WA and Eyre Peninsula, SA. Darker back, more grey on breast. Rump olive-yellow. **Size** 15 cm. **Juv.** As Eastern Yellow Robin. **Voice** Slow piping, lower, harsher than Eastern. **Hab.** Open forest, woodland, mallee, coastal scrub.

Wing bars in flight: typical of genus *Eopsaltria*

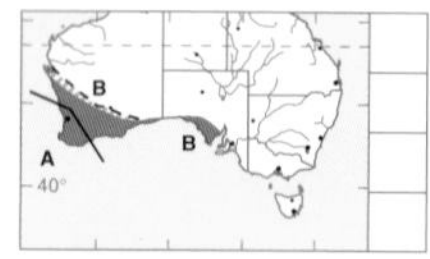

A = Race *griseogularis* **E**
B = Race *rosinae* **E**

White-breasted Robin *Eopsaltria georgiana* UC ◎ E

Upperparts blue-grey. Paler eyebrow; darker on lores, wings, tail. Inside of mouth rich gold-yellow. Breast grey-washed; white below. Wing bar only seen in flight. Tips of outer tail white. Smaller northern birds sooty-grey above. **Size** 14.5 cm. **Juv.** Head, wing coverts, mottled brown; breast mottled brown and grey. **Voice** Piping 'choo-chee'; whipcrack 'chee-rit'; sharp 'pit-pit'. **Hab.** Southern birds open forests, usually near streams. Northern birds in coastal thickets.

Trunk perching: typical of genus *Eopsaltria*

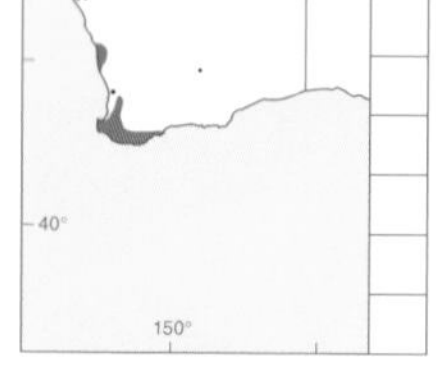

No races

Mangrove Robin *Peneoenanthe (Eopsaltria) pulverulenta* MC ◎

Often in families, on ground amid mangrove roots. In flight, pale wing bar, white panels in tail. Typical silent flight, quiet presence in shadows, but not shy. Long, thin black bill. Dark line through eye to ear coverts; contrasting white lower face, throat. Legs black. Race *cinereiceps* (A) Ash-grey above, whitish below, washed grey on sides of upper breast. Race *alligator* (B) Darker crown, face. Black eye-line, pale grey upper breast. Race *leucura* (C) Larger. Leaden grey above, dusky crown. **Size** 16 cm. **Juv.** Upperparts brown, streaked paler. Mottled buff breast. **Voice** Varied. Sweet rising 2-note whistle; compare Little Shrike-thrush. Falling 'pee-pee-peer'. Harsh 'chuk'; soft 'chrrr'. **Hab.** Mangroves.

Tail pattern

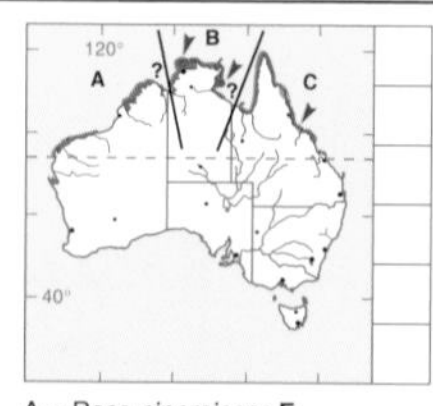

A = Race *cinereiceps* **E**
B = Race *alligator* **E**
C = Race *leucura*

Hooded Robin
Juv.
Hooded Robin
♂
Hooded Robin
Imm. ♂
Hooded Robin
♀
Eastern Yellow Robin
Race australis
Dusky Robin
Juv.
Dusky Robin
Eastern Yellow Robin
Race chrysorrhoa
Eastern Yellow Robin
Juv.
White-breasted Robin
Juv.
Western Yellow Robin
Race griseogularis
Western Yellow Robin
Race rosinae
White-breasted Robin
Mangrove Robin
Race leucura
Mangrove Robin
Race alligator
Mangrove Robin
Juv.
N. DAY.

Yellow-legged Flycatcher *Microeca griseoceps* **MC** ◎

Check Lemon-bellied Flycatcher and Grey Whistler (race *peninsulae*). Broad flat bill dark above, cream below. Pale lores, thin eye-ring. Head, nape grey; paler face, ear coverts. Back, upper-wing coverts, yellowish-olive. Throat, breast, dull white; lemon yellow below, washed grey-buff. Wings, tail brown, edged greenish. Legs pale orange-yellow. **Size** 12 cm. **Juv.** Buff feather tips above. Breast pale, dark-mottled. **Voice** Insect-like, descending trill; varying whistles. **Hab.** Rainforest and edges.

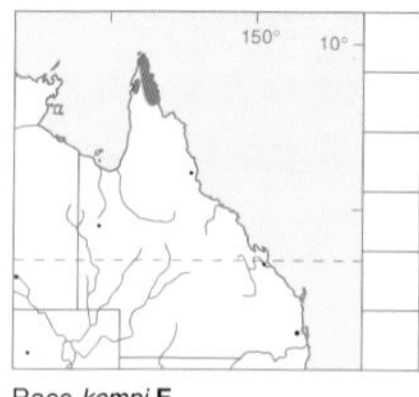

Race *kempi* **E**

Lemon-bellied Flycatcher *Microeca flavigaster* **C–LUC** ◎

Broad bill dark above, paler below. Pale lore streak. Olive-brown above, darker wings, tail. Rump yellowish. White throat, bright lemon breast, belly. Yellowish underwing coverts. Legs, feet black. Race *laetissima* (B) Larger. Pale lemon breast, washed grey. Race *tormenti* (C) 'Kimberley Flycatcher'. Greyer head, longer bill; silver-white breast, belly. Race *flavissima* (D) More yellow throughout. Rich yellow breast, belly. **Size** 12–12.5 cm. **Juv.** Browner; cream spots above. Cinnamon-buff wing feather edges; *tormenti* contrasting mottles, spots. **Voice** Sweet whistling songs; 'Please to come with me'. **Hab.** Along streams, woodland, mangroves; *tormenti* mangroves only.

Juv. moulting

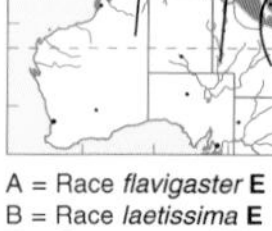

A = Race *flavigaster* **E**
B = Race *laetissima* **E**
C = Race *tormenti* **E**
D = Race *flavissima*

Poorly selected common names disguise the fact that all the birds on this plate are 'perfectly good robins' in the Australasian Family Petroicidae.

Jacky Winter *Microeca fascinans* **MC–LC** ◎

Perches, wags tail sideways; white edges show. Small winter groups. Check 'Kimberley Flycatcher', female Hooded Robin. Black bill. Narrow eye-line, whitish eyebrow. Head, back grey-brown; wings darker, white edges. Greyish breast; whitish below. Buff alula stripe. Tail blackish-brown; white outer feathers. Legs black. Race *assimilis* (B) Darker. White outer tail feathers become black towards base. Greyish wash over breast, flanks. Race *pallida* (C) Smaller, sandy brown, paling towards inland. **Size** 13 cm. **Juv.** Bill brown. Spotted white above; brown below. White wing, tail, feather edges. **Voice** Rapid, strong, 'jacky-jacky winter-winter-winter'. **Hab.** Open woodland, farmland.

Tail wag

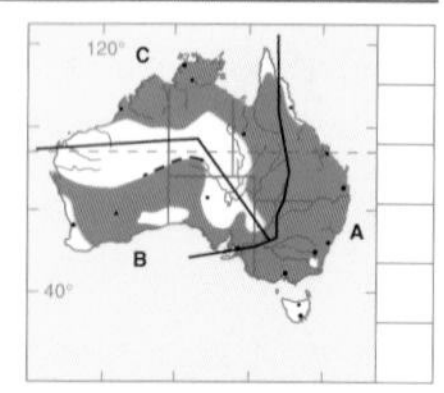

A = Race *fascinans* **E**
B = Race *assimilis* **E**
C = Race *pallida* **E**

Northern Scrub-robin *Drymodes superciliaris* **UC** ◎

Cinnamon-backed, long-tailed, long-legged ground-robin. Two white wing bars on black wing coverts. Black bill. Eye dark brown. Heavy black mark through eye, down cheek. Wings black, edged white-buff. Rump and central tail feathers rich cinnamon; broad white tips to black outer tail feathers. Cream lores, chin, throat, ear coverts, central underparts. Side of breast, long fluffy flank feathers, buff. Legs flesh-pink. **Size** 22 cm. **Juv.** Softer colours. Body speckled. **Voice** Four high, long notes, rising, falling. **Hab.** Rainforest floors.

Dorsal pattern

Race *superciliaris* **E**

'Presumed extinct' race colcloughi *of Roper R., NT, now considered invalid. Either two mis-labelled Cape York Penin. specimens, or a hoax (based on Schodde & Mason, 1999).*

Southern Scrub-robin *Drymodes brunneopygia* **UC–LUC** ◎ E

Cryptic grey-brown, long-tailed, long-legged robin. Flicks tail up. Bill black. Whitish lores; white partial eye-ring (behind eye). Dusky vertical mark through eye. Wings grey-brown, edged paler; whitish bars. Rump, upper tail, rufous; lower tail darker; four outer feathers tipped white. Fluffs out soft, greyish flank, belly plumage. **F** Less richly coloured. **Size** 23 cm. **Juv.** Browner above; softer; speckling over body; paler, mottled underparts. Two creamy wing bars visible. **Voice** Pleasant, varied 'chip, choo-wee?'. Warning chatter. **Hab.** Dense mallee, dry scrub.

Dorsal pattern

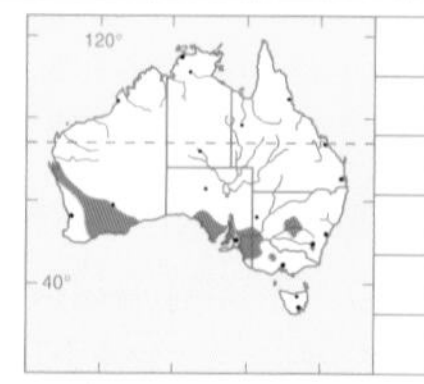

No races

Yellow-legged Flycatcher
Grey Whistler
Race *simplex*
Grey Whistler
Race *peninsulae*
Lemon-bellied Flycatcher
Juv.
Lemon-bellied Flycatcher
Race *flavigaster*
Jacky Winter
Race *fascinans*
Jacky Winter
Race *fascinans*
Lemon-bellied ('Kimberley') Flycatcher
Race *tormenti*
Jacky Winter
Juv.
Southern Scrub-robin
Juv.
Southern Scrub-robin
orthern
crub-robin
N.DAY.

Grey-headed Robin
Poecilodryas (Heteromyias) albispecularis **MC** ◎

Short black bill, yellow tip. Lores black. Narrow white, then black, lines behind eye. Crown grey to nape; paler eyebrow. Ear coverts pale rufous. White lower face, throat. Wings sooty-brown, two palest grey wing bars. Rump to tail base chestnut; lower tail dark brown, outer feather tips paler. Breast grey, belly whitish; buff flanks. Legs flesh. **Size** 17 cm. **Juv.** Brown above; head, underparts blotched rust. Bill pale. **Voice** Piping whistle; 2-note bell-like 'pee-per-per-per'. **Hab.** Rainforest above 300 m.

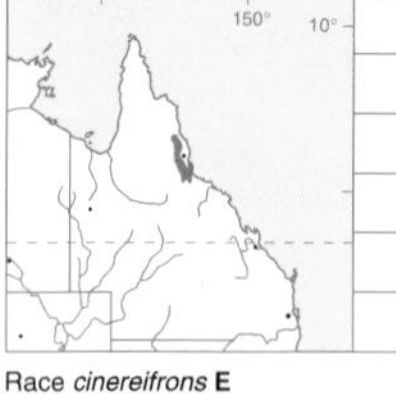

Race *cinereifrons* **E**

White-faced Robin *Tregellasia leucops* **MC** ◎

Small tropical robin. Olive-black head with white 'owl-like' face (incl. sides of forehead, lores, eye-ring, chin). Back, shoulders, rump, olive-green. Wings, tail, olive-brown, edged olive. Underparts bright yellow; olive wash on breast. Legs pale yellow. **Size** 13 cm. **Juv.** Browner above; duller below. **Voice** Harsh 'chee-chee'; sweet 5-note rising song. **Hab.** Rainforests.

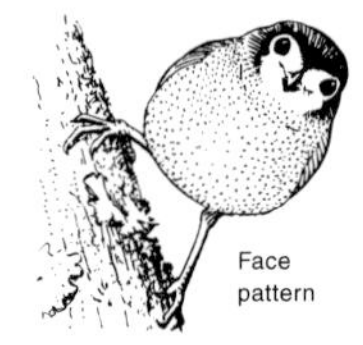

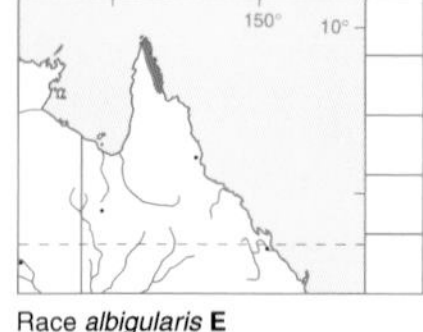

Race *albigularis* **E**

Pale-yellow Robin *Tregellasia capito* **MC** ◎ E

Head olive-grey, darker frons; paler ear coverts, nape. White lores, throat. Back, shoulder, rump, olive. Wings, tail, brownish, edged olive. Pale yellow below, flanks washed olive. Pinkish legs. Race *nana* (B) Smaller; lores buff. **Size** 13 cm. **Juv.** Browner. **Voice** Single notes, harsh scold, soft trill. **Hab.** Rainforest, edges.

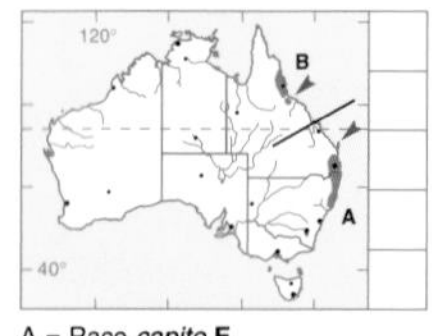

A = Race *capito* **E**
B = Race *nana* **E**

White-browed Robin *Poecilodryas superciliosa* **MC** ◎ EO

Dark brown above. Brow, patch below eye, white. White below, breast washed light grey. White wing patch; wing, tail tipped white. **Size** 15 cm. **Voice** Sweet piping; fast 'tu-tu-sweet-too'; 'ch-ch-choo'. **Hab.** Streams, rainforest, woodland, vine scrub.

Buff-sided Robin *Poecilodryas cerviniventris* **MC** ◎ E

As White-browed but head darker; broader eye band, longer stripe above, less white below. Buff flanks, undertail coverts. **Size** 16 cm. **Voice** Sweet piping. **Hab.** Mangroves, riparian thickets.

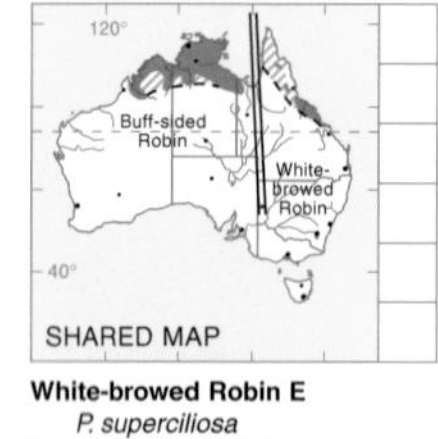

White-browed Robin E
P. superciliosa
Buff-sided Robin E
P. cerviniventris

Eastern Shrike-tit *Falcunculus frontatus* **MC–LUC** ◎–?♧ E

Swings on foliage, loose bark: bark-tearing may draw attention. Crested head. Robust black bill. Black head, bib: two broad white facial bands; lores white. Back, rump, olive-green. Yellow below. Wings, tail, darker grey. **F** Throat olive-green; longer-tailed. **Size** 17–19 cm. **Juv.** Pale throat; back brownish. **Voice** Like female Fan-tailed Cuckoo, but faster. Plaintive whistle 'knock-at-the-door'. **Hab.** Open woodland, rainforest, riparian eucalypts.

Western Shrike-tit *Falcunculus leucogaster* **LUC** ◎–?♧ E

Behaviour as Eastern. Yellower back. Yellow below, white abdomen. **F** Shorter crest; grey-green chin; longer tail. **Size** 15–17 cm. **Juv.** Pale throat; back brownish. **Voice** Plaintive whistle. **Hab.** Eucalypt forest, watercourses, woodland.

Northern Shrike-tit *Falcunculus whitei* **R–UC** ◎–?♧ E

Behaviour as Eastern. Smaller, duskier yellow. Slightly shorter tail. **F** Shorter crest; olive chin. **Size** 14–16 cm. **Juv.** Pale throat; back brownish. **Voice** Far-carrying plaintive whistle, rising, falling. **Hab.** Woodland. Endangered by habitat loss.

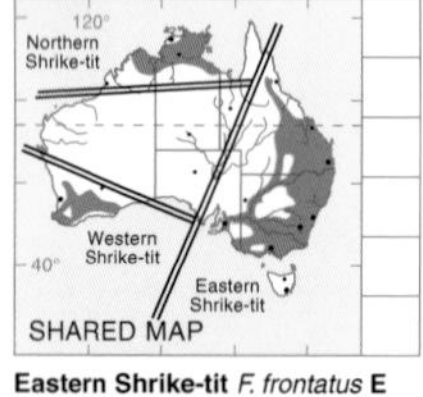

Eastern Shrike-tit *F. frontatus* **E**
Western Shrike-tit *F. leucogaster* **E Vulnerable**
Northern Shrike-tit *F. whitei* **E Endangered**

The Crested Shrike-tit complex, Family Pachycephalidae, shows morphological indications of distant alliances with Crested Bellbird and Grey Shrike-thrush. Schodde & Mason (1999) restored the three totally isolated shrike-tit populations to full species status. Tail-length proportions; wing-shape differences; wide geographic separation between species (formerly races), are all of importance.

Western Shrike-tit
♂
Northern Shrike-tit
♂
Eastern Shrike-tit
♂
Eastern Shrike-tit
♀
Grey-headed Robin
Race *cinereifrons*
White-faced
Robin
White-browed Robin
Pale-yellow Robin
Race *nana*
Pale-yellow Robin
Race *capito*
Buff-sided Robin
N. Day

Crested Bellbird *Oreoica gutturalis* **C–UC** ◎ E

Crown feathers erectile as a crest. Head mid-grey to nape, with central black line. Orange eye. White lores, throat, encircled by black band from crest through eye to breast. Back, wings, tail grey-brown, richer on rump. Buff side of breast, undertail coverts. **F** Eye red-brown. Lores grey. Black line on crown. Grey throat; no black on breast (and check Grey Shrike-thrush). Race *pallescens* (B) Paler generally. **Size** 21.5 cm. **M imm.** Dark throat patch. **F imm.** As adult female. **Voice** Distinctive, far-carrying; 2–4 clear liquid notes then bell-like 'p-link, p-link'. **Hab.** Low, dry, inland woodland and scrub.

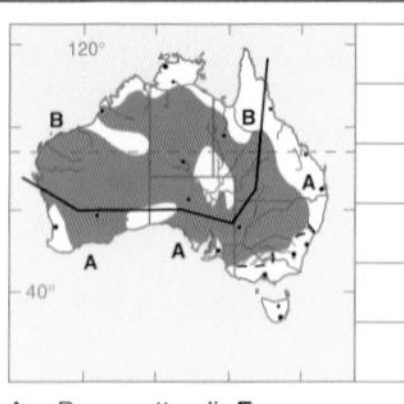

A = Race *gutturalis* **E**
B = Race *pallescens* **E**

Little Shrike-thrush *Colluricincla megarhyncha* **C–MC** ?◎

Seven races with subtle variation; the two best known described. Race *parvula* (A) Light brown above. Blackish-brown bill. White lores, eyebrow, throat. Faintly streaked throat, upper breast. Cinnamon-buff below. Race *rufogaster* (G) Olive-brown above; paler face. Pinkish-brown bill. Paler throat; slightly streaked upper breast. Rich cinnamon below. **Size** 19 cm. **Juv.** (all races) Smaller; paler bills; rufous wing edges. **Voice** Varied dialects: 'pu-lik, pu-lik'; 'weet-weet-weet'; 'wee-chew, wee-chew'. **Hab.** Mangroves, swamp thickets, rainforest, coastal woodland.

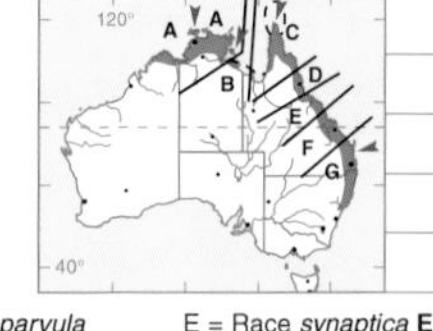

A = Race *parvula*
B = Race *aelptes* **E**
C = Race *normani* **E?**
D = Race *griseata* **E**
E = Race *synaptica* **E**
F = Race *gouldii* **E**
G = Race *rufogaster* **E**

Bower's Shrike-thrush *Colluricincla boweri* **MC** ◎ E

Black bill. Grey lores, eye-ring feathers. Large blue-grey head. Grey back. Wings, shorter tail, grey-brown. Pale throat, cinnamon breast, finely streaked grey. **F**, also **M imm.** Pale grey bill. Rufous lores, eyebrow; pale eye-ring feathers. **Size** 20.5 cm. **Juv./F imm.** Pale bill, eye-ring. Rufous lores, eyebrow. Variably rufous on wing feathers. Paler below, streaked. **Voice** Variable liquid trills, chirps; 'chip, chip, choo-wee', 'choo, chee-chee'. **Hab.** Rainforest above 300 m.

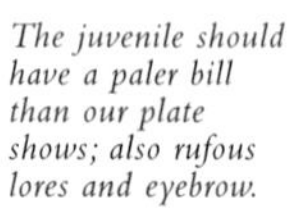
The juvenile should have a paler bill than our plate shows; also rufous lores and eyebrow.

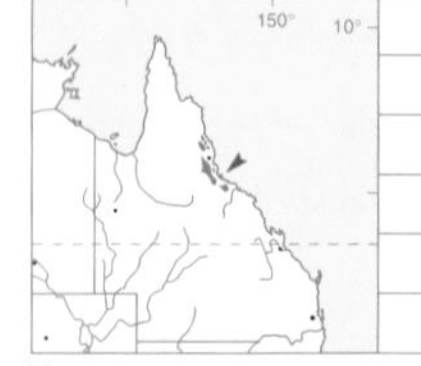

No races
Has affinities with Little Shrike-thrush.

Sandstone Shrike-thrush *Colluricincla woodwardi* **MC** ◎ E

Largest shrike-thrush. Flies across rocky gullies. Buff streak from bill to eye. Dull grey head. Olive-brown back, wings, tail. Finely streaked buff throat. Grey wash on finely streaked cinnamon breast. Abdomen cinnamon. **Size** 23–26 cm. **Juv.** Underparts paler, slightly streaked. Wing feathers edged rufous. **Voice** Rich, echoing 'pwee, pwee'. Lovely falling 'cheeeong'. Sings from rocky perches. **Hab.** Sandstone cliffs. Occurs almost entirely on ground; in crevices.

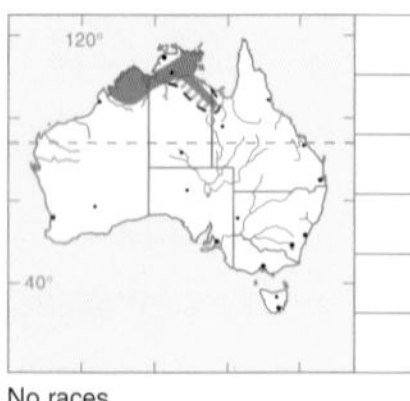

No races
Has affinities with Grey Shrike-thrush.

Grey Shrike-thrush *Colluricincla harmonica* **C** ◎–♧

Five races. Black bill. Head grey; white lores. Back brown. Wings, tail, grey. 'Longer-tailed' than Little Shrike-thrush. Underparts light grey. Race *rufiventris* (B) 'Western Shrike-thrush' Back, wings, darker grey. Cinnamon-buff undertail coverts. Race *brunnea* (E) Plain grey-brown upper-parts; underparts paler. **F** White eye-ring, eye-stripe, less distinct. Underside of greyer bill paler; fine streaking on throat. **Size** About 24 cm. **Juv./Imm.** Light brown eye-ring extends midway to bill. Tan to buff eyebrow; varies in extent. Strongly streaked throat, breast. **Voice** Old name 'Harmonious Thrush'. Very variable. Liquid melodious trills, clear whistles, 'cho-cho-weeee!'. Single ringing call in winter similar to Grey Currawong. **Hab.** Forest, woodland, scrub, mallee, gardens.

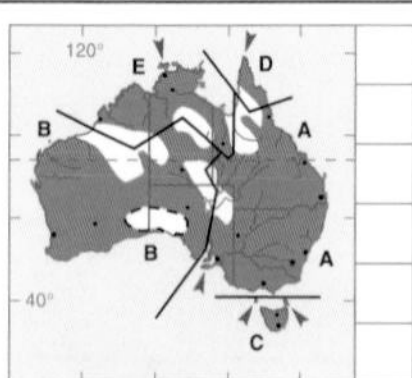

A = Race *harmonica* **E**
B = Race *rufiventris* **E**
C = Race *strigata* **E**
D = Race *superciliosa* **E**
E = Race *brunnea* **E**
Schodde & Mason (1999) have further subdivided these subspecies (races), where additional minor regional differences appear across Australia, and have allocated 'sub-subspecific' names to them ('quadrinomials').

Little Shrike-thrush
Race parvula
Little Shrike-thrush
Race rufogaster
Bower's Shrike-thrush
Juv./Imm.
Bower's Shrike-thrush ♂
Sandstone Shrike-thrush
Grey Shrike-thrush ♂
Race brunnea
Grey Shrike-thrush ♂
Race harmonica
Crested Bellbird ♀
Crested Bellbird ♂
Grey Shrike-thrush Juv.
Race harmonica
Grey ('Western') Shrike-thrush
Race rufiventris
N. Day

Golden Whistler *Pachycephala pectoralis* C–MC

Note Golden Whistlers may be darker, females greyer, than our plate shows. Black head to nape. Black band from nape extends around upper breast, enclosing white throat. Yellow nape, breast, abdomen. Back olive-green; wings black, edged citrine. Tail black, or grey and black. **F** Upperparts brownish-grey, sometimes washed olive. Pale grey wing stripe. Underparts plain grey-buff to dull white. In some northern birds, lemon wash on undertail coverts. **Size** 15–17 cm. **Juv.** Rich rufous; wings grey, edged rufous. This plumage (Mangrove Golden, Olive Whistlers also) is brief – only a few weeks. **Imm.** May be darker than female, wing feathers edged rufous. **Voice** Rich, melodious; often with whipcrack ending 'wi-wi-wi-whit!'. Contact call, rising 'seep'. **Hab.** Rainforest, open forest, woodland, mallee, coastal vegetation.

♂ Dorsal tail variation

Juvenile whistlers begin moulting their first plumage within a few weeks of fledging.

A = Race *pectoralis* **E**
B = Race *fuliginosa* **E**
C = Race *glaucura* **E**
D = Race *youngi* **E**

Mangrove Golden Whistler *Pachycephala melanura* MC

Similar to, but brighter, slightly smaller than male Golden Whistler. Yellow band of nape is broader, wings black, edged greyish-yellow; tail base sometimes yellow-green. **F** Upperparts buff-grey with olive wash on back and wings. Throat dull white. Rest of underparts yellow. Race *robusta* (B) Smallest race. **F** Tail dusky black. Race *spinicauda* (C) Largest race. **Size** 15–17 cm. **Juv.** Rich rufous; wings grey, edged rufous. **Imm.** As female, wing feathers edged rufous. **Voice** Faster, softer than Golden Whistler; 'wita-wheet'. **Hab.** Mangroves, riversides, coastal forest.

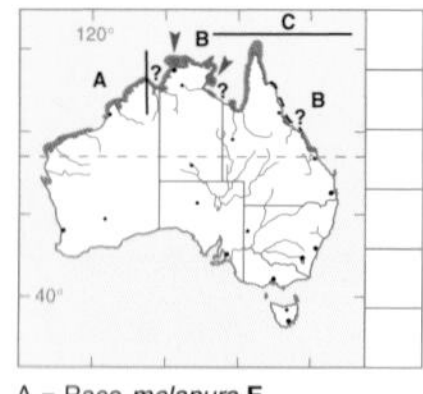

A = Race *melanura* **E**
B = Race *robusta* **E**
C = Race *spinicauda*

Gilbert's Whistler *Pachycephala inornata* MC E

Western birds darker than pale-bellied, longer-tailed, eastern birds (bold dotted line on map). Eye red. Black lores. Brownish-grey back. Throat, upper breast, deep orange. Lower breast, abdomen, pale grey. Undertail coverts buff-white. **F** Eye red-brown. Plain grey above. Lighter grey below, darker breast. **Size** 19.5 cm. **Juv.** Upperparts, breast, rufous-brown. **Voice** Repeated 'cheoo, cheoo' crescendo on one note. Hoarse 'cherak, cherak'. Rising whistle 'pooo-ee, choo-eeee'. **Hab.** Shrubby woodland, mallee.

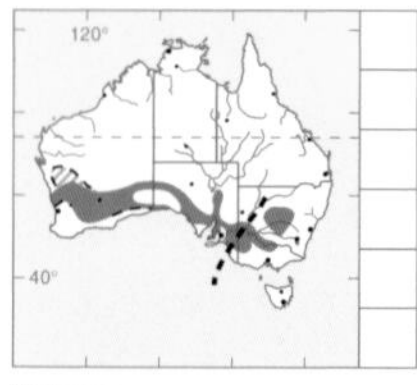

No races

Red-lored Whistler *Pachycephala rufogularis* UC E Vulnerable

Notoriously difficult to see. Slightly larger than Gilbert's Whistler. Eye red. Upperparts brownish-grey. Orange lores, chin, throat. Breast grey. Abdomen orange-buff. **F** Similar; paler overall. **Size** 20.5 cm. **Juv.** Paler about bill, lores. Upperparts, flanks rufous-brown. Underparts white, streaked dusky. **Voice** Clear whistle followed by sound like in-drawn breath. Small, meditative, 3-note 'see-di-oh'. **Hab.** Mallee, low shrubland.

Foraging on the ground

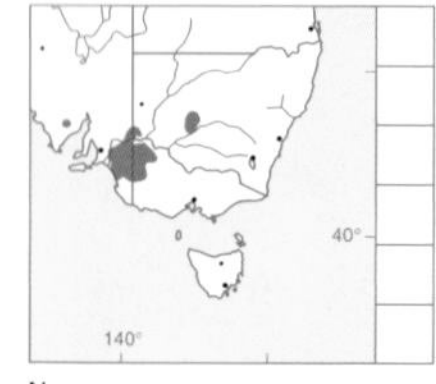

No races

Olive Whistler *Pachycephala olivacea* LMC–UC E

Shy, secretive. Bill black-brown. Head dark grey, back dark olive-brown. Throat white, barred broken grey. Buff-brown below, grey band on breast. **F** Head browner. Throat not barred. Race *macphersoniana* (B) Richer body coloration. Race (C) *bathychroa* Smaller, darker. Females faint pale breast band. Race (D) *apatetes* Duller. Females no breast band. Race (E) *hesperus* Paler. **Size** 20.5 cm. **Juv.** Rufous-brown. **Voice** Varied dialects. Rising thin whistle. Sweet drawn-out 'pee-oo'; loud territorial 'peee djo-djo-djo'; whipcrack 'pee-oo-wheet' or 'tee-u whit tu'. **Hab.** Tall wet forest; alpine heath. Beech forest.

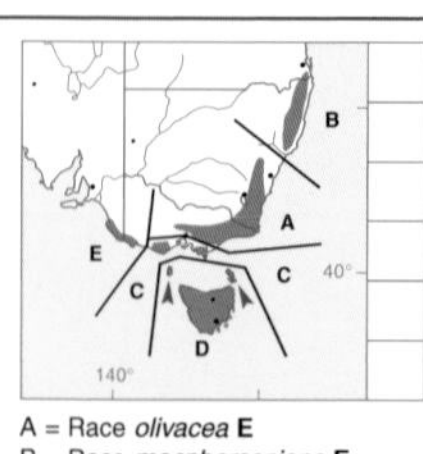

A = Race *olivacea* **E**
B = Race *macphersoniana* **E**
C = Race *bathychroa* **E**
D = Race *apatetes* **E**
E = Race *hesperus* **E**

Mangrove Golden Whistler ♂
Race *melanura*
Golden Whistler ♂
Race *youngi*
Mangrove Golden Whistler ♀
Race *melanura*
Mangrove Golden Whistler ♀
Race *robusta*
Golden Whistler
Imm.
Race *youngi*
Gilbert's Whistler ♂
Golden Whistler ♀
Race *youngi*
Red-lored Whistler ♀
Red-lored Whistler ♂
Gilbert's Whistler ♀
Olive Whistler ♂

Grey Whistler *Pachycephala simplex* MC ◎

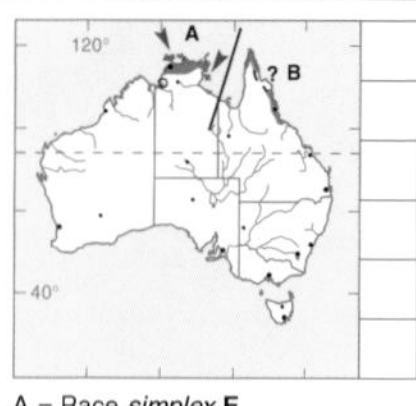

A = Race *simplex* **E**
B = Race *peninsulae* **E**

'Top End' race *simplex* (A) 'Brown Whistler' Upperparts uniform mid fawn-brown. Pale buff eyebrow. Pale fawn-buff smudge across faintly streaked upper breast. Underparts white-buff-white. NE Qld race *peninsulae* (B) 'Grey Whistler' Slightly larger. Head grey. Back olive-citrine. Wings olive-brown with small white 'flash' near bend of wing. Tail olive-grey. Throat buff-white; upper breast olive-buff merging with pale yellow lower breast, abdomen. Check Yellow-legged Flycatcher. **Size** 14–15 cm. **Juv.** Upperparts rufous-brown, lightly striated. Tinged rufous about throat, breast. Wings edged rufous. **Voice** *simplex* 'dee-doo pretty pretty', 'see-you whip'; *peninsulae* high, slow 4-note whistle, no whipcrack. **Hab.** *simplex* wet forest, mangroves; *peninsulae* coastal rainforest, mangroves.

Rufous Whistler *Pachycephala rufiventris* C ○ E

Black bill. Grey head and back. Black band of variable width from bill through eye extends around upper breast, enclosing white throat, edged with grey wash on sides of breast. Wings, tail blackish-brown, feathers edged light grey. Lower breast, abdomen deep buff. **F** Bill dark brown. Upperparts olive-grey. Wings, tail grey-brown. White throat merges into pale buff breast, abdomen, with dark brown streaking on throat, breast. Four races with two major patterns of variation, one of decreasing size (south to north); one of increasingly darker coloration (continental interior to coastal periphery). *Race rufiventris* (A) Large and dark (females more heavily streaked). Race '*maudeae*' (A1) A paler desert form of *rufiventris*. Race *pallida* (B) Palest race. Race *falcata* (C) Richly coloured but smaller than southern birds; male has grey lores. Richly coloured race *minor* (D) Only Melville Is. **Size** 16–18 cm. **Juv.** Plumage as female, but more olive above, with paler bill, rufous wash on ear coverts, paler below with heavier streaking. **M imm.** Lores not in adult colours for 2–3 years. **Voice** Ringing, whipcrack 'ee-chong!'; strong rippling 'joey-joey-joey'. **Hab.** Mostly open forest, woodland, mallee and scrub of arid interior; less common in wetter tall forest.

♂ Singing

At nest

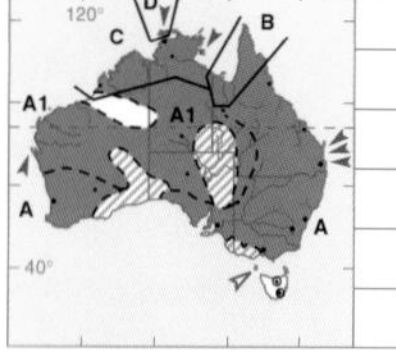

A = Race *rufiventris* **E**
A1 = Race '*maudeae*' (arid zone form of *rufiventris*) **E**
B = Race *pallida* **E**
C = Race *falcata* **E**
D = Race *minor* **E**

Nomadic or migratory species in parts of Australia.

White-breasted Whistler *Pachycephala lanioides* MC–UC ◎ E

Forages on mud at low tide. Often quiet, inconspicuous, but responds to 'calling up'. Bill black. Black head to nape. Black band from nape extends down around upper breast, enclosing white throat. Nape rufous, with narrower rufous band extending around below black band. Back grey to grey-black. Wings black, variably edged grey. Upper tail black. Rest of breast and abdomen white. **F** Bill brownish until several years old. Upperparts grey-brown, darker on wings, tail. Underparts creamy-buff, paler on throat. Pale grey wash on breast. Dark streaking on throat and breast. Race *carnarvoni* (B) Rufous band as wide as black band extends onto breast. Females brownish above, buff below. Race *fretorum* (C) Smaller than *lanioides*. Narrower black and rufous bands. **Size** 19.5 cm. **Juv.** As female but upperparts washed pale rufous; underparts more strongly streaked. **Voice** Shorter bursts of song than Rufous; melodious whistle, rising, accelerating. **Hab.** Mangroves; less common in adjacent coastal rainforest.

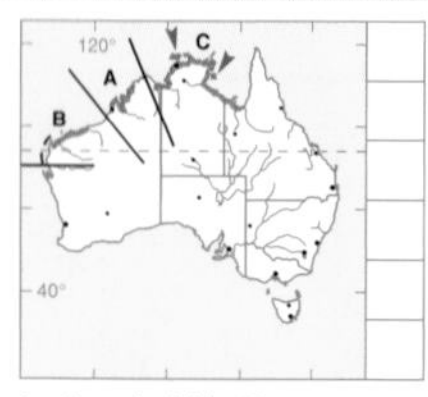

A = Race *lanioides* **E**
B = Race *carnarvoni* **E**
C = Race *fretorum* **E**

Grey Whistler
Race peninsulae
Yellow-legged
Flycatcher
Grey ('Brown') Whistler
Race simplex
Rufous Whistler ♂
Race pallida
Rufous Whistler ♂
Race rufiventris
Rufous Whistler ♀
Race rufiventris
White-breasted Whistler ♂
Race lanioides
White-breasted Whistler ♀
Race lanioides

Northern Fantail *Rhipidura rufiventris* **C** ◎

Perches quietly, unlike Grey. Hunts insects directly, like Leaden Flycatcher. Check Jacky Winter. Large black bill, brown eye. Narrow white eyebrow; no ear mark. Smoky-grey above; brown-washed wings. Tail grey; outer feathers edged white, three outer pairs with broad white tips. Throat white. Grey upper breast band, speckled white; cream-white below. **Size** 16–18.5 cm. **Juv.** Browner; throat, tail tips buff. **Voice** 6-note rising song like gerygones. **Hab.** Open forest, rainforest edges, mangroves.

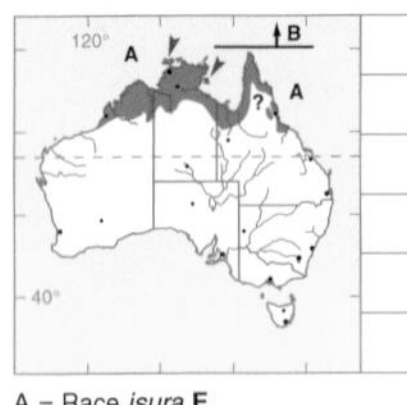

A = Race *isura* **E**
B = Race *gularis*

Grey Fantail *Rhipidura albiscapa (fuliginosa)* **C** ♧–O

Very active; erratic flight, fans tail constantly; perches sideways. Race *albiscapa* (A) Eye, bill, legs, black. Sooty-grey upperparts, tail. White eyebrow, ear mark, throat. Wide sooty breast band, chest marks. Sides of breast, upper flanks, deep grey. Two narrow wing bars. Narrow white tail tips (except central feathers); pale grey inner webs; outermost feather white. Rest of underparts rich cream. Race *alisteri* (B) Dark grey face. Mid-grey above, narrower breast band. Longer tail, edge bright white. No grey on flanks. Race *keasti* (C) Very dark above; pale buff below. Wide black breast band. Faint wing bars. Race *albicauda* (D) Brownish-grey above, paler grey breast. Broader wing bars. Tail distinctive, white except for central feathers. Race *preissi* (E) As *albiscapa*, *alisteri*, but breast grey. **Size** 15–17 cm. **Juv.** (all races) Browner; buffy wing bars, head markings. **Voice** Louder than Rufous. Cyclic tinkling song, ending with strong high note. Warning 'dik!'. **Hab.** Forest, woodland; *albicauda* mulga only.

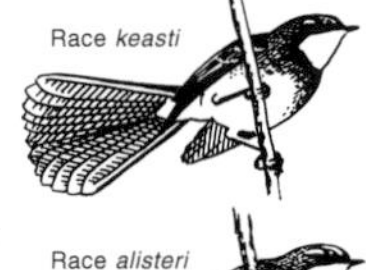

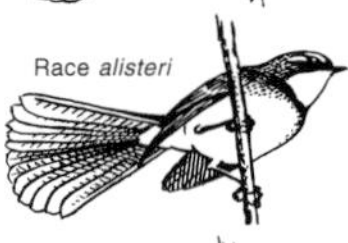

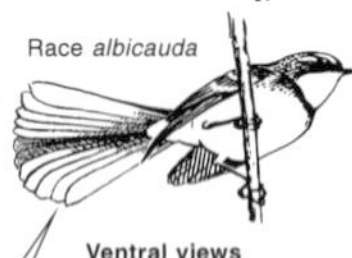

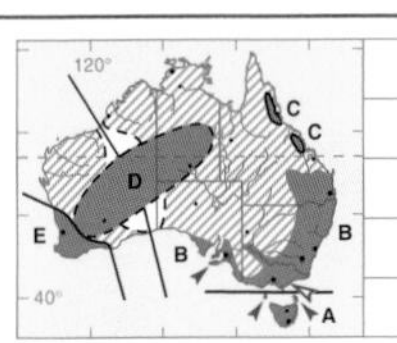

A = Race *albiscapa* **E**
B = Race *alisteri* **E**
C = Race *keasti* **E**
D = Race *albicauda* **E**
E = Race *preissi* **E**

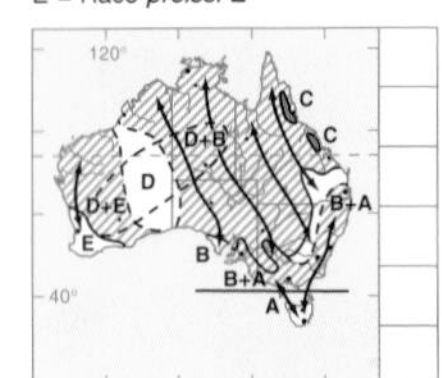

Right: probable non-br. (winter) movement of races A, B, E. After Schodde & Mason (1999).

Mangrove Grey Fantail *Rhipidura phasiana* **MC** ◎

Small. Check Grey Fantail. Light grey above; pale buff below. Narrow mid-grey chest band. Bill large. Wide white wing bars; broad white edges to tips on outer four tail feathers. **Size** 14.5–15.8 cm. **Juv.** Duller, browner; markings less distinct. **Voice** Softer than Grey Fantail; falling squeaky song. **Hab.** Mangroves.

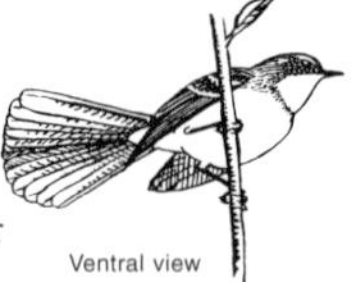

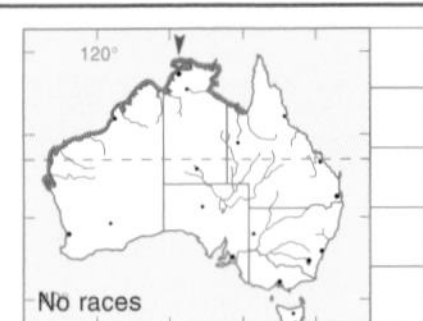

Rufous Fantail *Rhipidura rufifrons* **C–MC** ♧–O

Very active, often in shade near ground. Fans tail, swings body, wings slightly raised. Eye, bill, dark brown. Orange-rufous eyebrow, lower back, base of tail. Outer tail blackish, smudgy grey tips. Head, mantle, wings grey-brown. White throat, black band on upper chest; lower chest black, scaled white. White to buff below. Race *intermedia* (B) Tail tips, belly, whitish. **Size** 15–16 cm. **Juv.** Duller, brown. **Voice** Thin squeaks; twittering song, less structured than Grey. **Hab.** Prefers wetter forest.

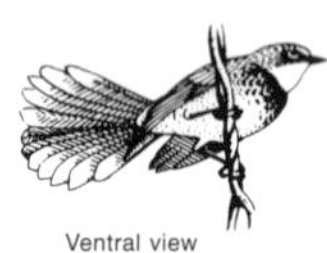

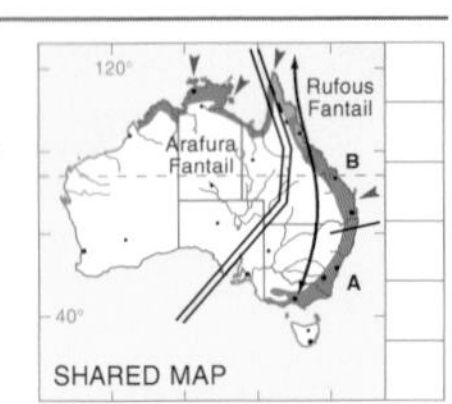

Rufous Fantail
A = Race *rufifrons* **Br. E**
B = Race *intermedia* **Br. E**
Arafura Fantail Race *dryas*

Arafura Fantail *Rhipidura dryas* **C–MC** ♧–O

Smaller than Rufous; duller, less rufous on tail. Long tail with dark leaden upper surface. Strong white tail tips. **Size** 15 cm. **Voice** High, silvery, falling song. **Hab.** Mangrove edges.

Willie Wagtail *Rhipidura leucophrys* **A–C** ◎–♧–?O

Hunts insects in foliage, from livestock, on ground; wags and fans tail. Aggressive. Check Restless Flycatcher. Eye, bill, legs, black. White eyebrow, lower cheek stripe. Upperparts glossy black. White belly. Brown-tinged wings. **Size** 19–21.5 cm. **Juv.** Buff spotting on tips of black feathers. **Voice** Sustained alarm, like rattling box of matches. Sweet repetitive song 'which are you, Willie, which are you?'; traditionally 'sweet, pretty creature'. May sing at night. **Hab.** Everywhere except very wet forest.

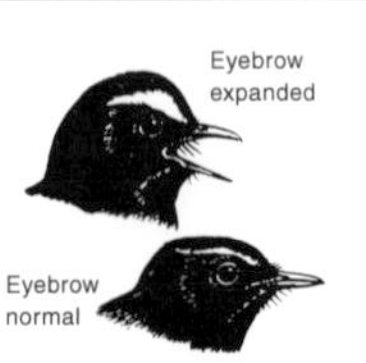

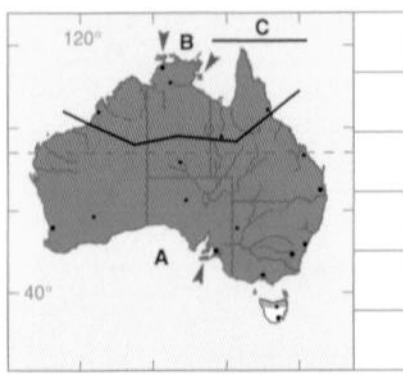

A = Race *leucophrys* **E**
B = Race *picata* **E**
C = Race *melaleuca*

Northern
Fantail
Race isura
Northern
Fantail
Juv.
Race isura
Grey Fantail
Race keasti
Grey Fantail
Juv.
Race alisteri
Grey Fantail
Race alisteri
Mangrove Grey
Fantail
Grey Fantail
Race albicauda
Rufous Fantail
Juv.
Race rufifrons
Arafura Fantail
Race dryas
Rufous Fantail
Race rufifrons
Willie Wagtail
Willie Wagtail
Juv.
N. DAY

Broad-billed Flycatcher *Myiagra ruficollis* **MC** ◎

Head: dorsal view

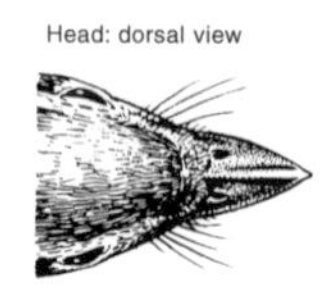

Bill blue-black; boat-shaped. Small erectile crest. Head, back, glossy blue-grey. Eye-ring pale. Eye brown. Chin, throat, upper breast rufous-orange (brighter than female Leaden). Underparts white. Wings, tail grey-brown, edged pale grey. Undertail darker than on our plate. Feet grey-black. **F** Paler. Lores light grey. Back greyer, leaden; whiter under tail. **Size** 14–17 cm. **Juv.** As juv. Leaden; pale eyebrow. **Voice** Frog-like 'brrrip' (harsher than Leaden, Satin); loud 'pee-ooo-uu', repeated. **Hab.** Mangroves, monsoon forest, nearby woodland.

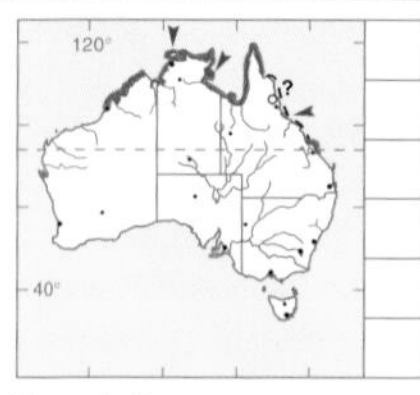

Race *mimikae*
This species shared with south coastal New Guinea.

Leaden Flycatcher *Myiagra rubecula* **C–MC** O

Head: dorsal view

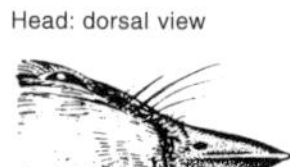

Juv. eyebrow pale in Broad-billed, Leaden, Satin Flycatchers.

Sexes dimorphic. Small erectile crest. Quivers tail. Bill blue, black tip; broad (not boat-shaped like Broad-billed). Eyes dark brown. Head, back, upper chest, leaden blue-grey. Underparts white. Undertail grey. Legs black. Race (B) *yorki* Lores often darker than face. **F** Check female Satin, also Broad-billed Flycatcher. Pale eye-ring; grey lores. Back dull grey. Rufous-orange on breast diffused into white underparts. Wings, tail feathers, pale-edged. **Size** 14–17 cm. **Juv.** Brown-grey above, whitish below. Wings pale-streaked. Breast mottled brown, washed rufous. **Voice** Deep frog-like 'zzrrup'. Buzzes; sweet repeated whistles 'tu-chee', 'chee-a, chee-a'. **Hab.** Open forest.

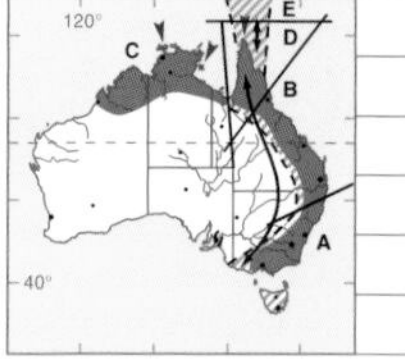

A = Race *rubecula* **Br. E**
B = Race *yorki* **Br. E?**
C = Race *concinna* **Br. E?**
D = Race *okyri* **Br. E?**
E = Race *papuana*

Satin Flycatcher *Myiagra cyanoleuca* **C–MC** O

Sexes dimorphic. Small erectile crest. Quivers tail. Glossy 'blue' in sunlight, blacker than Leaden in poor light, on head, back, upper chest. Undertail blackish. **F** Like female Leaden but smaller. Upperparts dark grey. Grey-brown wings, tail, pale-edged. Throat may be brighter. **Size** 15–18 cm. **Juv.** Like Leaden; upperparts darker, pale-streaked, buff-edged. Throat feathers darker-edged. **Voice** Questioning 'zurrp?'; rich, rapid repeated whistle 'shij-wee'. **Hab.** Wetter, denser forest, often at high elevations.

Incubating

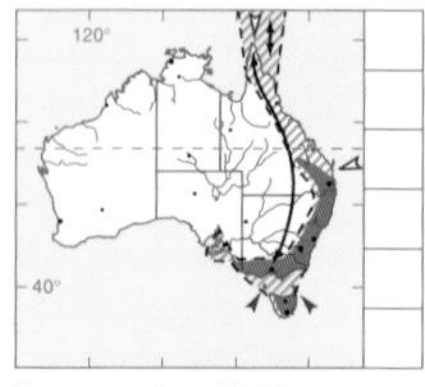

Race *cyanoleuca* **Br. E**

Shining Flycatcher *Myiagra alecto* **C** ◎

Sexes dimorphic, distinctive. Small erectile crest. Bill blue, tipped black. Males entirely glossy black with intense blue sheen. Race *melvillensis* (A) **F** Lores black. Crown, sides of face, nape, glossy blue-black. Upperparts rich rufous-chestnut; white below. Race *wardelli* (B) **F** Flanks, undertail coverts, buff. **Size** 15–18 cm. **Juv./Imm.** Like duller female. **Voice** Rapid whistling trill; clear sweet whistles; frequent soft buzzing; frog-like croaks. **Hab.** Tropical mangroves; forest streamside vegetation.

Foraging near ground

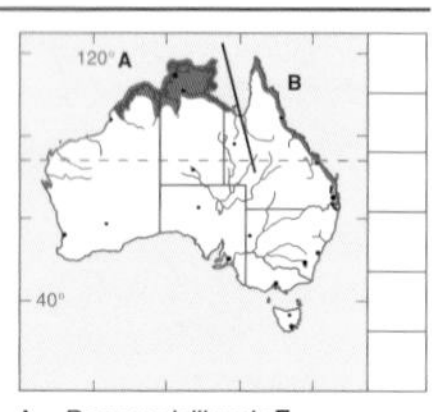

A = Race *melvillensis* **E**
B = Race *wardelli*

Restless Flycatcher *Myiagra inquieta* **C–MC** ◎–♧ E

Largest *Myiagra*. Small erectile crest. Check Willie Wagtail. Bill blue-black, iris dark brown, lores black. Glossy blue-black crown, sides of face. Dark satin grey back. Wings browner. White chin, throat to undertail coverts. Pale buff wash on breast variable. Legs black. **F** Lores grey. **Size** 19–21.5 cm; **Juv.** As adult; grey-black above. Wing feathers edged buff. Throat, upper breast washed creamy buff. **Voice** Hovers, buzzing ('scissors-grinder'), a pulsing whirr similar to Lyrebird. **Hab.** Open forest, farmland.

Hawking

Also called 'Scissors Grinder'.

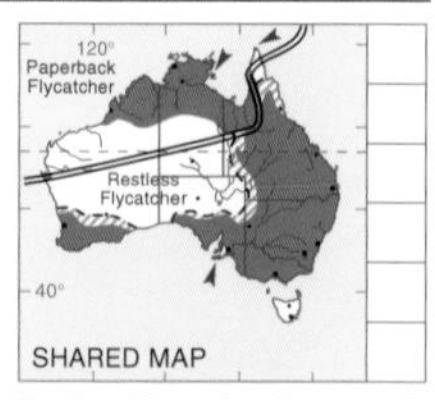

Restless Flycatcher *M. inquieta* **E**
Paperbark Flycatcher *M. nana* **E**

Paperbark Flycatcher *Myiagra nana* **C–MC** ◎–♧ E

Smaller; slightly wider bill than Restless. Check Willie Wagtail. Crown, back, glossy black. **F** Glossy head, satin grey back. **Size** 16–18 cm. **Voice** Clear rising 'chewee? chewee?'.

Paperbark Flycatcher not illustrated on plate.

Broad-billed Flycatcher
Broad-billed Flycatcher Juv.
Leaden Flycatcher ♀
Leaden Flycatcher ♂
Satin Flycatcher ♀
Satin Flycatcher ♂
Leaden Flycatcher Juv.
Shining Flycatcher ♀
Satin Flycatcher Juv.
Shining Flycatcher ♂
Restless Flycatcher ♂
Restless Flycatcher Juv.
N. DAY

Yellow-breasted Boatbill *Machaerirhynchus flaviventer* MC

Large black 'boat-shaped' bill (14 x 9 mm). Hovers before foliage. Cocks tail. Long black rictal bristles. Frons, long eyebrow stripe, bright yellow. Black crown, nape, mask through lores to ear coverts. Dull olive mantle. Narrow white shoulder bars. Bright yellow below, from chin to undertail. **F** Olive above. Chin, throat, white. Pale yellow eyebrow; grey-brown face mask, wings. Creamy-yellow below, duskier on flanks. Race *secundus* (B) Richer yellow throughout. Black crown and mantle. More prominent white shoulder bars. Chin, throat, white. Black tail, strongly tipped white. Legs, feet, leaden grey. **F** race *secundus* Black face band, wing coverts, tail. **Size** 11–12 cm. **Juv.** As females. Wings browner. Upper breast dull lemon yellow. Sides of breast, flanks, speckled/barred (may persist in adult females). Lower belly, undertail coverts whiter. **Imm./Sub-ad.** Green-grey upper shoulder, mantle, lower back to rump. **Voice** High warbles and insect-like buzzing. **Hab.** Rainforest.

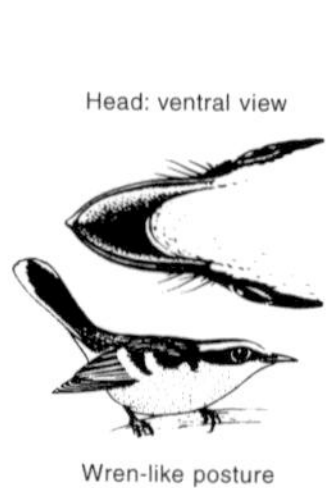

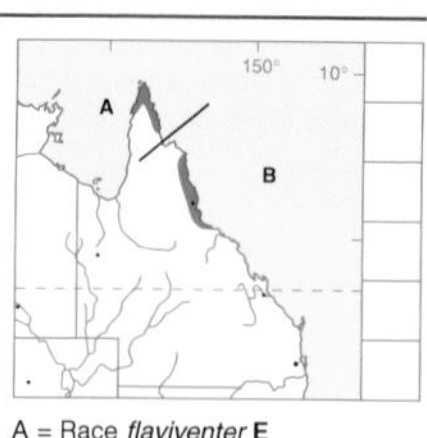

A = Race *flaviventer* **E**
B = Race *secundus* **E**

Black-faced Monarch *Monarcha melanopsis* C–MC Br. E

Grey-blue bill; hooked tip. Black 'face': frons, chin, throat patch. Dark eye surrounded by pale grey face and ear coverts. Soft, even, blue-grey crown, back, upper tail coverts. Darker grey wings, tail. Blue-grey upper breast contrasts with rufous lower breast, belly, undertail. Legs blue. **F** Duller; may have less black about face. **Size** 15–20 cm. **Juv.** Bill black. No black in face. Body, wings, olive-grey. **Imm.** No black in face, whitish lores. Wings brown-grey. **Voice** 'why-you-which ye-oo'; falling 'wee-chew', long whistles. **Hab.** Middle layers of rainforest, gullies, dense wet coastal forest. More open country during migration.

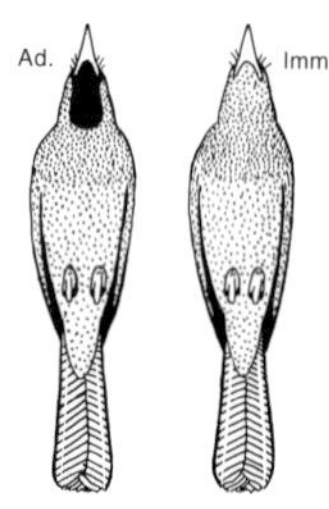

Ventral view

No races
Some winter in New Guinea.

Black-winged Monarch *Monarcha frater* C–MC

Race *canescens* Black face like Black-faced Monarch. Dark eye surrounded by pale grey face and ear coverts. Nape, mantle, rump, light pearly-grey. Black 'shoulder' mark. Conspicuous black wings, tail. Pearl-grey upper breast contrasts with rusty-orange lower breast, flanks, undertail coverts. **F** Whitish lores. **Size** 18–19 cm. **Juv.** Bill black. No black in face. Upper body, wings, brownish. **Note** Juvenile plumages for these monarchs are not yet adequately described. **Imm.** Face grey, not black. **Voice** Rising 'prreee', repeated. Falling 'wichooo'. **Hab.** Rainforest, adjacent forest.

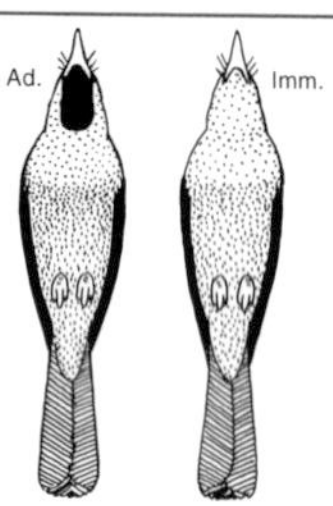

Ventral view

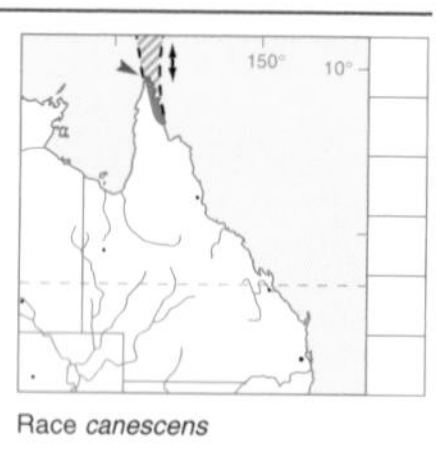

Race *canescens*

Spectacled Monarch *Monarcha trivirgatus* C–MC

Fans tail, showing broad white tips. Bill blue-grey. Black frons. Black entirely encloses eye, extends to ear coverts, chin, central throat. Slaty-grey upperparts, darker than Black-faced, Black-winged Monarchs. Cheeks, breast, flanks, variably rusty-orange. Legs leaden blue. Race *melanorrhoa* (B) Crown, mantle, wings, dark slate-grey. Uppertail blackish in males, grey in females. Race *albiventris* (C) 'White-bellied Flycatcher' has sharp demarcation of rusty-orange breast from white belly, flanks. **Size** 14–16 cm. **Juv.** Brown. **Imm.** Face grey, not black. Lores whitish, variable. Chin grey. Underparts from throat variable; duller rusty-orange; white lower belly, undertail coverts. **Voice** chirring 'swee, swee'; upward whistle; rosella-like twitters. **Hab.** Outer branches of lower canopy. Wet forest, mangroves.

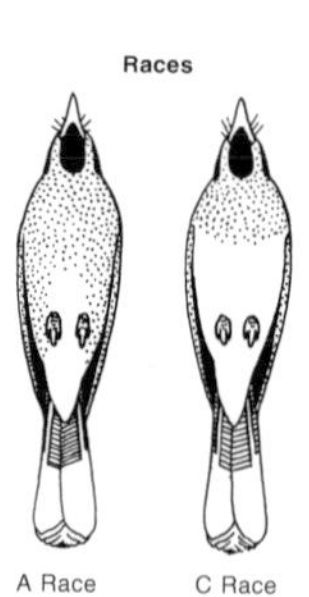

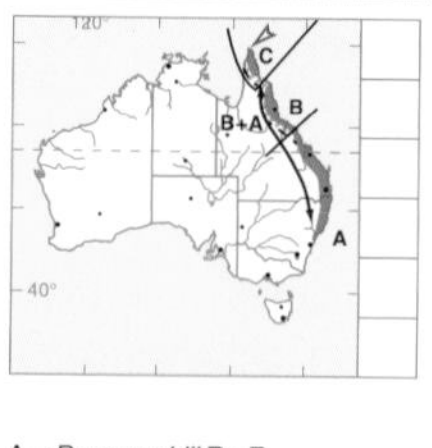

A = Race *gouldii* **Br. E**
B = Race *melanorrhoa* **E**
C = Race *albiventris* **Br E?**
Race *gouldii* migrates N in winter, through *melanorrhoa* (sedentary?) area, into and beyond *albiventris* area.

Yellow-breasted
Boatbill ♀
Race secundus
Yellow-breasted Boatbill ♂
Race secundus
Yellow-breasted Boatbill
Juv.
Race secundus
Black-faced
Monarch
Juv.
Black-faced
Monarch
Black-faced
Monarch
Imm.
Black-winged
Monarch Imm.
Race canescens
Black-winged
Monarch
Race canescens
Spectacled
Monarch
Race gouldii
Spectacled
Monarch
Imm.
N.DAY

Frill-necked Monarch *Arses lorealis* **MC** ◎

Bill blue. Eye-ring (wattle) sky-blue, vertically oval. Black frons, chin, lores, crown, nape, cheek, mantle. Erectile white collar (frill) extends from nape to plain white underparts. Frill complemented by crescentic white band of white scapulars, upper back. Wings black. **F** Duller; lores light grey, chin white. Speckles on white collar. May have buff wash on sides of chest and back crescent. **Size** 14–17 cm. **Juv./Imm.** White lores. Upperparts, tail brownish. Dirty white below; faintly mottled. **Voice** Strident, metallic; 'frog-like' squawk. **Hab.** Rainforest.

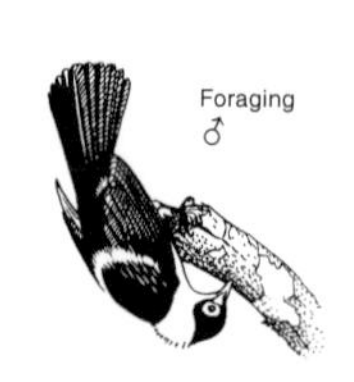

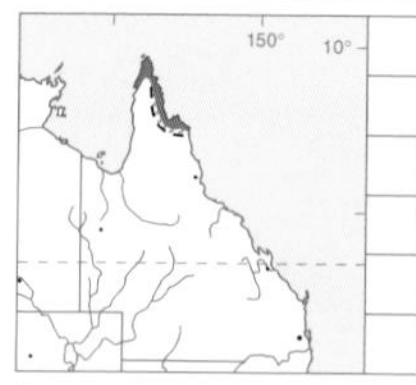

No races

Frill-necked Monarch is new species, A. lorealis, *split from Frilled Monarch, now* A. telescopthalmus harterti, *of northern Torres Strait islands only.*

Pied Monarch *Arses kaupi* **MC** ◎ E

As Frill-necked, but has glossy black chest band. Bluish, round eye-ring. Black chin spot tiny/absent. Dull black wings, tail (slightly longer in Pied). Legs, feet, leaden-blue. White erectile 'frill' extends from nape to white throat; is lightly speckled black. Race *terraereginae* (B) Narrower black chest band. Pure white 'frill'. **F** Greyish nape, more black speckles. Black lores. Black side of neck may join ear coverts to mantle. **Size** 14–15 cm. **Juv./Imm.** Yellowish bill, dark-tipped. Black lores. Greyish eye-ring. White nape, throat, heavily speckled black. Brownish wings, tail. Breast band irregular. **Voice** Ten or more soft, high whistles, getting louder; nasal 'brrreeep?'. **Hab.** Rainforest/fringes.

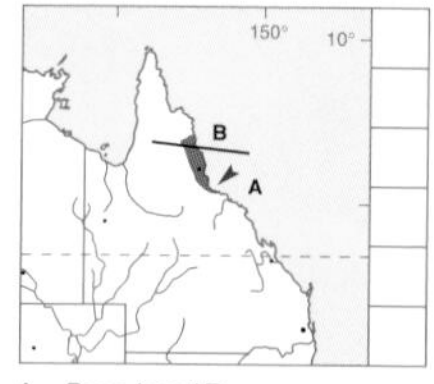

A = Race *kaupi* **E**
B = Race *terraereginae* **E**

White-eared Monarch *Monarcha leucotis* **UC** ◎ E

Small; distinctive face. Bill black, or with bluish base. Erectile black frons. White eyebrow, cheek, small spot before eye. Sooty black back, bold white wing bars. Rump white. Tail black, white-edged. Chin, throat, white. Black freckles form partial collar to side of lower neck. Underparts very pale grey. Legs blue-grey. **F** Duller, greyer; head markings less prominent. Reduced width of rump band. **Size** 13 cm. **Juv.** Face smudgy. White eyebrow. Upperparts sooty grey-brown; underparts washed buff. **Voice** As Horsfield's Bronze-Cuckoo 'thee-ou'; repeated 'bet-a-beee'; rising and falling 'pree?-proou'. **Hab.** Rainforest, mangroves.

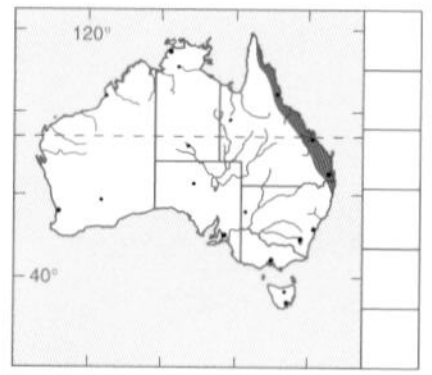

No races

Magpie-lark *Grallina cyanoleuca* **C** ◎–?

Glossy black and white. Plover-like walk. Congregates in winter flocks. Dimorphic. White bill, eye, eyebrow. Black face, throat. White wing bars show great individual variation. Slender black legs. **F** White face, upper throat, edged black. **Size** 27 cm. **Juv./Imm.** Dark bill and eye, white eyebrow and throat. Face pattern somewhat resembles smaller White-eared Monarch. **Voice** 'pee-wee'; also 'pee-o-wit'. Pairs perform wing-lifting duets – antiphonal song. **Hab.** Open areas, roadsides, often near water.

Other names are 'Australian Magpie-lark', 'Mudlark', 'Peewee' or 'Peewit'; also 'Murray Magpie'.

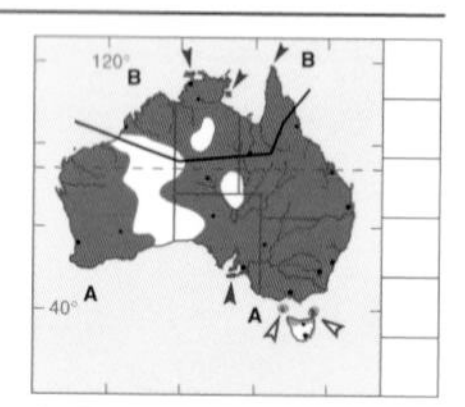

A = Race *cyanoleuca* **Br. E?**
B = Race *neglecta* **Br. E?**
Some southern birds fly north in winter.

Spangled Drongo *Dicrurus bracteatus* **C** ◎–

Glossy black with greenish sheen and reflective chest spangles. Flaring forked tail. Swift, erratic flight; hawks insects. Singly or pairs; small loose flocks (10–100+). Bill heavy, black; bristles at base. Eye red, prominent. Can erect 'ear-tufts'. **Size** M 30–32, F 28–30 cm. **Imm.** Dusky black; white throat spots, chevrons on undertail coverts. Brown eye. **Voice** Varied; rasping, hissing, crackling. Very vocal. **Hab.** Wet forest, urban areas.

Now known to be a monarch. WA, NT populations sedentary; E Aust. race bracteatus *migratory.*

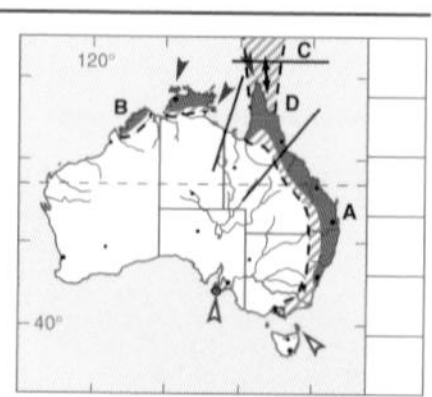

A = Race *bracteatus* **Br. E**
B = Race *baileyi* **E**
C = Race *carbonarius*
D = Race *atrabectus*

Frill-necked Monarch ♀
Frill-necked Monarch Juv.
Spangled Drongo Juv.
Spangled Drongo
Frill-necked Monarch ♂
Pied Monarch Juv./Imm.
Pied Monarch ♂ Race terraereginae
Pied Monarch ♀ Race terraereginae
White-eared Monarch ♂
White-eared Monarch ♀
Magpie-lark Juv.
White-eared Monarch Juv.
Magpie-lark ♂
Magpie-lark ♀
N.DAY

Yellow Oriole *Oriolus flavocinctus* **C** ◎–?

May accompany Figbirds, Great Bowerbirds, in fruit trees. Regional variation. Bill large, orange. Eye red. Uniformly rich yellow-olive plumage with fine black striations. Dark wing feathers edged yellow to creamy-white, appear as a patch and wing bars. Tail dark, variably tipped yellow to creamy-white. Yellow underparts, greener towards throat, not streaked in older males. **Size** 25–30 cm. **Juv.** Brownish bill. Eye grey-brown; paler with age. Thin yellow eyebrow. Bolder black streaks. Duller green back. Wing brownish; wing feathers edged white or pale cream. Underparts yellower. Small yellow tail tips. **Voice** Deeper-voiced than Olive-backed. Melodious roll of repeated notes; ventriloquial. **Hab.** Tropical forest, gardens, mangroves.

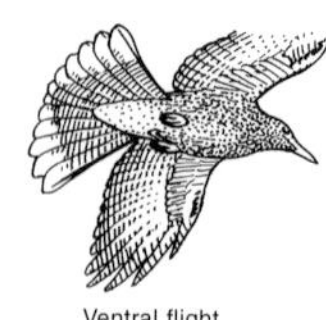
Ventral flight

Yellow Orioles have 5 distinct calls. One is like start of the 'cat' call of 'Spotted Catbird'. Many observers confuse this call.

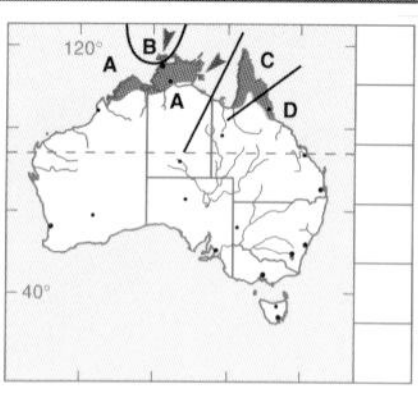

A = Race *flavocinctus* **E**
B = Race *tiwi* **E**
C = Race *flavotinctus* **E**
D = Race *kingi* **E**

Olive-backed Oriole *Oriolus sagittatus* **C–MC**

Large orange-red bill, red eye. Rich olive-green upperparts, lores darker. Back finely streaked black. Grey-brown wing feathers edged white or grey. Creamy-yellow sides of breast, flanks. Belly, vent, undertail coverts, whitish. Plain greyish throat. Heavy dark streaks over breast, belly. Tail dark grey, obvious white tips. **F** Chin, side of throat, greyer-green upperparts, more heavily streaked. Less white on wings. Race *grisescens* (B) Greyer, less yellow. Race *affinis* (C) Less richly coloured, appearing greyer or browner. Has brown, not black, breast streaks, which may partly reflect worn plumage in non-breeding season. **Size** 25–28 cm. **Juv.** Bill, eye, dark. Narrow buff-cream eyebrow, eye-ring. Upperparts olive-grey, streaked black. White breast, belly, strongly streaked. Cinnamon edges to all wing feathers. Light cinnamon-buff wash to underwing. Smaller whitish tail tips. **Imm.** Bill, eye lighter. Head, upper plumage become greener. Cinnamon wing feather edges may persist. **Voice** Ventriloquial; an excellent bird mimic. Rolling 'orry-orry-ole' (Peaceful Dove has somewhat similar call). Also sub-songs. **Hab.** Most wooded areas, parkland.

Ventral flight

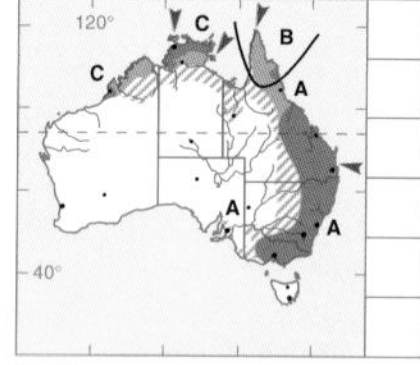

A = Race *sagittatus* **Br. E**
B = Race *grisescens* **Br. E?**
C = Race *affinis* **E**
Many of race *sagittatus* migrate north in winter; may mingle with *grisescens*.

Australasian Figbird *Sphecotheres vieilloti* **A–C** ◎–?

Undulating direct flight. Flocks, often of straggling groups. Dimorphic. Race *vieilloti* 'Green Figbird' Black bill. Facial skin red, pinkish or orange. Black head. Complete slate-grey collar. Rich green-yellow above, green below. Black primaries. Dorsal central tail feathers black; lateral tail feathers white. Hybrid zone *vieilloti/flaviventris* variable. Typically has green-grey breast, pale chin, throat; much yellower belly than southern birds. Race *flaviventris* (B) 'Yellow Figbird'. Less brilliant. Race *ashbyi* (C) 'Yellow Figbird'. Black bill. Facial skin red, pinkish or orange. Black head. Rich green-yellow above, brilliant yellow below from chin to lower belly. Black primaries. Central upper tail feathers black; lateral tail feathers white; these prominent in flight. White undertail coverts. **F** All races. Dark bill. Facial skin bluish. Head to mantle olive-brown, then greener to upper tail. Wings brown-black, edged cream. Chin, throat brown, heavily streaked. Lower underparts whitish to pale cream; flanks yellower. Faint white tail tips. **Size** 27–29.5 cm. **Juv.** As female, smaller. **Imm.** Patchy male characteristics appear within one year. **Voice** Short sharp yelps 'pow! pow! pow!'. Many soft musical calls. **Hab.** Tropical rainforest edges, parks.

Ventral flight ♀

B ♂ Race *flaviventris*   A ♂ Race *vieilloti*

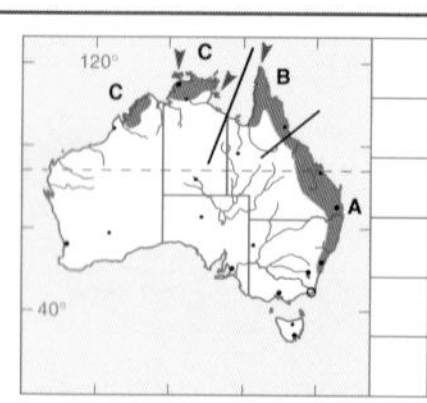

A = Race *vieilloti* **E**
B = Race *flaviventris* **E**
C = Race *ashbyi* **E**
Former species name *viridis* now confined to a population of smaller figbirds in Indonesia (East Lesser Sunda area). Name 'Australasian Figbird' proposed for separate Australo-Papuan superspecies group (based on Schodde & Mason, 1999).

Yellow Oriole
Juv.
Olive-backed
Oriole
Juv.
Yellow Oriole
Olive-backed
Oriole
♂
Olive-backed
Oriole
♀
Australasian Figbird ♂
Imm.
Race flaviventris
Australasian
('Yellow') Figbird ♂
Race flaviventris
Australasian Figbird
Juv.
Australasian
Figbird ♀
Australasian
('Green') Figbird ♂
Race vieilloti
N. DAY.

Paradise Riflebird *Ptiloris paradiseus* **MC** ◎ E

Listen for birds tearing rotten wood. 'Rustling' flight (males). Black males display on bare poles, branches; females visit to mate. Long, narrow bill. Bright yellow in mouth. Velvet black gorget, crown, central tail has blue-green, purple iridescence. Lower breast, silky black with oil-green scallops. **F** Longer, more decurved bill. Long white brow. Dark olive-brown above, buff below, blackish chevrons, barring. Chestnut wings, tail. **Size** 29–30 cm. **M juv.** As female until black feathers develop. **Voice** Double, explosive 'yaass'. **Hab.** Rainforest, nearby forest.

♀ Foraging

No races

Victoria's Riflebird *Ptiloris victoriae* **MC–UC** ◎ E

As Paradise Riflebird, but more greyish velvet-black between smaller gorget and uniform bronze abdomen. Central tail, iridescent blue-green. **F** As Paradise but rich cinnamon-buff below, more spotted. Longer, more decurved bill than male, but shorter than Paradise female's. **Size** 23–25 cm. **Juv.** As Paradise. **Voice** Double 'yaass'; Atherton Tableland, single 'sshhhh'. Contact 'kek'. **Hab.** Rainforest, adjacent woodland, orchards.

♂ Displaying

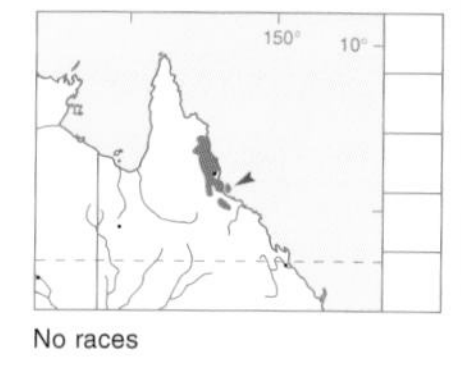

No races

Magnificent Riflebird *Ptiloris magnificus* **MC–UC** ◎

Elusive. Velvet-black with magenta iridescence. Gorget greenish-blue reflecting magenta; edged jet black, bronze-green below. Underparts, long filamentous flank plumes, black, suffused purple-red. In display, underwing shows iridescent blue-white edge. **F** Longer bill. Cinnamon above, dull white below, barred brown. **Size** M 34 cm, F 28 cm. **Juv.** As F, less barring. **Voice** Iron Range 'wheew-whit'; Cape York 'whit, whit'. **Hab.** Wet forest.

Imm. ♂ moulting

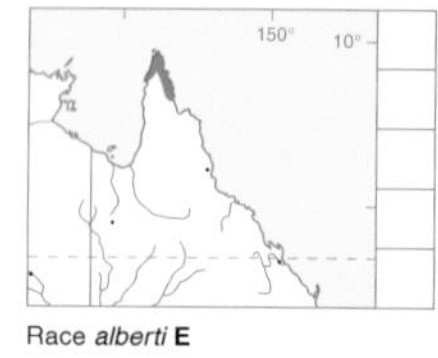

Race *alberti* **E**

Trumpet Manucode
Phonygammus (Manucodia) keraudrenii **MC–R** ?♣–?◎

Check male Koel (larger); Spangled Drongo. Glossy black. Red eye; elongated nape plumes. Often flicks long rounded tail. Race *jamesii* (A) Blue-green sheen; violet over wings, tail. Race *gouldii* (B) Dull oily-green sheen. **Size** 27–32 cm. **Voice** Powerful, vibrating, trumpet-like blast. **Hab.** Tropical rainforest.

Nape plumes

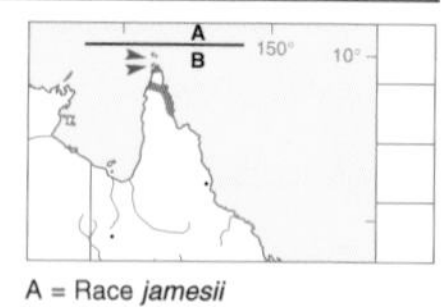

A = Race *jamesii*
B = Race *gouldii* **E**

See also comparative diagram of 'black birds', p. 260.

Tooth-billed Bowerbird *Scenopoeetes dentirostris* **LMC** ◎ E

Stocky, brown, with legs much shorter than 'Spotted Catbird'. Stout black bill. Pale buff cheeks. Upperparts dark olive-brown. Dirty white, streaked underparts. **Size** 24–27 cm. **Voice** Over unique display court ('stage'): strong, varied, very loud or sweetly soft bird mimicry; 'chuck'. Otherwise silent save for harsh flight alarm call. **Hab.** Tropical rainforest approx. 600–1400 m.

Singing over court

Prior name 'Stagemaker'.

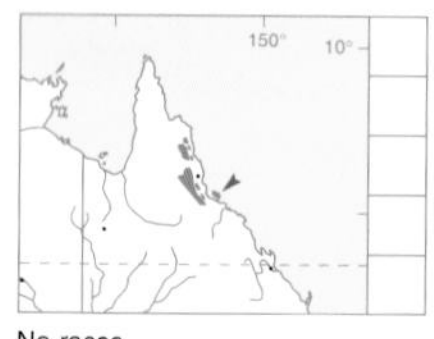

No races

Green Catbird *Ailuroedus crassirostris* **MC–LUC** ◎

Check 'green' Satin Bowerbird (eye blue or brown). Stout green bird, red eye, strong whitish beak. White wing bars. Greater coverts, secondaries, tipped white. Tail green above, grey below, white tips. Light olive-green below, streaked white. Race *maculosus* (B) 'Spotted Catbird' Head dusky, spotted dull white. Black ear patch. Dirty whitish spots streaking onto mantle. Underparts mottled with heavy olive-yellow chevrons. Race (C) *joanae* As 'Spotted', smaller, with brighter face pattern. Black crown, densely spotted cream. Black ear patch. Dusky green below, scalloped white. **Size** 26–33 cm. **Juv.** Duller. **Voice** Crying, cat-like mewing, resembles a baby crying; single, double high 'chip', 'tick'. **Hab.** Temperate and highland rainforest.

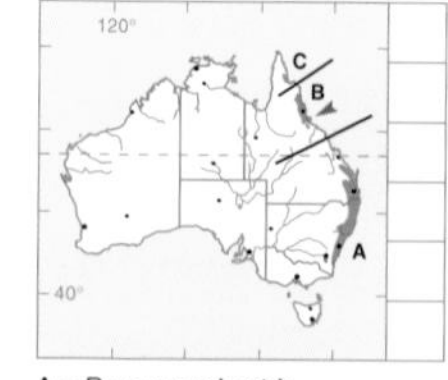

A = Race *crassirostris*
B = Race *maculosus* 'Spotted Catbird' **E**
C = Race *joanae* 'Spotted Catbird' **E**

Trumpet
Manucode
Victoria's
Riflebird
♂
Paradise
Riflebird
♂
Magnificent
Riflebird ♂
Race *alberti*
Victoria's
Riflebird
♀
Magnificent
Riflebird ♀
Race *alberti*
Green ('Spotted')
Catbird
Race *maculosus*
Paradise
Riflebird
♀
Green Catbird
Race *crassirostris*
Tooth-billed
Bowerbird
N. Day

Golden Bowerbird *Prionodura newtoniana* **R** ◎ E

Dimorphic. Solitary. Imm. males in groups of 2–6. Small, slender, yellow-eyed, long-tailed bowerbird. Face, upperparts, central tail feathers, golden olive-brown. Central crown, nape, underparts, golden-yellow. **F** Olive-brown, ash-grey below. **Size** 23–25 cm. **Juv.** Dark eye. Belly, flanks washed yellow. Yellow feathers increasingly show before moult to adult. **Voice** Rattles, croaks, mimicry. **Hab.** Tropical rainforest above approx. 900 m.

Bowerbird males of all species build the bowers. Females mate there, but build nests and raise young alone.

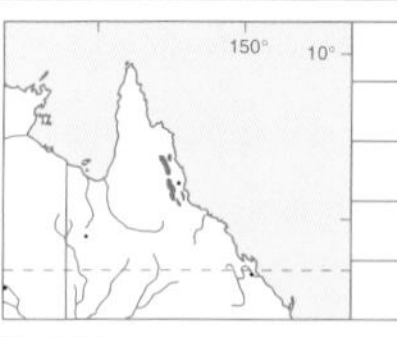

No races

Satin Bowerbird *Ptilonorhynchus violaceus* **C–MC** ◎–? E

Dimorphic. Nomadic winter flocks of 'green' birds. Glossy blue-black. Eye blue. Bill whitish. **F** Bill dark. Olive; rufous wings, tail. Pale green below, lightly scalloped brown. Race *minor* (B) Greyer. **Size** 27–33 cm. **Juv./Imm.** Dark eye. As female to 4th year. **M imm.** Bill paler. Fine, dense scalloping across breast. Odd blue-black feathers until full 7th year moult. **Voice** Strong slow downward double whistle; also harsh 'haaars'; hissing, buzzing, mimicry. **Hab.** Rainforest, wetter tall forest and edges.

Mixed flock

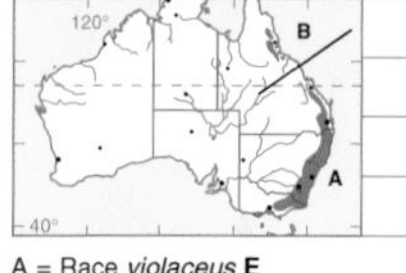

A = Race *violaceus* **E**
B = Race *minor* **E**

Regent Bowerbird *Sericulus chrysocephalus* **LMC–UC** ◎ E

Dimorphic. Pale bill. Yellow eye. Black body; gold crown, nape, shoulders, wing-patch. Variable red-gold tinge to frons, neck. **F/Juv.** Brown eye. Black bill, rear of crown, throat patch. Wings, tail, brown-olive. Body greyish or fawn, mottled and scalloped brown. Tail longer. **Size** 24–28 cm. **M imm.** Gradual plumage change from 2nd–5th years. Grey-brown males first show yellow bill, eye. **Voice** Infrequent: scolds, chattering, mimicry. **Hab.** Rainforest and adj. areas: forest, scrub, orchards, parks.

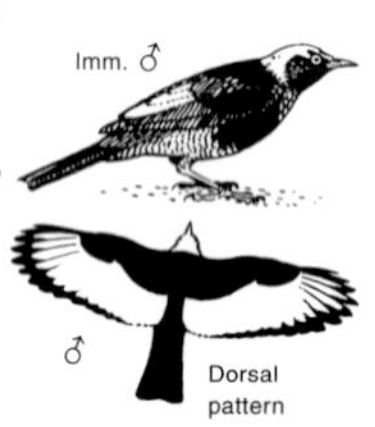

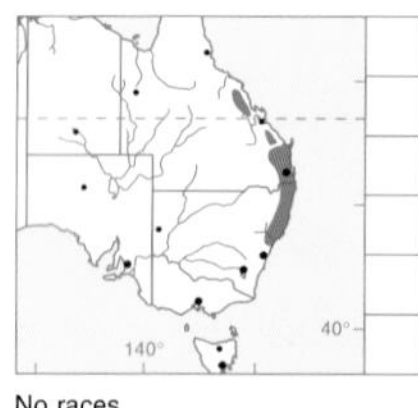

No races

Spotted Bowerbird *Chlamydera maculata* **UC** ◎ E

Fawn-brown to blackish-brown body, boldly spotted cream to buff. Head paler; ash-grey hind neck below lilac-pink nape (nuchal crest). Throat, breast, finely spotted black. Underparts paler buff-grey than Western Bowerbird. **F** Crest smaller. **Size** 27–31 cm. **Juv.** Lacks lilac crest. **Voice** Grating hissings; mechanical sounds, mimicry. **Habitat** Dry open woodland.

Courtship behaviour crest presentation ♂

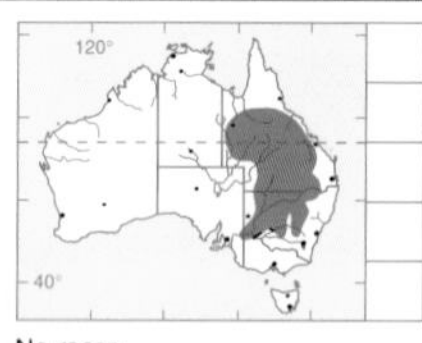

No races

Western Bowerbird *Chlamydera guttata* **MC** ◎ E

Smaller, more richly coloured than Spotted. Lilac-pink nuchal crest. Throat, back, black, boldly spotted orange-buff; tail tip same colour. Deep buff underparts, paling to throat. **F** Larger. Finer markings. **Size** 25–28 cm. **Juv.** Lacks crest. **Voice** Generally similar to Spotted. **Hab.** Arid open woodland.

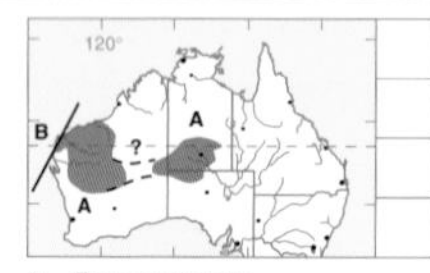

A = Race *guttata* **E**
B = Race *carteri* **E**

Great Bowerbird *Chlamydera nuchalis* **C** ◎ E

Stout decurved bill. Grey with brownish-grey back. Wings, tail heavily marked pale grey. Lilac nuchal crest forms rosette in display. **F** Smaller, paler. Often lacks crest. **Size** 32–37.5 cm. **Juv.** Slight barring abdomen, flank. **Voice** Mimicry; churring. **Hab.** Drier woodlands, low open forest, near watercourses.

Courtship behaviour: parade posture ♂

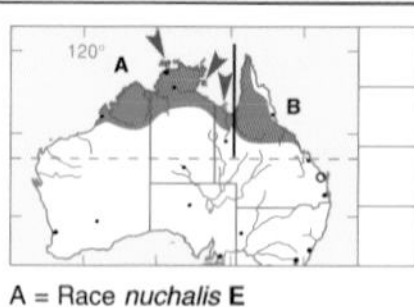

A = Race *nuchalis* **E**
B = Race *orientalis* **E**

Fawn-breasted Bowerbird *Chlamydera cerviniventris* **R** ◎

Decurved stout black bill. Grey-brown with back, wings, tail feathers, finely tipped whitish. Whitish streaks on cheeks, throat, neck to breast. Plain fawn lower breast, abdomen, flanks. **Size** 25–30.5 cm. **Voice** Hoarse hissing, mimicry. **Hab.** Coastal vegetation near rainforest; mangroves, vine forest, woodland.

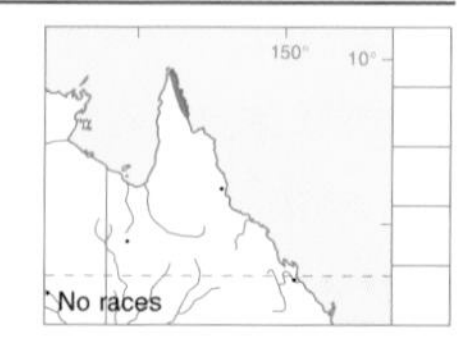

No races

Golden
Bowerbird
♂
Golden
Bowerbird
♀
Satin
Bowerbird
♂
Regent
Bowerbird
♂
Satin
Bowerbird
♀
Western
Bowerbird
Regent
Bowerbird
♀
Spotted
Bowerbird
Great
Bowerbird
Fawn-breasted
Bowerbird

Black-faced Cuckoo-shrike *Coracina novaehollandiae* **C–MC**

Undulating flight. 'Shuffles' wings on landing. Slender; deep grey above; mid grey below. Black mask over face and throat. Dark, white-edged flight feathers. Plain white underwing, undertail coverts. Race *melanops* (B) Dove grey; smaller in north of range. Race *subpallida* (C) Silvery grey. **Size** 33 cm. **Juv./Imm.** Broad blackish eye-stripe, bill to behind eye. Pale throat, breast finely barred. Check other cuckoo-shrikes. **Voice** Creaky, trilling 'kreeark'. **Hab.** Open woodland, forest.

Wing shuffle

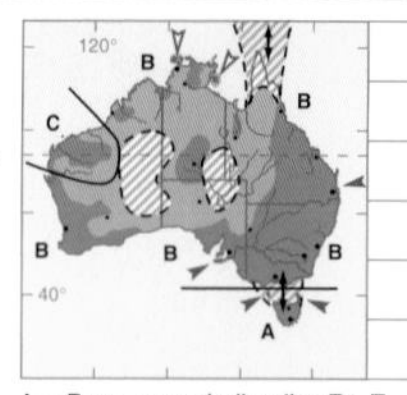

A = Race *novaehollandiae* **Br. E**
B = Race *melanops* **Br. E**
C = Race *subpallida* **E**

Barred Cuckoo-shrike *Coracina lineata* **LC–UC**

Pairs or large groups. Check larger male Oriental Cuckoo. Black lores. Dark grey above; also chin to upper breast. Wings darker, edged whitish. Breast to abdomen white, strongly barred black. **F** Dark grey lores. **Size** 26–28 cm. **Juv./Imm.** Whitish below, finely barred, densest at chin, breast. **Hab.** Rainforest, open forest.

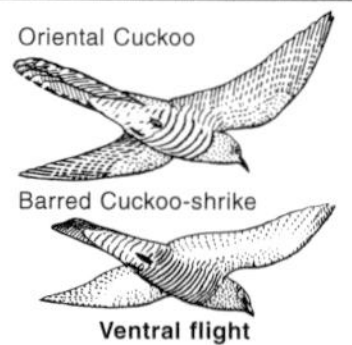

Ventral flight

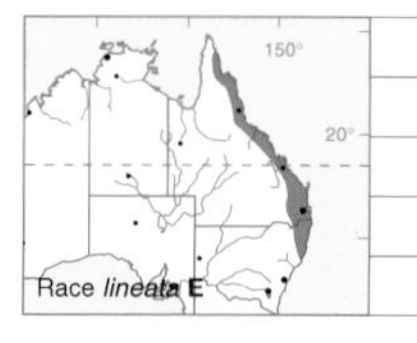

Prior name 'Yellow-eyed Cuckoo Shrike'.

White-bellied Cuckoo-shrike *Coracina papuensis* **C–MC** ?

Check imm. Black-faced, Barred Cuckoo-shrikes. Race *robusta* (A) Also called 'dark morph'; the largest race. Black lores, face, throat; grey breast, flecked black (all variable). Barred undertail; broad white tail tip. Paler races: Race *artamoides* (B) Black narrow lore bar to ear coverts. Race *hypoleuca* (D) Tiny white mark behind eye. Light–mid grey above. Clear white below; grey bloom on breast. **F/Imm.** Greyer lores. Most races lightly barred below. **Size** 26–28 cm. **Voice** Shrill 'kseak'. **Hab.** Woodland.

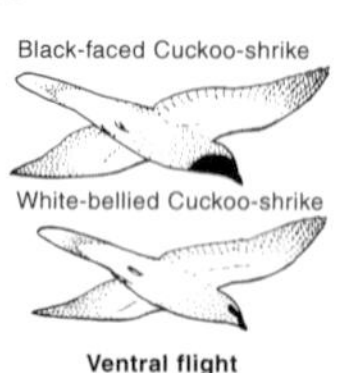

Ventral flight

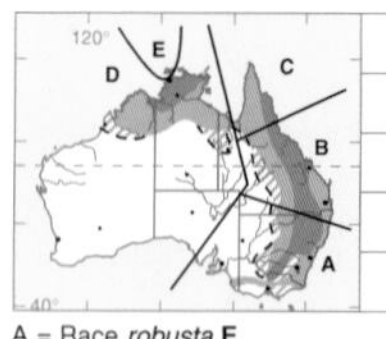

A = Race *robusta* **E**
B = Race *artamoides* **E**
C = Race *oriomo* (also PNG)
D = Race *hypoleuca* **Br. E?**
E = Race *apsleyi* **E**

Cicadabird *Coracina tenuirostris* **UC–MC**

Small blue-grey cuckoo-shrike. Flight, tail feathers black, edged grey. **F** Like female trillers. Pale eyebrow. Browner above, creamy buff below, fine barring. **Size** 24–26 cm. **Juv./Imm.** Heavier bars. **Voice** Cicada-like trill; 'pee-uh' repeated; NE Qld birds, ringing Rosella-like call. **Hab.** Forest, woodland.

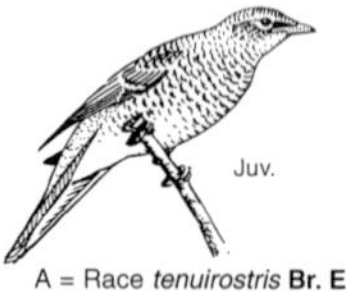

A = Race *tenuirostris* **Br. E**
B = Race *melvillensis* **E**

Ground Cuckoo-shrike *Coracina maxima* **UC** E

Largest cuckoo-shrike. A ground feeder; often in family groups. Face dark grey; eye yellow. Silvery body. Black wings, forked tail. Rump, uppertail coverts, belly, distinctly barred black. Long legs. **Size** 33–37 cm. **Juv./Imm.** Barred upperparts. **Voice** Distinctive, metallic. **Hab.** Drier inland, open woodland.

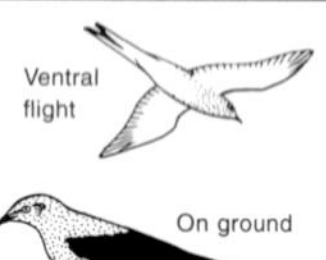

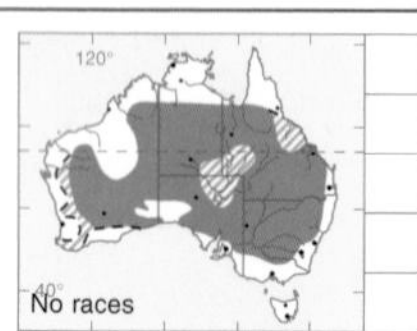

White-winged Triller *Lalage tricolor* **LC–UC** E

Dimorphic. Check Varied Triller, Cicadabird, Rufous Songlark. Black above, white below. No eyebrow. Bright white cheek, shoulder, wing edges. Light grey rump. **M non-br.** White brow. Brown mantle, grey rump; white below. **F/Imm.** Brown above; buff head, wing, breast marks; white belly, vent. **Size** 18 cm. **Voice** Fast falling 'chooee, chooee'. Trill. **Hab.** Woodland.

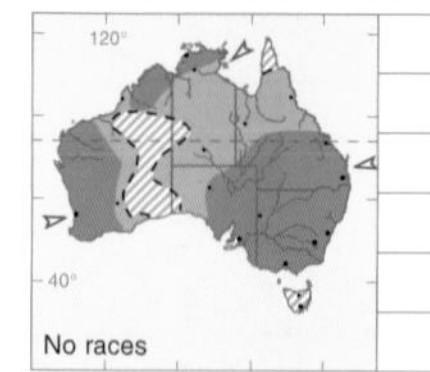

Varied Triller *Lalage leucomela* **LUC**

Dimorphic. White eyebrow. Black above; grey rump. White on wings, tail tip, duller than White-winged. Faintly barred breast; cinnamon-buff belly, vent. Race *yorki* (B) Rufous vent. Races *rufiventris* (C), *macrura* (D) Heavier breast bars; rufous belly, vent. **F/Imm.** Females variably grey to brown above. Barred grey-buff below; cinnamon vent. **Size** 19 cm. **Juv.** Back scalloped. **Voice** Rich, falling 'brreeorr'. **Hab.** Rainforest, woodland.

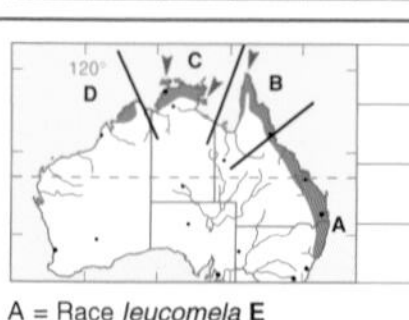

A = Race *leucomela* **E**
B = Race *yorki*
C = Race *rufiventris* **E**
D = Race *macrura* **E**

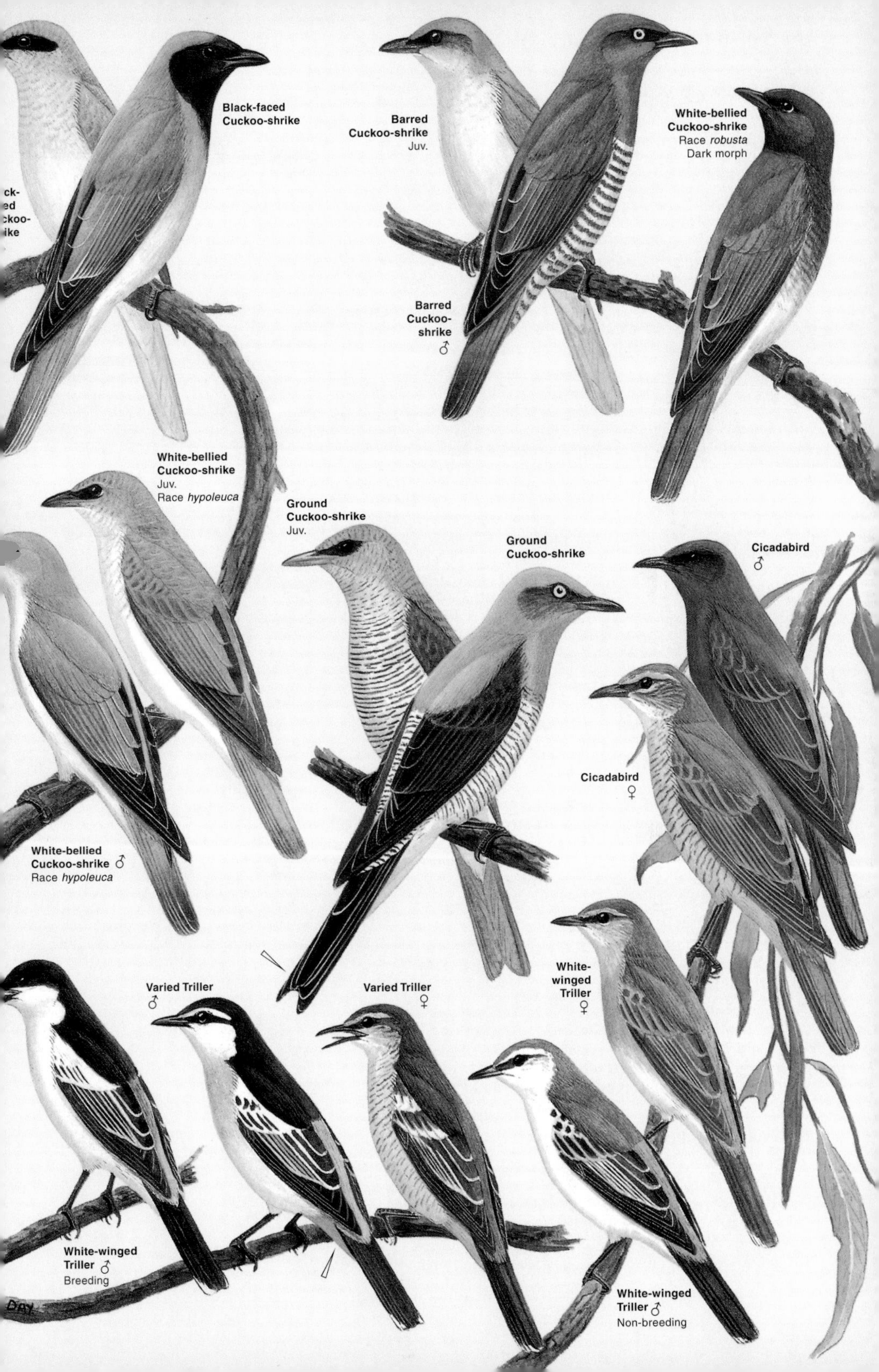
ck-
ed
ckoo-
ike
Black-faced
Cuckoo-shrike
Barred
Cuckoo-shrike
Juv.
White-bellied
Cuckoo-shrike
Race *robusta*
Dark morph
Barred
Cuckoo-
shrike
♂
White-bellied
Cuckoo-shrike
Juv.
Race *hypoleuca*
Ground
Cuckoo-shrike
Juv.
Ground
Cuckoo-shrike
Cicadabird
♂
Cicadabird
♀
White-bellied
Cuckoo-shrike ♂
Race *hypoleuca*
White-
winged
Triller
♀
Varied Triller
♂
Varied Triller
♀
White-winged
Triller ♂
Breeding
White-winged
Triller ♂
Non-breeding

White-breasted Woodswallow
Artamus leucorynchus **C–MC** ◎–⁂

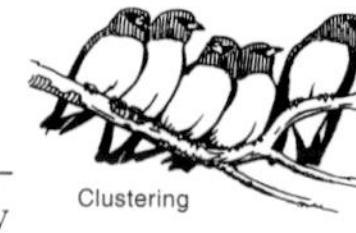
Clustering

All adult woodswallows have a bluish bill, tipped black, as do butcherbirds and Aust. Magpie.

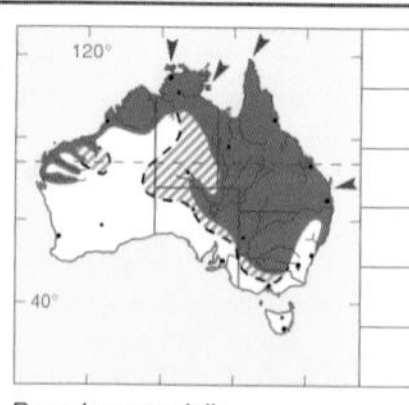

Race *leucopygialis*

Conspicuous flocks in towns. White rump gleams in sunlight. Slate-grey hood, wings. Warm 'soft' grey-brown mantle, back. All-dark tail. White breast, underparts. **Size** 17 cm. **Juv.** Thin creamy eyebrow. Upperparts brown, mottled/striped buff-rufous. Cream to buff rump, underparts. Wing, tail feathers dark grey, tipped buff. **Voice** 'pert, pert'; chatters. **Hab.** Most in its range.

Masked Woodswallow *Artamus personatus* **LA–MC** ⁂ E

Common Starling in silhouette may resemble woodswallows, in flight or when perched on power lines.

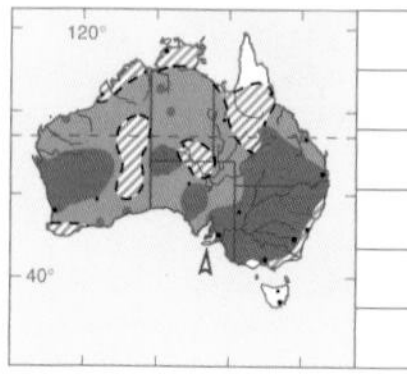

No races

Nomadic; often travels with White-browed Woodswallows. Long bill. Clean-cut black mask on face, throat, edged with a white crescent. Mid blue-grey body, wings. Paler grey underparts, underwing. **F** Dull black face, with pale crescentic edging. Underparts washed pinkish-grey. **Size** 19 cm. **Juv.** Face, throat, upperparts grey, mottled/spotted whitish-buff. Underparts pale buffy grey. **Imm.** Partial eyebrow. Buff feather tips remain on wings. **Voice** 'chap, chap'; chattering. **Hab.** Inland.

White-browed Woodswallow *Artamus superciliosus* **LA–MC** ⁂ E

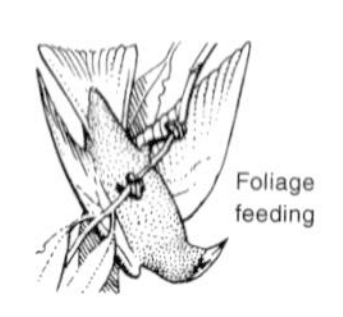
Foliage feeding

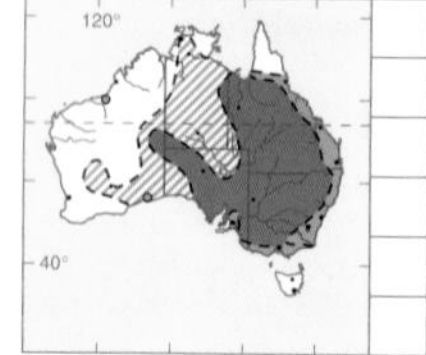

No races

Widely nomadic. Bill long. Long white eyebrow, wider at nape. Face, chin black, grading to deep blue-grey on back and upper breast. Rich chestnut lower breast to undertail coverts. **F** Dull white eyebrow, black lores. Body grey-brown; underparts pinkish-fawn. **Size** 18–19 cm. **Juv.** Bill brown, black tip. Lores black. Head, body, brown, spotted, mottled buffy white. Wing feathers grey, narrow buff-white tips. **Imm.** Partial eyebrow. Buff wing-feather tips. **Voice/Hab.** As Masked Woodswallow.

Black-faced Woodswallow *Artamus cinereus* **C** ◎–?⁂

Undertail variation

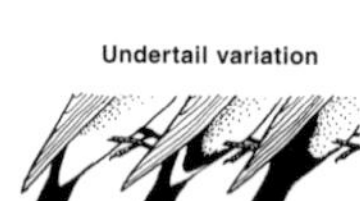
Races B and D — Hybrid — Races A and C

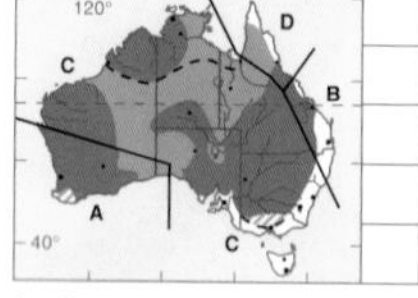

A = Race *cinereus* **E**
B = Race *dealbatus* **E**
C = Race *melanops* **E**
D = Race *normani* **E**

Smoky grey; black face mask from lores to upper throat. Black rump. Short white tail tip. Light grey breast grading darker to black under tail. Underwing silvery. Race *dealbatus* (B) Mid grey, white under tail, broad white tail tip. Race *melanops* (C) Black mask extensive, reduced in tropics; black under tail. Race *normani* (D) Small mask, white undertail coverts, white tail tip. **Size** 18 cm. **Juv.** Bill pale, dark tip. Black lores. Brown body, buff streaks, mottles. Pale throat. Wings grey; narrow buff-white tips. **Imm.** Warmer brown above; buff wash below. **Voice** 'chep, chep'; chattering. **Hab.** Open forest, plains, farmland.

Dotted line on map is broad boundary between 'dark, small-masked' northern population and 'pale, larger-masked' southern population of race melanops (C).

Dusky Woodswallow *Artamus cyanopterus* **C–LUC** ↻ E

Tail wag

Typical of genus *Artamus*

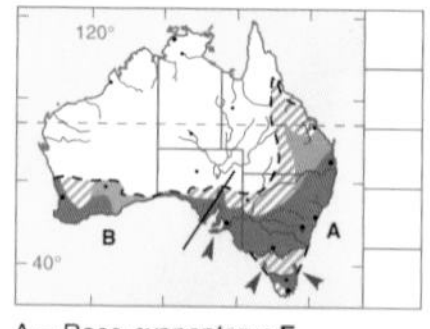

A = Race *cyanopterus* **E**
B = Race *perthi* **E**

Warm smoky-brown head, body. Lores black. Bold white edge on dark blue-grey wing. Silvery underwing. Black tail, broad white tip. Race *perthi* (B) Narrow white wing stripe, tail tip. **F** Larger. **Size** 18 cm. **Juv.** Bill grey-brown, dark tip. Lores brown. Grey-brown body streaked/mottled buff. Dark grey wing has white stripe. **Voice** 'vut vut'; chatters. **Hab.** Open forest, woodland.

Little Woodswallow *Artamus minor* **C** ◎–?⁂ E

Favours escarpments

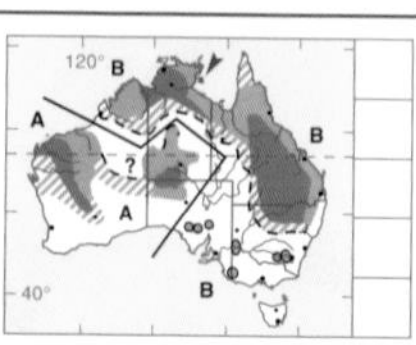

A = Race *minor* **E**
B = Race *derbyi* **E**

Rich chocolate body (black in poor light). Darker face than Dusky. Dark grey-blue wings; no white stripe. Tail black, broad white tip. Underwing dull grey. Race *derbyi* (B) Darker, smaller. **F** Slightly paler. **Size** 12 cm. **Juv.** Body speckled cream. Wings grey, buff tips. **Voice** 'peat-peat'; chattering. **Hab.** Gorges, escarpments, tropical forest, grassland, near termite spires.

White-breasted Woodswallow
White-browed Woodswallow
White-breasted Woodswallow
White-breasted Woodswallow
Masked Woodswallow
Dusky Woodswallow
Little Woodswallow
Black-faced Woodswallow
Masked Woodswallow Juv.
Masked Woodswallow ♀
sked
odswallow ♂
White-breasted Woodswallow Juv.
White-browed Woodswallow Juv.
White-browed Woodswallow ♀
Black-faced Woodswallow Juv.
Black-faced
Voodswallow
ace *cinereus*
White-browed Woodswallow ♂
Little Woodswallow Juv.
Little Woodswallow
Dusky Woodswallow
Dusky Woodswallow Juv.
N.DAY.

Black Butcherbird *Cracticus quoyi* MC ◎

Shy; plumage entirely bluish-black. Typical strong hooked bill. **F** Smaller. **Size** Races *jardini* (B) 42–44 cm; *rufescens* (C) 33–38 cm. **Juv./Imm.** Only *rufescens* has two morphs. Dark morph entirely dull blue-black. Rufous morph brown, streaked rufous above, plain light cinnamon below (some reported to breed in this plumage). All black when adult. **Voice** Variable, strong, musical, yodel; sub-songs. **Hab.** Rainforest, mangroves; adjacent fringes.

Singing

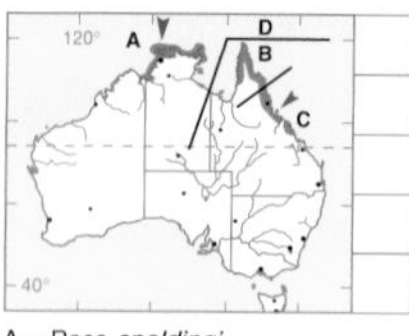

A = Race *spaldingi*
B = Race *jardini* **E**
C = Race *rufescens* **E**
D = Race *alecto*

Grey Butcherbird *Cracticus torquatus* C–LUC ◎–☘ E

Direct 'flat' glide. Strong hooked bill. White lores, half collar. Black head; dark grey back. Black wing, thin white stripe. Black tail; white tip. White below, washed grey. Race *cinereus* (B) Larger, duskier. Race *leucopterus* (C) Smaller, lores less white; wing whiter. **F** Duskier. **Size** 28–32 cm. **Juv.** Dark bill. Brown above; buff where adults white or greyish. Mottled brown, buff below. **Imm.** Bill base pale; dusky bird. **Voice** Rich melodious piping. **Hab.** Open forest, woodland, mallee; urban, farmland.

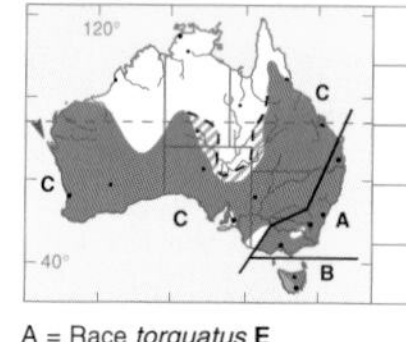

A = Race *torquatus* **E**
B = Race *cinereus* **E**
C = Race *leucopterus* **E**

Silver-backed Butcherbird *Cracticus argenteus* C ◎ E

As Grey; smaller; black lores. Some have partial throat band; black chin spot. Pale grey back; silver-white wing stripe, underparts. Race *colletti* (B) Smaller. Chin, throat, breast clear silver-white.

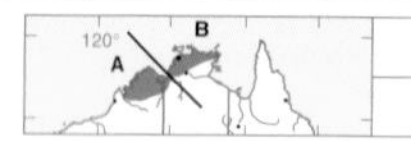

A = Race *argenteus* **E**
B = Race *colletti* **E**

Black-backed Butcherbird *Cracticus mentalis* C ◎

Striking pied bird. Black head, back. Black back edged silver-grey to rump. White partial collar to shoulder. White chin has small dark patch. White below. Black-edged tail; white terminal band. **F** Greyish collar, rump. **Size** 25–27 cm. **Juv.** Brown; back greyer. **Voice** Melodic, unlike Grey's. **Hab.** Tropical open forest.

Ventral flight

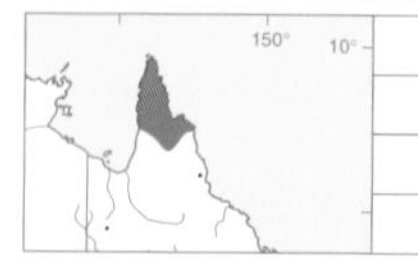

Race *kempi* **E**

Pied Butcherbird *Cracticus nigrogularis* C ◎ E

Black hooded with bib; white below. Wide white collar; narrow black back. White bar on black wing. White corner tips to black tail. Dull white rump. Race *picatus* (B) Brighter white; broader collar extends further down back. **F** Duskier; narrow, greyer collar. **Size** 32–35 cm. **Juv.** Bib buff; dirty white below. **Imm.** Grey-brown, not black; faint collar is lighter brown. **Voice** Lovely, flute-like. **Hab.** Open woodland, scrub and rangeland.

Pied Butcherbird Magpie-lark ♂

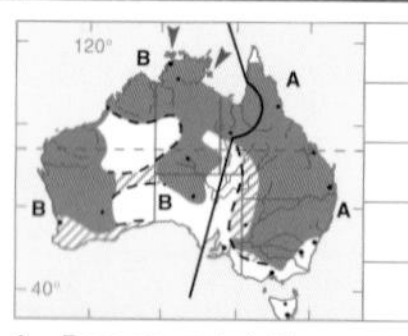

A = Race *nigrogularis* **E**
B = Race *picatus* **E**

Australian Magpie *Gymnorhina tibicen* LA–C ◎–☘

Feeds on ground. Very territorial. Strong, direct flight; loud wing 'swish'. Bill bluish, tipped black. Glossy black and white. 'Black-backed Magpie group': races *tibicen* (A), *terraereginae* (B), *eylandtensis* (C), *longirostris* (D) Black head. White nape/collar. Black back, wings. White shoulder, rump, underwing and undertail coverts. Black terminal band on white tail. Underparts black. **F** Glossy black, white-winged as male, but nape, lower back, pale to medium grey with soft darker streaks, mottles. 'White-backed Magpie group': race *dorsalis* 'Western Magpie' (E) White-backed. **F** Central back feathers black, white-edged; looks 'mottled'. Races *telonocua* (F), *tyrannica* (G), *hypoleuca* (H) Whole back white. **F** Back mottled grey. **Juv.** (all races) As females but dull grey-brown, not black. **Imm.** (all) As females; future black areas mottled brown and black. Fully black-breasted by approx. 2–3 years. **Size** 36–44 cm. **Voice** Flute-like carolling; harsh shrieks. **Hab.** Open forest, farms, urban land.

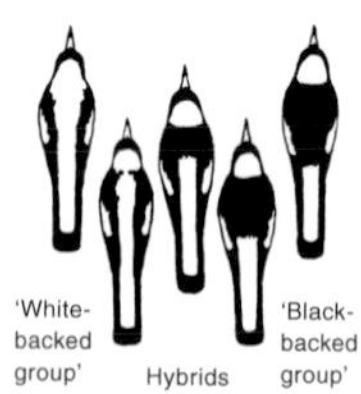
'White-backed group' Hybrids 'Black-backed group'

Nine variable races in two major 'groups'; wide hybrid zones between them. Former race leuconota *replaced by* telonocua *(an anagram).*

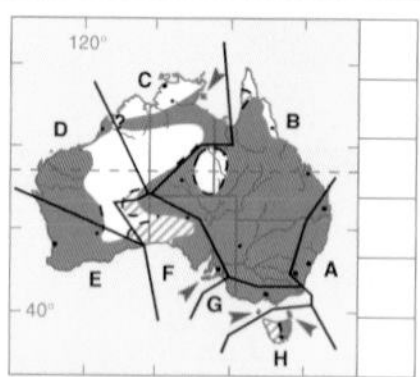

'Black-backed group':
A = Race *tibicen* **E**
B = Race *terraereginae* **E**
C = Race *eylandtensis* **E**
D = Race *longirostris* **E**
[Also race *papuana* in southern N.G.]
'White-backed group':
E = Race *dorsalis* **E**
F = Race *telonocua* **E**
G = Race *tyrannica* **E**
H = Race *hypoleuca* **E**

Silver-backed Butcherbird ♂
Race colletti
Black Butcherbird
Juv./Imm.
Race rufescens
Rufous morph
Black-backed Butcherbird
Imm.
Black Butcherbird
Pied Butcherbird
Imm.
Black-backed Butcherbird
Grey Butcherbird ♂
Grey Butcherbird
Imm.
Pied Butcherbird
Australian Magpie
Australian Magpie ♂
Race tyrannica
Australian ('Western') Magpie ♀
Race dorsalis
Australian Magpie ♀
Race tyrannica
Australian Magpie ♂
Race tibicen
Australian Magpie ♀
Race tibicen
Australian Magpie Juv.
Race tibicen

Pied Currawong *Strepera graculina* **LA–C** ♧–Ↄ E

Winter flocks. 'Rowing' flight when travelling. Robust hooked bill. Yellow eye. Black upper body with prominent white crescent-shaped patch (window or speculum) on wing. Crescentic 'rump' (tail base) and undertail coverts form broad white ring around base of tail. White tail tip. Sooty-black underparts. Outside the breeding season, look for mixture of races as members of some populations move north (A) or westerly (D). Race *magnirostris* (B) Heavier bill, shorter tail. Race *robinsoni* (C) Smaller, shorter bill. Narrow white tail tip. Race *nebulosa* (D) Larger. Sooty black with slate-grey belly, less white on wings, 'rump'; broader white tail tip. Race *ashbyi* (E) Slate-grey back, belly, grading sooty on breast. Vestigial white on wings, tail base; broadest white tail tip. Races *nebulosa, ashbyi* may be confused with Grey Currawong. **F** Smaller, shorter-billed, slightly duller. **Size** 41–51 cm. **Juv./Imm.** Washed brown. Less white on wings, tail base. Pale gape; dark eye gets paler with age. Again, check Grey Currawong. **Voice** Noisy, distinctive, ringing, double call 'curra-wong'. **Hab.** Open forest, woodland, scrubland, farms, urban.

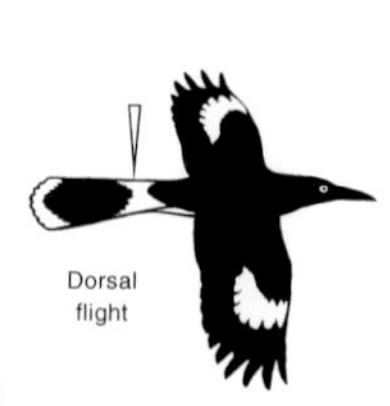

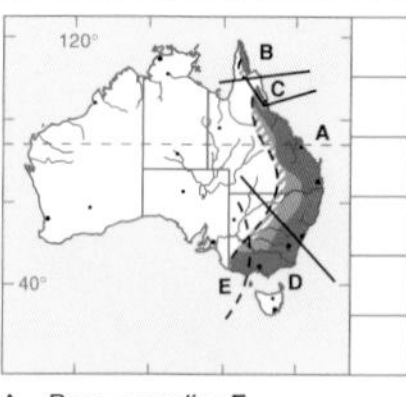

A = Race *graculina* **E**
B = Race *magnirostris* **E**
C = Race *robinsoni* **E**
D = Race *nebulosa* **E**
E = Race *ashbyi* **E Endangered**

Appears that race ashbyi (E) *in western Victoria, may be in process of being 'hybridised out of existence' by race* nebulosa (D), *moving in from the east. Based on Schodde & Mason (1999).*

Black Currawong *Strepera fuliginosa* **C** ◎ E

Identify from Forest Raven (Tas. only). Island races smaller. Bill more robust than Pied, with well-defined hook. Black body; prominent white tips to wing primaries. Tail white-tipped; much shorter than Pied and Grey. No white speculum in dorsal wing. Small greyish patch on underwing. **Size** 46–48 cm. **Juv**. Pale gape; dark eye. Brown on scapulars, upperwing coverts. **Imm.** Retains pale yellow gape until second year. Duller. **Voice** Usual call a musical 'kar-week week-kar' (also described as a yodelled croak). **Hab.** Open forest, woodland, scrub, heathland and agricultural lands.

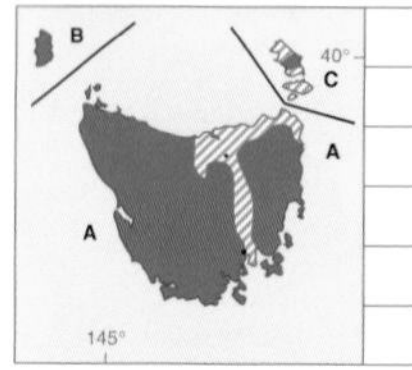

A = Race *fuliginosa* **E**
B = Race *colei* **E Vulnerable**
C = Race *parvior* **E**

Grey Currawong *Strepera versicolor* **C** ◎–♧ E

'Rowing' flight. Forages in trees from canopy to ground. May resemble Laughing Kookaburra when flying away from observer. Darker races: check Pied Currawong, but upper bill base wider; no white rump. Bill slender, without well-defined hook. Smoky grey, sootier on face, throat. Large, prominent white speculum in wing. Flight feathers, tipped white; white undertail coverts, broad white tail band. **F** Slightly smaller; lighter grey. Race *arguta* (B) 'Clinking Currawong' Darkest race, almost black, scalloped satin-black on body. More extensive white speculum in wings, some grey-tipped flight feathers. **F** Matt black lower abdomen, more grey at base of tail. Race *intermedia* (C) 'Brown Currawong' Dull sooty black, darker and browner than nominate. Off-white markings. Race *melanoptera* (D) 'Black-winged Currawong' Darkest mainland race; dull charcoal grey, faint dull grey speculum. Check for ravens, Little Crow. **F** Sooty-grey, dusky throat. Race *halmaturina* (E) Dark sooty black. Race *plumbea* (F) Deep leaden grey, washed brown; sooty face, throat. White wing speculum, tips. **F** Uniform brownish-grey. **Size** 45–53 cm. **Juv.** Cream gape obvious; persists for some months. Duller, browner. **Imm.** Markings as for adult, but body generally greyer; more brownish on throat, mantle. Adults in body moult may briefly resemble imm. birds. **Voice** Ringing, clinking call; also repeated loud bell-like 'chimes'. **Hab.** Open, low open forest; woodland generally, mallee heath, scrub and agricultural lands, urban fringes.

Dorsal flight

A Race *versicolor*

B Race *arguta*

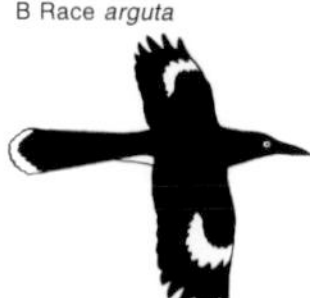

D Race *melanoptera*

A = Race *versicolor* **E**
B = Race *arguta* **E**
C = Race *intermedia* **E**
D = Race *melanoptera* **E**
E = Race *halmaturina* **E**
F = Race *plumbea* **E**

Australian Raven
Black Currawong
Pied Currawong
Grey Currawong
Race *versicolor*
Pied Currawong
White-winged Chough
Grey Currawong
Race *versicolor*
Grey ('Clinking') Currawong
Race *arguta*
Black Currawong
Grey ('Black-winged') Currawong
Race *melanoptera*
Grey
('Brown')
rrawong
Race
ntermedia
N. Day

Australian Raven *Corvus coronoides* **C–LUC** ◎–⁂ E

Note Apart from minor size differences, sexes almost alike in Aust. ravens and crows. Black plumage glistens in bright sun. In hand, crows have white basal down to feathers; all ravens have grey to grey-brown basal down.

Largest corvid in Aust. When calling, throat hackles fanned to form long 'beard'. Large black bill. White eye. Glossy black plumage. Long, floppy, pointed throat hackles. Race *perplexus* (B) Smaller body, bill; shorter hackles. **Size** 52 cm. **Juv./1st yr** Extensive bare pink skin on sides of chin. Brown eye. **Voice** High, far-carrying, child-like wailing; a series of slow notes 'aaaa ...' with strangled, drawn-out finish; also quiet croaking. Race *perplexus* Shorter, 'more clipped and *mellori*-like' (Schodde & Mason, 1999). **Hab.** Most except closed forest.

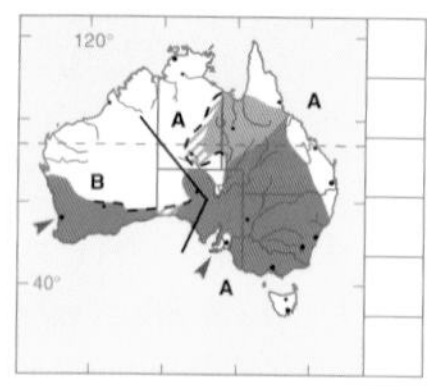

A = Race *coronoides* **E**
B = Race *perplexus* **E**

Forest Raven *Corvus tasmanicus* **LC** ◎–⁂ E

SE mainland populations but only corvid in Tas. Looks 'heavily built'; wide-tailed, a little ponderous in flight. Very prominent bill. Black palate. White eye, blue inner ring. Inconspicuous throat hackles. Black plumage. Feather bases ashy brown. Short tail. Race *boreus* (B) 'Relict Raven' Larger bird. Longer tail, larger wing. **F** Tail shorter than male. **Size** 52 cm. **Juv.** Eye blue-grey. Gape, palate, pink. **1st–3rd yr** Brown–hazel eye. Palate black with pink. **Voice** Very deep; guttural and harsh; 'rolls its Rs'. Utters notes slowly, last fading away. **Hab.** Prefers dense eucalypt forest.

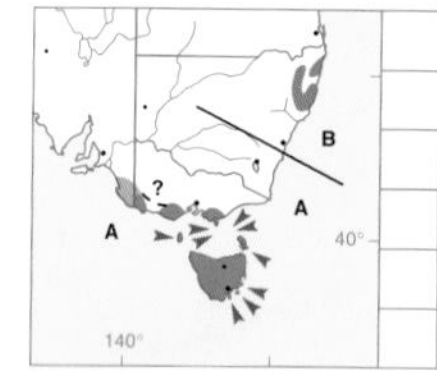

A = Race *tasmanicus* **E**
B = Race *boreus* **E**

Little Raven *Corvus mellori* **LA–MC** ⁂–? E

Often in large flocks. Flight quicker than other ravens. When alighting or perched, movements accompanied by flick of wings above back. Slightly smaller than other ravens. Slightly larger than Aust. Magpie where occur together. 'Round-headed'. Slender bill. White eye. Small bifurcated throat hackles. Black plumage. **Size** 50 cm. **Juv.** Pale pinkish gape. **1st yr** Brown eye. **Voice** Series of rapid-fire, short, rather deep, guttural barks, notes abruptly cut off. Wing flick with each note. **Hab.** Most types (not closed forest).

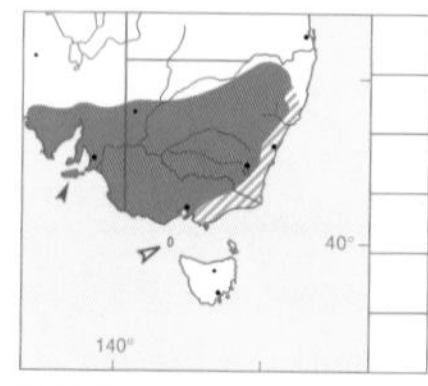

No races

Little Crow *Corvus bennetti* **C** ◎–⁂ E

Flight more rapid, agile, than Torresian Crow, to which related. Small crow in comparison to other Aust. corvids. Often seems disproportionately 'long-legged'. Slender bill. White eye. Black. **F** Slightly smaller. **Size** 48 cm. **Juv.** Fleshy gape. **1st yr** Brown eye. **Voice** Flat, hoarse, very nasal, rather deep; a monotonous series of notes uttered rather rapidly but with each note prolonged. **Hab.** Arid, semi-arid zones, roadsides, outback towns.

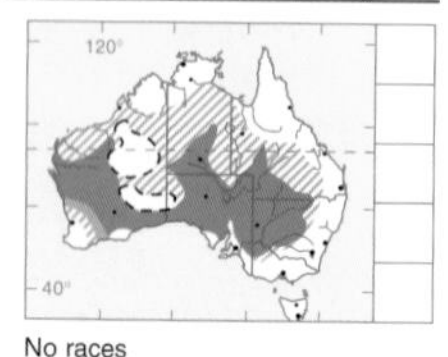

No races
Recent changes in distribution around Perth, WA.

Torresian Crow *Corvus orru* **C–MC** ◎–⁂

After perching, often lifts and settles the wings several times. Slightly smaller than Australian, Forest Ravens. Depending on your location, check Little Crow and any likely raven species. More heavily built, tail broader, squarer, than Little Crow. Nominate race *orru* (A), north Torres Strait islands. Mainland race *cecilae* (B) White eye. Black. **Size** 50 cm. **Juv.** Fleshy gape. **1st yr** Brown eye. **Voice** High-pitched series of staccato honkings, usually rapid but can finish with one or more longer notes; also a series of harsh, snarling notes, the last note dying away. In the arid zone, also a loud falsetto stutter. **Hab.** Most types within its range.

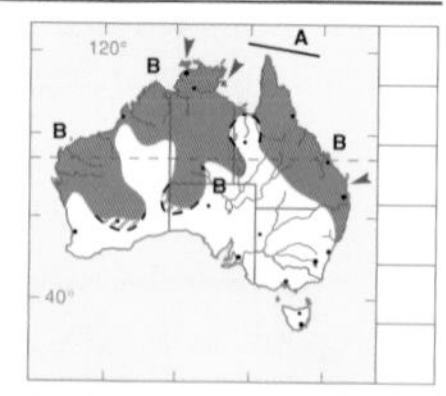

A = Race *orru*
B = Race *cecilae* **E**

House (Columbo) Crow *Corvus splendens* see **Vagrant Bird Bulletin** p. 298.

Little
Raven
Australian
Raven
Forest
Raven
Little
Raven
Australian
Raven
Juv.
Little
Crow
Australian
Raven
Torresian
Crow
Little
Crow
Torresian
Crow
Torresian
Crow
Juv.
House Crow

White-winged Chough *Corcorax melanorhamphos* **C** ◎– E

Check currawongs, ravens, crows. Highly social. Breed, forage on ground in families of 6–14. Flocks to 100+ in winter. In display (single or groups) red eyes bulge; wings held wide open, drooped, fanned; tail wagged, spread. Builds ‘pudding bowl’ mud nest; similar to, but larger than, Apostlebird’s. Groups roost, preen, in ‘clumps’ along branches. Long, black, stout, down-curved bill. Dusky black, the faintly iridescent body plumage often ruffled. Wings, in display or flight, show large white circles with a black line along each feather. Long broad tail. Legs, feet, strong, black. **Size** 45 cm. **Juv.** Black, brownish tinge to head, neck. Eye brown. Thin, wispy white eyebrow persists for 1–4 months. **Imm.** Browner plumage; eye brown; redder with age. **Voice** Alarm – a series of loud descending whistles by whole group; also harsh gratings. **Hab.** Dry open woodland, mallee.

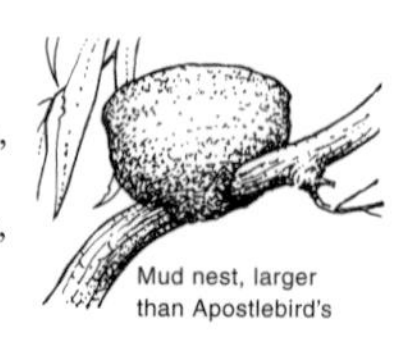
Mud nest, larger than Apostlebird’s

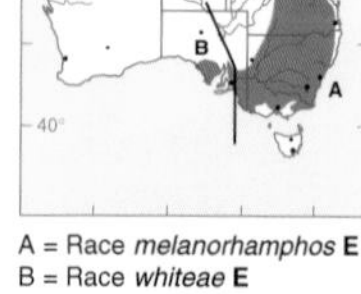

A = Race *melanorhamphos* **E**
B = Race *whiteae* **E**

‘Clumping’

Wing display

Apostlebird *Struthidea cinerea* **C** ◎– E

Highly social. In family parties of 8–14 when breeding; flocks of up to 100+ in winter. Birds walk around on the ground in groups; also huddle, preen, roost in a row on a branch. Builds medium-sized mud nest; slightly larger, stouter, than that of Magpie-lark. Stout black bill. Grey body, pale streaks. Brown wings. **Size** 29–32 cm. **Juv.** Fluffier than adults; less streaked. **Voice** Harsh chattering. **Hab.** Open forests, woodlands and scrub.

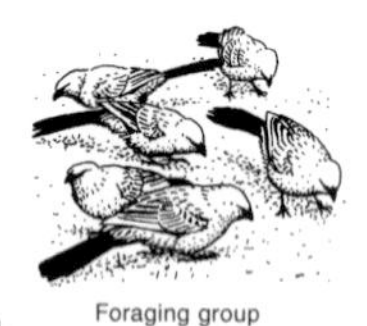
Foraging group

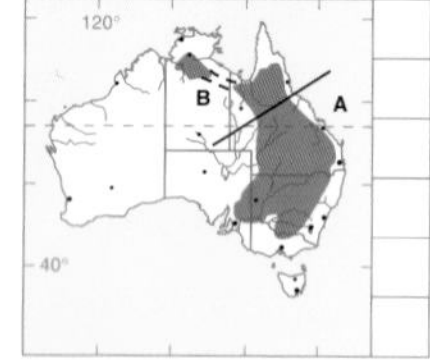

A = Race *cinerea* **E**
B = Race *dalyi* **E**

Relative sizes of the ‘black’ bush birds of Australia

1. Satin Bowerbird (Ad. M) 2. Paradise Riflebird (Ad. M) 3. Spangled Drongo 4. Metallic Starling 5. Trumpet Manucode 6. Black Butcherbird 7. Shining Flycatcher (M) 8. Common Koel (M) 9. Common Starling 10. Common Blackbird (M) 11. Red-tailed Black-Cockatoo 12. Little Black Cormorant 13. Black Falcon 14. White-winged Chough 15. Black Currawong 16. Little Crow 17. Australian Raven.

White-winged
Chough
White-winged
Chough
White-winged
Chough
Imm.
White-winged
Chough
White-winged
Chough
Juv.
Apostlebird
Juv.
Apostlebird
N. DAY

White-backed Swallow *Cheramoeca leucosternus* **MC** ◎ E

Flight more fluttering than other swallows, martins. Appears black at height. Strong light enhances black/white contrast. 'Square' nest burrows in colonies in sandy banks. Burrowing adults may stain buff-orange. Communal winter roosting in a burrow. Crown mottled brown-white. Eyebrow narrow, white to cream. Lores, face black. Plain brown across nape. White throat, mantle, upper back, underwing coverts. Rest of body, wings, deeply forked tail, all dull black. **Size** 13–15 cm. **Juv.** Duller; tail shorter, belly mottled. **Voice** Single 'chhk' in flight. **Hab.** Inland sandy country.

Perched

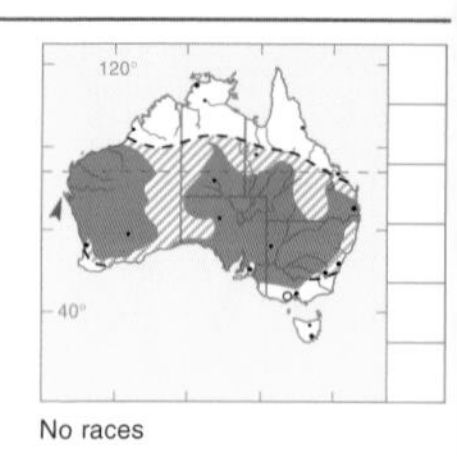

No races

Barn Swallow *Hirundo rustica* **MC**

Perches on wires, fences. Chestnut throat, frons. Narrow blue-black upper breast band. Glossy blue-black above. Browner wings, deeply forked tail. White band on inner side of longest tail feathers. White below (some reddish in NW Aust.). **Size** 15 cm. **Juv.** Smaller; duller. Pale, narrower breast band, mottled reddish. Tail shorter. Faint buff wash to belly, undertail coverts. **Voice** Twitter; soft warbling. **Hab.** Open agricultural, urban areas.

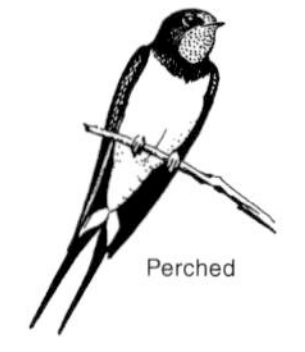

Perched

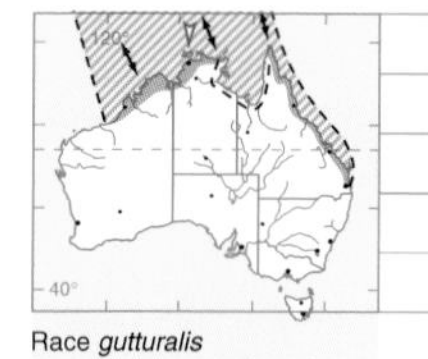

Race *gutturalis*
Annual migrant to Aust. in small numbers.

Welcome Swallow *Hirundo neoxena* **C** – – ◎ E

Often in large flocks. May feed with swifts, woodswallows, martins. May migrate with martins. Local birds smaller, shorter-tailed at extreme NE of range (size cline). Rufous throat, frons. Glossy blue-black above. Browner wings. Deeply forked tail. White band on inner of longest tail feathers. Whitish to dull grey-brown below. Undertail coverts with dusky chevrons. Race *carteri* (B) Bill slightly longer; proportionately shorter-tailed. **F** Outer feathers (streamers) shorter, broader. **Size** 14–15 cm. **Juv.** Forehead, throat dull rufous. Cream gape. Less glossy above. Shorter tail. **Voice** Twittering. **Hab.** All types near water.

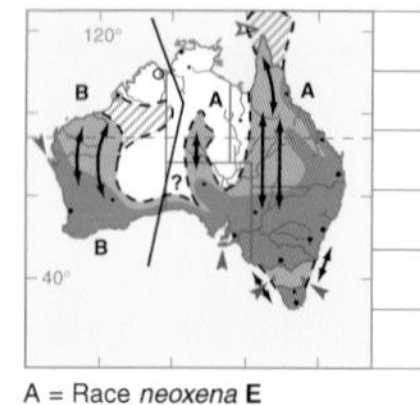

A = Race *neoxena* **E**
B = Race *carteri* **E**

Red-rumped Swallow *Cecropis (Hirundo) daurica* **UC**

Typical swallow. Check Barn Swallow. Dark blue-black crown, upper parts, wings. Rufous eyebrow extends to rufous collar, and is narrowest just above mantle. Rufous-buff rump. Heavy dark streaks on white to pale rufous underparts. Deeply forked tail; longer tail streamers than any Aust. swallows. **Size** 16–18 cm. **Juv.** Paler; less streaked below. **Hab.** open areas; woodland.

Perched

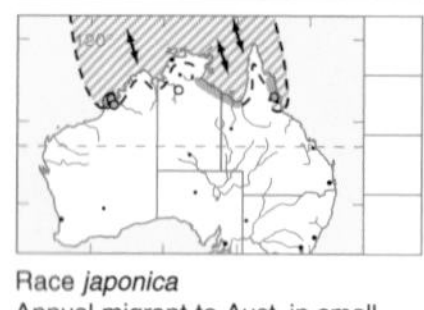

Race *japonica*
Annual migrant to Aust. in small numbers.

Tree Martin *Petrochelidon (Hirundo) nigricans* **C** –? ?Br. E

Aerial. Black-headed in flight. Dirty-white rump (cf. Fairy Martin). Short, slightly forked tail looks square in flight. Bill black. Rufous frons. Glossy blue-black crown, mantle, lower back. Wings, tail feathers brown. Chin, throat, breast, flanks cream to buff, lightly striated. Race *neglecta* (B) Frons creamy rufous. Paler rump. Underparts off-white, striated. **Size** 13 cm. **Juv.** Browner; breast streaked brown. **Voice** Pleasant twitter. **Hab.** Most. Large migratory flocks often roost in reedbeds.

Perched

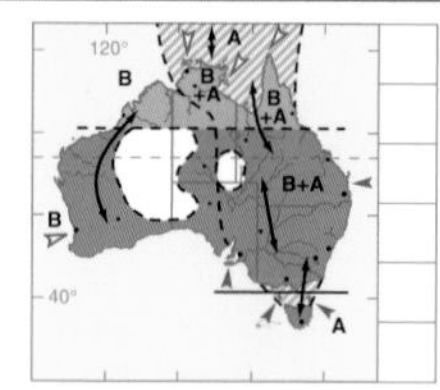

A = Race *nigricans* **?Br. E**
B = Race *neglecta* **E**

Fairy Martin *Petrochelidon (Hirundo) ariel* **C** Br. E

Aerial. 'Red-headed' in flight. Pale buff rump gleams white (cf. Tree Martin). Short tail appears square. Head rufous. Bill black. Fine white nape streaks. Blue-black mantle, back. Wings, tail brown. Faintly streaked throat. Whitish underparts; **Size** 12 cm. **Juv.** Smaller, duller. Chin, throat greyer. **Voice** Distinct chirrup; also sweet twittering. **Hab.** Open country near water. Often about its nest sites, culverts, bridges, cliffs – the 'Bottle Swallow'.

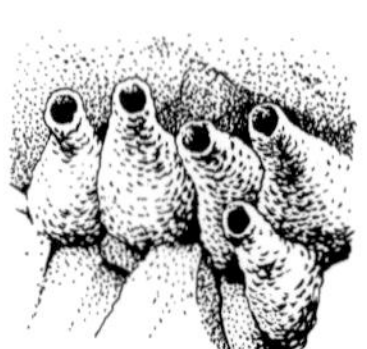

'Bottle-shaped' mud nests

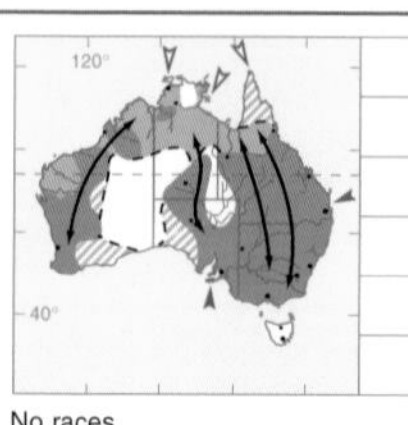

No races

White-backed Swallow
Welcome Swallow
Barn Swallow
Welcome Swallow
Red-rumped Swallow
Tree Martin
White-backed Swallow
Red-rumped Swallow
Fairy Martin
Fairy Martin
Tree Martin
Barn Swallow
Welcome Swallow
White-backed Swallow Juv.
White-backed Swallow
Tree Martin Juv.
Welcome Swallow Juv.
Red-rumped Swallow
Tree Martin
Fairy Martin
Fairy Martin Juv.
N. DAY

Australian (Richard's) Pipit *Anthus australis* C–MC ◎

Wags tail up and down. Runs along ground. Check Skylark, Singing Bushlark. Slender bill. Pale buff eyebrow stripe and below cheek. Brown bird with darker streaks above. Long white-edged tail. Underparts buff with brown spots and streaks on whitish breast. Unstreaked flanks. Long pinkish legs. Short hind toe. **Size** 17–18 cm. **Imm.** Like adults. **Voice** Chirrups; trilling calls in undulating song flight. **Hab.** Open country.

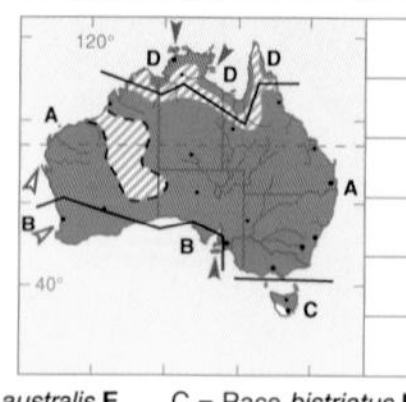

A = Race *australis* **E** C = Race *bistriatus* **E**
B = Race *bilbali* **E** D = Race *rogersi*

Yellow Wagtail *Motacilla flava* UC ○

Three races recorded in Aust.; not mapped. Eyebrow runs to sharp point at bill base. Olive-green back; dull rump. No wing bars. Long black tail edged white; black legs. Race *simillima* Grey head; broad white eyebrow; underparts yellow; slight breast band. Race *taivana* Bright olive-green head, back; yellow eyebrow. Race *tschutschensis* Grey crown; eyebrow, throat white. **Non-br.** Races hard to separate. Dull olive upperparts; cream to yellow eyebrow; buffish below. **1st yr** Greyer above, whitish below (no yellow at all), dull breast band. Some show two thin wing bars. **F/Imm.** Brownish breast band. **Size** 15–17 cm. **Voice** Shrill, trilling. **Hab.** Salt works, paddocks, marshes, grassy wetlands.

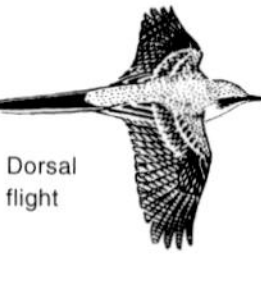

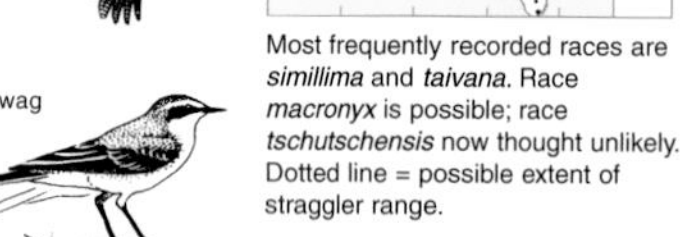

Most frequently recorded races are *simillima* and *taivana*. Race *macronyx* is possible; race *tschutschensis* now thought unlikely. Dotted line = possible extent of straggler range.

Grey Wagtail *Motacilla cinerea* V–R

White eyebrow; stripe above black throat. Grey head, mantle. Yellowish-green rump, uppertail coverts. Tail very long, black, edged white. Yellow below, brighter under tail. Pale legs. **M non-br./F** Narrow, white, wing bar obvious in flight. Breast washed yellow. **Size** 17–18 cm. **Juv.** Brown tinge above, buffish below; speckled breast. Yellow only on tail coverts. **Voice** Sharp 'tit' or 'chichit'. **Hab.** Higher altitudes near fast running water. Recently reported almost annually in northern Australia, from the Kimberley, WA, to south-east Qld.

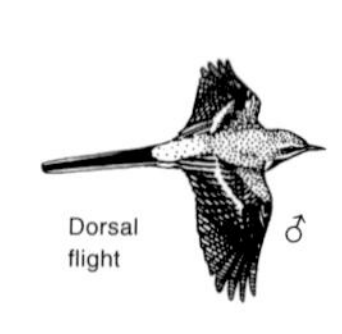

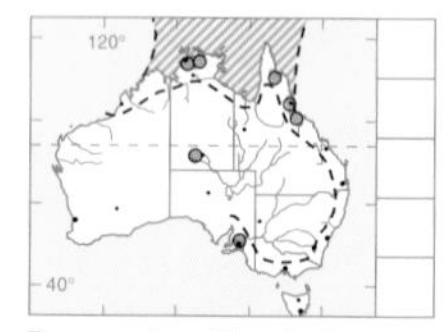

Two races (possibly *robusta*, *melanope*) may reach Australia. Identity not confirmed. These are shorter-tailed than foreign nominate *cinerea* but it may not be a useful field feature.

White Wagtail *Motacilla alba* V–R

Check (smaller) White-fronted Chat. Wags tail up and down, as do all these wagtails. Thin black eye-line to nape. Black and white bird with long black tail, edged white. Conspicuous white wing bars. Back grey; white underparts. Rare in Aust. in this plumage. **M Non-br./F** Grey upperparts; white-edged wing feathers. Identify from Black-backed Wagtail. **Size** 18 cm. **Juv.** Grey above; dusky below. Complicated dark face, throat, pattern. Two wing bars. **Imm.** Grey-brown above. Faint yellow blush to face, breast. **Voice** Given as 'chissick'. **Hab.** Aust. records in coastal areas. Some other sightings not sufficiently detailed to differentiate between White and Black-backed Wagtails.

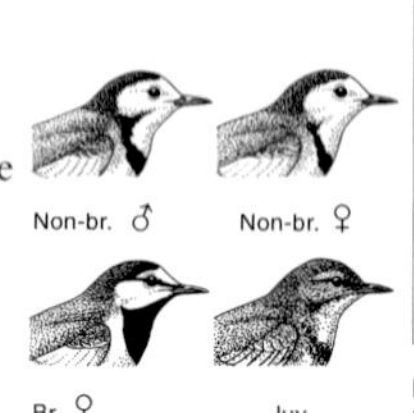

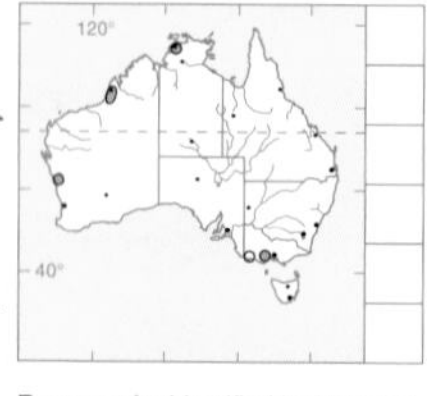

Races so far identified in Aust. are:
Race *leucopsis*
Race *baicalensis*
Race *ocularis*

1. Despite present vagrant status of some wagtail species, increasingly frequent records (all species) suggest more regular dispersal to Aust.

2. Plumages of all motacillid wagtails vary greatly with sex, age and season. Pay attention to facial detail. Be very careful with identification. For corroboration, drawings and photos will be required.

Red-throated Pipit *Anthus cervinus*, **Pechora Pipit** *Anthus gustavi*, **Citrine Wagtail** *Motacilla citreola*, **Black-backed Wagtail** *Motacilla lugens* see **Vagrant Bird Bulletin** pp. 298, 299.

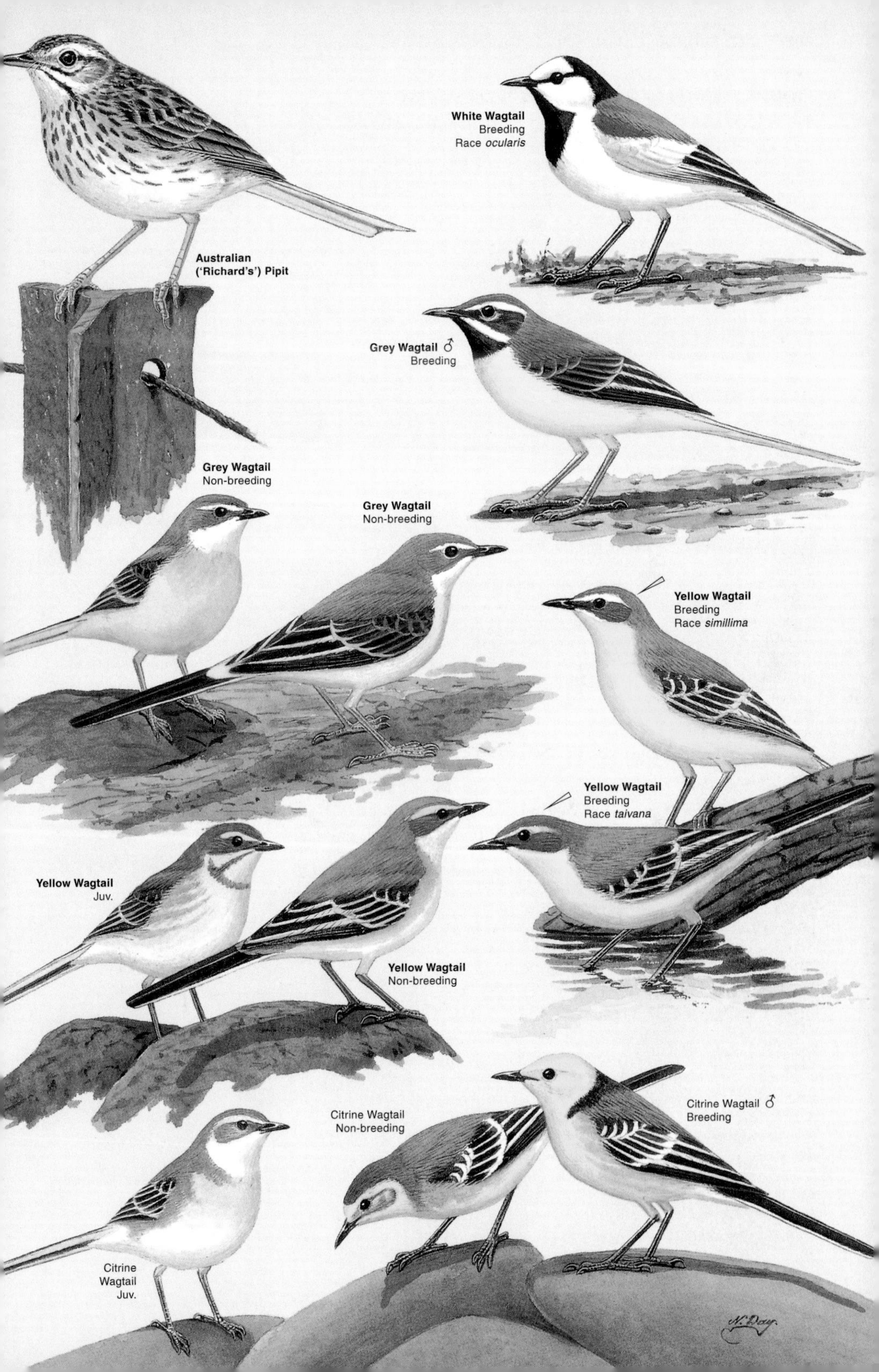
Australian
('Richard's') Pipit
White Wagtail
Breeding
Race *ocularis*
Grey Wagtail ♂
Breeding
Grey Wagtail
Non-breeding
Grey Wagtail
Non-breeding
Yellow Wagtail
Breeding
Race *simillima*
Yellow Wagtail
Breeding
Race *taivana*
Yellow Wagtail
Juv.
Yellow Wagtail
Non-breeding
Citrine Wagtail
Non-breeding
Citrine Wagtail ♂
Breeding
Citrine
Wagtail
Juv.
N. Day

Horsfield's (Singing) Bushlark *Mirafra javanica* C ⟳ E

Runs on ground. Like small Skylark, no crest. In flight, rufous wing patch; white tail shafts. Northern races larger. Race *horsfieldii* (A) Bill short, sparrow-like. Distinct pale eyebrow. Grey-brown above, streaked dark brown; wing feathers scalloped lighter. Buff breast, speckled black. Race *rufescens* (B) Larger, more rufous, plainer. Race *soderbergi* (C) Dark, heavily marked. Race *melvillensis* (D) Rich rufous. Race *forresti* (E) Tawny-brown. Race *halli* (F) Grey above, buff below, clearly spotted. Race *woodwardi* (G) Cinnamon, plainer. Race *secunda* (H) Small, plain, tawny. Race *athertonensis* (I) Warm brown, heavily marked, medium bill. **Size** 12–15 cm. **Imm.** Paler all races. **Voice** Melodious songs, including mimicry. **Hab.** Grassland, crops.

Dorsal flight

Foot comparison

Horsfield's Bushlark

Australian Pipit

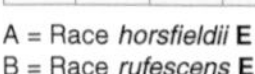

A = Race *horsfieldii* **E**
B = Race *rufescens* **E**
C = Race *soderbergi* **E**
D = Race *melvillensis* **E**
E = Race *forresti* **E**
F = Race *halli* **E**
G = Race *woodwardi* **E**
H = Race *secunda* **E**
I = Race *athertonensis* **E**

Skylark *Alauda arvensis* C ◎–⁂ Intro.

Sings as ascends, then hovering aerial song before diving sharply to earth. Runs along ground. Flies low, showing bold white outer tail shafts. No rufous wing patch. Identify from songlarks. Larger, paler than Horsfield's (Singing) Bushlark. Darker than Australian (Richard's) Pipit. Bill brownish. Entire head, upper body surface light brown with strong, dark streaks. Some Tas. birds greyer. Small dark crest sometimes visible. Buff eyebrow. Whitish chin, throat. Strongly streaked breast. Wing feathers brown, edged pale buff. Legs flesh to pale tan brown. Extremely long hind claw (16–18 mm). **Size** 17–19 cm. **Juv.** Pale, sandy dorsal plumage has strong buff feather edgings (appears 'button-quail-like'). Chin, throat, belly plain whitish-buff. No crest, shorter tail. **Imm.** Paler than adult. **Voice** Chirrup; long-lasting musical warbling whilst in flight over territory. **Hab.** Grassland, crops, roadside verges.

Skylark

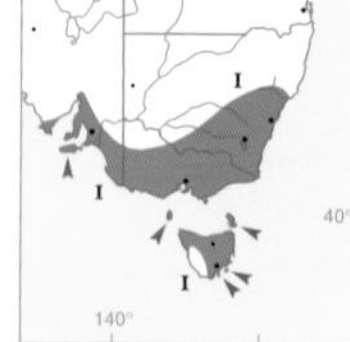
Race *arvensis*

Australian Pipit

Dorsal flight

Probable future name will be 'Eurasian Skylark'.

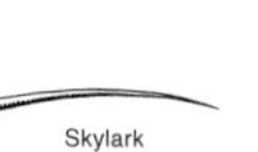
Skylark

Rufous Songlark *Cincloramphus mathewsi* C–MC ⟳ E

Singing male conspicuous in breeding season. Pale, white eyebrow. Streaky-brown upperparts. Rufous rump, uppertail coverts. Whitish underparts. Dark brown tail. **M br.** Bill, mouth, black; breast may have fine spots. **F** Smaller. Bill pale brown. **Size** M 19, F 16 cm. **Juv.** Paler; dark spots on breast, throat. **Voice** Lengthy melodious song (in flight or perched). **Hab.** Woodland, parkland, hedges, lightly timbered grassland. Often at edges of timber stands, roadside reserves.

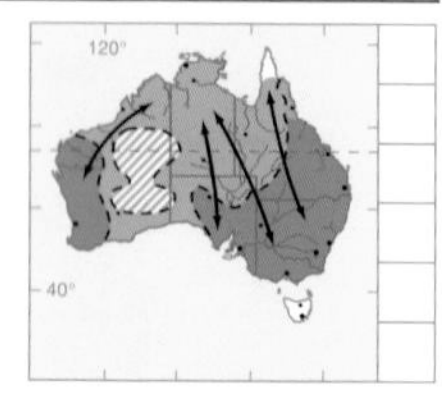
No races
Map shows dispersal to non-breeding (wintering) areas

Brown Songlark *Cincloramphus cruralis* C–MC ⟳ E

Male often perches with crown, tail raised; often appears very dark in grassland localities; black in poor light. Conspicuous ascending, then gliding, song flight. Note very different sex sizes. Pale eyebrow. Streaked brown upperparts. Dark brownish-black underparts. Longish, pointed tail. **M br.** Bill, mouth black when breeding. **F/Juv.** Much smaller; paler. Pinkish-brown bill. Pale throat. Breast light buff, faintly streaked. Black-brown belly. Identify female from Rufous Songlark, Skylark, Australian Pipit and female White-winged Triller (worn plumage of these species may make them appear very pale in the field). **Size** M 23–25, F 18–23 cm. **Voice** Loud, creaky. **Hab.** Grassland, crops.

♂
Singing in flight

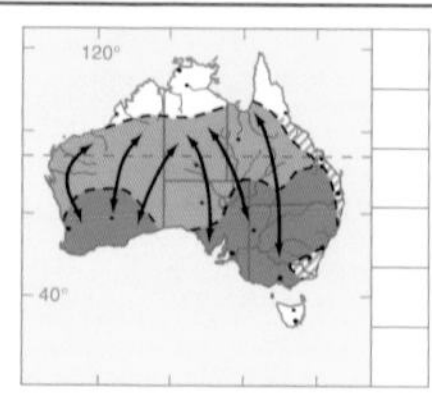
No races
Map shows dispersal to non-breeding (wintering) areas

Horsfield's ('Singing') Bushlark
Juv.
White-winged Triller
♀
Rufous Songlark
♂ Juv.
Horsfield's Bushlark
Ad. Red
Rufous Songlark
♀ Ad.
Horsfield's Bushlark
Ad. Dark
Rufous Songlark
♂ Ad.
Skylark
Race arvensis
Skylark
Juv.
Brown Songlark ♂
Ad. Breeding
Australian ('Richard's') Pipit
Brown Songlark
♀ Ad.
Brown Songlark ♂
Ad. Non-breeding
Brown Songlark ♂
Moult
N.DAY.

Australian (Clamorous) Reed-Warbler *Acrocephalus australis* **C–LC**

Flies low over water. May sing from taller trees near water. Bill dark above, pale below; slender. Eyebrow, throat cream. Upperparts plain warm brown; buffy-cream below. Race *gouldi* (B) Larger. Deep walnut brown above; more rufous below. **Size** 17 cm. **Voice** Clear, sweet varied 'crut-crut-crut, deet-deet-deet, crotchy-crotchy-crotchy'; various scolding calls. **Hab.** Reed, cumbungi beds; willows; other dense vegetation near water.

Incubating

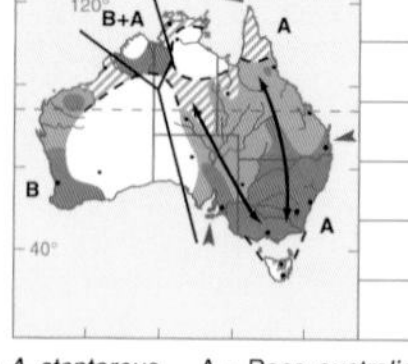

Species *A. stentoreus* now considered Asian.
A = Race *australis*
B = Race *gouldi* **E**

Oriental Reed-Warbler *Acrocephalus orientalis* **R–UC**

Like Australian Reed-Warbler; bill shorter, thicker. Fine streaks on throat and upper breast. **Size** 19 cm. **Voice** As Australian but harsher, faster and lower. **Hab.** Reed beds.

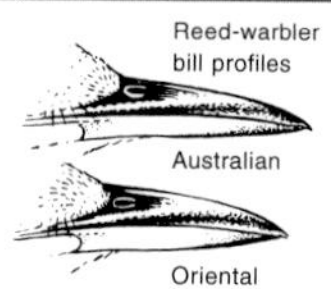

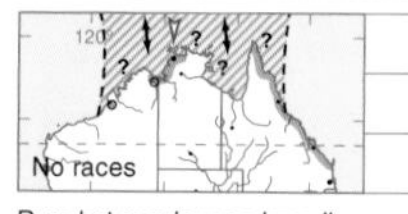

Rare but regular non-breeding migrant.

Spinifexbird *Eremiornis carteri* **MC–UC** ◎ E

Rufous crown, nape. Upperparts uniform plain rufous-brown. Whitish underparts. Very long tail coverts. Long, graduated, dark tail with rounded buff tip. Small feet. **Size** 15 cm. **Voice** Pleasant warble. **Hab.** Spinifex, low scrub, dense grasses on stony hills.

Tail cocked

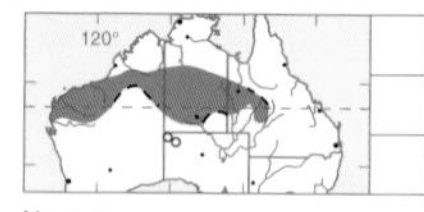

No races

Zitting Cisticola *Cisticola juncidis* **MC–LC** ◎

Crown, nape mid-brown, faintly striped. Back cinnamon, streaked black. Tail tipped white. White below, flanks rufous. Undertail pale, sub-terminal black spots. **F br.** Crown, back, heavily striped black. Rump bright cinnamon. **M/F non-br.** Upperparts streaked; tail longer. Race *normani* (B) Paler, faint stripes. Race *laveryi* (C) Brightest. **Size** 10 cm. **Voice** insect-like 'tik-tik'; 'see-sick, see-sick'. **Hab.** Rank grassland.

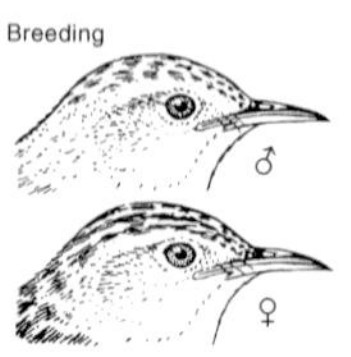

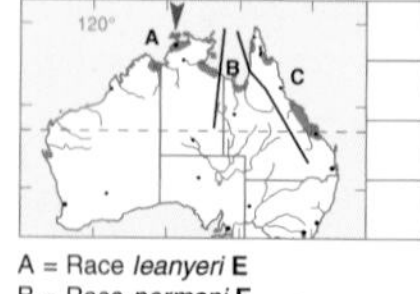

A = Race *leanyeri* **E**
B = Race *normani* **E**
C = Race *laveryi*

Golden-headed Cisticola *Cisticola exilis* **C** ◎–?

Uniform golden crown, nape. Back tawny-rufous, heavy black streaks. Underparts cream to golden buff. Dark undertail, tipped cinnamon. **M non-br./F** Striped crown; back rich tawny-rufous, finely streaked black. Tail becomes longer after breeding. Races *diminuta* (B), *lineocapilla* (C) Deeper rufous. Race *alexandrae* (D) Sandy, paler. **Juv.** Duller. **Size** 10 cm. **Voice** 'churr, lik-lik'. **Hab.** Long grasses.

Display flight

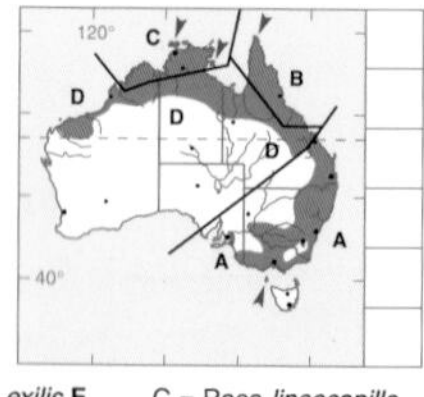

A = Race *exilis* **E**
B = Race *diminuta*
C = Race *lineocapilla*
D = Race *alexandrae* **E**

Tawny Grassbird *Megalurus timoriensis* **LC–UC** ◎

Rich red-brown crown, faintly streaked. Brown to pale-brown mantle, back, with moderate dark streaks. Whitish to buff-washed sides of unstreaked underparts. Long mid-brown tail. **Size** 19 cm. **Voice** Descending wren-like reels; scolding calls. **Hab.** Reeds, tussocks, low bushes in swamps; also open grassland.

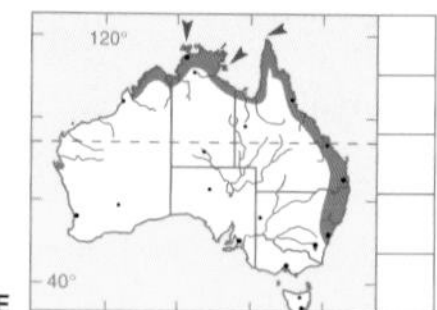

Race *alisteri* **E**

Little Grassbird *Megalurus gramineus* **C–UC** ◎

Darker, smaller than Tawny Grassbird; larger than cisticolas. Check Striated Fieldwren. Olive-brown above, distinctly dark streaked. Long wing feathers edged white. Olive-grey below, spotted. Race *goulburni* (B) Paler, plainer. Race *thomasi* (C) Smaller, very dark. **Size** 14 cm. **Voice** Plaintive whistled 't-thee-thee' or 'to-too too'. **Hab.** Reeds, tussocks, swamp vegetation.

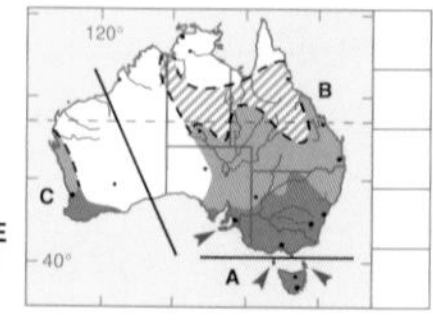

A = Race *gramineus* **E**
B = Race *goulburni* **E**
C = Race *thomasi* **E**

Arctic Warbler *Phylloscopus borealis* see **Vagrant Bird Bulletin** p. 300.

Arctic Warbler
Oriental Reed-Warbler
Australian ('Clamorous') Reed-Warbler
Zitting Cisticola ♂ Breeding Race *leanyeri*
Spinifexbird
Golden-headed Cisticola ♂ Non-breeding
Tawny Grassbird
Golden-headed Cisticola ♂ Breeding
Little Grassbird
N. Day.

Eurasian Tree Sparrow *Passer montanus* **LC** ◎ Intro.

This smaller species sometimes feeds with House Sparrows. Sexes alike. Bill black. Bright chestnut crown. Small crescent-shaped black spot on white cheek. Black throat. Whitish collar. Upperparts streaked brown and black; two white wing bars. Brown rump. Greyish below. **Non-br.** Bill blackish-brown to yellow at base. Less black on throat. **Size** 14 cm. **Juv.** Paler bill; pale brown plumage. **Voice** Soft 'tek' and twittering song. **Hab.** Urban, industrial areas.

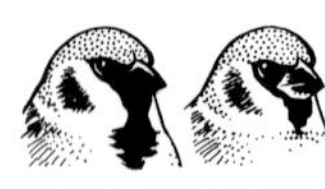

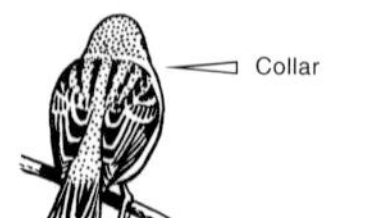

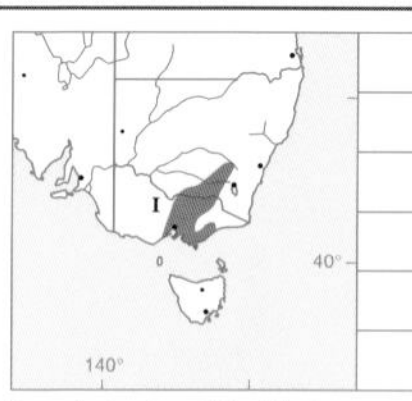

Race in Aust. not identified. Patchy distribution within range. Appears to be spreading north from Melbourne along Hume Hwy and railway line.

House Sparrow *Passer domesticus* **C** ◎ Intro.

Flocks often seen along roadsides. Identify from Little Grassbird in reeds. Sometimes feeds with Eurasian Tree Sparrows. Bill black. Prominent grey crown. Chestnut ear coverts, nape. Large black bib. White bar on shoulder. Whitish-grey cheeks, underparts and rump. Tail brownish-grey. **M non-br.** Bill horn-brown; breast less smudged with black. **F** Horn-brown bill; pale brown head. Pale buff stripe behind eye. Pale wing bar. Whitish-grey underparts. **Size** 15 cm. **Juv.** Paler, yellowish-ivory bill with yellow gape flanges. **Voice** Harsh 'cheer-up', and chirruping song. **Hab.** Human habitation; farmland; may roost in reed beds.

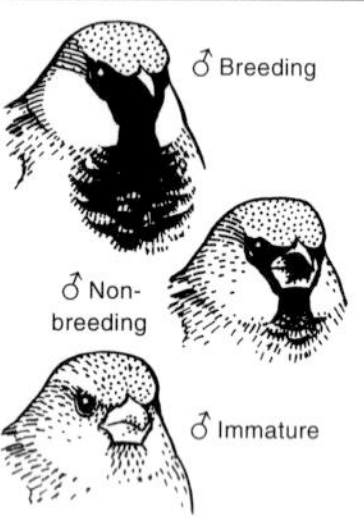

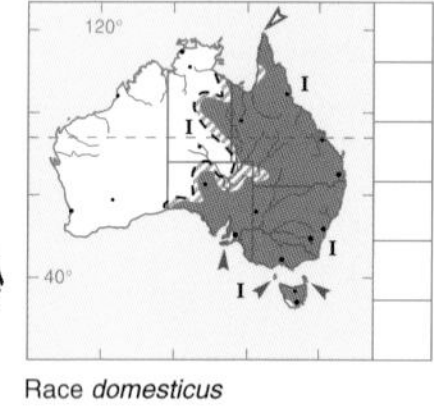

Race *domesticus*

European Greenfinch *Carduelis chloris* **LC** ♧–◎ Intro.

In pairs or flocks; flight undulating. Stout, olive-green finch with grey and yellow streaked wings. Heavy ivory bill; large head; dark lores, eyeline. Tail forked; base yellow; black centre, terminal bar. **F** Duller, yellow less obvious. **Size** 15 cm. **Juv.** Duller bill and plumage. **Voice** Frequently calls from very top of tree. Song is trill followed by ascending 'zeep'; 'chip-chip-chip'; nasal 'twe-e-ee'. **Hab.** Urban areas; gardens, parks, farmland and coastal areas; often where foreign trees, windbreaks are well established. Commonly on cypress and pine trees.

Song posture, and a typical song perch

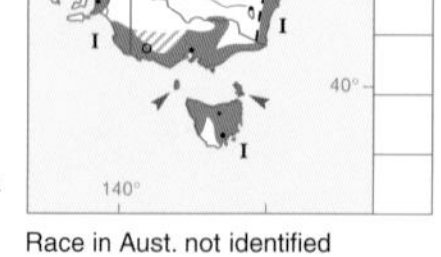

Race in Aust. not identified

European Goldfinch *Carduelis carduelis* **LC** ♧–◎ Intro.

Distinctive head pattern, bright red face. Black, white and brown finch; large yellow wing bars conspicuous in undulating flight. Pinkish-white pointed bill. Black lores, crown, shoulders. Tail and trailing edge of wing tipped white. Back and flanks tawny-brown. Side of head, throat, rump, abdomen, white. **F** Slightly less red on face. **Size** 13 cm. **Juv.** Brownish head, streaked plumage. Yellow and black wings. **Voice** Calls in flight. Liquid 'tu-leep', 'tsi-i-it'; liquid twittering song. **Hab.** Settlements and agricultural areas, particularly in patches of thistles; rank grasses on industrial, railway land; lawns. Minor pest in some orchards.

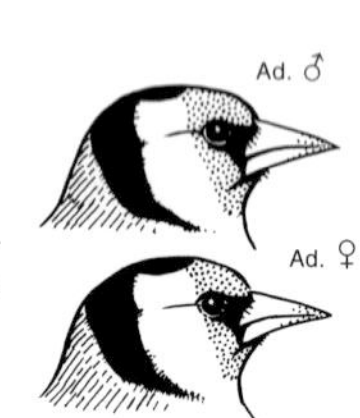

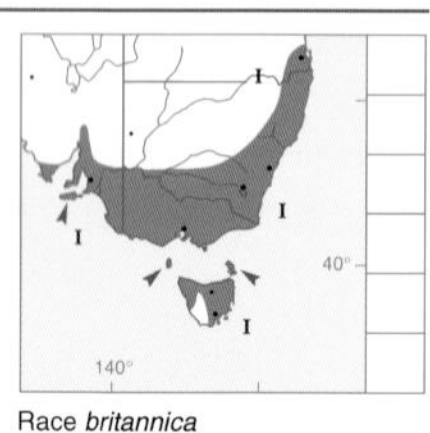

Race *britannica*

Common aviary escapes

♀ Non-breeding Bishop or Wydah *Euplectes* sp.

Canary *Serinus canaria* Yellow and striated varieties

Eurasian Tree Sparrow
Eurasian Tree Sparrow Juv.
House Sparrow ♀
DRY
House Sparrow ♂ Breeding
House Sparrow ♂ Non-breeding
House Sparrow ♀
House Sparrow ♂
Eurasian Tree Sparrow
European Greenfinch
European Greenfinch Juv.
European Greenfinch
European Goldfinch
European Goldfinch Juv.
European Goldfinch
N.DAY

 (and see p. 330)

Double-barred Finch *Taeniopygia bichenovii* **C** ⁂ E

Neat 'owl-faced', brownish-grey and white finch. Bill greyish-blue. Face white, bordered black. Black wings spotted white. Upper tail coverts, rump, white. Black tail. White underparts with two narrow black bands above and below chest. Legs blue-grey. Race *annulosa* (B) Upper tail coverts, rump, black. **Size** 10–11 cm. **Juv.** Duller; chest bars indistinct. **Voice** High-pitched, 'floating', nasal 'tiaah'. **Hab.** Varied; open forest, grassland, beside creeks.

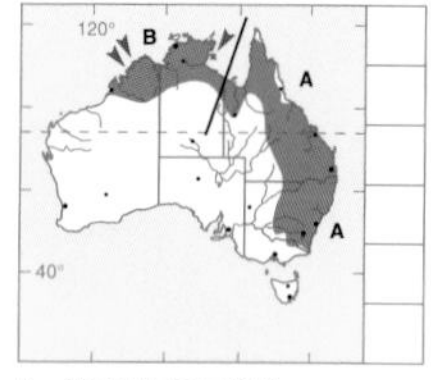

A = Race *bichenovii* **E**
B = Race *annulosa* **E**

Zebra Finch *Taeniopygia guttata* **C–UC** ⁂

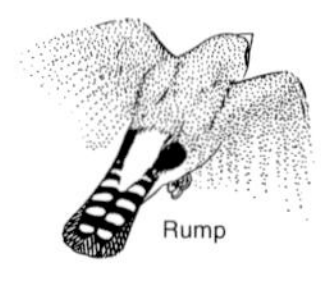

White rump and zebra-barred tail coverts conspicuous in flight. Wax-red bill; black and white tear stripes before and below eye. Light rufous ear patch. Mid-grey to brownish above. Fine black and white barring on throat; black chest bar. Flanks light chestnut, spotted white. White abdomen. **F** Buff abdomen. **Size** 10 cm. **Juv.** As female, bill black. **Voice** Nasal twang 'tiaah'; soft rhythmic song. **Hab.** Most inland open country, farms. Often in mature introduced boxthorn bushes.

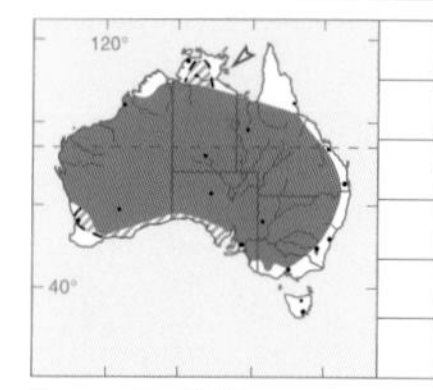

Race *castanotis* **E**

Long-tailed Finch *Poephila acuticauda* **C** ⁂–◎ E

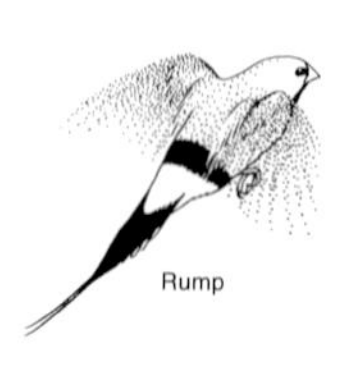

Jerks head on landing. Bill varies from waxy yellow in race *acuticauda* (A; WA) to orange or coral-red in race *hecki* (B; NT, Qld). Fawnish-tan with powder blue-grey head, black lores. Large black bib. Long, sharply tapered black tail; white rump; orange legs. **F** Smaller bib. **Size** 15–16.5 cm. **Juv.** Duller; bill black. **Voice** Soft 'tet', and loud, long pure whistle; soft musical song. **Habitat** Eucalypt and paperbark woodland near creeks.

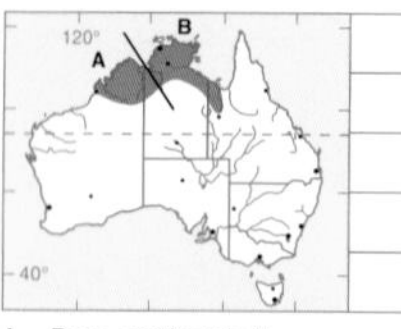

A = Race *acuticauda* **E**
B = Race *hecki* **E**

Masked Finch *Poephila personata* **C–MC** ?⁂–◎ E

Flicks tail frequently. Bill heavy, waxy-yellow. Black mask and chin. Slender body; dusky-cinnamon above, buff below. White rump; long black pointed tail. Race *leucotis* (B) Smaller; pale on cheeks and lower flanks. **F** (both races) Smaller mask; less black on chin; tail shorter. **Size** 12–13.5 cm. **Juv.** Duller; bill black. **Voice** Long nasal 'tiat'; soft 'tet'; soft mechanical song. **Hab.** Eucalypt and paperbark woodland.

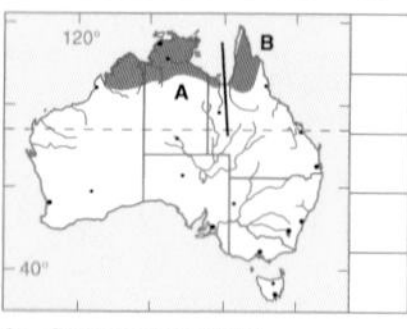

A = Race *personata* **E**
B = Race *leucotis* **E**

Black-throated Finch *Poephila cincta* **LMC–UC** ⁂–◎ E

Courtship display

Jerks head up and down on landing. Stocky pinkish-fawn; mid to pale blue-grey head; black bill, lores. White rump. Short black tail. Large black bib. Race *atropygialis* (B) Grey dorsal 'bloom'; pinkish ventral 'bloom'. Black rump. **F** Smaller; rounder bib. **Size** 10 cm. **Juv.** Duller. **Voice** Hoarse 'floating' whistle; soft 'tet'; very soft musical song. **Hab.** Open forest, woodland.

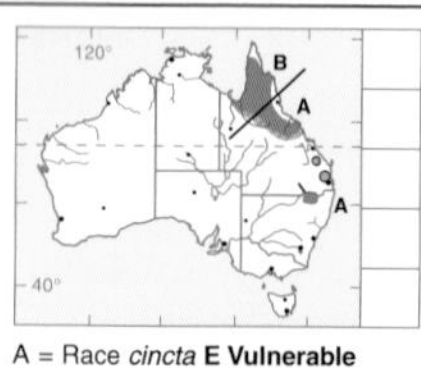

A = Race *cincta* **E Vulnerable**
B = Race *atropygialis* **E**

Plum-headed Finch *Neochmia modesta* **UC** ⁂ E

Courtship display

Bill, lores and tail black. Forehead, crown, chin, deep claret. White cheeks. Olive-brown above; spotted white on wings. White ventrum, strongly barred brown; white undertail coverts. **F** Thin white line above and to rear of eye. No claret chin spot. **Size** 11–12.5 cm. **Juv.** No claret head markings; no barring at fledging. **Voice** Long, drawn out 'ting'. **Hab.** Open woodland, grassland, tall crops bordering watercourses.

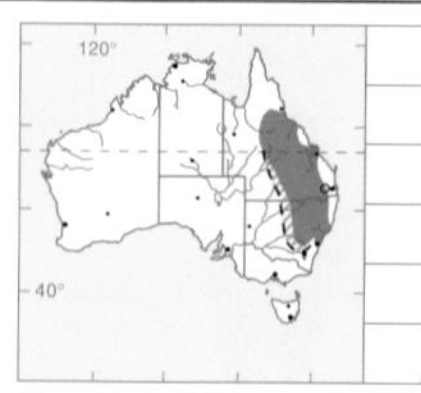

No races

-barred
ichenovii
Double-barred
Finch
Race annulosa
Zebra Finch Juv.
Race castanotis
Zebra Finch ♀
Race castanotis
Zebra Finch
♂
Long-tailed Finch
Race acuticauda
Masked Finch
Race personata
Long-tailed Finch
Race hecki
Masked Finch
Race leucotis
Long-tailed Finch
Juv.
Plum-headed
Finch
♀
Black-throated Finch
Race cincta
Plum-headed
Finch
♂
Black-throated Finch
Race atropygialis

Crimson Finch *Neochmia phaeton* **C–MC** ?◎

Slender 'upright' deep crimson finch, flicks long tapered tail. Crown, nape grey. Upperparts grey-brown washed crimson. Fine white flank spots. Belly, undertail coverts black. **F** Dark crimson face, throat. Underparts brownish-grey. Some white flank spots. Race *evangelinae* (B) Lighter crimson. White belly, undertail coverts. **Size** 12–14 cm. **Juv.** Duller; bill black. **Voice** Piercing 'che-che-che'. **Hab.** Watercourses with tall grass, pandanus; paperbark woodland, cane fields.

Race phaeton *(A) includes former race* iredalei.

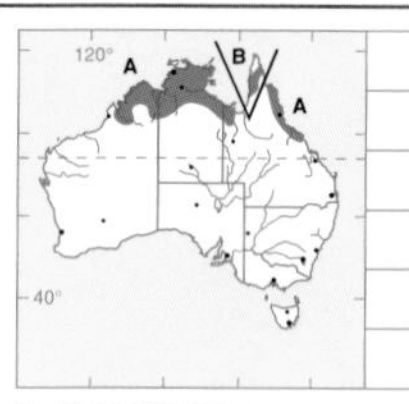

A = Race *phaeton* **E**
B = Race *evangelinae* **Vulnerable**

Red-browed Finch (Firetail) *Neochmia temporalis* **C** ◎ E

Small flocks, families. Olive-green, with scarlet 'eyebrow' from red bill through eye to hind crown. Crown leaden-grey. Rump scarlet. Tail dark grey to black. Grey-brown below. Race *minor* (B) Wider eyebrow, brighter dorsal colour, black tail. **F** Duller (both races). **Size** 11–12 cm. **Juv.** Duller, browner. Bill black; eyebrow barely visible. **Voice** High-pitched, piercing 'seee'. **Hab.** Varied; dense shrubs interspersed with grass; near water.

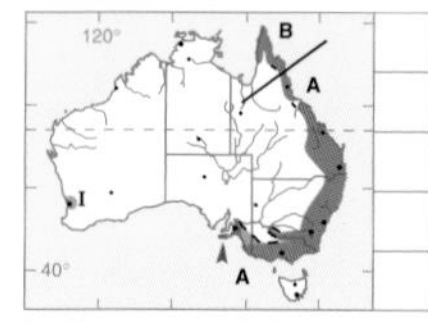

A = Race *temporalis* **E**
B = Race *minor* **E**

Star Finch *Neochmia ruficauda* **R–MC** ♧ E

Red face to chin. Dark olive above, yellow-olive below. Chest, rump, flanks, tail coarsely spotted white. Race *ruficauda* Sexes alike. Race *clarescens* (B) Greyer; scarlet extends to upper throat. Race *subclarescens* (C) Lighter olive; finely spotted. **F** Races B, C Red only on frons, cheeks, chin. **Size** 10–12 cm. **Juv.** Paler; bill black. **Voice** penetrating 'sseet'. **Hab.** Grasslands near water.

Declining in eastern Australia.

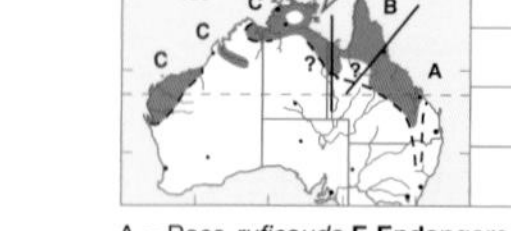

A = Race *ruficauda* **E Endangered**
B = Race *clarescens* **E Endangered**
C = Race *subclarescens* **E**

Red-eared Firetail *Stagonopleura oculata* **UC** ◎ E

Crimson rump, uppertail coverts, prominent in flight. Red bill. Black lores. Pale blue eye-ring. Crimson ear patch. Olive-brown back, throat, finely barred black. White oval spots on black below. **F** Paler bill, ear patch. **Size** 11.5–12 cm. **Juv.** Plainer; bill black. Head, face, brown only. Vague barring. **Voice** Piercing, 'floating', single note 'oooee'. **Hab.** Dense coastal forest, scrub.

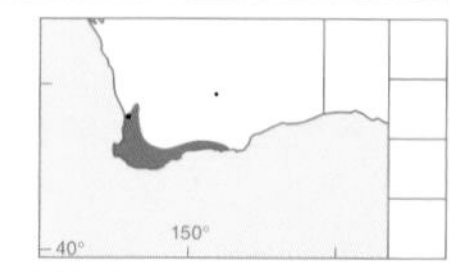

No races

Beautiful Firetail *Stagonopleura bella* **UC** ◎ E

Red bill; black mask. Pale blue eye-ring. Olive-brown above. Rump, uppertail coverts, crimson. Finely black-barred chest, flanks bolder; central belly black. **M br.** Belly, undertail, black. Race *interposita* (B) Lighter; belly not black. **Size** 11–12 cm. **Juv.** Bill black; vague barring. **Voice** Mournful 'floating' whistle. **Hab.** Dry forest, shrubby heath; she-oak, tea-tree thickets.

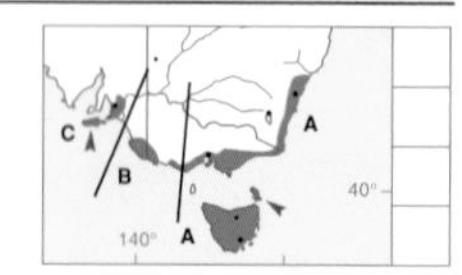

A = Race *bella* **E**
B = Race *interposita* **E**
C = Race *samueli* **E**

Diamond Firetail *Stagonopleura guttata* **MC** ♧–◎ E

Solid, upright, hops vigorously. Maroon bill; lores black. Grey above, white below. Crimson rump. Black chest band. Flanks black, spotted white. **F** Bill coral; lores brown. **Size** 12 cm. **Juv.** Black bill; dull markings; part red rump. **Voice** Double, 'sad' whistle falls, rises. **Hab.** Woodland, heaths.

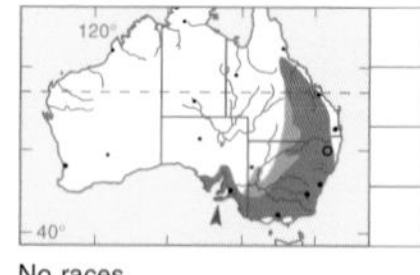

No races

Painted Finch (Firetail) *Emblema pictum* **MC** ?◎ E

Slim bird. Pale eye; long bill, blue base tapers to red tip. Scarlet face, chin, mid-belly, rump. Brown crown, back. Sides of black throat, flanks, boldly spotted white. **F** Face duller; red bill-tip, rump; faint reddish lores. Larger white spots on black from throat to flanks. **Size** 10–12 cm. **Juv.** Duller; red only on rump. **Voice** Loud, harsh 'trut'. **Hab.** Stony hills, gorges, spinifex plains.

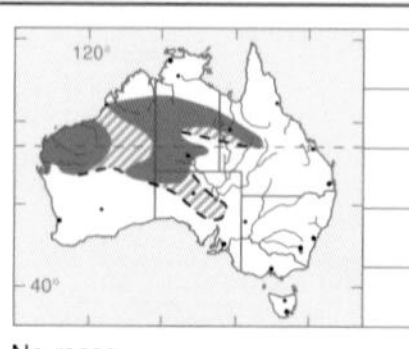

No races

Crimson Finch ♀
Race *phaeton*
Crimson Finch ♂
Race *phaeton*
Crimson Finch ♂
Race *evangelinae*
Red-browed Finch
Juv.
Red-browed Finch
Beautiful Firetail
Red-eared Firetail
Painted Finch ♀
Painted Finch ♂
Star Finch
Juv.
Star Finch ♂
Diamond Firetail
Juv.
Diamond Firetail

Pictorella Mannikin *Heteromunia pectoralis* **LC** E
Black-masked rosy-fawn finch. Thick blue-grey bill. Cinnamon crescent over eye and ear to side of neck. Fine white spots on wings. White breast mottled black above plain pinkish flanks. **F** Face brownish-black, more black on breast. **Size** 11 cm. **Juv.** Bill dark; plumage grey-brown. **Voice** Loud 'teet'. **Hab.** Tropical woodland; tussock grassland.

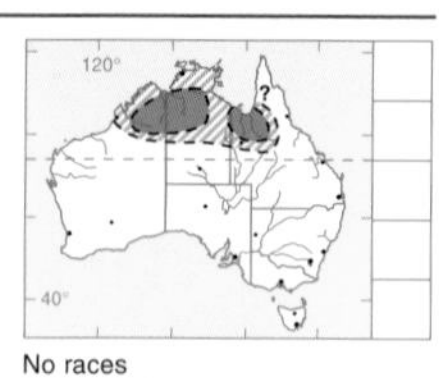

No races

Black-headed Mannikin *Lonchura malacca* Intro.
Local introduced population in SE of Aust. now considered extinct. The text for this species has therefore been removed from the *Field Guide*. Stray birds are aviary escapes.

Nutmeg Mannikin *Lonchura punctulata* **C–UC** Intro.
Flicks dull yellow tail constantly. Bill grey. Face, throat chocolate-brown. Upperparts plain grey-brown. Underparts dull white, scalloped dark brown. **Size** 11 cm. **Juv.** Brownish buff below. **Voice** 'ki-ki-te-te'. **Hab.** Reeds, rank grass, crops.

Tail flick

Also called 'Spice Finch'.

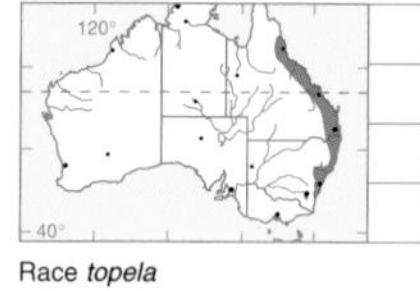

Race *topela*

Yellow-rumped Mannikin *Lonchura flaviprymna* **LC** E
Solid finch. Thick, greyish bill, typical of mannikins. Pale grey head. Back and wings cinnamon-brown; cream-buff underparts. Straw-brown rump and tail. Black undertail coverts. **Size** 10 cm. **Juv.** Dark bill. Olive brown above; buff-brown below, paler abdomen. **Voice** Bell-like 'teet'. **Hab.** Reeds and rank grasses, tall crops.

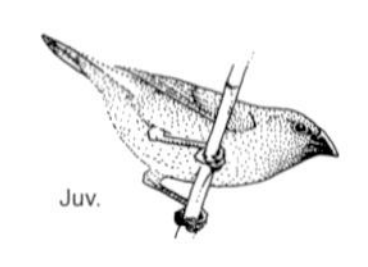
Juv.

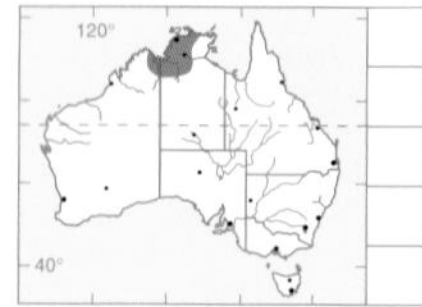

No races

Chestnut-breasted Mannikin *Lonchura castaneothorax* **C**
Solid brownish finch with black face and chin. Heavy silver-grey bill. Deep brown crown to upper mantle covered in fine grey chevrons. Warm-brown back; orange-brown rump and straw-yellow tail. Bright chestnut breast divided from white abdomen by narrow black band. Narrow short black bars edging flanks. **F** Similar, paler. **Size** 10 cm. **Juv.** Dark bill; olive-brown above, buff below. **Voice** Bell-like 'teet'. **Hab.** Reed beds, rank grass.

Ventral pattern

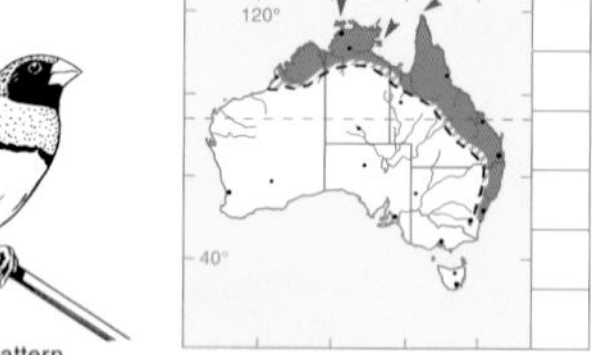

Race *castaneothorax*

Blue-faced Parrot-Finch *Erythrura trichroa* **UC** ?–◎
Small flocks show vivid green backs in flight. Distinctive grass-green finch with cobalt-blue face and throat. Black bill. Dull scarlet rump and uppertail coverts. **F** Duller, with less blue. **Size** 12 cm. **Juv.** Dull, with pale grey bill. **Voice** High-pitched 'tseet-tseet'. **Hab.** Edges of rainforest, mangroves.

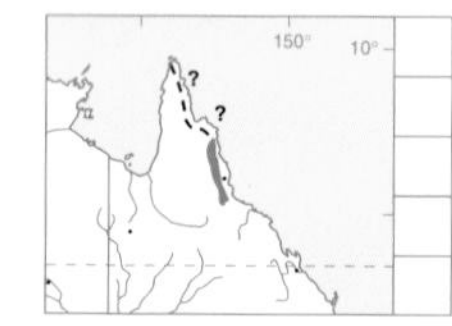

Race *macgillivrayi*

Gouldian Finch *Erythrura gouldiae* **UC** –◎ E Endangered
Elegant, colourful finch. Grass-green above, cobalt-blue rump, lilac chest, yellow abdomen. Ivory bill, red tip. Face black in most but crimson in some and yellow-ochre in rare individuals. Face colour variation not linked to regions. Black tail drawn into fine, thin wisps. **F** Duller; tinged olive. **Size** 14 cm. **Juv.** Upper bill blackish, lower bill pinkish-white, tipped red. Plumage ashy-grey and olive. **Voice** 'ssitt'. **Hab.** Open woodland and grassland.

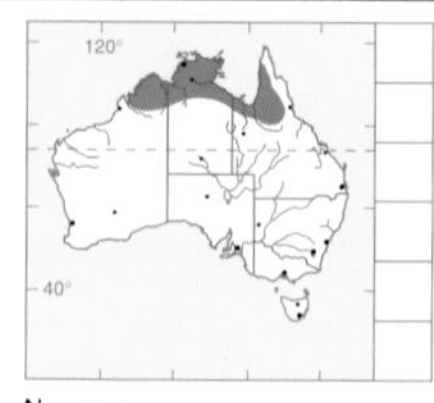

No races

Pale-headed Munia *Lonchura pallida* see **Vagrant Bird Bulletin** p. 300.

Pictorella Mannikin ♂
Black-headed Mannikin
Blue-faced Parrot-Finch ♂
Race macgillivrayi
Nutmeg Mannikin
Yellow-rumped Mannikin
Chestnut-breasted Mannikin
Juv.
Gouldian Finch ♂
Yellow-faced morph
Chestnut-breasted Mannikin
Race castaneothorax
Gouldian Finch ♂
Red-faced morph
Gouldian Finch ♂
Gouldian Finch
Juv.
Gouldian Finch ♀

Olive-backed (Yellow-bellied) Sunbird *Nectarinia jugularis* C ?◎

Small. Long, slender, curved black bill. Narrow yellow eyebrow, cheek stripe. Chin, upper breast bib (gorget) dark metallic blue sharply divided from deep yellow lower breast, undertail coverts. Upperparts bright citrine-olive. Wings darker. Tail black, tipped white. Legs, feet black. **F** Fine yellow eyebrow. Rich yellow chin, underparts. **Size** 10–12 cm. **Juv.** Like female. **M imm.** Blue bib develops along midline. **Voice** High-pitched 'dzit-dzit'; hissing whistle; trill. Also single loud call like caged Canary. **Hab.** Rainforest edges, mangroves, gardens. Nests around houses.

♂ bib development

The name 'Olive-backed Sunbird' has recently come into international use.

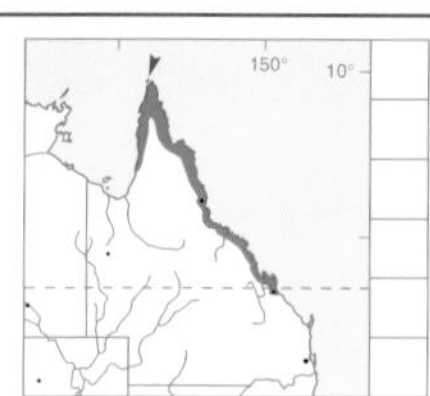

Race *frenata*

Mistletoebird *Dicaeum hirundinaceum* C–MC ?◎ ?E

'Swallow-like' in flight. Dark short bill. Glossy blue-black above. Throat, breast, undertail coverts bright scarlet. Underparts grey-white; wide central dull black streak. Marked sexual dimorphism. **F** Grey above; white below. Greyish belly streak. Undertail coverts pale scarlet. **Size** 10–11 cm. **Juv.** As female; bill, gape orange. Undertail paler. **Voice** Sharp, high double note; warble; soft mimicry. **Hab.** Varied; wherever mistletoe grows.

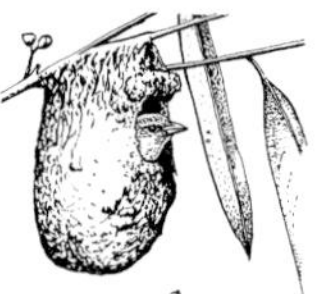

Incubating ♂

Race *hirundinaceum* **?E**

Pale (Pale-bellied) White-eye *Zosterops citrinellus* MC ◎

Bill, eye dark brown. White eye-ring. Pale grey-green above. Frons, chin, upper throat pale lemon. Breast, belly off-white. Pale buff flanks. Undertail coverts lemon. **Size** 12 cm. **Juv.** Yellowish. **Voice** Warbling song; strong contact calls. **Hab.** NE Qld islands.

All adult male white-eyes, and Silvereye, are slightly brighter-coloured than their females.

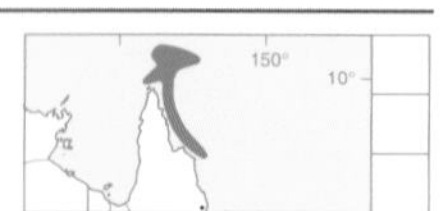

Race *albiventris* **E**
Recent record Saibai Is., Torres Strait.

Yellow White-eye *Zosterops luteus* C ♧–?◎ E

White eye-ring. Bill, eye dark brown. Rich citrine-yellow above. Forehead, underparts rich lemon. Bold yellow alula line on dark wing edges. Race *balstoni* (B) More olive above; dull yellow washed grey below. **Size** 10.5 cm. **Juv.** *luteus* Upperparts more olive; underparts dusky lemon. **Juv.** *balstoni* Greyer-green above. Chin, throat yellow. Buff-grey tinge to underparts. **Voice** Rapid, loud warbling. **Hab.** Mangroves, adjacent thickets.

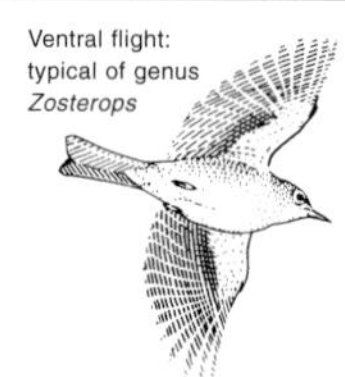

Ventral flight: typical of genus *Zosterops*

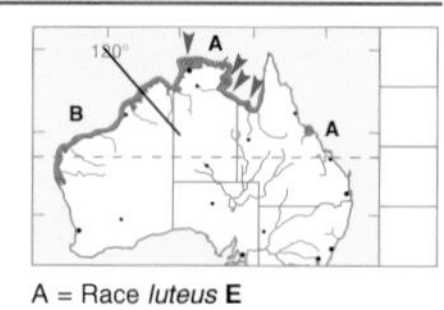

A = Race *luteus* **E**
B = Race *balstoni* **E**
Isolated colony of race *luteus* south of Ayr (Burdekin R. mouth), Qld.

Silvereye (Grey-backed Silvereye) *Zosterops lateralis* C ○–♧

Note Eight continental Aust. races; five (in SE, E Aust) are grey-backed. Some are highly migratory (*lateralis* (A) colonised NZ). In 'summer' all Silvereye races should be in their breeding (core) areas, enabling accurate identification. Identify from Weebill, gerygones.

Bill black, faint bluish base. Bold white eye-ring, dark lores. Head, wings bright olive green. Dark grey mantle. Pale grey throat, breast, grading to whitish under tail. Rich brown flanks, darker in males. Race *vegetus* (B) Small; richly coloured, paling south from Cape York. Yellow under tail, flanks washed grey (cf. Green-backed Honeyeater). Race *chlorocephalus* (C) 'Capricorn Silvereye' Large, sedentary island race; yellow-green head, pale grey to cream below. Race *cornwalli* (D) Smaller; throat bright yellow. White to lemon under tail. Race *westernensis* (E) Pale yellow throat, paler brown flanks. Race *pinarochrous* (F) Olive above blending into dull grey mantle; grey breast, deep brown flanks, grey under tail. Includes Kangaroo Is. birds (prior *halmaturina*) Lemon under tail. Race *chloronotus* (H) Small, olive-backed, only Aust. Silvereye with this feature. Greenish throat, under tail; dull grey breast, flanks. **Size** 12 cm. **Juv.** (all races) Paler than adults. **Voice** Repeated high, mournful 'tee-oow'; warbling song. **Hab.** All types; orchards, gardens.

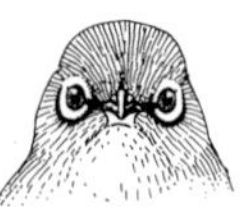

Facial pattern

Radical revision of Silvereye races has recently occurred.

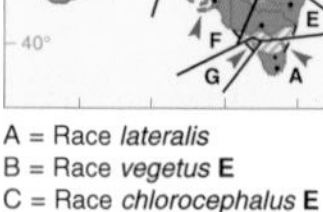

A = Race *lateralis*
B = Race *vegetus* **E**
C = Race *chlorocephalus* **E**
D = Race *cornwalli* **E**
E = Race *westernensis* **E**
F = Race *pinarochrous* **E**
G = Race *ochrochrous* **E**
H = Race *chloronotus* **E**

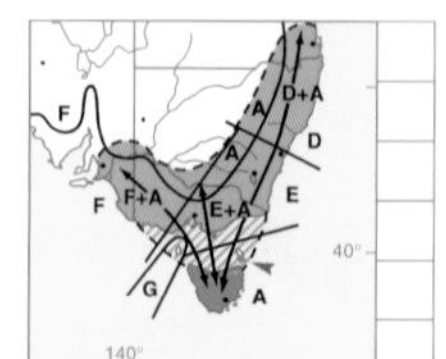

Non-br. winter migration of race *lateralis* (A)

Olive-backed ('Yellow-bellied') Sunbird ♀
Race frenata
Mistletoebird ♂
Race hirundinaceum
Olive-backed ('Yellow-bellied') Sunbird ♂
Race frenata
Mistletoebird ♀
Race hirundinaceum
Mistletoebird
Juv.
Yellow White-eye
Race balstoni
Pale White-eye
Race albiventris
Yellow White-eye
Race luteus
Silvereye
Race westernensis
Silvereye ('Capricorn Silvereye')
Race chlorocephalus
Silvereye
Race chloronotus
Silvereye
Race lateralis
Green-backed Honeyeater
Green-backed Gerygone
N.DAY.

Red-whiskered Bulbul *Pycnonotus jocosus* **C–LC** ?◎ Intro.

Black bill. Red tuft behind eye. Black head, pointed vertical crest. Black malar stripe, collar. White cheek, throat. Olive to grey-brown above; paler below. Undertail coverts red. Outer tail broad white tips. Size 20 cm. **Juv.** No red on face; pink undertail. **Voice** Melodic whistles, sharper than Blackbird. **Hab.** Urban.

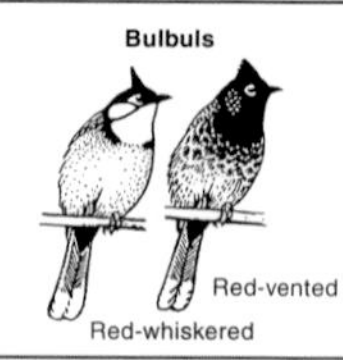

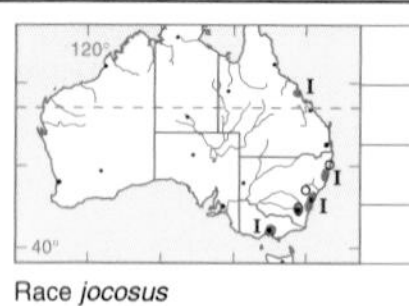

Race *jocosus*

Bassian (Ground) Thrush *Zoothera lunulata* **MC–LC** E

'Scaly thrush'. Runs with head low. Dark eye; whitish lores, eye-ring. Black face mark. Black scallops on rich olive-brown upperparts, whitish below. Pale wing bar in flight. Race *cuneata* (B) Rich copper-brown above, rufous wash below. **Size** 26–27 cm. **Juv.** More heavily mottled buff above. **Voice** Sweet falling, rising 'swee-oo-wee'. **Hab.** Usually on forest floor.

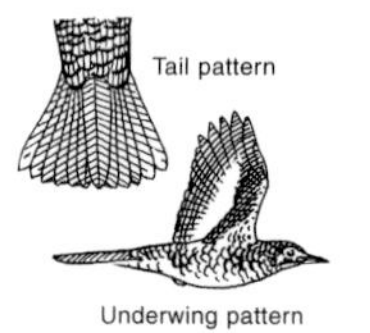

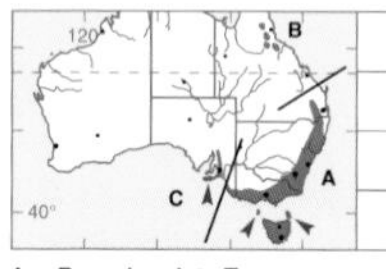

A = Race *lunulata* **E**
B = Race *cuneata* **E**
C = Race *halmaturina* **E**

Russet-tailed Thrush *Zoothera heinei* **LUC** ◎

Like Bassian. Smaller; paler face, finer black scallops. Richer copper-brown plumage, especially on rump, uppertail. **Size** 23–25 cm. **Juv.** Rufous plumage; heavier buff mottling above. **Voice** Strong 2-note 'theea thooa'. **Habitat** Coastal rainforest.

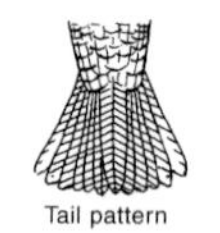
Tail pattern

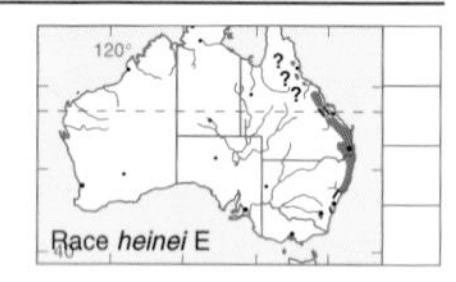
Race *heinei* E

Common (Eurasian) Blackbird *Turdus merula* **C–LC** ◎ Intro.

Black male sings from perch at dawn, dusk. Ground feeder; soft fruits raided. Bill, eye-ring, orange-yellow. **F** Dark grey-brown; blackish wings, tail. Pale chin. Faintly streaked breast. **Size** 25 cm. **Juv.** Dark bill. More rufous, strongly mottled. **Voice** Complex liquid song; 'pink pink' alarm; mimicry. **Hab.** Varied.

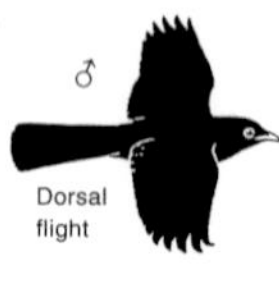

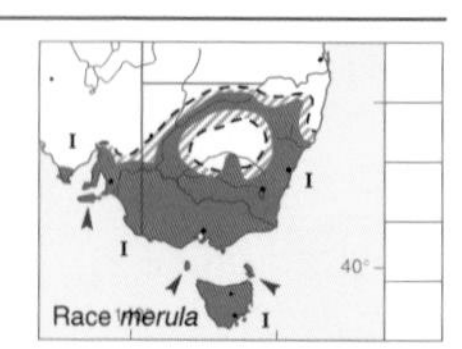

Race *merula*

Song Thrush *Turdus philomelos* **LUC** ◎ Intro.

Bi-coloured bill. Warm olive-brown above, creamy buff below. Pale eyebrow. Black spotted breast. No wing bar. Legs flesh. **Size** 23 cm. **Juv.** Mottled buff above. **Voice** Mimics. Superb, complex song. **Hab.** Urban; older gardens, parks.

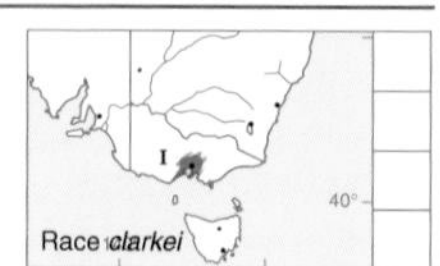

Race *clarkei*

Metallic Starling *Aplonis metallica* **C–LC**

Flight fast, lorikeet-like; flocks. Strong black bill. Red eye. Lustrous oil-green black body; long pointed tail. **Size** 21–24 cm. **Juv.** Brown eye, body. Whitish below, striated. **Imm.** Red eye. Duller black above; white below, fine black streaks. **Voice** Harsh chatters; wheezes. **Hab.** Tropical forests.

Nest colony

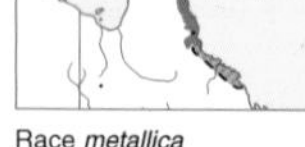

Race *metallica*

Common Starling *Sturnus vulgaris* **A–LC** ◎–?–Intro.

Massed evening flights. Flocks feed on ground. Roosts colonially. Glossy oil-green, black in most lights. Bill straw-yellow; bluish base. After annual moult, bill black, body very speckled. **F** Pinkish bill base. **Size** 20–22 cm. **Juv.** Mouse-brown, bill dark. **Voice** Twitters, whistles; mimicry. **Hab.** Urban, country.

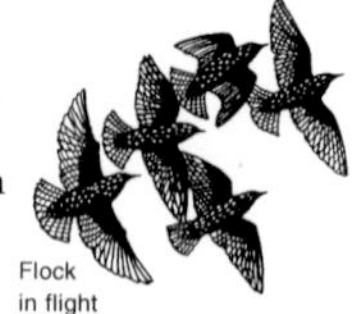

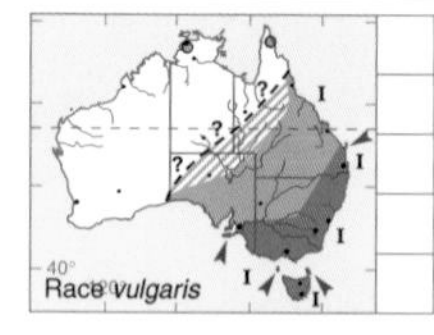

Race *vulgaris*

Common Myna *Acridotheres tristis* **LA–C** ◎ Intro.

White wing patches in flight. 'Arrogant' walk on ground. Roosts colonially. Yellow bill, facial skin, legs, feet. Black head, throat. Cocoa-brown body; white abdomen, undertail. **Size** 23–25 cm. **Juv.** Duller; brownish, less 'black-hooded'. Wing feathers edged rufous. Short tail. **Voice** Varied, noisy. **Hab.** Urban.

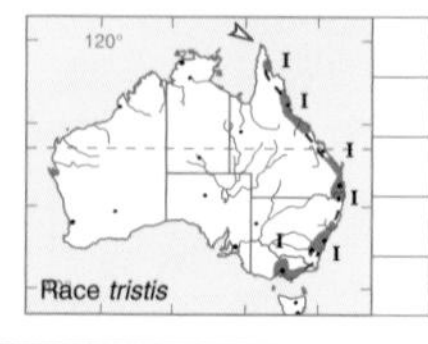

Race *tristis*

Narcissus Flycatcher *Ficedula narcissina*, **Blue-and-White Flycatcher** *Cyanoptila cyanomelaena*, **Isabelline Wheatear** *Oenanthe isabellina*, **Blue Rock Thrush** *Monticola solitarius* see **Vagrant Bird Bulletin** pp. 300, 301.

Red-whiskered Bulbul
Metallic Starling Imm.
Metallic Starling Ad.
Metallic Starling Juv.
Common Starling Ad. Breeding
Common Starling Juv.
Common Starling Ad. (Post moult) Non-breeding
Common Myna
Russet-tailed Thrush
Bassian Thrush
Song Thrush
Common Blackbird Juv.
Common Blackbird ♀
Common Blackbird ♂
N. DAY

Vagrant Bird Bulletin

An expert committee referees new bird records to establish their authenticity in relation to the Australian species list (only reports proved to be wrong are rejected). We strongly encourage you to report your observations of true rarities, or any unusual range extensions of more common species in Australia or its territories. Send all facts of the sighting, including date, precise locality, time of day, very detailed written field descriptions and comparisons, drawings, photographs, size relationships, measurements and also names of corroborating observers to: Birds Australia Rarities Committee, 415 Riversdale Rd, Hawthorn East, VIC 3123, Australia; ph. (03) 9882 2622; fax (03) 9882 2677.

If you find the body of a rare or unidentifiable bird, contact your nearest state museum, fauna authority or university zoology department for instructions, then send it to them.

As discussed in the **Introduction**, we have transferred a great deal of information concerning 'true vagrants' recorded in Australia from the **Field Information** pages to this expanded section. Not all of these have been re-illustrated yet, but will be as the opportunity occurs. In the meantime, refer to the original colour plates. Generally (there are some exceptions), birds from the islands listed under **Island Territories' Checklists** (pp. **332–41**) are not illustrated. We remind you that the sequence of Families in the **Vagrant Bird Bulletin** follows Christidis & Boles (1994) as closely as possible and is slightly different to the sequence in the main body of the field guide.

To facilitate the identification of the principal Australian species contained in the main text, the vagrants are best dealt with here. As the book progresses down the years, we shall continue to update and improve the Vagrant Bird Bulletin. Increasingly, birdwatchers in Australia are visiting out-of-the-way localities and finding more overseas vagrants and rarities. Additionally, Australian birds outside their 'normal' range are being found as atlassing proceeds across the continent.

The addition of so many new species to the Australian list has necessitated some further changes to the layout of our book. Reconstruction of an existing book is a complex exercise and not all changes can be made at once. Texts and illustrations have been thoroughly cross-referenced.

Discussion with a number of ornithologists since the Sixth Edition has convinced us to follow the path we are taking here. If records of a 'vagrant' become so regular that the species is recognised as a minor part of the Australian avifauna, to some extent dependent on Australia to maintain its population, it will be transferred to the main field guide. Some species remain in the main text because we anticipate, from recent sightings, that soon they will no longer be 'vagrants'. The House Swift is an example. We may eventually move the Spotted Whistling-Duck to the main text, as it has recently been found breeding in Queensland.

The reference given as *HANZAB* refers to *Handbook of Australian, New Zealand and Antarctic Birds*, Vols **1–6**, (1990–2003), OUP, Melbourne, and a page reference is given for each species, where possible. Family names are based on Sibley & Monroe (1990) and intended to help you locate rare birds in other reference texts. These Family names are at the top of each page.

Acknowledgment: We sincerely thank Mike Carter, Stephen Debus and Fred T.H. Smith for their participation in a major revision of this section of the book.

Gentoo Penguin *Pygoscelis papua* V

See also Plate, p. **27**. Distinctive. Bill black and orange. White triangular patches over eyes just meet on crown. Head, side of neck, lightly speckled white. Black above; white below. Long stiff tail. Underflipper tip has small black patch. Feet orange. **Size** 71–76 cm. **Hab.** Oceanic. Breeds subantarctic islands. Approx. six records in Tas. waters.

HANZAB (1990), Vol. **1**, Part A, *Ratites to Petrels*, p.147.

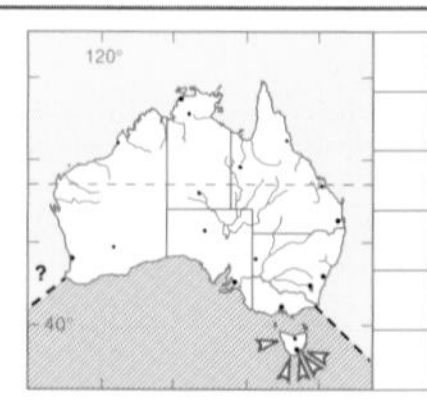

Race *papua*

Adelie Penguin *Pygoscelis adeliae* V

See also Plate, p. 27. Distinctive. White eye-ring diagnostic. Black above, including black hood; white below. Long tail. Underflipper tip has small dark mark. **Size** 60–79 cm. **Juv./Imm.** Chin whitish; black about eye. **Hab.** Oceanic. Breeds Antarctic islands, coastline. Two Aust. records: Portland, Vic. 1933; Tas. 25–31.12.1983.

HANZAB (1990), Vol. **1**, Part A, *Ratites to Petrels*, p.158.

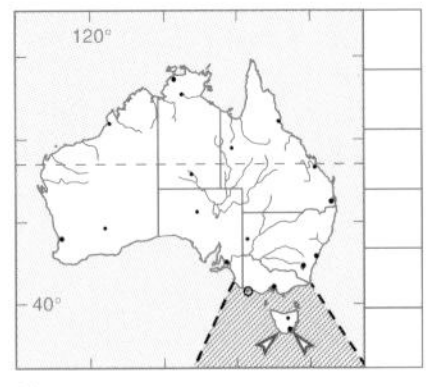

No races

Chinstrap Penguin *Pygoscelis antarctica* V

See also Plate, p. 27. Distinctive. White face; thin black line forming 'chinstrap' diagnostic. Bill, crown, nape, black. Black above; white below. Long tail. Underflipper tip has small blackish mark. **Size** 69–77 cm. **Hab.** Oceanic. Breeds Antarctic islands. Two Tas. records: one on 22.11.1968, died Jan. 1969; also Jan. 1980. One at Venus Bay, Vic., 24.11.1985.

HANZAB (1990), Vol. **1**, Part A, *Ratites to Petrels*, p.174.
Proeger, M. (1987), 'A Chinstrap Penguin *Pygoscelis antarctica* in Victoria', *Aust. Bird Watcher* **12**: 67.

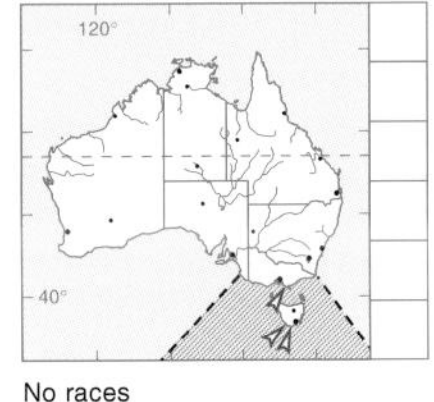

No races

Erect-crested Penguin *Eudyptes sclateri* V

See also Plate, p. 27. Shape, position, of front of upswept, silky-textured lateral eye-stripe/crest, dipping toward gape, diagnostic. White mandibular skin. Cheeks glossy black. Black above, white below. Underflipper tip has very broad black area. Legs, feet, flesh. **Size** 67 cm. **1st yr** Chin, throat, pale; eye-stripe white, short; fully defined. **Imm.** Chin, throat, greyish. **Hab.** Oceanic. Breeds on several subantarctic islands of New Zealand. Approx. nine Aust. records.

HANZAB (1990), Vol. **1**, Part A, *Ratites to Petrels*, p. 215.

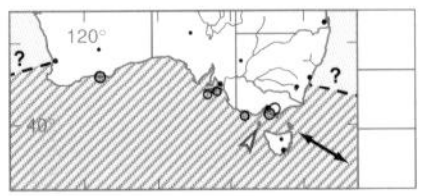

No races

Position: anterior tip of crest/stripe in adult

Snares Penguin *Eudyptes robustus* V

See also Plate, p. 27. Position of front end of pale yellow, silky textured, lateral eye-stripe/crest, diagnostic. White mandibular skin. Cheeks glossy black. Black above; white below. Long tail. Underflipper tip has large black patch. Legs, feet, flesh. **Size** 51–61 cm. **1st yr** Eye-stripe short; paler; fully defined. Chin, throat, greyish. **Hab.** Oceanic. Breeds on four islands of Snares Group, N.Z. Approx. seven Aust. records.

HANZAB (1990), Vol. **1**, Part A, *Ratites to Petrels*, p. 205.

Snares Penguin Ad.
Position: anterior tip of crest/stripe

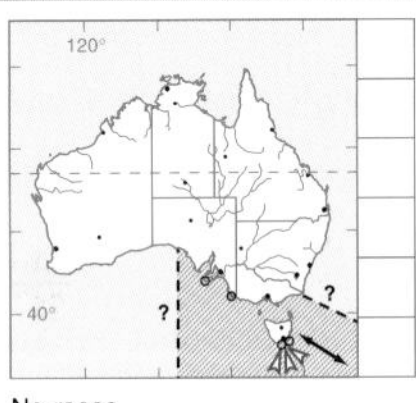

No races
Has close affinity with Fiordland Penguin.

Fiordland Penguin Ad.
Position: anterior tip of crest/stripe

Rockhopper Penguin Ad.
Position: anterior tip of crest/stripe

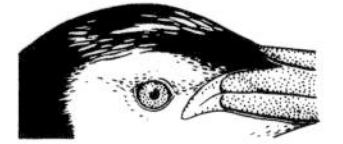

Royal (Macaroni) Penguin
Imm. 1–2 yrs: early development of frontal crest

Magellanic Penguin *Spheniscus magellanicus* V

See also Plate, p. 27. Bill black. Pink about eyebrow, eye-ring. Black cheeks, upperparts. White below. Two white bands of about equal width, each above similar blackish bands on throat and breast; combination is diagnostic. Underflipper whitish, edged grey. Legs, feet, black. **Size** 68–72 cm. **Hab.** Oceanic. Breeds southern coastline, islands, of South America; also Falkland Islands. One record, beach-washed, Phillip Is., Vic., 31.3.1976 (? ship-assisted).

Enticott, J. & Tipling, D. (1997), *Photographic Handbook of the Seabirds of the World*, New Holland, Frenchs Forest, pp. 22–3.
HANZAB (1990), Vol. **1**, Part A, *Ratites to Petrels*, p. 259.

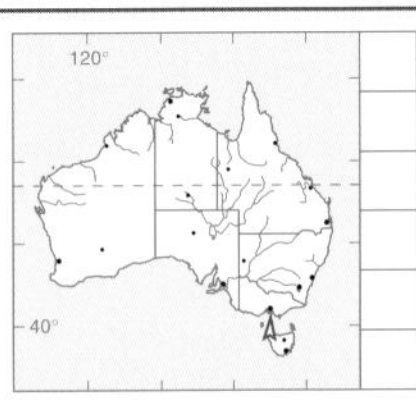

No races

South Georgian Diving-Petrel *Pelecanoides georgicus* V

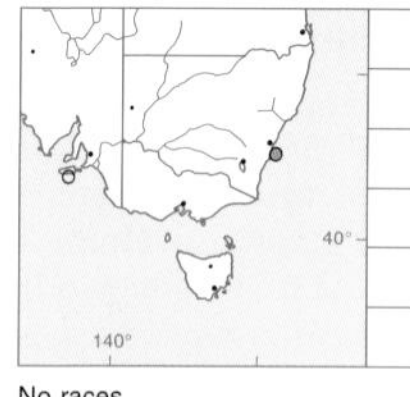

No races

See also Plate, p. **47**. Almost impossible to identify at sea. 'Auk-like' when swimming. Like Common Diving-Petrel, appearing black above, white below. Some individuals of each species have white scapular bands. Bill sides rounded (diagram). Underwing coverts white. **Size** 20–25 cm. **Hab.** Oceanic. Breeds on subantarctic islands: South Georgia, Prince Edwards, Crozets, Kerguelen, Heard and McDonald; a few on Codfish Is. in N.Z. seas. One beach-washed, Bellambi Beach, NSW, Dec. 1958.

HANZAB (1990), Vol. **1**, Part A, *Ratites to Petrels*, p. 719.

Antarctic Petrel *Thalassoica antarctica* V

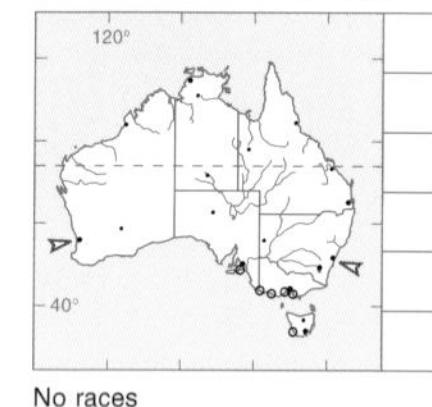

No races

See also Plate, p. **35**. Flight stiff-winged; quick flapping then gliding. Bill longer than Cape Petrel; brown on sides. Like Cape Petrel, but browner or greyer, with a broad unbroken white stripe through centre of upper wings; all-dark mantle. Rump, most of tail, white. Feet greyish-flesh. **Size** 40–45 cm. **Hab.** Oceans. Breeds in Antarctica. Mostly beach-washed birds in southern Aust.

HANZAB (1990), Vol. **1**, Part A, *Ratites to Petrels*, p. 384.

Juan Fernandez Petrel *Pterodroma externa* V

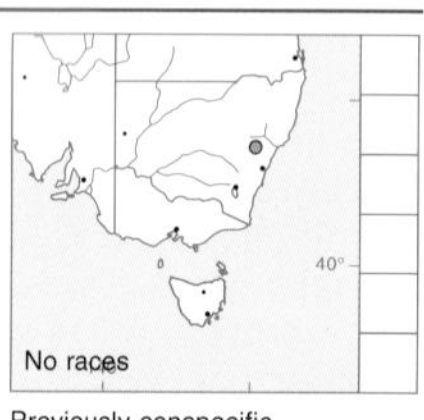

No races

Previously conspecific with White-necked Petrel.

Dark above; pale below. Grey-brown crown; shows little white in neck. Broad black 'M' across wings. Less black on leading edge of underwing than similar White-necked Petrel; tail darker. **Size** 43 cm. Breeds at Juan Fernandez island group off west coast of Chile. One captured at Cessnock, inland NSW.

HANZAB (1990), Vol. **1**, Part A, *Ratites to Petrels*, p. 468.

Barau's Petrel *Pterodroma baraui* V

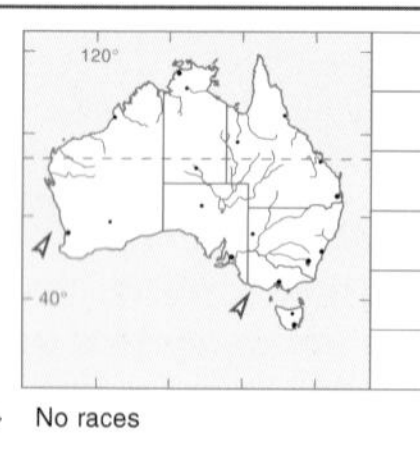

No races

Check similarly-sized White-necked and Juan Fernandez Petrels, also smaller Gould's and Black-winged Petrels. Grey above with broad black 'M' on wings. Diagonal black line in white underwing. **Size** 38 cm. Breeds Rodrigues, Reunion Islands, west Indian Ocean. Records west Vic. and off WA.

Carter, M., et al (1989), 'Barau's Petrel *Pterodroma baraui*, a new species for Australia', *Aust Bird Watcher* **13**: 39–43.

HANZAB (1990), Vol. **1**, Part A, *Ratites to Petrels*, p. 475.

Warham, J. (1990), *The Petrels, Their Ecology and Breeding Systems*, Academic Press, London & San Diego, pp. 131–40.

Bulwer's Petrel *Bulweria bulwerii* V–LMC

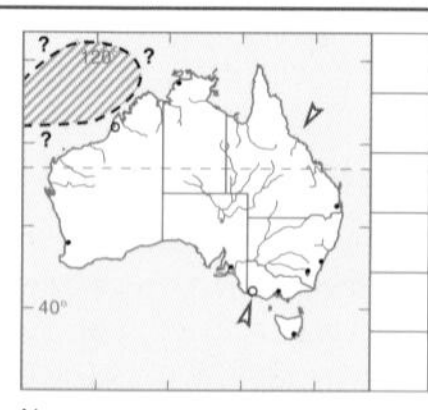

No races

Allied to *Pterodroma* petrels; identify from largest all-dark storm-petrels. Erratic, buoyant flight, low to sea. Very small, 'prion-sized', but body plumage dark sooty-brown. Bill black; large nail at tip. Tail long, wedge-shaped. Feet may be bicoloured grey to pink. Sexes alike. **Size** 26–28 cm. **Hab.** Tropical, subtropical seas of all oceans. Breeds islands of north-west, central, Pacific Ocean, also north-east Atlantic. Three confirmed Aust. records. More common than previously known: recent numerous sightings off northern WA. Now considered a regular migrant in the pelagic zone.

HANZAB (1990), Vol. **1**, Part A, *Ratites to Petrels*, p. 554.

Schulz, M. (1992), 'A beach-washed specimen of Bulwer's Petrel *Bulweria bulwerii* in Victoria', *Aust. Bird Watcher* **14**: 204–5.

Jouanin's Petrel *Bulweria fallax* **V–R**

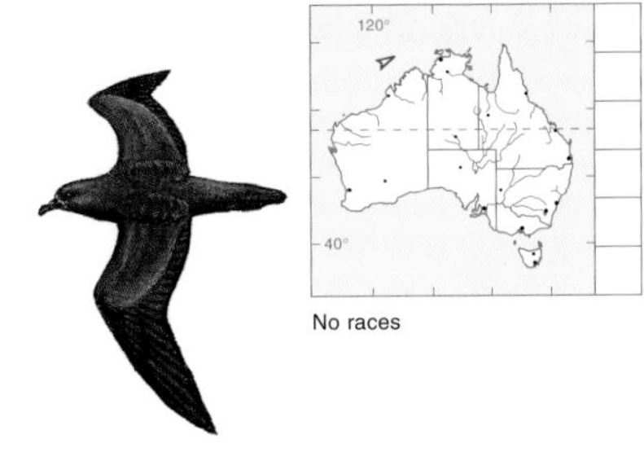

No races

Check Bulwer's Petrel, Wedge-tailed Shearwater. Looks all dark at sea; flies low; rarely near ships. Larger than Bulwer's. Bill black, 'angled down' in flight. Blackish-brown above and below. Faint covert bar as wing feathers wear. Tail broader than Bulwer's. **Size** 31 cm. **Hab.** Pelagic; a little known species. Breeds in Arabian Sea; recorded in southern Red Sea, Gulf of Aden. Disperses southward, eastward, into northern Indian Ocean, travelling to the south of India, Sri Lanka, towards Sumatra. Probably regular off northern WA. Only one Aust record, south-west of Ashmore Reef, 15.10.2000.

Enticott, J. & Tipling, D. (1997), *Photographic Handbook of the Seabirds of the World*, New Holland, Sydney, pp. 72–3.
Taleb, N.M.A. (2002), 'The discovery of a breeding colony of Jouanin's Petrel *Bulweria fallax* on Socotra, Yemen', *Sandgrouse* **24**: 105–8.

Fulmar Prion *Pachyptila crassirostris* **V**

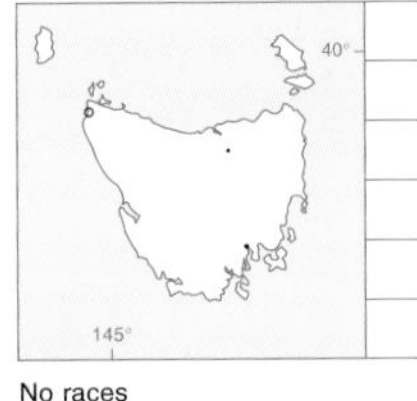

No races

See also Plate, p. **39**. Slightly larger, normally indistinguishable at sea from Fairy Prion, flanks tend greyer. Bill short; thicker, nail large. Eyebrow faint. Bold black 'M' on wings. Tail band twice as broad as Antarctic Prion. Undertail broadly tipped black; central grey smudge. **Size** 28 cm. **Hab.** Oceans, coastal islands. Breeds Heard Island, some N.Z. subantarctic islands. One Aust. record: beach-washed, north-west Tas., Sept. 1996.

HANZAB (1990), Vol. **1**, Part A, *Ratites to Petrels*, p. 550.

Pink-footed Shearwater *Puffinus creatopus* **V**

No races

Identify from Streaked Shearwater, light morph Wedge-tailed Shearwater, by heavier build, shorter tail. Dark-tipped pink bill. Dark grey-brown above, scaled paler. Head, throat, flanks, underwing, undertail coverts, variably grey-brown. Mainly white below. Legs, feet, pink. **Size** 48 cm. **Hab.** Coastal, oceanic. Breeds Juan Fernandez Is. group, off Chile, E. Pacific. One Aust. record 21 km off Wollongong, NSW, March 1986.

HANZAB (1990), Vol. **1**, Part A, *Ratites to Petrels*, p. 616.

Great Shearwater *Puffinus gravis* **V**

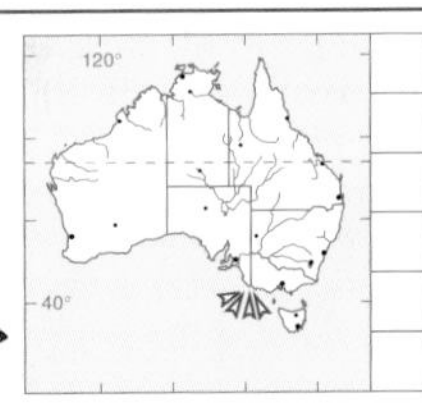

No races

Check White-necked Petrel. Slender dark bill. Distinctive dark cap. White collar, uppertail coverts. Upperparts dark grey-brown, scaled paler. Underwings white; dark streaks forming diagonals on inner wing; broad black trailing edge. White below; belly smudged sooty. **Size** 43–51 cm. **Hab.** Oceans. Breeds Tristan da Cunha group, Gough Is., Falkland Is., south Atlantic. Recorded twice off Robe, SA, Jan–Feb. 1989; off Portland, Vic., 11.4.1999; off Port Fairy, Vic. April 2002.

HANZAB (1990), Vol. **1**, Part A, *Ratites to Petrels*, p. 619.

Manx Shearwater *Puffinus puffinus* **V**

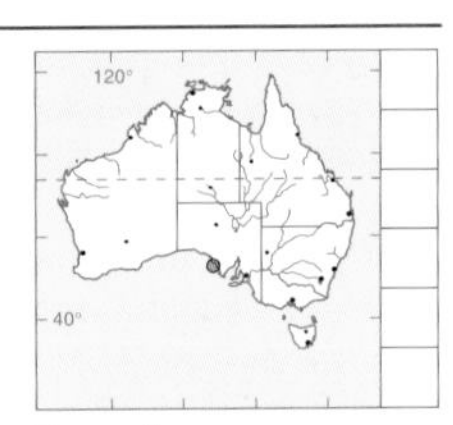

Race *puffinus*

See also Plate, p. **45**. Flies like Short-tailed Shearwater but less 'dashing'. Nominate race smaller than Short-tailed Shearwater. Bill larger, more robust than Fluttering, Hutton's, Shearwaters. Upperparts black. Underparts, throat to tail, white. Underwing, axillaries, white; primaries black. Thin black leading edge. Legs, feet, light pink; outer edge blackish. **Size** 30–38 cm. **Hab.** Coastal, oceanic. Breeds on islands in North Atlantic, Mediterranean, north-east Pacific Ocean. One Aust. record, beach-washed at Venus Bay, SA, 1961.

HANZAB (1990), Vol. **1**, Part A, *Ratites to Petrels*, p. 646.

Audubon's Shearwater *Puffinus lherminieri* **V**

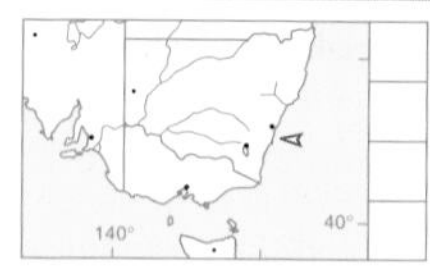

Races *dichrous, gunax* and *heinrothi* are possible vagrants

See also Plate, p. **45**. Glides close to water. Like Fluttering Shearwater, with shorter bill, longer tail. Underwing as Little Shearwater, but broader black margins. Undertail coverts black. **Size** 27–33 cm. **Hab.** Oceanic, coastal. Breeds islands of tropical Atlantic, Indian, Pacific, Oceans. One Aust. record, 20 km off Wollongong, NSW, 28.2.1987.

HANZAB (1990), Vol. **1**, Part A, *Ratites to Petrels*, p. 662.

Laysan Albatross *Diomedea immutabilis* **V**

No races

Bill pink, black tip. Black lores through eye, grade to grey smudge on face. Head, neck, underparts, white. Blackish upperparts, upperwings. Rump white. Tail dark grey. White underwings, broadly edged black; coverts largely marked black (variable). **Size** 80 cm; wingspan 195–203 cm. **Hab.** Tropical, northern Pacific Ocean; pelagic. Breeds northern Hawaiian islands. One at Norfolk Is., visited over 2–3 years; was banded.

Enticott, J. & Tipling, D. (1997), *Photographic Handbook of the Seabirds of the World*, New Holland, Sydney, pp. 30–1.

Leach's Storm-Petrel *Oceanodroma leucorhoa* **V**

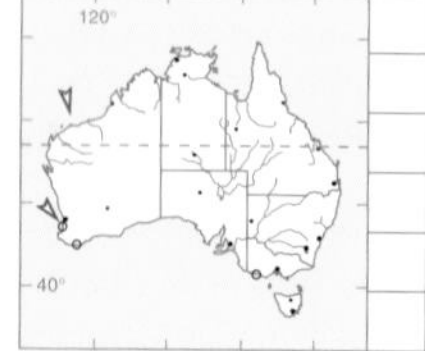

Race *leucorhoa*

See also Plate, p. **47**. Bill black. Brownish-black body. Rump usually white (can be black) with complete or broken black central line. Paler grey-brown greater upperwing coverts. Deeply forked tail. **Size** 19–22 cm. **Hab.** Oceanic. Breeds north Atlantic, north Pacific Oceans. Four Aust. records: one beach-washed, Tower Hill, Vic., 1965; three from WA 1978–84. Several recent unconfirmed sightings off northern WA.

HANZAB (1990), Vol. **1**, Part A, *Ratites to Petrels*, p. 713.

Swinhoe's Storm-Petrel *Oceanodroma mornorhis* **V**

No races

Medium-sized, dark storm-petrel; smaller than Matsudaira's, Tristram's. Fast flight, swoops. Rarely near ships. Bill black. Almost uniform dark grey-brown above and below, slightly paler covert bar. Wings black; white primary bases rarely show at sea. Dark tail has shallow fork. Legs, feet, blackish. **Size** 20 cm. **Hab.** Oceanic. Breeds islands of north Pacific, incl. Japan, Taiwan. Post-breeding dispersal south-west in Pacific, across to north Indian Ocean, Arabian Sea, NE African coast. Recorded off Broome, WA, 1.11.1999, and unconfirmed reports from same area 2000, 2001.

Enticott, J. & Tipling, D. (1997), *Photographic Handbook of the Seabirds of the World*, New Holland, Sydney, pp. 100–1.

Tristram's Storm-Petrel *Oceanodroma tristrami* **V**

No races

Check Bulwer's Petrel, Matsudaira's Storm-Petrel, other dark storm-petrels. Banking, side-slipping, gliding flight over sea; appears 'long-winged'. Large mid-dark brown storm-petrel. Bill, legs, feet, black. Head dark sooty brown, contrasting paler body. Pale tan carpal bars. Rump pale; tail deeply forked. **Size** Approx. 26–28 cm. **Hab.** Oceanic. Breeds Japan, Laysan, Midway Islands, central Pacific Ocean. Only Aust. record 9.10.2000, off Sydney, NSW.

Palliser, T. (2002), 'Tristram's Storm-Petrel … off Sydney, NSW: A New Bird for Australia', *Aust. Bird Watcher* **19**: 215–18.

Abbott's Booby *Papasula abbotti* **V** Endangered

Check Masked Booby. Distinctive shape; narrow wings, slender body. Whitish bill, black tip. Grey-black lores. White body. Black scapulars; scattered white feathers along central upper wing. White underwing, black tip, narrow trailing edge. Lower rump, upper tail spotted/striated black. Tail black. Legs blue; feet proximal half blue, distal half black. **F** Larger. Pinkish bill, black-tip. Lores as male. **Size** 79 cm approx. **Juv./Imm.** As adult male; bill slightly greyer. Breeds Christmas Is.; feeds in Javan Trench, Indian Ocean; does not disperse widely. One claimed (Darwin, NT). First confirmed Aust. record at Eco Beach, Broome, WA, 16.12.1999.

No races
Previously in genus *Sula*.

HANZAB (1990), Vol. **1**, Part B, *Pelican to Ducks*, p. 791.
Hassell, C.J. & Boyle, A.N. (2000), 'Abbott's Booby: First Record for Mainland Australia', *Aust. Bird Watcher* **18**: 255–8.

Christmas Frigatebird *Fregata andrewsi* **V** Vulnerable

Black. Red throat pouch. White abdominal patch. Brown wing panels. **F** Like Lesser Frigatebird female, but more white on breast, belly, underwing. Conspicuous black 'spur' markings on upper breast. **Size** 90–100 cm. **Juv.** Difficult to separate from other juv. frigatebirds. **Hab.** Tropical north-west seas. Breeds Christmas Is., Indian Ocean. One at Darwin, NT, 21–27.1.1974 and one at Port Hedland, WA, Jan. 1990.

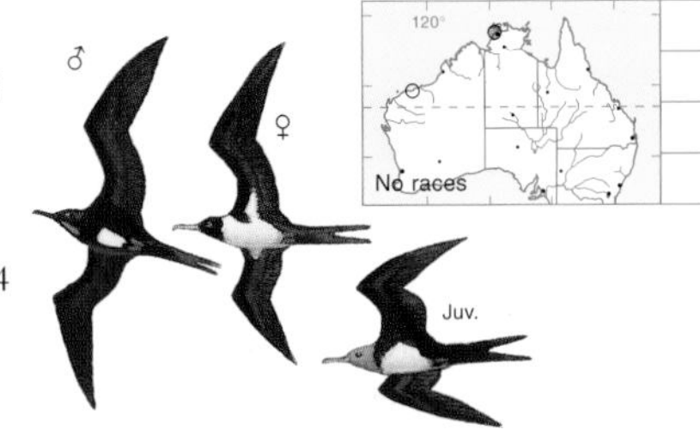

HANZAB (1990), Vol. **1**, Part B, *Pelican to Ducks*, p. 928.

Little Grebe *Tachybaptus ruficollis* **V**

Resembles Australasian Grebe. Bill black; lower mandible 'chisel-shaped'. Very prominent cream patch of bare skin at gape. Eye red. Throat, cheeks, red-rufous. Front, sides of neck, wholly red-rufous. Marked 'peak' or small crest at rear of crown. No wing bar in flight. Flanks blackish. Small white patch shows in undertail region when swimming. **Size** 25–27 cm. **Hab.** As for Australasian Grebe. Breeds across Eurasia, Africa, south-east Asia to Solomon Islands. One confirmed record, adult at Darwin, NT, 26.9–5.10.1999.

Also called Eurasian Little Grebe.

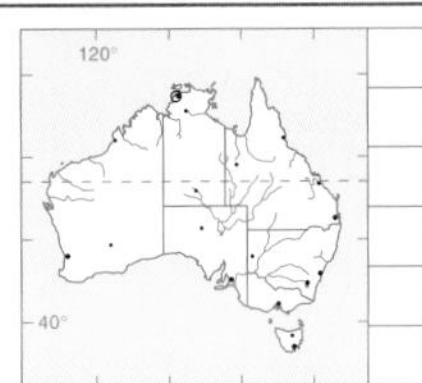

Race in Aust. not identified (10 races worldwide).

Carter, M. (1999), 'Little Grebe *Tachybaptus ruficollis*', *Bird Observer* No. **803**: 20–1.
Konter, A. (2001), *Grebes of Our World*, Lynx Edicions, Barcelona, Spain, pp. 49–61.

Spotted Whistling-Duck *Dendrocygna guttata* **V–? LMC**

Associates with, identify from, Wandering Whistling-Duck. Groups, flocks. White-spotted flanks diagnostic. Deeply dished dark grey bill has pink edge, base. Crown grey-brown. Face, eyebrow, neck to upper breast, pale grey. Dorsum dark brown, feathers edged cream to buff. Rufous sides to breast. Many variable black-bordered white flank spots to undertail coverts. **Size** 43–50 cm. **Juv.** Dull brown body (not rufous brown). Dark eyeline; pale supercilium. Little or no spotting on flanks. 'Streaks' from black-edged flank feathers, resemble Wandering Whistling-Duck. **Voice** 'wee-ow'; also longer 'wee-a-whu-whu'. **Hab.** Wetlands. Breeds Philippines, Sulawesi, to New Guinea. First record Weipa, Qld, 25.12.1995 but now regular. Adults with fledglings, 8.12.2000, at Weipa, suggests breeding locally. Flocks with young reported, photographed, in Iron Range, Portland Roads area; also Boigu Is.

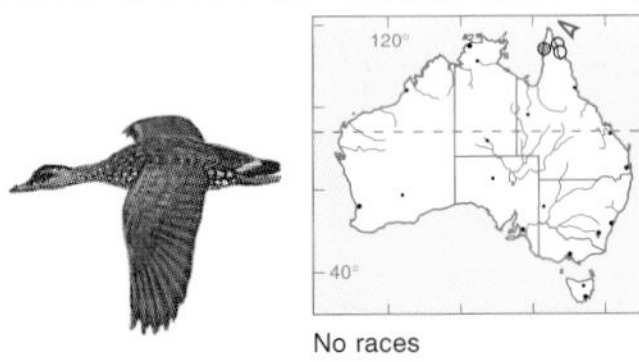

No races

Beruldsen, G. (2002), 'Spotted Whistling-Duck *Dendrocygna guttata* – Probable Breeding in Australia', *Aust. Bird Watcher* **19**: 143–6.
Ogilvie, M. & Young, S. (1998), *Photographic Handbook of the Waterfowl of the World*, New Holland, Cape Town, South Africa, pp. 14–15.

Northern Pintail *Anas acuta* V–R

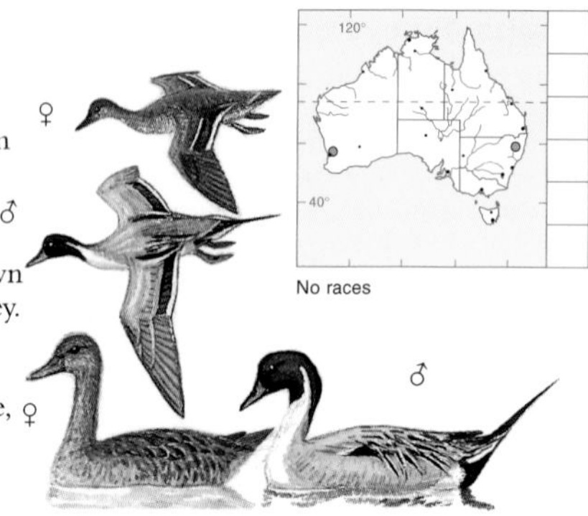

Distinctive, slender-necked. Bill pale grey, marked black. Head dark brown. Neck black, white stripe to breast. Upperparts, flanks, pale grey-brown. Scapulars striped black. Green speculum in wing. Underparts white. Undertail black. Legs grey. **M eclipse** As female; identify from female Australasian Shoveler, also Mallard and other feral ducks. **F** Bill grey. Head, neck, brown, fine pale buff streaks. Upperparts, underparts, brown with buff and white edges, chevrons. Speculum brown. Legs grey. **Size** 50–65 cm. **Hab.** Coastal wetlands, farmland, reservoirs. Breeds north Eurasia, North America; migrates to Africa, China, Central America. Two records: One ad. male, br. plumage, Chandala Swamp, 50 km NE of Perth, WA, July 1985. One at Grafton, NSW, 3.8.2000.

HANZAB (1990), Vol. **1**, Part B, *Pelican to Ducks*, p. 1301.

Northern Shoveler *Anas clypeata* V

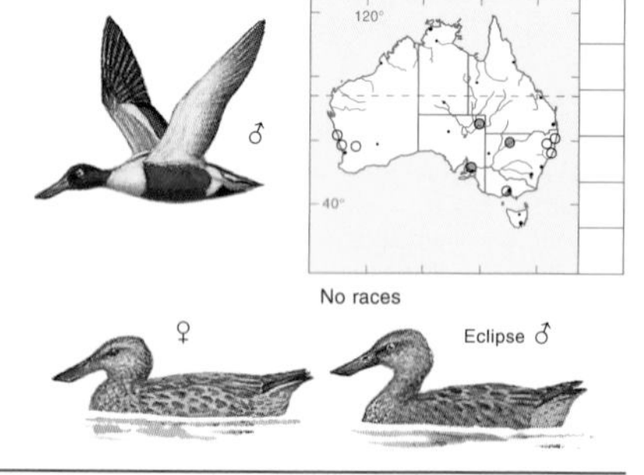

See also Plate, p. **63**. Differs from Australasian Shoveler male by uniform green head, pure white breast, sides of back. **M eclipse** Resembles dark female, but uniformly redder brown (green head, white markings absent). Hard to identify from eclipse male Australasian Shoveler. **F** Bill flanges orange; check Mallard, Mallard-cross. White tail edges visible in flight and on water; female Australasian Shoveler has grey bill, brown tail edges. **Size** 45–55 cm. **Hab.** Mainly vegetated freshwater swamps. Breeds Palearctic, Nearctic, wintering southward. Records from all states except NT.

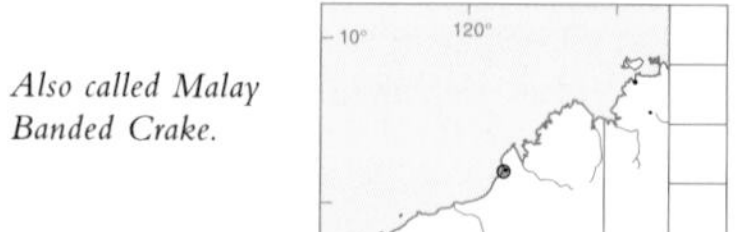

HANZAB (1990), Vol. **1**, Part B, *Pelican to Ducks*, p. 1348.

Red-legged Crake *Rallina fasciata* V

Also called Malay Banded Crake.

No races

See also Plate, p. **69**. Smaller than Buff-banded Rail, Red-necked Crake, which it resembles. Bill reddish or brown; base red. Head, neck, breast, rich rufous. Upperparts olive and chestnut; white wing barring. Mid-chest to vent black, barred white. Legs red. **Size** 23–25 cm. **Juv.** Brown (not chestnut); duller white barrings. Legs brownish. **Voice** Variety of pumping, screaming calls; scolding. Tends to call at dawn, dusk, night. **Hab.** Wet areas in open country, crops, grassland, scrub, forest. Breeds north-east India, south Burma, Malaysia, to Philippines, Borneo, Indonesian archipelago. One Aust. record (specimen), Broome, WA, 16.7.1958.

HANZAB, (1993), Vol. **2**, *Raptors to Lapwings*, p. 493.
Taylor, B. (1998), *A Guide to the Rails, Crakes, Gallinules and Coots of the World*, Yale Univ. Press, New Haven & London, pp. 201–3.

Yellow Bittern *Ixobrychus sinensis* V

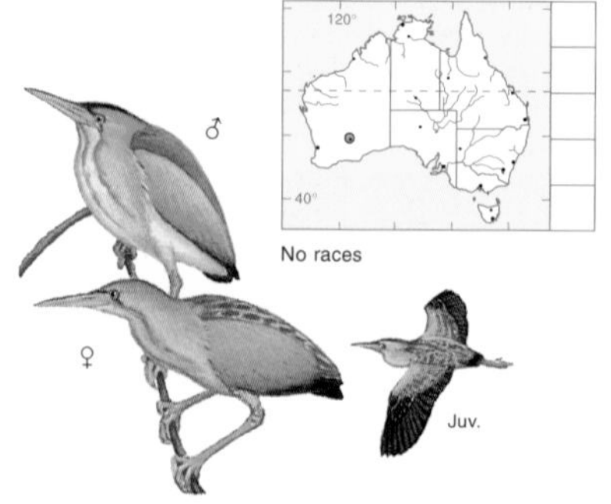

See also Plate, p. **79**. Like male Little Bittern but no black on back. Bill longer, more slender, than Little. Differs from female Little by black wings, less obvious wing patches. **Juv.** Heavily streaked. **Size** 30–40 cm. **Hab.** As for Little Bittern. Breeds India, south-east to north-east Asia, Japan, Indonesia; has colonised some islands in Indian, SW Pacific Oceans. One certain Aust. record: Imm. at Kalgoorlie, WA, 23.1.1967, after a cyclone. Earlier Aust. records discounted.

HANZAB (1990), Vol. **1**, Part B, *Pelican to Ducks*, p. 1047.

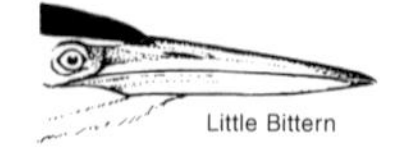

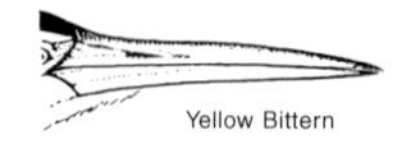

Eurasian (European) Curlew *Numenius arquata* **V ?**

Race *orientalis* more likely in Aust.

See also Plate, p. **85**. Like Eastern Curlew but shorter, finer bill (also check Whimbrel). No eyebrow or crown stripe. White lower back, rump. Tail barred. **Size** 50–60 cm. **Voice** Varies from Eastern Curlew by sharper, 'fluting' calls. Contact call single, rising 'coorloo'. **Hab.** Coastal, estuarine. Breeds Eurasia, incl. Britain; migrates far southward, spreading widely, often erratically. Several reports; no confirmed Aust. records.

HANZAB (1996), Vol. **3**, *Snipe to Pigeons*, p. 116.

Upland Sandpiper *Bartramia longicauda* **V**

No races

See also Plate, p. **85**. Upright stance; 'plover-like'. Long tail, neck. Buffy coloured, heavy dark streaks. Bill short, tip slightly down-curved; yellowish base. Large brown eye; white eye-ring. Small head; dark crown. Rump, tail, dark-centred, edged white. Underwing heavily barred dark brown. Legs, feet yellowish. **Size** 28–32 cm. **Voice** In flight 'quip-ip-ip-ip', last note lower. **Hab.** Coastal. Breeds across central North America. Migrates to eastern area of south central South America. One old record, Sydney, 1848.

Underwing pattern

HANZAB (1996), Vol. **3**, *Snipe to Pigeons*, p. 125.
Hayman, P., Marchant, J. & Prater, T. (1987), *Shorebirds: An identification guide to waders of the world*, Christopher Helm, London, p. 322.

Spotted Redshank *Tringa erythropus* **V**

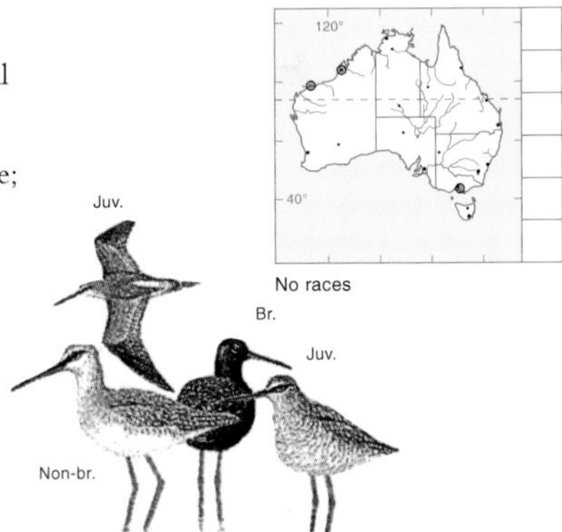

No races

Solitary or in groups. May swim. Check Common Redshank. Bill long, slender. Entirely black; back, upperwings, spotted white. Underwings white. **Non-br.** Lower bill base orange. Eyebrow white; black eye-line. Mantle, wing feathers edged, notched, white; no white trailing edge to wing. Dorsum greyish; lower rump speckled black. Tail dark-barred. White below; greyish breast; barring on flank, undertail coverts. Legs orange-red. **Size** 29–31 cm. **Juv.** Finely barred grey below. **Voice** Whistle in flight 'chew-it'. **Hab.** Marshes, mudflats. Breeds Eurasian Palaearctic: Sweden to Kamchatka Penin. Winters central Africa. Confirmed Port Hedland, WA, 26.10.1986; one in winter plumage Carrum Downs, Vic. Mar.–Sept. 1992; one near Broome, WA, 11.6.1993.

HANZAB (1996), Vol. **3**, *Snipe to Pigeons*, p. 128.

Short-billed Dowitcher *Limnodromus griseus* **V**

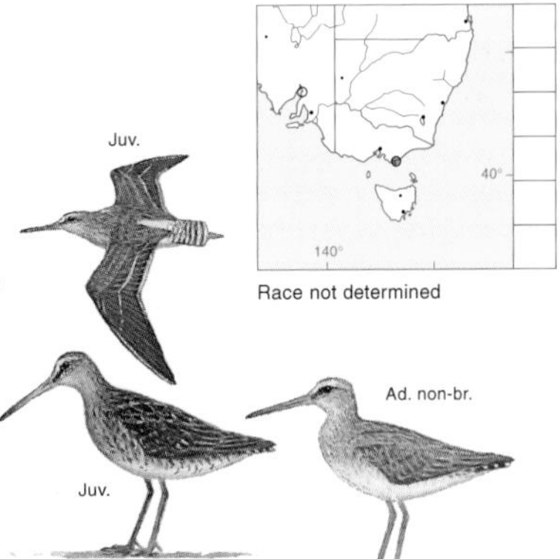

Race not determined

Accompanies other waders. Feeds in rapid 'sewing-machine' manner. In flight, faint bars in axilla; pale grey-white lower back, rump (black-barred and speckled when seen closely); narrow black tail bars. Toes project beyond tail. Check Asian, Long-billed, Dowitchers, Bar-tailed Godwit, knots. Bill snipe-like. White eyebrow. Dorsum boldly patterned black, white, buff. Throat, neck, breast, side of belly, flushed salmon-rufous. Central belly white. Pale underwing has thin pale bars. Undertail white or tinged rufous; lightly barred, spotted. Sexes alike; female larger. **Non-br.** Thin black eye-line below white eyebrow. Crown not striped. Dorsum greyish. Grey breast, streaked lower down. Pale belly. Legs grey-greenish. **Size** 25–29 cm. **Juv.** Richer coloured, reddish buff. Scapulars, tertials, barred. Legs paler. **Voice** Soft 'tu-tu-tu' in flight; allegedly like Ruddy Turnstone. **Hab.** Estuaries, muddy shorelines. Breeds across northern North America. Migrates to tropical central America. First record, an adult, non-br. plumage, Corner Inlet, Vic., June 1995, originally thought to be a Long-billed Dowitcher *L. scolopaceus*. One at Price Saltfields, Gulf St Vincent, SA, 1.12.1999.

Hayman, P., Marchant, J. & Prater, T. (1987), *Shorebirds: An identification guide to waders of the world*, Christopher Helm, London, p. 360.

Green Sandpiper *Tringa ochropus* V

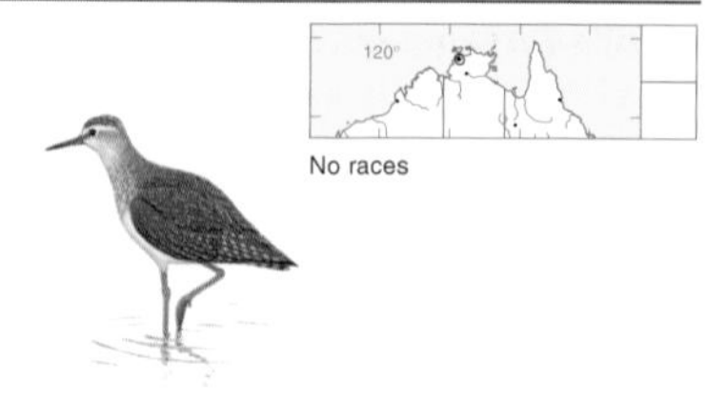

See also Plate, p. **85**. Distinguish from slightly smaller, longer-legged Wood Sandpiper (difficult). White supercilium joins eye-ring. Lores black. Crown, neck, streaked. Dark dorsum with extremely fine white spots. Brilliant white rump, upper tail coverts. Strongly striated throat, upper breast. White below; little flank streaking (Wood Sandpiper has more). **Non-br.** In flight, uniform blackish upperparts, no wing bar, contrast with white rump. Tail broadly barred black. Underwing blackish. **Size** 21–24 cm. **Hab.** Fresh water, esp. ditches, irrigation areas. Breeds across Palaearctic Eurasia. Migrates to tropical Africa, eastern Mediterranean, India and south-east Asia to China. One, Darwin, NT, 4.3.1998.

HANZAB (1996), Vol. **3**, *Snipe to Pigeons*, p. 158.
McCrie, N. (2000), 'A sighting of a Green Sandpiper *Tringa ochropus* at Darwin, Northern Territory', *Aust. Bird Watcher* **18**: 229–32.

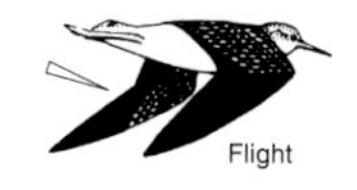

Nordmann's (Spotted) Greenshank *Tringa guttifer* V ?

See also Plate, p. **87**. Like Common Greenshank. Yellowish short legs barely trail in flight. Bill stouter; yellowish base. Underwing white. Obvious spotting on breast. **Size** 29–32 cm. **Voice** Piercing 'keyew'. **Hab.** As Common Greenshank. Breeds Sakhalin Is., north of Japan; perhaps on nearby mainland; a poorly known, rare species. Winters to south-east Asia; scattered records. No acceptable Aust. records, although three northern Aust. reports.

HANZAB (1996), Vol. **3**, *Snipe to Pigeons*, p. 152.

Lesser Yellowlegs *Tringa flavipes* V

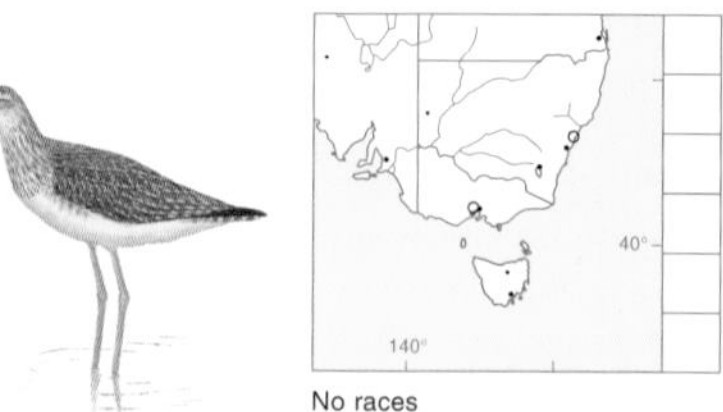

See also Plate, p. **87**. Dark above; breast, neck, heavily streaked. Long slender straight bill, long neck. **Non-br.** Breast streaked. Legs bright yellow–orange, trail in flight. **Size** 23–25 cm; bet. Common Greenshank and Marsh Sandpiper. **Voice** Soft, high 'ti-di-ti', 'ti-dup'. **Hab.** As Common Greenshank, Marsh Sandpiper. Breeds Nearctic north-west and north central North America. Migrates to central and South America. Aust. records: in Vic. at Reedy Lake near Moolap 9–20.3.1983; also Werribee, 9–12.3.1995 and Jan 2001. One at Newcastle, NSW, 13.8.2001. A number of other unaccepted reports.

HANZAB (1996), Vol. **3**, *Snipe to Pigeons*, p. 153.

Hudsonian Godwit *Limosa haemastica* V

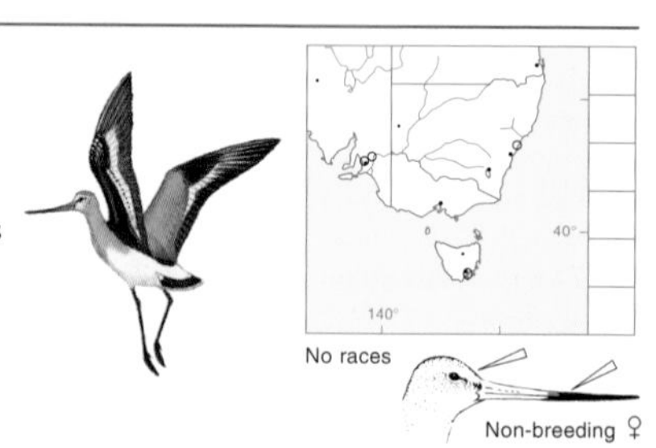

See also Plate, p. **89**. **Br.** (not described here). **Non-br.** Like Black-tailed Godwit. Underwing almost all black; central wing bar less distinct than Black-tailed. Rump less white. Legs shorter than Black-tailed. **Size** 37–42 cm. **Hab.** As other godwits. Breeds in scattered sites across northern North America. Migrates south-east coasts of South America. Only three accepted Aust. records: Kooragang Is., NSW; Lauderdale-Orielton Lagoon, Tas.; Dry Creek Saltfields, SA. Other reports incl. one from Werribee, Vic.

HANZAB (1996), Vol. **3**, *Snipe to Pigeons*, p. 77.

'Cox's Sandpiper' *Calidris paramelanotus* R

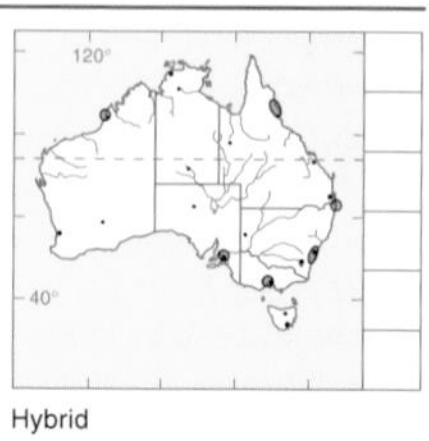

See also Plate, p. **91**. DNA proves it to be a hybrid between Pectoral and Curlew Sandpipers. Check Dunlin. Like Pectoral Sandpiper, but smaller, paler, less well-marked. Bill black, longer, less curved than Pectoral; shorter than Curlew Sandpiper. Small head. Breast not strongly marked, nor sharply cut-off as Pectoral. Legs olive; same length or shorter than Pectoral. **Size** Approx. 19–20 cm. **Voice** As Pectoral; shriller. **Hab.** Marshes, saltworks.

HANZAB (1996), Vol. **3**, *Snipe to Pigeons*, p. 307.

Baird's Sandpiper *Calidris bairdii* **V**

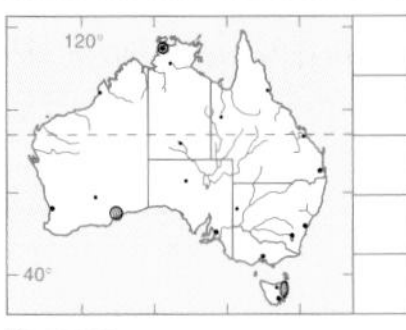

No races

See also Plate, p. **91**. 'Large stint' sized. Check Red-necked Stint (smaller), Sharp-tailed Sandpiper (larger). **Br.** (not described here). **Non-br.** Folded wings project well past tail; looks to have 'horizontal stance'. Wing bar barely seen in flight. Bill black. Buff-white eyebrow almost to rear of crown. White chin, throat. Feathers of back, wings, dark brown; more scalloped than Red-necked Stint. Rump dark. Legs dark olive. **Size** 14–16 cm. **Juv.** Buff scaling above. **Voice** High-pitched, melodious, rolling 'krreep'. **Hab.** Shallow lakes, lagoons, mudflats, sewage ponds. Breeds north-east Siberia, Alaska, Canada. Migrates Mexico, South America; some to Patagonia. About six confirmed Aust. records; no recent reports.

HANZAB (1996), Vol. **3**, *Snipe to Pigeons*, p. 283.

White-rumped Sandpiper *Calidris fuscicollis* **V**

No races

See also Plate, p. **91**. **Br.** (not described here). **Non-br.** Resembles small Curlew Sandpiper, Baird's Sandpiper. Wings long; when folded protrude beyond tail. Short, faintly decurved bill has 'swollen' tip. Whitish eye-line. Fine streaks on neck, breast, flanks. Narrow white wing bar. White rump, uppertail coverts, but smaller patch than on Curlew Sandpiper. Short legs. **Size** 15–17 cm. **Voice** Like Pectoral; shriller, 'tzeeet'. **Hab.** Coastal, sub-coastal tidal flats. Breeds north Alaska, Canada. Migrates to West Indies, and Argentina in South America. Several accepted Aust. records.

HANZAB (1996), Vol. **3**, *Snipe to Pigeons*, p. 279.

Western Sandpiper *Calidris mauri* **V ?**

See also Plate, p. **91**. A stint (despite name); resembles Red-necked Stint; very slightly larger. Bill longer, black, slightly decurved. White eyebrow, brightest at front. Rufous basal patches on mantle feathers. Grey chevrons, triangles, form striations on anterior white underparts. **Non-br.** Crown pale grey in centre. Lightly striated across upper breast. Legs dark. **Size** 14–17 cm. **Juv.** Black centre to crown; rufous wash about head, ear coverts. **Hab.** Typically coastal areas, mudflats. Breeds each side of Bering Straits: north-east Siberia, north-west Alaska. Several unconfirmed Aust. reports.

HANZAB (1996), Vol. **3**, *Snipe to Pigeons*, p. 247.
Hayman, P., Marchant, J. & Prater, T. (1987), *Shorebirds: An identification guide to waders of the world*, Christopher Helm, London, pp. 196, 367.

Dunlin *Calidris alpina* **V**

Races visiting Aust. not reliably identified; *sakhalina* and/or *pacificus* are most likely.

See also Plate, p. **93**. Like Curlew Sandpiper, smaller. Check 'Cox's Sandpiper'. Chestnut above; black belly. Black centre to rump. **Non-br.** Grey-brown above; white below. Broad white wing bar in flight. **Size** 20 cm. **Voice** Nasal 'tree'. **Hab.** Coastlines. Breeds northern Palaearctic, across northern temperate Europe; also Nearctic. Migrates southward to temperate and subtropical areas from these continents. Accepted record, Cairns, Qld, 4.1.1983; Cape Bowling Green, Qld, 1.7.1999. All others retracted as doubtful, largely because of possible confusion of early records with 'Cox's Sandpiper'.

HANZAB (1996), Vol. **3**, *Snipe to Pigeons*, p. 308.

Stilt Sandpiper *Micropalama himantopus* **V**

See also Plate, p. **93**. Resembles Marsh Sandpiper, but forehead flatter, slopes. Bill black. Whitish eyebrow. Chestnut ear coverts, nape. Blackish upperparts, pale fringes. Underparts heavily barred black. **Non-br.** Upperparts mid-grey; underparts white, breast finely streaked darker to belly. No wing bar. Long thin yellow-green legs. **Size** 18–23 cm. **Juv.** As adult; buffer neck, breast; darker back. **Voice** 'too too'. **Hab.** Swamps, shallow wetlands, pasture, tidal flats. Breeds Nearctic; migrates to southern temperate South America.

HANZAB (1996), Vol. **3**, *Snipe to Pigeons*, p. 326.

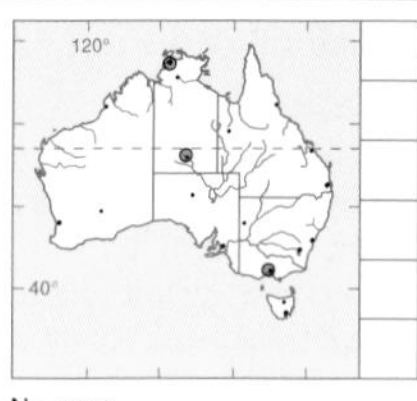

No races

Grey Phalarope *Phalaropus fulicarius* **V**

See also Plate, p. **95**. Second largest phalarope. Shorter, stouter black bill than other species; often yellowish at base (adults). **M** Slightly duller than female. **F** Bill yellow; black tip. Forehead, crown black. Face white. Black above, strongly patterned golden-buff. Entire underparts red-brown. **Non-br.** Paler on head; has large, black, 'phalarope eye-patch'. Uniform grey upperparts; black line through rump. White wing bar. White below. Feet lobed. **Size** 20–22 cm. **Juv.** Buffer, strong golden-buff pattern on wings. **Voice** Shrill 'twit'. **Hab.** Oceans, bays, lakes, swamps. Breeds northernmost Palaearctic, Nearctic. A small number of Aust. records.

HANZAB (1996), Vol. **3**, *Snipe to Pigeons*, p. 360.

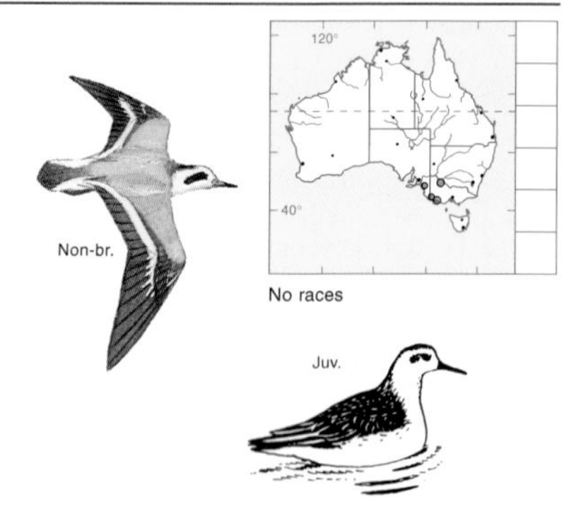

Wilson's Phalarope *Steganopus (Phalaropus) tricolor* **V M**

See also Plate, p. **95**. Feeds by swimming. Occasionally spins. More often ashore than other phalaropes. Bill longer, more needle-like, than Red-necked Phalarope. **M** Much duller than female. White nape spot. **F** Broad black eye-stripe extends down side of neck to red-brown shoulder, back stripes. Crown, back of neck, grey; buffy lower neck. White nape spot. Legs black. **Size** 22–24 cm. **Non-br.** Resembles Marsh Sandpiper but bill shorter, finer; shorter legs; lobed feet; lack of white on lower back. Smaller, narrower, grey, curving, 'phalarope' eye-mark than Grey, Red-necked. Uniform pale grey forehead, eyebrow, upperparts. White on rump only. Tail grey. Underparts white. Yellow-greenish legs. **Juv.** Buffer. Golden-buff wing pattern. **Voice** Low-pitched honking. **Hab.** Lagoons, lakes, mudflats, swamps. Breeds across central North America; migrates to western, southern South. America. A few south-east Aust. records; none recently confirmed.

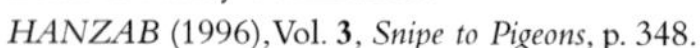

HANZAB (1996), Vol. **3**, *Snipe to Pigeons*, p. 348.

Non-br.

No races

Juv.

Pheasant-tailed Jacana *Hydrophasianus chirurgus* **V**

See also Plate, p. **97**. **Br.** Unlikely in Aust. In flight, white wings with black tips. **Non-br.** Neck pale gold, bordered by line of black, becoming brown. Upperparts dark olive-brown; underparts white. **Size** 31 cm. **Juv.** As non-br. adult but rufous crown, neck less yellow; fainter breast bar. Identify from juv. Comb-crested Jacana. **Hab.** Open swampy areas. Breeds India to Philippines; also Taiwan, Indonesian islands (Java). One bird recorded at Paraburdoo, WA, Dec. 1974. This sighting recently reviewed; now accepted. Other claims not submitted.

HANZAB, (1993), Vol. **2**, *Raptors to Lapwings*, p. 675.
Palliser, T. (2002), 'Rare Birds in 2001', *Wingspan* **12** (3): 19.

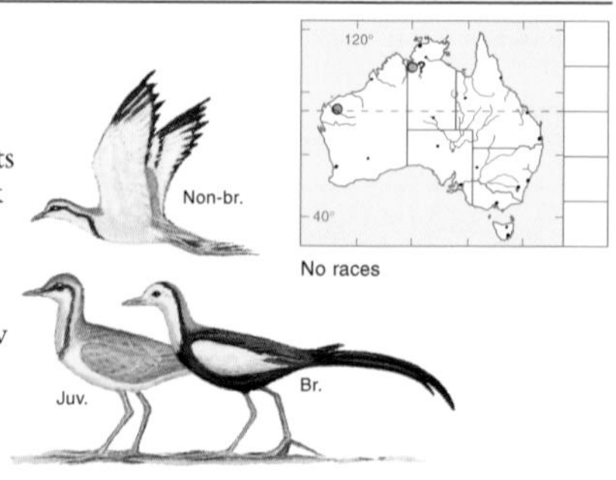

South Island Pied Oystercatcher *Haematopus finschi* V

Like Pied Oystercatcher but much shorter legs, more white on back and on both upper- and undersides of wings. Orange-red bill; eye-ring. Upperparts, upper breast, black; white below. Wide, angled, white wing bar in flight; extends to innermost secondaries. White upper tail coverts, rump, extends in sharp triangle pointing up upper back (square across in Pied Oystercatcher). Black tail. Legs, feet, pinkish (flesh) red. **F** Larger; longer bill. **Size** 46 cm. **Imm.** As adult, duller. **Voice** Loud alarm call like Pied; quieter in flight; piping in courtship, aggression. **Hab.** Sub-alpine lakes, riverine and pasture areas; ocean, bayside, beaches and estuaries. Most breed inland in South Island of New Zealand; post-breeding, some disperse locally but many to North Island coasts. One at Ballina, NSW, in prob. 2nd year plumage, from 6.11.1998 to at least 14.2.1999. One Patches Beach, near Ballina, NSW, 22.1.1999. One Manly Boat Harbour, Qld, 24.11.1999. One Woody Point, near Brisbane, Qld, 10–27.4.2001.

Carter, M.J. (1999), 'South Island Pied Oystercatcher on the Australian mainland', *Aust. Birding* **5** (1): 14–15, 23.
HANZAB, (1993), Vol. **2**, Raptors to Lapwings, p. 727.

Previously considered a race of the worldwide species Eurasian Oystercatcher *Haematopus ostralegus*.

American Golden Plover *Pluvialis dominica* V

Extremely difficult to separate from Pacific Golden Plover (Plate p. 99). Fractionally larger. Bill larger. Toes rarely project beyond tail tip in flight. When standing, primary feather tips project further beyond tail tip than do Pacific's. Relative lengths of these, and position of tip of longest tertial, critical in determination (but not reliable in moulting birds). Finer speckling on dark upper parts, wing coverts; wider white patches to side of breast; more black about flanks, undertail, than Pacific. **Non-br.** Pale supercilium, dark crown; whiter about face than Pacific. Greyer shades in body plumage than Golden. **Juv.** Blackish upperparts, some yellowish on covert tips. Check non-br. Grey Plover. **Size** 23–27 cm. **Hab.** As for Pacific Golden Plover. Breeds across northern North America; most migrate to inland central eastern South America and coast. One accepted record Byron Bay, NSW, 7–11.11.1994; many unverified claims.

HANZAB, (1993), Vol. **2**, *Raptors to Lapwings*, p. 810.
Patterson, R.J. (1996), 'RAOU Records Appraisal Committee: Opinions and Case Summaries 1992–1996', *RAOU Report* No. **101**, p. 37.

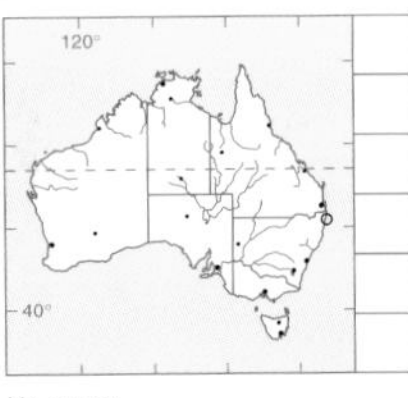

No races.
Recently 'split' taxonomically from Pacific Golden Plover, *P. fulva*.

Not yet illustrated.

Eurasian Golden Plover *Pluvialis apricaria* V ?

See also Plate, p. **99**. Like a bulkier Pacific Golden Plover except eye-line, face, underwing lining, white. Black face, central underparts. **Non-br**. Eyebrow vague. Dorsum, breast, golden; white belly, undertail coverts. **Size** 26–29 cm. **Juv.** As adult, but duller; fine grey scallops on belly. **Hab.** As Pacific Golden Plover. Breeds Iceland, Scotland, north-west Palaearctic; migrates to western Europe, Mediterranean area. An unlikely vagrant. No confirmed Aust. sighting. Two pre-1919 museum skins with insufficient data.

HANZAB, (1993), Vol. **2**, *Raptors to Lapwings*, p. 811.
Hayman, P., Marchant, J. & Prater, T. (1987), *Shorebirds: An identification guide to waders of the world*, Christopher Helm, London, pp. 98, 277.

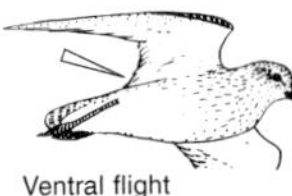

Ventral flight

Caspian Plover *Charadrius asiaticus* V

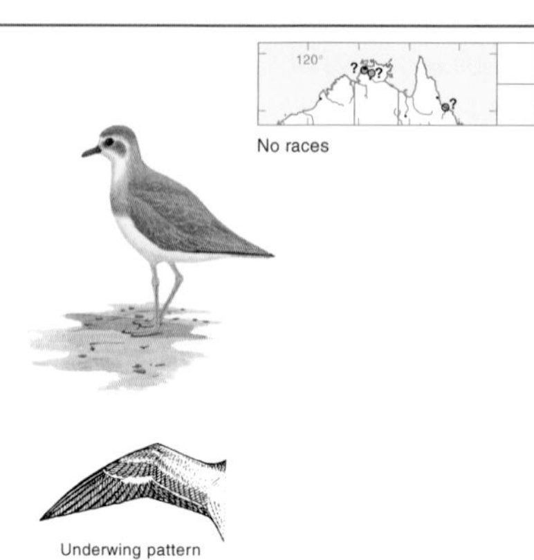

See also Plate, p. **101**. Like Oriental Plover, slightly smaller. In flight, thin white wing bar, widest at base of inner primaries. Black bill. Large dark eye. Thin dark eye-line. White frons, face, eyebrow, chin. Brown above. Blackish tail rounded, thin white border. Rich chestnut breast band, thin black border; white below. Whitish underwing. Dull greenish legs, slightly shorter than Oriental. **F** Dull buff-grey crown, nape, chest band; no black line beneath it. **Non-br.** Brown plumage paler, more buff. Chest band mottled pale grey-fawn. **Size** 18–20 cm. **Hab.** As Oriental. Breeds east of Caspian Sea, eastern Europe. Early specimen Pine Creek, NT, 26.9.1896. One Lake Finnis, NT, 5.10.1994. The few other Aust. claims unconfirmed.

HANZAB, (1993), Vol. **2**, *Raptors to Lapwings*, p. 876.
McCrie, N. (1999), 'Sighting of a Caspian Plover *Charadrius asiaticus* at Lake Finnis, Northern Territory', *Aust. Bird Watcher* **18**: 81–6.

Kentish Plover *Charadrius alexandrinus* V

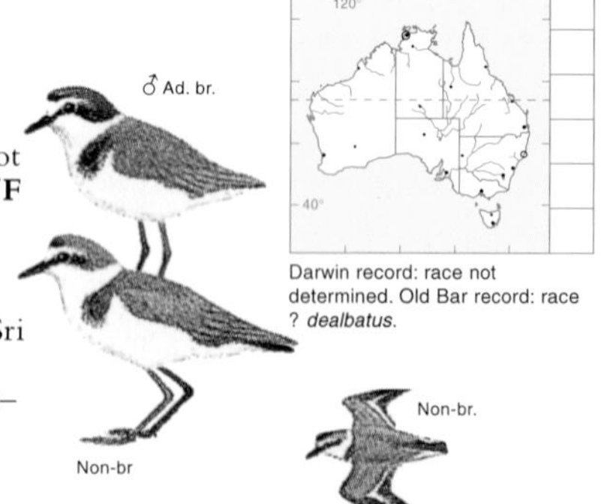

See also Plate, p. **103**. Like large, closely related, Red-capped Plover. Check other non-br. plovers. Bill thicker, longer. White eyebrow extends further. White frons wider. Crown browner. Complete white collar. Blackish patches at side of breast larger, not extending across upper mantle edge. Longer legs paler. **Non-br./F** Dark marks on head, sides of breast browner, contrast less with upperparts. **Size** 15–17.5 cm. **Juv.** As female. More buffy, paler dorsum. **Hab.** Shallow water of beaches, tidal flats, salt lakes with soft sediments. Breeds Africa, west Europe to central Asia, Japan, Sri Lanka, Java. Two accepted records: one ad. male, Darwin, NT, late 1988; one non-br. female at Old Bar, near Taree, NSW, 14.2.2002–15.4.2002. One other reported Port Hedland, WA, 4.4.1993.

HANZAB, (1993), Vol. **2**, *Raptors to Lapwings*, p. 836.
Johnstone, R.E. & Storr, G.M. (1998), *Handbook of Western Australian Birds*, Vol. **I**, *Non-Passerines*, WA Museum, Perth, p. 213.

Black-tailed (Japanese) Gull *Larus crassirostris* V

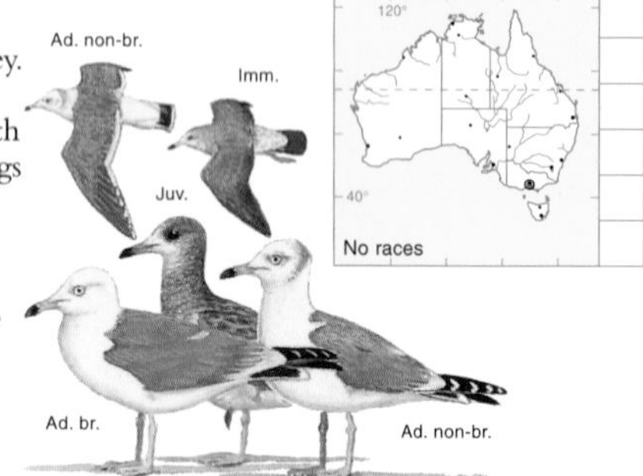

Bill lemon, tipped red with black sub-terminal band. Eye honey. Body white. Slate-grey back, upperwings. White trailing edge ends at central primaries; rest of primaries black. Tail white with black sub-terminal band. **Non-br.** Grey markings on head. Legs olive-brown. **Size** 46–48 cm. **Juv.** Bill flesh-pink, tip black. **Imm.** Greyer head, grey extending to flanks. Broad tail band. **Hab.** Coastal/sub-coastal. Breeds China Sea, Japan Sea. Confirmed record, bird over-wintered in Port Phillip Bay, Vic., Mar.–Sept. 1978. Also a more recent WA sighting.

HANZAB, (1996), Vol. **3**, *Snipe to Pigeons*, p. 485.
Wild Bird Society of Japan (1983), *A Field Guide to the Birds of Japan*, Wild Bird Soc. Japan, Tokyo (pp. 88–9).

Black-headed Gull *Larus ridibundus* **V**

Identify from Laughing, Franklin's Gulls by wing pattern. **Br.** (Europe) Brown hood. Incomplete eye-ring. Bill dark red-brown. Back, upperwings, pale grey. Nape, neck, underparts to tail, white. Primaries broad white leading edge; thin black trailing edge. Legs red-brown. **Non-br.** Bill tipped black; head white; dark ear spot. **2nd** (northern) **summer** Bill orange, tipped black. Hood incomplete. Brown marks on wing. **Size** 38–44 cm. **Juv.** Bill pink, tipped black. Incomplete buff-brown hood. Back, wings scaled brown. Underparts white; sides of breast marked brown. Legs flesh. **Imm.** Like juv. Head whiter. Back pale grey. **Hab.** Coasts, freshwater wetlands. Breeds Iceland, across northern Eurasia to Alaska; non-br. birds to coastal areas of North Africa, Asia, India to south-east Asia, Philippines and southern Japan. One Broome, WA, present Oct.–Dec. 1991; also one Darwin, NT, Feb. 1998.

HANZAB, (1996), Vol. **3**, *Snipe to Pigeons*, p. 558.

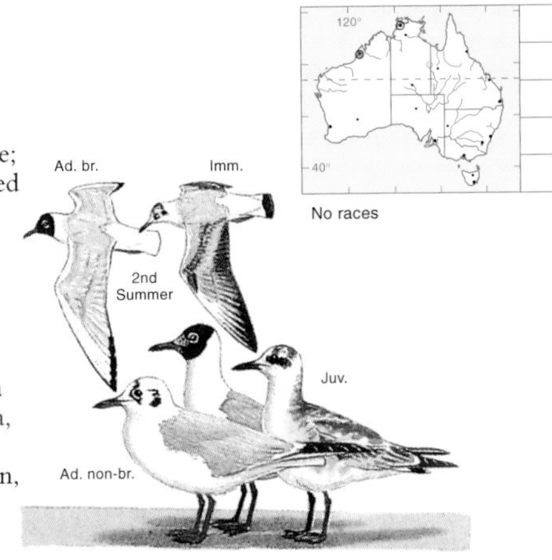

Laughing Gull *Larus atricilla* **V**

Identify from Franklin's Gull by wing pattern. Smaller, darker than Silver Gull. 'Longer' than Franklin's when standing. Appears long-winged in flight. **Br.** (America) Black hood. White eyelids. Upperparts slate grey. Wings tipped black; trailing edge white. **Non-br.** Like Franklin's, less hood. Smaller wing mirrors. White tail in flight. **Size** 36–41 cm. **Juv.** Like Franklin's; darker-winged. **1st yr/Imm. winter** Like non-br. Dusky breast and flanks. Broader tail band. In flight (illus.) partly based on photos of Cairns birds. **Hab.** Coastal, oceanic. Breeds eastern tropical Americas. Two birds, adult and 1st year, at Cairns, north Qld, from 11.12.1987, both in winter plumage (autumn 1988; then intermittently until Sept. 1990). Adult achieved full breeding plumage. Also singles at Eyre, WA (Dec. 1988–Jan. 1989); Triabunna, Tas. (Dec. 1988–Jan. 1989); Lakes Entrance, Vic. (Nov.–Dec. 1989). New records 2002: Portland Roads, N Qld, and Bribie Island, SE Qld.

HANZAB, (1996), Vol. **3**, *Snipe to Pigeons*, p. 561. [1st Cairns records are more than verified, *contra* Vol. **3**, p. 563.]

Harrison, P. (1987), *Seabirds of the World – A Photographic Guide*, Christopher Helm Ltd, Bromley, UK.

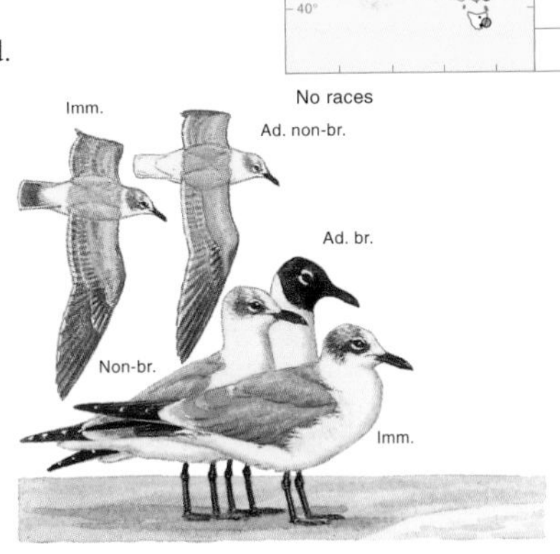

Franklin's Gull *Larus pipixcan* **V**

Smaller than Silver, Laughing Gulls. Black bill, tipped red. White eyelids. Black hood. Upperwings, back, slate-grey; white trailing edge curves behind black outer band on white-tipped primaries. Pink tinge on newly feathered underparts. Tail white, pale grey centre (hard to see in field). Legs red. **Non-br.** Partial hood: black hind crown to eyes; streaked crown; white frons, throat. Blackish legs. **Size** 32–36 cm. **Imm.** Like non-br.; outer primaries black; black sub-terminal tail band. **Hab.** Breeds central North America; migrates to coasts of Caribbean, South America. Several records: most recent Broome, WA, Dec. 1996; Peterborough, Vic., 18.4.1999; Adelaide, SA, 2002.

HANZAB, (1996), Vol. **3**, *Snipe to Pigeons*, p. 565.

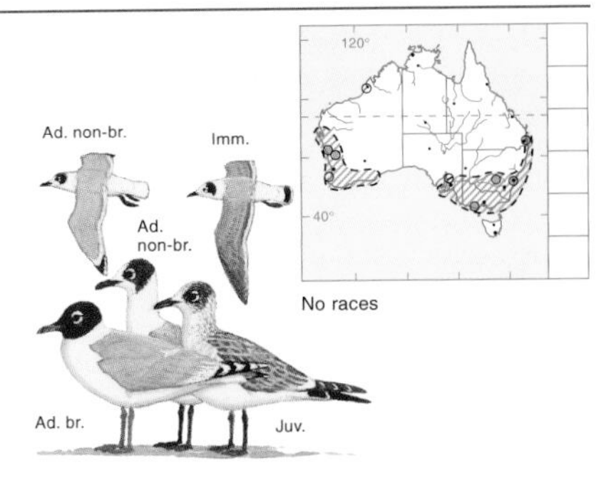

Sabine's Gull *Larus (Xema) sabini* V

Black hood. Black bill, tipped yellow. Forked white tail. Upperwing has grey shoulder, black outer primaries with white tips and white triangular trailing edge. **Non-br./Imm.** White head; dark nape. **Juv.** Eye to mantle and shoulders scaly grey-brown. Tail tip black. **Size** 27–32 cm. **Hab.** Coastlines and seaward. Breeds Nearctic and Northern Palaearctic; migrates to western Americas and western Africa, exhibiting 'semi-pelagic' behaviour along continental shelves. Four confirmed records: Darwin, 1982; Port Macdonnell, SA, 1984; offshore from Wollongong, NSW, 1985; Coconut Well, N of Broome, WA, 14.12.2001. Also seen Port Hedland, 1989, 1990.

HANZAB, (1996), Vol. **3**, *Snipe to Pigeons*, p. 569.
Johnstone, R.E. & Storr, G.M. (1998), *Handbook of Western Australian Birds*, Vol. **I**, *Non-Passerines*, WA Museum, Perth, p. 230.

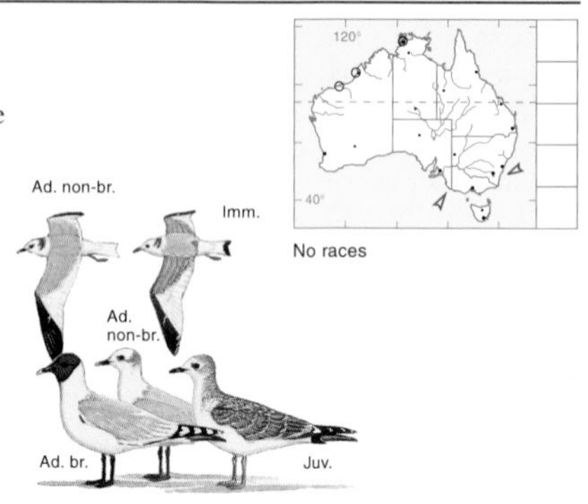

No races

Black Tern *Chlidonias niger* V

See also Plate, p. **109**. Like White-winged Black Tern but long slender bill; longer wings and tail (which is obviously forked). Confusion with moulting White-winged Black Terns is extremely likely. Bill black. Like White-winged Black but no black on underwing, whiter upperwing, paler (greyer) dorsum. **Non-br.** As White-winged Black; look for blackish mark ('droop') extending from mantle to breast sides. **Size** 22–24 cm. **Juv.** Darkest of *Chlidonias* terns at this age; upperwing, mantle, back, dark grey; brownish fringes to latter. **Hab.** Lakes, estuaries, oceans. Breeds north-west Eurasia; migrates to Mediterranean and eastward to Asia Minor. Also breeds North America; migrates to USA, central and northern South American coastline. Two confirmed records: The Entrance (1958) and Newcastle (1968), both NSW. Others reported in SE Aust. (none accepted).

HANZAB, (1996), Vol. **3**, *Snipe to Pigeons*, p. 785.

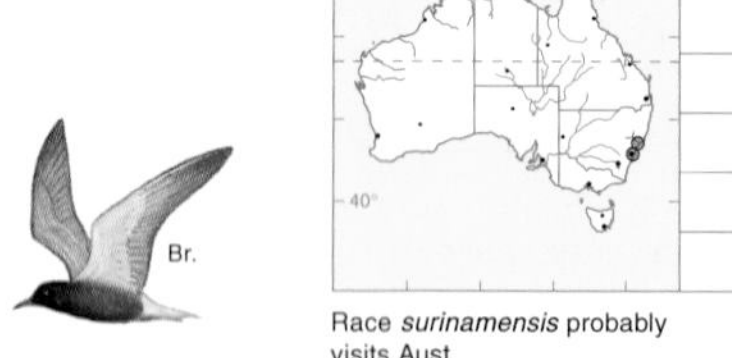

Race *surinamensis* probably visits Aust.

Antarctic Tern *Sterna vittata* V

Identify from Arctic, Common, perhaps from White-fronted, Roseate, Terns. Resembles these, but 'bulkier' size; heavier, brighter bill. Most like Arctic. Bill red. White facial stripe separates black cap from grey throat. Upperparts grey. Dark leading wing edge fainter than Common. Underwing lacks well defined black trailing edge of Arctic. Underparts grey, paling to white undertail. **Non-br.** Bill duller red. Lores, forehead, crown whiter than Common, Arctic. Some grey on underparts. **Size** 32–36 cm. **Juv.** Like Common Tern. Upperparts more strongly scaled brown; breast washed brown. **Hab.** Breeds on subantarctic islands. Two beach-washed records: south of Busselton, WA, July 1978; islet near Kangaroo Is., SA, Nov. 1982. One live, west end of Kangaroo Is. on 12.11.2001.

HANZAB, (1996), Vol. **3**, *Snipe to Pigeons*, p. 677.
Johnstone, R.E. & Storr, G.M. (1998), *Handbook of Western Australian Birds*, Vol. **I**, *Non-Passerines*, WA Museum, Perth, p. 243.

No races

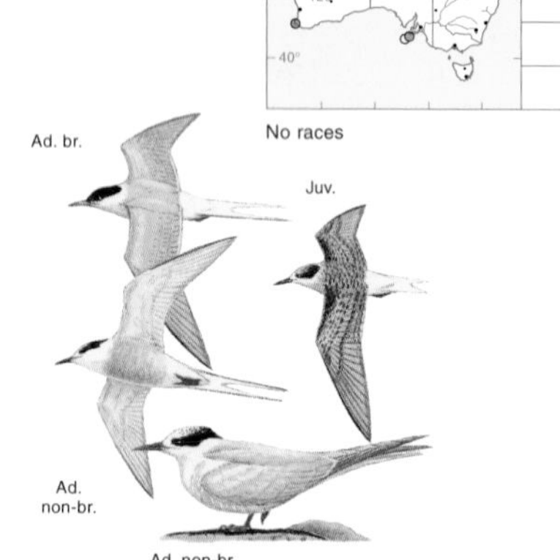

Eastern Marsh Harrier *Circus spilonotus* or Papuan Harrier *Circus approximans spilothorax* V

A race (or species) with a chequered taxonomic history. The latest global raptor field guide (Ferguson-Lees & Christie, 2001) regards this PNG raptor a race of Swamp Harrier *C. approximans spilothorax*, formerly a race of Eastern Marsh Harrier *C. spilonotus spilothorax*.

See also Plate, p. **125**. Papuan Harrier, of PNG, difficult to determine because of poorly known development of plumages; taxonomy unsettled. Compare possible Aust. sightings with various plumages of Swamp, Spotted Harriers. Identify carefully from pale, dark-hooded, 1st yr Spotted Harrier moulting into 2nd yr plumage. Black hood, nape. Black and silver-grey above. Pale dorsal wing bar with narrow black trailing wing-edges. Rump white. White below, streaked on breast dark. Colour morphs occur. **F** May have a brown morph, with pale scapulars. **Size** 47–53 cm. **Hab.** In PNG, open grassland, mainly in highlands. Breeds across PNG. First Darwin record withdrawn. Possible sightings more recently, Darwin, NT; Torres Strait; several in N Qld (Daintree River to Atherton). Many claims; none yet authenticated for Aust.

Coates, B.J. & Peckover, W.S. (2001), *Birds of Papua New Guinea and the Bismarck Archipelago: A Photographic Guide*, Vol. **1**, *Non-Passerines*, Dove, Brisbane, p. 117.
HANZAB, (1993), Vol. **2**, *Raptors to Lapwings*, p. 105. [Listed as Eastern Marsh Harrier *Circus spilonotus*].

Collared Imperial-Pigeon *Ducula mullerii* V–LMC

Crown pink. Broad black collar. Mantle, sides of chest, glossy claret. Silver-grey throat band between black collar and dark mauve-pink underparts. Wings, back, tail, dark grey. Broad silver-grey mid-tail band. **Size** 41 cm (approx. size of White-headed Pigeon). **Voice** Little known. **Hab.** Tree-lined creeks, low-lying woodlands, mangroves. Breeds Irian Jaya (except Vogelkop), Papua New Guinea; also on Aru Island. Single bird Boigu Is., north Torres Strait, Jan. 1980. Others seen on recent visits and on Saibai Is.; suggest now resident there. Three on Fantome Is., Palm Islands Group, Qld, 27.1.2002.

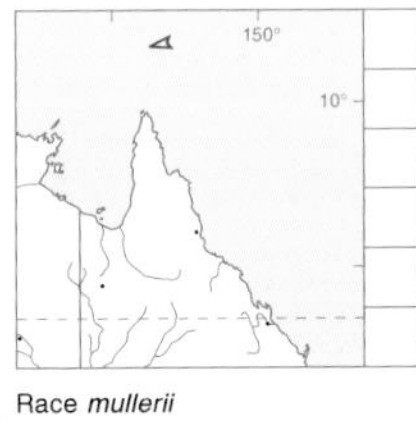

Race *mullerii*

HANZAB, (1996), Vol. **3**, *Snipe to Pigeons*, p. 999.

Elegant Imperial-Pigeon *Ducula concinna* V

Larger than Pied (Torresian) Imperial-Pigeon. Bill dark. Eye gold to yellow. Head, face, nape, chin, throat, silver-grey. Hind neck, mantle, underparts, silvery grey, tinged pale salmon. Wings, upper tail, iridescent (dark green to purple). Underwing blackish-green. Chestnut undertail coverts. Legs, feet, red-pink. **F** Slightly paler on grey and salmon parts. **Size** Approx. 42–44 cm. **Juv./Imm.** A little duller. Breeds on small islands between Sulawesi and Irian Jaya, including Aru Islands north of Australia. One in suburban gardens, Nightcliff, Darwin, NT, from Sept. 1993, for some weeks.

Also called 'Blue-tailed Imperial-Pigeon', 'Gold-eyed Imperial-Pigeon'.

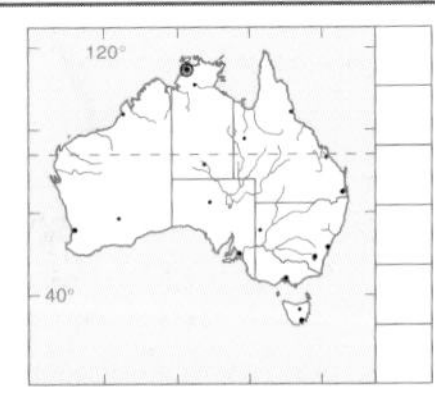

Race *concinna*
Considered part of the Green Imperial-Pigeon 'superspecies' based on *Ducula aenea*. The group ranges from India to Wallacea.

HANZAB, (1996), Vol. **3**, Snipe to Pigeons, p. 994.

Brown Hawk-Owl *Ninox scutulata* V

Indistinct facial mask. Uniform dark brown above; paler to white, strongly streaked with brown, below. Tail longish, dark brown, lighter bars. **Size** 27–33 cm. **Voice** Musical double hoot; second note brief and double-pitched. **Hab.** Forests, woodlands. Race *japonica* breeds Japan, Korea, east China; migrates south to Philippines, Malaya, Borneo and most western islands of Indonesia. Two Aust. records: One dead on Ashmore Reef (off north-western Aust.), 6.1.1973; one (race not known) alive, later died, at Exmouth, WA, 6.2.1991. Two said to have lived on an oil rig in Timor Sea, Nov.–Dec. 1988.

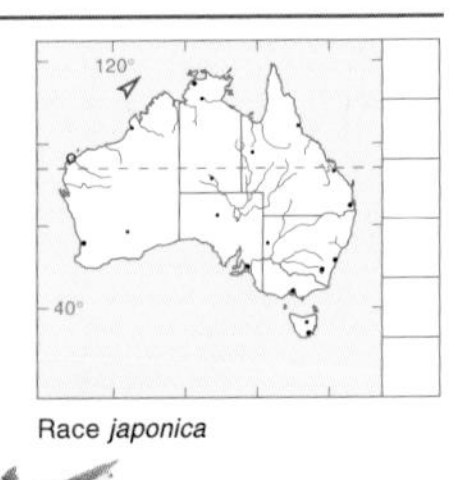

Race *japonica*

HANZAB, (1999), Vol. **4**, *Parrots to Dollarbird*, p. 875.
Johnstone, R.E. & Storr, G.M. (1998), *Handbook of Western Australian Birds*, Vol. **I**, *Non-Passerines*, WA Museum, Perth, p. 323.

Blue-winged Pitta *Pitta moluccensis* **V**

See also Plate, p. **169** for similar Noisy, Fairy, Pittas. Broad pale brown eyebrow. Wing coverts, rump, violet-blue. Broad white wing patch in swift, direct flight, as in all pittas. White throat with small black chin mark. Rufous-buff underparts. **Size** 18–21 cm. **Voice** Loud disyllabic whistle; second note highest. **Hab.** Mangroves, rainforests. Breeds south-east Asia in China, Burma, Malaya, Thailand; migrates to Sumatra, Borneo. Four north-west Aust. records: (Mandora Station Nov. 1927; Derby 'late' 1930; Burrup Peninsula 6.11.1994; Coconut Well, 10 km N of Broome, 20.12.1995–96).

Erritzoe, J. (1998), *A Monograph of the Pitta Family*, The Lutterworth Press, Cambridge, UK.
HANZAB, (2001), Vol. **5**, *Tyrant Flycatchers to Chats*, p. 103.
Johnstone, R.E. & Hamilton, N. (1995), 'A Blue-winged Pitta (*Pitta moluccensis*) in Western Australia', *W. Aust. Naturalist* **20** (2): 120.

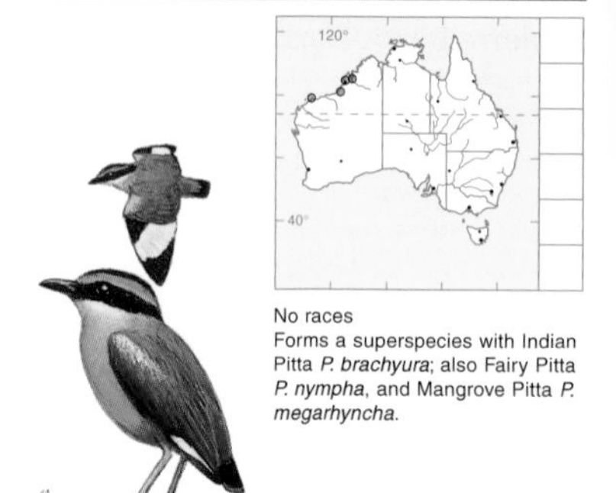

No races
Forms a superspecies with Indian Pitta *P. brachyura*; also Fairy Pitta *P. nympha*, and Mangrove Pitta *P. megarhyncha*.

House (Columbo) Crow *Corvus splendens* **V**

See also Plate, p. **259**. Like other corvids but smaller, thinner; flies faster. Dark bill. Brown eye. Mostly black; broad pale grey to grey-brown nape, collar, mantle, breast. Legs short. **Size** 43 cm. **Voice** 4–5 closely repeated 'caws', short, higher, than Little Raven. **Hab.** Urban areas. Largely commensal on humans. Breeds India, Sri Lanka, Maldive Islands, Burma, Malaysia, south-west Thailand, south China. Ship-assisted potential colonist from southern Asia. Three Aust. records: Fremantle, WA; one with paler mantle than colour plate p. **259**, near Melbourne Zoo, Vic., 1991; one with Little Ravens, Phillip Island, Vic., 17–28.1.2001, had dull grey mantle (little contrast between hood, mantle, in poor light). Bill had arched culmen, characteristic of race *insolens*.

Day, N. (2001), 'House Crow *Corvus splendens* at Phillip Island, Victoria', *Bird Observer* No. **812**: 25.
Madge, S. & Burn, H. (1994), *Crows and Jays: A Guide to the Crows, Jays and Magpies of the World*, Christopher Helm (A. & C. Black), London.

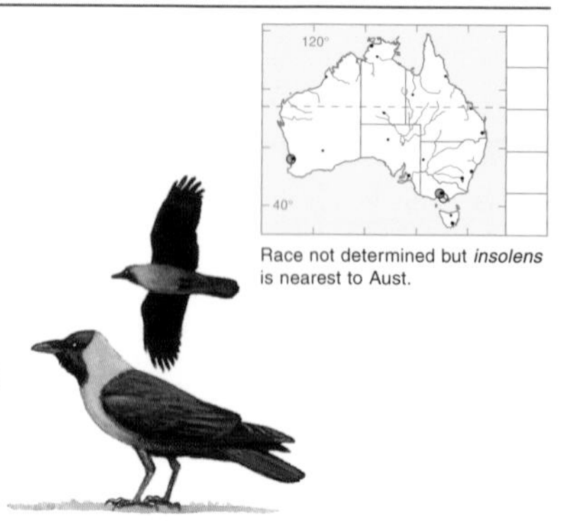

Race not determined but *insolens* is nearest to Aust.

Red-throated Pipit *Anthus cervinus* **V**

Identify from Australian (Richard's) Pipit (larger, paler, flanks not striped); from Horsfield's Bushlark (smaller). Red-throated stands 'more horizontally' than Aust. Pipit; is shorter tailed, darker backed. Reddish throat, breast. White belly has strong black striations. **Non-br.** Little or no red; body stripes remain. **Size** 14.5 cm. **Hab.** Seen in short wet grass. Breeds Eurasian Holarctic (Scandinavia–E Siberia); migrates to tropical Africa, Asia, reaching Borneo. One dead (ship-assisted?) on wharf, Albany, WA (May 1983). One at Broome, north-west Aust. (6–9.1.1992).

Carter, M.J. (1997), 'Red-throated Pipit *Anthus cervinus* in Australia', *Aust. Bird Watcher* **17** (1): 3–10.

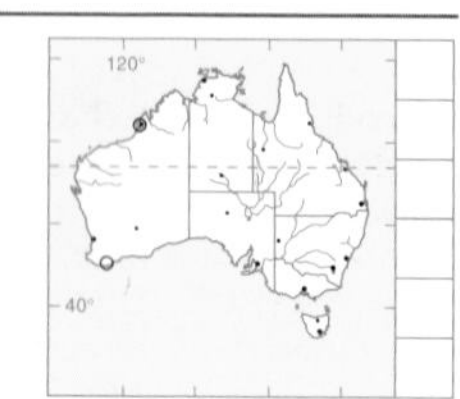

No races

Pechora Pipit *Anthus gustavi* V

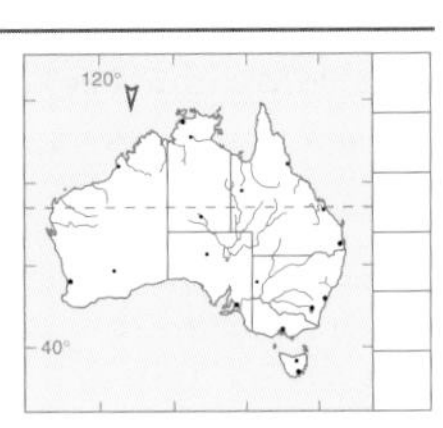

Race *gustavi* most likely in Aust.

Smaller; shorter legs, tail than Australian (Richard's) Pipit. May have yellowish tinge to face. Bill pink; culmen ridge, tip dark. Dark stripe in lores but not reaching bill (very pale in Red-throated Pipit). Broad white eyebrow. Dark eye has broad, white, half eye-ring beneath it. Ginger forehead, crown, finely streaked brown. Black malar stripe. Back has two off-white vertical streaks on each side; these not always obvious. Two fine wing bars. Longest primary feathers project beyond tertials at rest (only pipit with this feature). White chin, throat. White below with breast, flank, streaked. White undertail coverts. Legs, feet, bright pink. **Size** 14.5 cm.
Voice Ashmore Reef bird not heard to call. **Hab.** When wintering, typically in dense cover. Kept within or close to shrubs at Ashmore Reef. Breeds Western Palaearctic to Siberia and Bering Strait, usually between 60–70° N. Migrates to south-east Asia, and Wallacea including Sumba, Timor. One at West Island, Ashmore Reef, off NW of WA, 5.11.2001.

Carter, M.J. (2003), 'Pechora Pipit *Anthus gustavi* in Australia', *Aust. Field Ornithology* (formerly *Aust. Bird Watcher*) **20** (for June 2003).

Citrine (Yellow-headed) Wagtail *Motacilla citreola* V

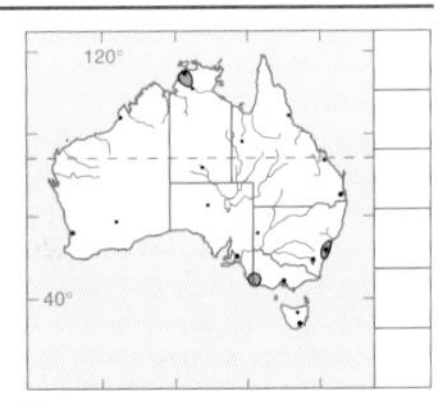

No races

See also Plate, p. **265**. Dimorphic. Bright yellow head; neck with black nape. **M non-br./F br.** Both similar to non-br. Yellow Wagtail race *taivana*. Paler yellow on sides of head, dark-edged mark about ear coverts; dark crown, nape. Greyer on back. Double white wing bars sometimes regarded as diagnostic, but may be present in Yellow Wagtail. Rump dark grey. **Size** 16–17 cm.
Juv. Soft grey upperparts; white underparts; often no yellow in plumage. **Voice** Louder, shriller than Yellow Wagtail. **Hab.** Wet grasslands. Breeds across Eurasia. Few Aust. records.

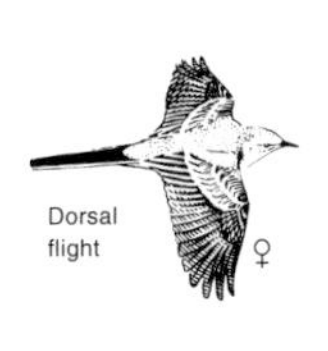

Wild Bird Society of Japan (1983), *A Field Guide to the Birds of Japan*, Wild Bird Soc. Japan, Tokyo, pp. 222–3.

Black-backed Wagtail *Motacilla lugens* V

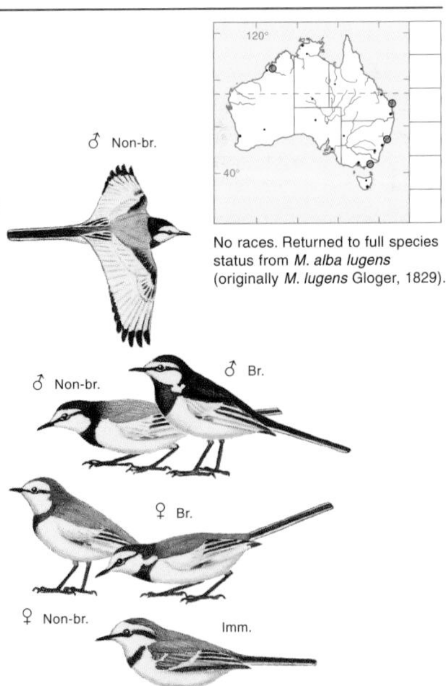

No races. Returned to full species status from *M. alba lugens* (originally *M. lugens* Gloger, 1829).

Identify from White Wagtail race *ocularis* (both have dark line through eye). Black throat, breast band, collar, but white chin. Black eye-stripe; black crown, nape, back, scapulars, rump. Long black tail edged white. Dorsal wings in flight mostly white.
M non-br. Grey back, anterior scapulars; less black on breast; retains narrower black collar. **F** Charcoal-grey crown, nape, breast band, collar. Grey back, scapulars, rump. **F non-br.** Paler grey crown, nape, back, rump, scapulars. Greyer, narrower breast band, collar. Size 17–18 cm. **Juv./Imm.** (See 2nd ref. below).
Hab. Tends to be on coastal plains, farmland, in migratory period. Breeds Manchuria, Korea, Kurile Islands, Kamchatka, east China, northern Japan (Hokkaido), etc.; wintering to southern Japan, Taiwan, south China. Aust. records: Fraser Is., Qld, May–Sept. 1987; two at Derby, WA in Dec. 1995; Broome, WA, 15.3.1998; Glendale, NSW, 4–10.4.1998: a 'first summer female'. Many other sightings not sufficiently detailed to differentiate between White and Black-backed Wagtails.

Howell, S. (1990), 'Identification of White and Black-backed Wagtails in alternate plumage', *Western Birds* **21**, 41–9.
Sibley, D. & Howell, S. (1998), 'Identification of White and Black-backed Wagtails in basic plumage', *Western Birds* **29**: 180–98.
Wild Bird Society of Japan (1983), *A Field Guide to the Birds of Japan*, Wild Bird Soc. Japan, Tokyo (pp. 224–5).

Arctic Warbler *Phylloscopus borealis* **V**

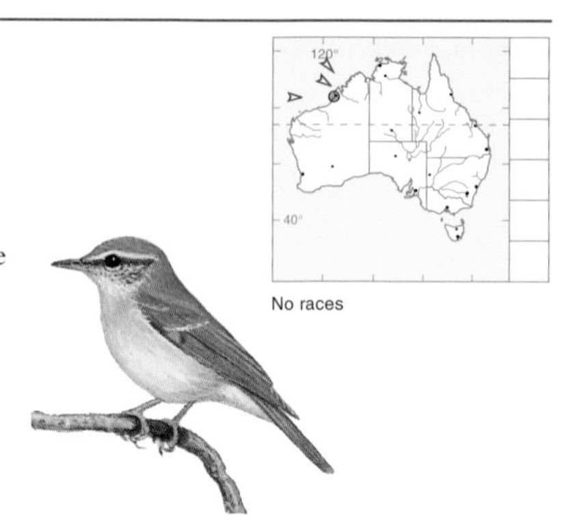

No races

See also Plate, p. **269**. Small songbird. One of several similar warblers which could reach Australia. Dark olive upperparts. Yellowish-white, long, straight eyebrow. Whitish below.
Size 12 cm (just larger than Mangrove Gerygone).
Voice Distinctive loud 'twzee-et'. **Hab.** Wooded areas, mangroves. Breeds (seven races) across Arctic Eurasia, Japan; some migrate to south-east Asia, Philippines, Borneo, Sumatra. Aust. records (all north-west WA): one dead, Scott Reef, Nov. 1979; one alive on oil rig off Dampier, 24.12.1985; one alive at Lacepède Island off Beagle Bay 17.12.1997; one caught alive, remained locally at Broome 23–28.1.1998; three filmed on Ashmore Reef, 24–25.10. 2001.

Hassell, C.J. (1998), 'Arctic Warbler: First confirmed record for mainland Australia', *Aust. Bird Watcher* **17**: 365–9.

Pale-headed Munia *Lonchura pallida* **V**

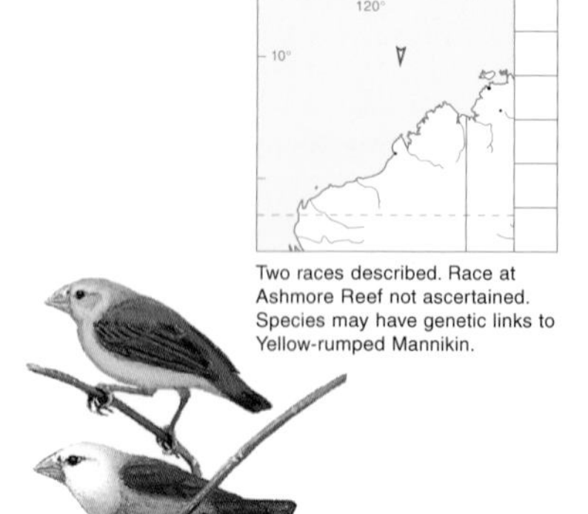

Two races described. Race at Ashmore Reef not ascertained. Species may have genetic links to Yellow-rumped Mannikin.

Typical mannikin shape; appears pale-headed. Bill pale grey. Eye dark brown. Pale creamy-white head, face, throat. Crown, nape, buffer. Mantle to lower back, wings, bright brown. Rump darker. Tail pale. Mushroom-fawn chest, grades to cinnamon belly, thighs, flanks. Undertail dark reddish brown. Legs grey.
F Underparts paler. Slightly darker head, breast. **Size** 10–11 cm.
Juv./Imm. Plain brown above; pale below. **Voice** M 'pseet'; F 'psit'. Louder 'peep' in flight (Restall, 1996). **Hab.** Grassy scrub, grassland, crops. Found in bushes at Ashmore Reef. Breeds Indonesian islands from Lombok to Weta, Timor; also southern Sulawesi. Three on West Island (Lat. 12° 14' S; Long. 122° 58' E), Ashmore Reef, off north-west Aust., 22.12.2000. Another record Jan.–Feb. 2003.

Palliser, T. (2002), 'Rare birds in 2001', *Wingspan* **12** (3): 19.
Restall, R. (1996), *Munias and Mannikins*, Pica Press, Mountfield, East Sussex, UK.

Narcissus Flycatcher *Ficedula narcissina* **V**

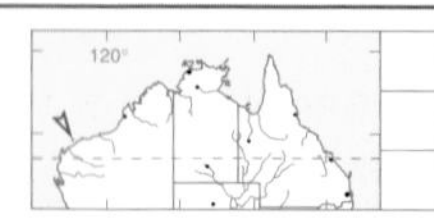

Race not determined; ? *narcissina*

Small. Black upper parts. Bright yellow eyebrow, rump. Bold white wing bar. Chin, throat washed orange. Rest of underparts yellow fading to white belly, undertail coverts. **F/Juv.** Olive brown above, tail washed rufous. Pale eye-ring, throat; rest of underparts pale brownish grey, mottled, washed, brown on breast, flanks. Others may have yellowish underparts. **Size** 13–14 cm.
Voice Low melodious warble; two-three syllable contact call.
Hab. In Aust., found in acacia-spinifex scrub. Breeds Japanese islands. Migrates to Philippines, North Borneo. First Aust. record: Barrow Is., off north-west WA following Cyclone 'Frank', two males, 26–28.11.1995; one male photographed 20.12.1995, about 5 km away.

Doig, P. & Fritz, S. (1996), 'Narcissus Flycatcher in Australia', *Wingspan* **6** (2): 23.
Mackinnon, J. & Phillipps, K. (1993), *A Field Guide to the Birds of Borneo, Sumatra, Java and Bali*, O.U.P., Oxford, UK.

Blue-and-White Flycatcher *Cyanoptila (Ficedula) cyanomelaena* V

Small songbird. Glossy blue upperparts, black face. Black breast sharply demarcated from white underparts. White bases to outer tail feathers. **F** Brown with pale eye-ring. Rump washed rufous. White throat patch, belly; rest of underparts pale brown. **Size** 16.5–17 cm (slightly larger than Hooded Robin). **Juv./Imm. M** As female, but blue wings, rump, tail. **Voice** Sweet warble; ending in distinctive double note. **Hab.** Within range, forests on hills near streams. Breeds Japan–Korea area; winters to south-east Asia, Indonesian region. One adult male found dead, beach-washed, near Cossack, east of Dampier Archipelago, WA, 5.12.1995. One ad. male Broome, WA 15–19.11.2002.

Johnstone, R.E. & Darnell, J.C. (1996), 'A Blue and White Flycatcher (*Ficedula cyanomelana*), a new bird for Australia', *Western Aust. Naturalist* **21**: 43–8.
Mackinnon, J. & Phillipps, K. (1993), *A Field Guide to the Birds of Borneo, Sumatra, Java and Bali*. O.U.P., Oxford, UK.
Wild Bird Society of Japan (1983), *A Field Guide to the Birds of Japan*, Wild Bird Soc. Japan, Tokyo (pp. 224–5).

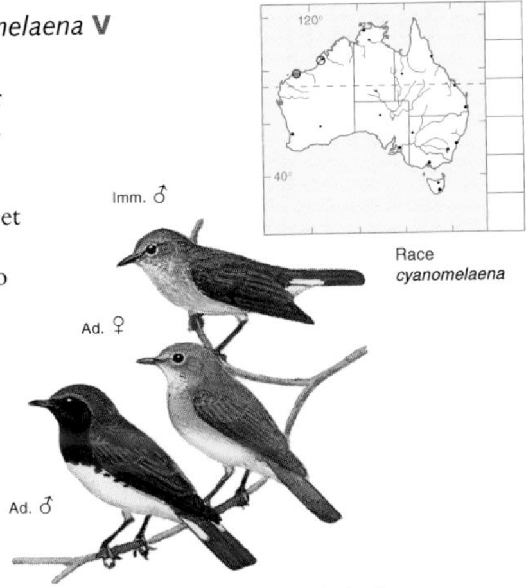

Race *cyanomelaena*

Two spellings encountered in books: cyanomelaena; *also* cyanomelana.

Isabelline Wheatear *Oenanthe isabellina* V

Check Gibberbird, female White-winged Triller. 'Thrush-shaped'. Has upright, 'long-legged' stance. Tail shorter than Australian (Richard's) Pipit, held well off ground. Pale, generally sandy wheatear. Bill dark, pointed. Soft whitish eyebrow, strong black eye-line. White rump, upper tail. Wide blackish terminal band, two central feathers blackish to base. Pale buff breast, paler below. **Size** Approx. 16.5 cm. **Voice** Chirping; whistles. **Hab.** Breeds on level steppes, stony areas, low hillsides in south central Eurasia (Turkey to China); migrates south-west to Central Africa, Arabia, Pakistan and north-west India. One at Mt Carbine, Qld., 15–25.11.2002.

Carter, M.J. (2003), 'Isabelline Wheatear: Another new bird for Australia', *Bird Observer* No. **822**: 28.

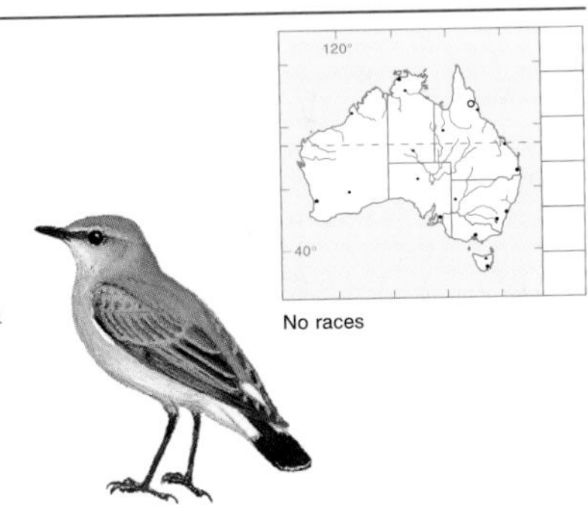

No races

Blue Rock Thrush *Monticola solitarius* V

Starling size, shape. Dark blue with rufous belly, undertail and underwing coverts. **M non-br.** Black and white scaling on dorsum. **F** Brownish. Dark-backed with bluish wash, pale buff underparts with dark scaling. Indistinct white throat is paler than breast. **Size** 23 cm. **Juv.** As female; scaling on dorsum more obvious. **Imm. M** As the Noosa individual and as M non-br., plumage scaled with white and black. Darker below. **Hab.** Qld bird seen on coastal cliffs, rock platforms, perching prominently in sheokes, dead trees. Widespread, variable species. Race *philippensis* breeds north-east Asia, Japan; migrates south to Philippines, parts of Indonesia. Nearest prior record Port Moresby, PNG. Recorded 26.10.1997 at Noosa Heads NP, south-east Qld, until end Nov. 1997.

Carter, M. & Shaw, R. (1998), 'Blue Rock Thrush *Monticola solitarius*: First record for Australia', *Aust. Bird Watcher* **18**: 101–5.
Mackinnon, J. & Phillipps, K. (1993), *A Field Guide to the Birds of Borneo, Sumatra, Java and Bali*, O.U.P., Oxford, UK.

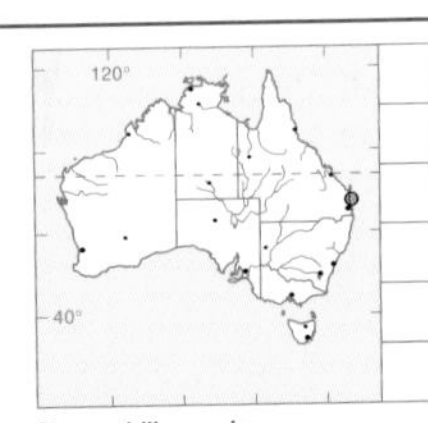

Race *philippensis*

Where the Birds Live

Vegetation and landform habitats of Australia

Geology, climate and soils, together with latitude, altitude and surface topography, determine the kinds of plants that are found in particular areas. The following pages first give a summary of those habitats in which the vegetation is the dominant visible feature, then those in which the landform is dominant. The purpose of these descriptions is to amplify the very brief descriptions of habitat given in the Field Information section. Space limitations have meant that the precise terms introduced here have not always been used in the prior section.

The sequence of presentation is broadly based on a structural classification proposed by Professor R. L. Specht during the 1970s and modified since by Walker & Hopkins (1984). The classification looks at identifiable plant habitats and plant communities as a whole and analyses, not so much what species are present, as how each community exists in terms of density and heights of its component plant species. In addition, the number of horizontal layers that the member species impart to the structure is taken into account (there may be several layers, or just one).

Habitats often merge with each other. Some of the richest bird localities are those where several habitat types meet. You are likely to see the endemic birds of each 'pure' habitat, plus the species which thrive in several habitats or in the fringe zones.

Line drawings, photographs and maps of each vegetation type can be found in Volume 6, *Vegetation*, of *Atlas of Australian Resources*. We are pleased to acknowledge the permission of the General Manager, Australian Surveying and Land Information Group, AUSLIG (now Geoscience Australia), Department of Administrative Services, Canberra, ACT, to reproduce these modified vegetational structural diagrams from this atlas. We acknowledge the assistance of Dr Robert Parsons and Dr Keith McDougall for their 6th edition update of these habitat notes.

We urge *all* field observers, ornithological or otherwise, to use the terminology of the *Atlas of Australian Resources*, and to identify correctly the vegetational categories they are working in, to improve the quality of their reports.

Vegetation heights in the diagrams are given in metres.

Closed forest

Closed forest (**rainforest** and **monsoon forest**) is forest closed in by dense, umbrella-like tree canopies so that little sunlight reaches the ground. Usually luxuriant, often majestic, it occurs in high rainfall areas and is named tropical or temperate depending on the mean annual temperature. Vines are prominent in the tropical types; ferns and mosses become more prominent in the temperate ones. Dense fringes may make physical entry difficult. Once under the canopy, reasonable mobility is possible. Birds can be clearly heard, but to see and identify them in the canopy is often a real challenge. Included here is the vegetation variously called monsoon forest, dry rainforest or vine thicket, in which up to 90% of species may be seasonally deciduous. This is found in patches in northern parts of WA, NT and Qld.

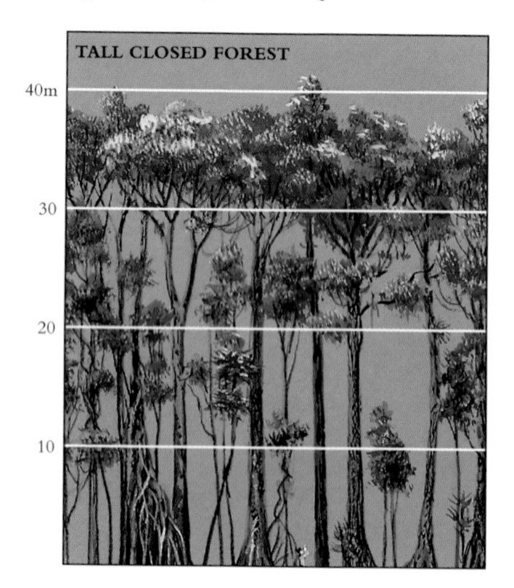

Open forest

Open forest (**wet** or **dry sclerophyll**; **eucalypt forest**) consists of trees spaced with *no* continuous canopy. In high rainfall areas, tall open forest (i.e. more than 30 m tall) is also called wet sclerophyll and often contains tall shrubs and tree ferns.

Most open forest is in drier areas with understoreys of low shrubs, grasses or both. Eucalypts usually dominate these forests, but some are dominated by acacia (e.g. brigalow) or various casuarinas. Open forest less than 30 m tall may be known as dry sclerophyll forest.

Woodland

Once the tree density drops (usually with declining rainfall) so that the average distance between tree crowns is more than one quarter of the average crown diameter, the vegetation is called woodland, *not* forest. Eucalypts are usually dominant but *Acacia*, *Banksia*, *Callitris* and *Melaleuca* dominate some types. The ground cover can be grassy or shrubby depending on various factors including soil fertility. Spinifex is the main understorey in parts of northern Australia. In open woodland, the distance between tree crowns can be 1–20 m.

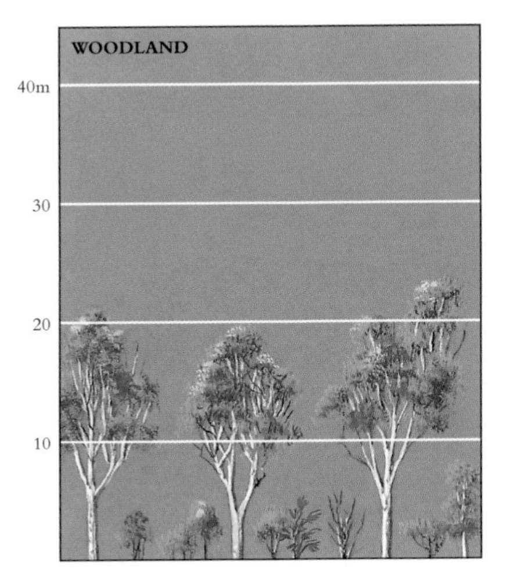

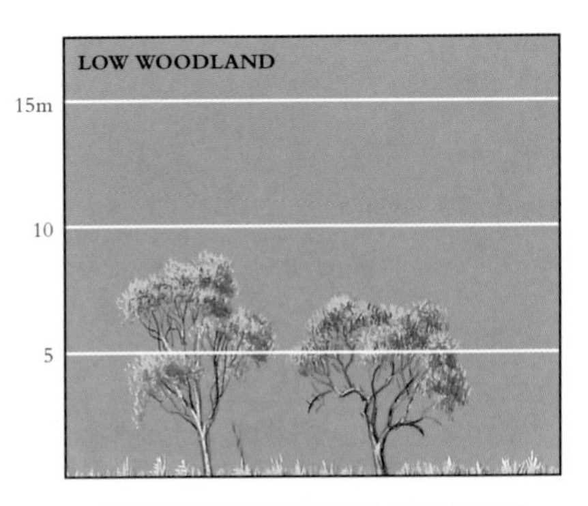

Eucalyptus scrubs and tall shrublands

Woody plants 2–8 metres tall with many stems arising at or near the base are regarded as shrubs, not trees, and dominate vegetation types called scrubs or, as shrub density declines, tall shrublands. Such types dominated by eucalypts include the well-known 'mallee scrub' of much of semi-arid southern Australia.

The soils can range from very infertile deep white sands to fertile calcareous loams and clays. Depending on soils and climate, the understorey can be dominated by:

a tussock grasses like spear grass and wallaby grass
b spiny hummock grasses like spinifex, *Triodia*
c low, hard-leaved (sclerophyllous) shrubs like *Leptospermum* and *Hakea* – types with this understorey have been called 'mallee-heath' in South Australia and Victoria
d dense, erect shrubs of the 'broombush' type, e.g. *Melaleuca uncinata*
e semi-succulent low shrubs, especially of the Family Chenopodiaceae (saltbush family).

Mallee vegetation can sometimes be found on rocky, infertile or otherwise unfavourable sites in some wet, mountainous areas.

The scrub known as 'mallee-heath' of southern Australia likewise has suffered from grazing and clearance for often ephemeral wheat farming. In the late 1940s, it was discovered that addition of soil trace elements such as zinc and copper allowed pasture growth for sheep in the 'mallee-heaths'. Some habitat has been preserved in national parks but much has been lost. Fire has become all too common.

Acacia scrubs and tall scrublands

The most common types are dominated by mulga *Acacia aneura* and a few other wattles. These dominate about 20 per cent of inland Australia, usually in areas drier than the main mallee ones. Low shrubs such as *Senna* (previously called *Cassia*) and *Eremophila* (emu-bushes) often occur, as do some chenopods. A layer of perennial tussock grasses is often present, along with ephemeral herbs. On some central and north-western Australian sandplains, hummock grasses ('spinifex') dominate the understorey.

Vast areas of these inland scrubland formations are available for sheep and cattle grazing. Stock there rely heavily on top feed, particularly during droughts, resulting in destruction of many mature mulga stands. In addition, rabbits have often prevented seedling establishment. Many regions of scrubs and shrublands have been severely degraded and are subject to soil erosion. Huge areas were cleared for wheat production, resulting frequently in eventual over-cropping, oversupply of superphosphate and inevitable degradation, leading to erosion and, in many places, rising salinity levels. Excess fertilisers can inhibit native vegetation growth, by favouring introduced pasture grasses.

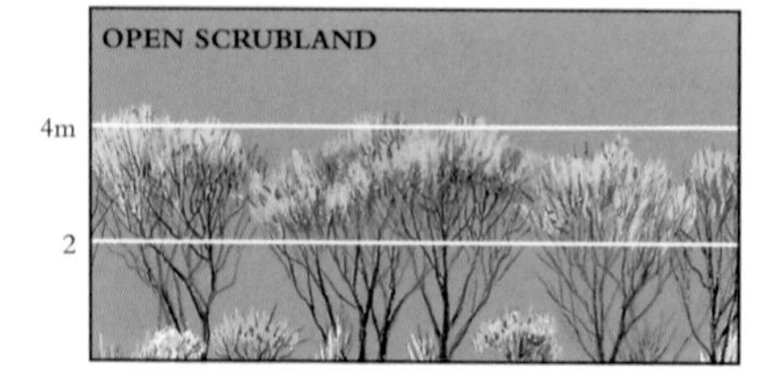

Heath

If the vegetation has its tallest layer dominated by evergreen, hard-leaved (sclerophyllous) shrubs less than two metres high, it is called heath. For many of these shrubs, the leaves are both hard and small (less than 2.5 cm long). Such leaves are called 'ericoid'.

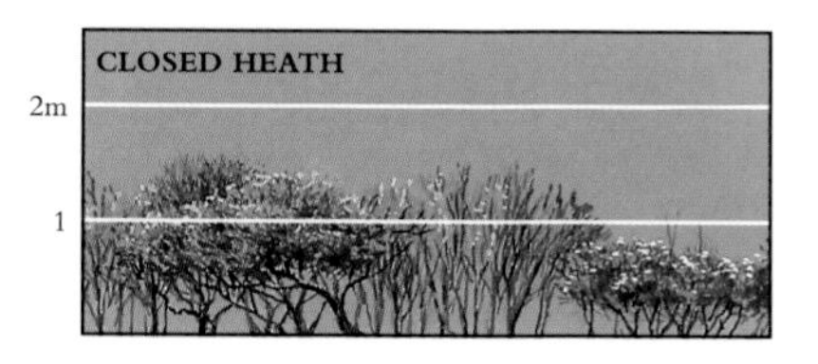

Heaths occur in two distinct habitat types, on coastal lowlands and in some alpine and sub-alpine areas. Heaths, particularly lowland heaths, have very diverse floras, with representatives of many plant families, including Casuarinaceae, Proteaceae, Mimosaceae, Myrtaceae, Xanthorrhoeaceae, Epacridaceae. A ground layer of grass-like plants such as sedges and Restionaceae is often present. Heath communities are mostly confined to areas of southern and eastern Australia where mean rainfall exceeds about 300 mm annually and where soils are very infertile.

Low nutrient levels in heath soils have meant that comparatively little has been cleared for farming, although the addition of fertilisers does render some areas suitable. Main threats to this formation come from coastal and alpine recreational and housing developments, and also from the increasing amount of sand mining being carried out in coastal heaths on stabilised dune systems.

Fairy-wrens, emu-wrens, scrubwrens and honeyeaters are often well represented in heathlands. The Ground Parrot may be found in a patchy distribution through some coastal heaths.

Low shrubland

Low shrubland (formerly called **shrub steppe**) is dominated by well-separated shrubs, up to two metres tall, of the Family Chenopodiaceae. The plants are semi-succulent, often with hairy leaves, and are well-adapted to soils with a high clay content and to periodic drought conditions. The most common dominants are species of *Maireana* (bluebushes) and *Atriplex* (saltbushes). After rains, grasses and ephemeral plants in the Families Compositae, Cruciferae and Leguminosae occur, along with lichens and fungi.

Salt marshes around coastal tide inlets and the salt pans of inland and central Australia are also structurally part of this formation but are discussed separately. Gibber plains are often covered with a very open low shrubland (see below).

Low shrublands are important sheep grazing areas. The sheep eat the chenopodiaceous shrubs in times of drought. Over-stocking has lead to the destruction of the flora of many such areas and its replacement by annual grasses. Often there is little shrub regeneration and much topsoil erodes.

Parrots, cockatoos, small doves, fairy-wrens, some honeyeaters, chats and woodswallows are seen in low shrubland. Flooding attracts wader species and a variety of waterfowl.

Gibber plains

Gibber plains ('stony deserts') consist of a sheet of continuous small- to medium-sized stones and rocks which effectively determine how the sparse plants are spaced and perhaps to what height they will grow. These deserts have formed over millions of years as widespread regional erosion of an earlier land surface dumped (deflated) the most resistant siliceous rocks (largely quartzites, although other rock types may also be involved). A visit to one of the remaining flat-topped hills will show you how it came about.

Sparse low vegetation also occurs on gibber plains; the *Atlas of Australian Resources* maps these areas as **sparse open herbfield**. The most common plants are non-woody species of the chenopods *Atriplex* and *Sclerolaena*; in drier years virtually all vegetation disappears. Cattle graze on gibber plains and erosion problems develop about artificial water sources such as stock tanks, bore drains and dams. Emu, birds of prey, Banded Lapwing, Inland Dotterel, Australian Pratincole and chats may be seen on gibber plains.

Closed grassland

Closed grassland is dominated by grasses of short or medium height where masses of individual plants are in close contact at their bases and have interlacing leaf canopies. Smaller herbs are also present. These communities are typical of the flood plains of many rivers draining Australia's north coast where the heavy black soils flood during the monsoon, then dry and crack deeply toward the end of the dry season. In some areas, sedges are dominant or co-dominant with the grasses.

The grazing of cattle, frequent firings that encourage green grass in the dry season, and destruction by introduced pigs and water buffalo, all severely damage areas of these grasslands.

Closed grasslands are also found in alpine and sub-alpine areas of south-eastern Australia where tussocks of *Poa* and *Danthonia* merge to form closed tussock grasslands. Some types are rich in perennial daisies and other herbs. The closed grasslands grade into moss-beds or bogs in the wetter hollows. They are covered by snow for several weeks or months each year. Such habitats were previously known as closed herbfield. Botanists now classify all of the low alpine/sub-alpine vegetation which was called 'herbfield' as grassland.

Fire (which in some areas occurs far too frequently) and also cattle grazing and trampling in the alpine areas of Tasmania, Victoria and New South Wales have caused extensive damage. To a lesser extent, so has the provision of firebreaks, ski runs, telecommunication towers, vehicle access tracks and car parks, lodges and other buildings, and the general trampling of some popular places by humans in the summer season. Exotic weeds are appearing along tracks and in stream courses.

Most of the small number of bird species that inhabit these alpine habitats in summer tend to move out (down) in the winter – altitudinal migration or nomadism.

Tussock grassland

Tussock grassland mostly occurs in northern Australia along the southern edges of the high summer rainfall zone (monsoonal influence) on calcareous cracking clay soils. Mitchell Grass (*Astrebla*) dominates these rolling treeless plains, the tussocks occurring about one metre apart. Except in drought years, a dense cover of short grasses and herbs occupies the spaces. The tussocks die back during the dry season or drought and, following rains, regenerate from the root stock. In western Victoria, the geologically Recent basalt plain carried a closed tussock grassland dominated by *Themeda* and *Danthonia* species, but most has been destroyed by grazing, improved pastures and land clearance.

Hummock grassland

Hummock grassland mostly occurs on skeletal or deep sandy soils, in arid or semi-arid areas where mean annual rainfall is 130–350 mm. It is dominated by large, perennial, evergreen, usually pungent and sharply pointed plants of the grasses *Triodia* and *Plectrachne*, which trap wind-blown sand to form mounds ('hummocks') up to a metre in diameter. The clumps die in the middle, spreading outward to form a doughnut-shaped ring. Flowering stems may be up to 1.5 metres high. The spaces between the hummocks are often bare; ephemeral plants may appear after rain. Over many years, these mounds enlarge and begin to overlap each other, forming a complex land terrain in some areas. A good example is in the Simpson Desert, where the lower sides of the many parallel dunes have hummock grassland associations.

It is noticeable in hummock grassland, and in the habitat descriptions following, that the geological component of the land surface becomes more dominant, largely controlling the vegetation structure and spacing.

Salt marshes and mangroves

Salt marshes and mangroves are very often found together along the coastline, occurring on tidally inundated areas of sheltered coasts. Mangroves dominate the seaward fringe of many estuaries and bays. By definition, mangroves are trees and tall shrubs found in sites flooded by tides, and are best developed in tropical areas where a number of different, often very well-defined, zones occur. Their structure ranges from forest to shrubland, with height and species-richness declining progressively southward. Only one mangrove species, *Avicennia marina*, is found in southern Australia. No single bird species is a specific frequenter of this species, but in the tropics a number of bird species may spend virtually all their lives in the mangrove communities – more work on this aspect of ornithology is needed.

Immediately inland of the mangrove zones, it is quite common to find various zones of salt marsh. These are usually shrublands dominated by nearly leafless chenopods called samphires. Further inland, high soil salinity produces a zone bare of almost all vegetation in many areas. Various bird species use salt marshes differently and many migratory waders enter them at high tide to roost after feeding on tidal mud or sand flats. The endangered Orange-bellied Parrot is in part a frequenter of salt marsh in south-eastern Australia during the winter months.

Salt marshes also occur about inland salt lakes, in basins or hollows from which there is mainly evaporative escape for the water. Where poor farming practices, over-grazing and tree clearance have radically altered the soil/water relationship, high soil salinity occurs.

Coastal dunes

Coastal dunes are readily recognisable. Exposed low coastal shorelines are usually backed by a series of coastal sand dunes formed during the recent geological past. A marked plant succession occurs from the seaward fringe of the frontal dune inland, resulting in a gradual stabilisation of the sand. The zones frequently parallel the coastline for several kilometres inland. The succession is from dune grasses to low shrubland to woodland. Freshwater lakes or swamps may lie in hollows (swales) between the dunes.

Coastal dune systems all around Australia are under considerable pressure. Development of coastal resorts has involved destruction of dune vegetation, and building of houses and roads, often just above high tide mark. As a result, severe beach erosion has occurred. Groynes and sea walls have been built in an attempt to control sand loss or movement in popular areas. More recent threats to other major coastal dune systems are sand mining operations for heavy minerals (for instance rutile, ilmenite, monazite and zircon) and increasing problems posed by dune buggies, trail bikes and rabbits.

Inland waters

Inland waters across the continent are variable, intermittent or virtually non-existent, because of low and unreliable rainfall, high evaporation and fairly level topography. Perennial streams are confined to the northern and eastern coasts and along small stretches of the southern coast. The largest river system is the Murray/Darling and its tributaries, but even there flow is very variable as no permanent snow fields exist to maintain river levels in summer months.

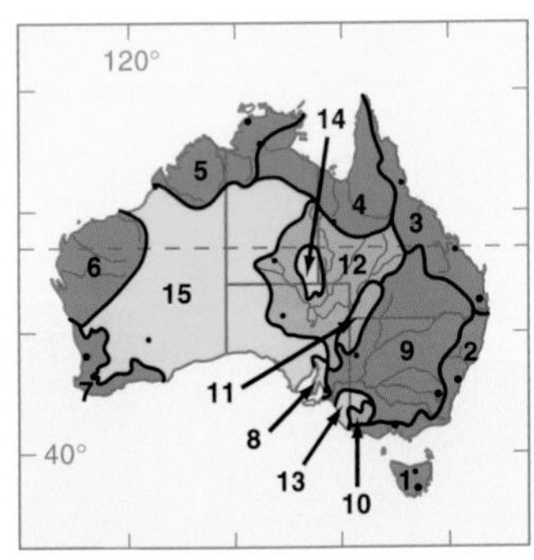

Drainage basins of Australia

Drainage to sea
1 Tasmanian
2 South-eastern slopes
3 North-eastern slopes
4 Gulf of Carpentaria
5 Timor Sea
6 Indian Ocean
7 South-west slopes
8 Adelaide coastal
9 Murray-Darling Basin

Internal Drainage
10 Wimmera internal
11 Bulloo internal
12 Lake Eyre internal

Uncoordinated drainage
13 South-eastern 'Mallee area'
14 'Central' Lake Eyre basin area
15 'Central Australia' area

Map modified from Lake, J.S. (1971), *Freshwater Fishes & Rivers of Australia*, Nelson, Melbourne.

Major streams in Australia often change within one year from a peak flow that inundates vast areas of flood plain to a chain of pools and billabongs with little or no flow between them. Rivers in more arid regions generally do not flow every year and drainage is toward the generally extensive playa basin areas rather than towards the coast. The rivers are 'grouped' into catchments or basins of drainage, such as Lake Eyre Basin.

The most extensive areas of **swamp** (wetland) in Australia are associated with the northern coastal rivers and the Murray/Darling Basin. Other smaller swamps are widely scattered through higher rainfall areas where they may occur in natural or man-made depressions. Apart from sub-alpine bogs, most swamps dry out during the summer.

The only extensive **freshwater lakes** in Australia are those of the Tasmanian central plateau. Here, lakes, lakelets and ponds ranging in depth from less than a metre to more than 200 m resulted from the last glaciation period. Similar lakes occupy glacial basins in the Australian Alps. The remaining freshwater lakes in Australia are confined to the higher rainfall areas; the majority of these either dry out annually or have been dry a number of times since European settlement. Minor exceptions are flooded volcanic craters, such as Lakes Eacham and Barrine in northern Queensland.

Pollution from mining waste, industrial and household effluent, uncontrolled boating, conversion of lakes into reservoirs for the generation of hydro-electric power or for water storage – often with release of cold, de-oxygenated bottom water – plus land clearance and creeping salinity levels, pose the main threats to the comparatively small number of our natural freshwater lakes, streams and wetland areas.

Obviously, all Australia's birds are dependent in one way or another on the limited freshwater complexes of the continent. The nomadic lifestyle of many species reflects their capacity and need to follow the rains and they breed only if local conditions are right.

Saline lakes vary in character in terms of dissolved salts and the presence or absence of water itself. They include some of the volcanic crater lakes of western Victoria, some mound springs south-west of Lake Eyre which are the natural outlets of the subterranean Great Artesian Basin, and the numerous salt pans of arid Australia. In most years these lakes, including the vast bed of Lake Eyre, consist of extensive areas of white salt crust supporting no vegetation at all and, in the interior, with surface summer temperatures reaching 50°C.

Marine habitats

Marine habitats divide into three types, each having their own birds and each sharing some birds with adjacent habitats.

Estuaries occur where freshwater streams meet the tide's influence. These estuarine or 'mixing of the waters' zones could be said to extend seaward as far as the diluting influence of the freshwater reaches. This will vary with the season, the amount of rainfall or melting snow contributed, the range and reach of normal and king tides, and the width and depth of the embayment into which the freshwater flows. Estuaries are also areas of active sedimentation from the land. Mangroves often fringe the seaward side and salt marshes may develop behind them as new land is formed and edges outward.

Our definition of **coastal seas** includes all of the comparatively shallow seas lying directly on the submerged portions of the continental shelf of the Australian continental plate. By this definition, Bass Strait, Torres Strait, the Gulf of Carpentaria, the Timor and Arafura Seas and the Great Barrier Reef are all coastal areas (see map at front of book).

The **oceans** include all sea areas beyond the continental plate margin, where the really deep water lies. The boundary between these pelagic (oceanic) areas and the edge of the continental shelf is proving a very rich area to visit for seabird watching. Take a bird- or whale-watching trip on a small boat if you possibly can. The rewards can be high. But do remember to consult a pharmacist if you are prone to sea sickness – it can be largely overcome!

Cliffs and exposed rock faces

There are thousands of cliffs and exposed rock faces around Australia. Many contain caves or deep joints, faults, crevices; some have vegetation on them, some are bare. Only a fairly small number of bird species *consistently* breed on, or under, rock ledges in Australia. These include the Little Penguin, Fairy Prion, Common Diving-Petrel, gannets and boobies, Great Cormorant, Black-faced Cormorant, Red-tailed Tropicbird, Osprey, Wedge-tailed Eagle, White-bellied Sea-Eagle, Peregrine Falcon, Nankeen Kestrel, Silver, Pacific and Kelp Gulls, Rock Dove, Rock Parrot, Barn and Masked Owls, swallows and martins, Grey and Sandstone Shrike-thrushes, Rockwarbler, pardalotes, House Sparrow, Common Starling and Common Myna. In south-western Victoria, some Long-billed Corella breed in holes in the tuff, the volcanic ash crater walls of Tower Hill.

Other species breed opportunistically in such sites. Quarry faces, open-cut mines, mullock heaps, road and railway cuttings, embankments and cave entrances are all used. Large office buildings, silos, factories and hangars may be regarded as 'human cliffs'. Birds often use such sites.

We exclude from examples of bird species using this habitat, those that nest on telegraph poles, aerials, telecommunication towers and land-line (cable) towers – they are using them as substitute trees.

Islands

Islands may merely be sand or mud banks exposed at low tide in an estuary or bay, or rocky offshore mountain tops or ranges, as are many of the islands of our continental shelf. Sometimes these are enlarged by the growth of coral upward from the floor of the shallow seas, or along the edge of the shelf itself, e.g. the Great Barrier Reef. Such islands may have no vegetation, an individual plant character, or extensions of the flora of the adjacent mainland. Islands usually have fewer land bird species than does the nearby land mass.

Caves

Caves form in many ways: by solution in limestone areas, by rifting and jointing in almost every rock type, by the flowing on of molten lava to form lava tunnels, by plucking or grinding of sea or river in cliffs of coastlines or gorges, and by the abrasion of windblown sand. Mines, railway and pipeline tunnels may be regarded as 'human caves'.

Only one bird species in Australia, the White-rumped Swiftlet, is fully adapted to total blackness and a cave-dwelling way of life. It uses echo-navigating clicks to find its way in the dark. Swallows and martins, the Grey Shrike-thrush and the Masked Owl at times use the twilight zone of caves and mines. If exploring, take a torch, leave a note or marker at the entrance of any cave you enter, watch out for snakes, do not smoke, wear a helmet and be very slow, quiet and responsible – caves and their fauna are extremely vulnerable to human interference.

Agricultural and pastoral lands

Agricultural and pastoral lands now dominate a huge proportion of the continent. Even those wilderness regions which remain directly uncontaminated by Europeans and their crops, stock, feral plants and animals receive indirect pollution from airborne or waterborne chemicals. Direct human interference with the land is the rule, not the exception. We urge all persons interested in any way in natural history, at any level, to increase their efforts in the documenting of entire communities and their ecological webs, and in saving and rehabilitating the natural vegetation.

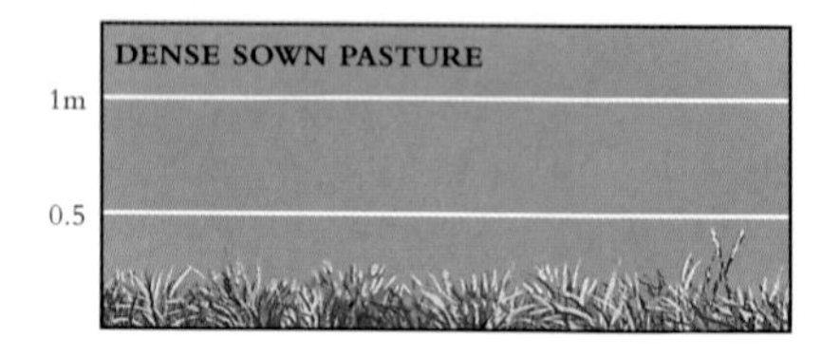

Urbanised land

Urbanised land represents the end of the road for most of the Australian native bird fauna! But some are able to adapt and hang on in gardens and reserves. They, with introduced bird species, constitute completely new bird communities to be studied, although frequently such communities are species-impoverished.

Relief for birds and other fauna must come in the form of massive green belts, with a linking web of 'green corridors' between these. Selected species plantings, wetland provision and preservation, and coastal reserves are needed. So too is a ruthless onslaught against feral animals and weed species, and a far-reaching educational programme for humans.

Reading

AUSLIG (1990), *Atlas of Australian Resources, Third Series, Volume 6, Vegetation,* Commonwealth of Australia, Division of National Mapping.

Beard, J.S. (1990), *Plant Life of Western Australia,* Kangaroo Press, Kenthurst, NSW.

Bradstock, R.A., Williams, J.E. & Gill, A.M. (eds) (2002), *Flammable Australia: The Fire Regimes and Biodiversity of a Continent,* Cambridge University Press, Cambridge, UK.

Brock, J. (1993), *Native Plants of Northern Australia,* Reed New Holland, Frenchs Forest, NSW.

Costermans, L. (1981), *Native Trees and Shrubs of South-Eastern Australia,* Rigby, Adelaide.

Gibbons, P. & Lindenmayer, D. (2002), *Tree Hollows and Wildlife Conservation in Australia,* CSIRO Publishing, Collingwood, VIC.

Holliday, I. (2002), *A Field Guide to Australian Trees,* 3rd edition, New Holland, Frenchs Forest, NSW.

Low, T. (2001), *Feral Future,* Penguin, Ringwood, VIC.

Specht, R.L. (1970), 'Vegetation', in Leeper, G.W. (ed.), *The Australian Environment,* 4th edition, CSIRO in association with Melbourne University Press, Melbourne.

Walker, J. & Hopkins, M.S. (1984), 'Vegetation', in McDonald, R.C., et al, *Australian Soil and Land Survey: Field Handbook,* Inkata Press, Melbourne.

White, M.E. (1998), *The Greening of Gondwana: The 400 Million Year Story of Australia's Plants,* 3rd (revised) edition, Kangaroo Press, East Roseville, NSW.

White, M.E. (2000), *Running Down: Water in a Changing Land,* Kangaroo Press, East Roseville, NSW.

Breeding Information

The life cycle of a bird

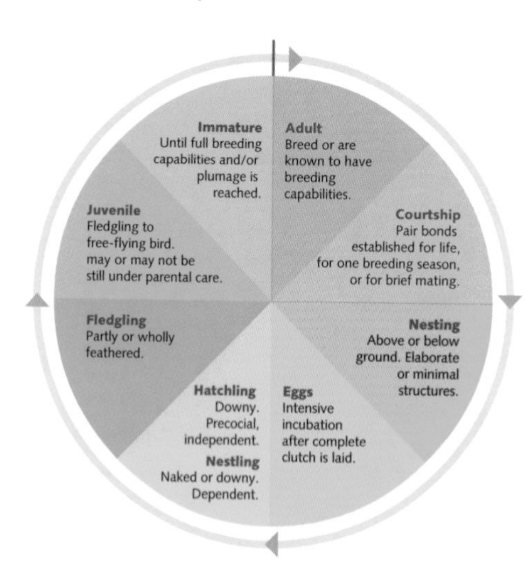

HATCHLING Downy, in or about the nest. Precocial. May leave nest quickly. Often fully or partly independent.

NESTLING Naked or downy (downy = before true feathers develop). Dependent.

FLEDGLING (after leaving the nest) Partly or wholly feathered. Flightless or partly flighted, but almost always *before* full flight capacity.

Note These first three categories are colloquially known as 'chicks'.

JUVENILE (= Juvenal) Fledged to free-flying birds, with the feathers which first replaced the natal down. May or may not be still under parental care. This plumage duration may be short-lived, a few weeks only in some species.

IMMATURE (= Sub-adult) All plumages which *follow* first moult *until* full breeding capacity and/or breeding plumage is attained. Sometimes given as 1st year, 2nd year, and so on.

ADULT Birds which breed or are known to have breeding capabilities. Adult plumages are those that do not change in appearance in subsequent moults (allowing for alternating eclipse plumages in some species, e.g. waders, fairy-wrens, and lifelong slow change by Wandering Albatross).

Courtship

Males and females meet for courtship with the intention of breeding. Elaborate courtship ceremonies occur between the sexes in many birds; in others courtship is inconspicuous. Pair bonds are established, either for life, for one year or breeding season, or for brief matings, and are followed by nesting and brooding by one of the sexes, sometimes assisted by the partner, sometimes alone.

Nesting

Availability of the correct nest site, safely located and typical of its species, is vital for successful breeding. Environmental damage probably affects this period of a bird's life cycle more severely than any other. Nesting may be above or below ground. It may be colonial, where only the immediate nest area is defended, or solitary, in a defended territory of variable size. Site choice usually dictates nest materials. Some birds do not build a nest; others have elaborate structures.

Nest and territory defence may be by direct physical attacks and vocalising, by distraction displays designed to lead an attacker away, or by immobility and skilful camouflage. The number of broods per season varies. One brood is considered normal for most Australian birds, but many species have demonstrated a capacity to breed from two to four times in a season when optimum environmental conditions prevail.

Eggs

Eggs of most bird species are plain white or pastel in colour and may have darker speckles, spots, blotches or patterns for recognition or camouflage. Eggs of hollow-breeding species may have a high gloss, and those of a burrow-breeding species a chalky surface. Shapes vary between species, from well-rounded to pyriform.

Eggs are often given minimal care until the entire group (clutch) is laid. Then intensive incubation (covering and heating) commences in earnest. The period of incubation depends, to some extent, on external temperatures, body bulk, egg-size ratios and, to a large extent, on the degree of independence of the chick at hatching. Incubation does not last long in species in which chicks are born naked, blind and virtually helpless. In species that have advanced (precocial) and largely or entirely independent hatchlings, incubation may take much longer.

Hatchlings usually have a tiny 'egg tooth' – a hard protuberance on the upper bill tip which helps them chip a hole in the eggshell. Hatching may take from a few minutes to several days, depending on egg size, thickness of shell, external air temperature and degree of parental assistance.

Hatchlings – fully or partly independent

Hatchlings must recognise and bond with (imprint on) their parents at time of hatching and vice versa.

Nestlings – dependent

Natal covering of nestlings varies from quite naked to lightly or fully clad in fluffy down, depending on egg size, incubation period and future lifestyle. Suitable food must be provided fairly soon after hatching as the yolk reserves of the chick are quickly exhausted. Warmth, shading and protection from predators and territorial neighbours are also required. Education of the chick proceeds by mimicry of adults, observation, and trial and error. Cuckoos may be an exception: do hosts and neighbouring birds imprint on them? Or perhaps there is delayed imprinting: juvenile cuckoos meeting their real parents later.

Moulting

Every bird species undergoes a series of feather moults, from natal down into juvenile plumage, then into immature plumage (which may continue annually for several years) and finally adult breeding plumage. In adult life, all the feathers change once a year, either in a pre-breeding or post-breeding moult. However, there are plenty of exceptions to this. Many have a partial moult, changing either body or wing feathers in turn, or moulting the wing feathers in series, so that flight capacity is not lost. Penguins have a total body moult over a short period for re-waterproofing purposes. Many migratory birds arrive in or leave Australia in a state of partial or complete moult. They moult into, or out of, a drab, less conspicuous winter or 'eclipse' plumage. As you will appreciate, it is important that you work hard to identify the visiting seabird and wader species, gulls, and foreign wagtails, because plumages may vary greatly.

Death

Death of birds, as with other animals, may come in many guises and a high proportion does not survive the first year. Birds may die *(a)* by mechanical means – by shooting or trapping (usually illegal), traffic, choking or entangling accidents, becoming prey, being tossed out of the nest by a cuckoo or a sibling; or *(b)* by physiological (systemic) means – disease, starvation, exposure, overwhelming internal or external parasite load, poison, pollutants, or even old age!

The bodies of dead birds are rarely found because they are quickly taken by predators or scavengers.

Legend for breeding bars

- Main breeding season
- Casual breeding and breeding in response to unseasonable rainfall

Breeding season is taken as the beginning of nest construction to fledging of the young

Breeding summary

In the pages that follow we give more detail about the breeding and nesting of the birds described in the **Field Information** section. Remember that we only cover families occurring in the Australasian avifaunal region. The sequence of families follows that of the **Key to Families** (pp. **8–17**), but within each family, the sequence is that of Christidis & Boles (1994). Most of the original data for the Breeding Bars came from our interpretation of Gordon Beruldsen's *A Field Guide to Nests and Eggs of Australian Birds* (1980), Rigby, Adelaide, S.A. Since then, many other published sources have been used, including *HANZAB*, the set of *National Photographic Index of Australian Wildlife* volumes and Schodde & Mason (1999), as well as our own knowledge, and information from some of our contributors. Far more information exists in the **Core Library** (pp. **351–6**), so please use those books to extend your knowledge.

All birds that breed in Australia have been given a diagrammatic representation of their breeding seasons, although there are many exceptions and anomalies. Some species really require several breeding bars, because of asynchronous breeding in different parts of the continent, caused either by climate and nomadism, or variation in the number of breeding attempts in any season. The latter, and the species particularly prone to variation, are indicated by '(★ = variable)' at the head of appropriate breeding bar sequences, and an asterisk for each species. Introduced species are indicated by a bold '**Intro.**'.

In this **Breeding Summary**, we accept nest building as the beginning, and the departure of fledged young from the nest as the end, of a breeding period. Most entries begin with a brief introduction concerning aspects of breeding, such as courtship, monogamy or polygamy, age of parents at sexual maturity, size of the breeding group (pair, colonial, family group with 'helpers'), and breeding frequency per season. All information should be regarded as 'approximate', to be used only as a guide. Look at other texts for fine detail.

The following standard headings are used:

Nest Nest site, type of nest, materials, position, builder.

Eggs Their number (clutch size), and very brief summary of colour.

Inc. Incubation period by male or female or both and given in days. Also, who feeds who?

Hatchl. Hatchling.

Nestl. Nestling.

Fledge Age at fledging, i.e. the time of leaving the nest, given in weeks. May be partly or fully feathered; partly or fully flighted.

Care Any subsequent parental or other care, from fledging to independence.

Cassowaries, Emu *Family Casuariidae* pp. 18–19

Females polygamous. Males build nest, incubate eggs alone for about 2 months; rear chicks.

Southern Cassowary: **Nest** Well-drained platform of forest litter. **Eggs** 2–5; large, green, embossed. **Care** Approx. 9 months.

Emu: **Nest** Thin mat of grass or twig-lined shallow scrape on ground. **Eggs** 6–14, large, green–black, embossed. Larger clutches by two females in one nest. **Care** Approx. 18 months.

Breeding Seasons

J F M A M J J A S O N D

Southern Cassowary

Emu

Mound-builders (Megapodes) *Family Megapodiidae* pp. 20–1

Females polygamous. **Nest** Sand, soil or leaf-litter 'incubating' mound. Males tend nest-mound, control temperature and humidity; turn eggs. **Eggs** 3–30, pinkish, chalky, stained by vegetation; laid at varying intervals. **Inc.** 50 days or more. **Hatchl.** Precocial, independent from hatching. **Care** None.

Breeding Seasons

J F M A M J J A S O N D

Orange-footed Scrubfowl

Malleefowl

Australian Brush-turkey

Quails, Pheasants *Family Phasianidae* pp. 20–1

Native quail are fairly nomadic, breeding frequently after good rains. **Nest** Female builds shallow saucer in tall grass. **Eggs** 4–12, pale buff, speckled or heavily blotched brown. **Inc.** By female. 14–21 days (quail); 20–28 days (Peafowl, Common Pheasant). **Hatchl.** Precocial, dependent. **Fledge** 2–3 weeks. **Care** Mostly by female; about 12 weeks.

Breeding Seasons (* variable)

J F M A M J J A S O N D

Stubble Quail

Brown Quail*

King Quail

Red Junglefowl* **Intro.**

Common Pheasant **Intro.** (Insufficient information)

Indian Peafowl **Intro.**

Wild Turkey **Intro.** (Insufficient information)

New World Quails *Family Odontophoridae* pp. 22–3

Monogamous. Little Aust. information. Probable spring breeders. Small groups (coveys) in autumn, winter. From NZ studies: **Nest** Ground scrape. **Eggs** 13; pointed, dull white to buff. **Inc.** Female only. **Nestl.** Precocial. **Care** Both parents guard chicks. Attain full size after 4 months.

Breeding Season

J F M A M J J A S O N D

California Quail **Intro**

Button-quails *Family Turnicidae* pp. 24–5

Breed after rain. Females polygamous, mating with several males each breeding season. **Nest** On ground near tussocks, lined with grass, some with interwoven canopy. **Eggs** 2–5, spotted red-brown, lavender. **Inc.** Approx. 14 days. **Hatchl.** Precocial, dependent. **Fledge** Approx. 2½ weeks. **Care** Male incubates, rears young.

Breeding Seasons (* variable)

J F M A M J J A S O N D

Red-backed Button-quail*

Painted Button-quail

Chestnut-backed Button-quail

Buff-breasted Button-quail

Black-breasted Button-quail

Little Button-quail*

Red-chested Button-quail*

Penguins *Family Spheniscidae* pp. 26–7

Little Penguin breeds in Australia. **Nest** Colonial or solitary nesters in burrows, under rocks or suitable built structures. **Eggs** 1–2, whitish, stained. **Inc.** Approx. 42 days. **Fledge** 8–10 weeks. **Care** Adults return at dusk to feed nestlings.

Breeding Season

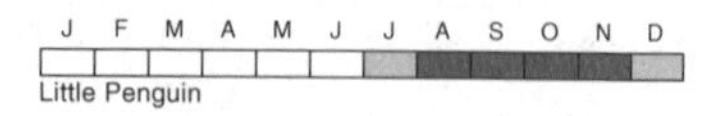

Little Penguin

Albatrosses *Family Diomedeidae* pp. 28–33

Only albatross breeding in Australia is the Shy, nominate race *cauta*, on Albatross Island off north-west Tasmania, Pedra Branca, and The Mewstone, off southern Tasmania. Breeds at 7 years. Colonial. **Nest** Raised platform of earth and faecal material. **Eggs** 1, white, clouded at one end. **Inc.** 70 days. **Fledge** 4–5 months. **Care** Both parents, for possibly 8 months (little data).

Breeding Season

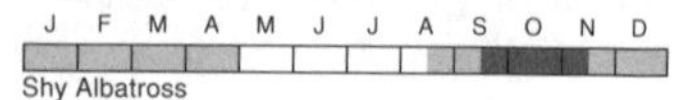

Shy Albatross

Diving-Petrels, Petrels, Prions, Shearwaters
Family Procellariidae pp. 34–47

Colonial nesters. **Nest** In burrows or rock crevices. **Eggs** 1, white. **Inc.** Approx. 42–63 days. **Nestl.** Downy, dependent. **Fledge** Shearwaters at approx. 14 weeks; smaller petrels less. **Care** Both parents. Shearwaters leave older downy young in burrows until the fledging is complete, when young leave independently. Similar pattern for most petrel species.

Breeding Seasons

J F M A M J J A S O N D

Common Diving-Petrel

Great-winged Petrel

Herald Petrel*

Soft-plumaged Petrel (insufficient information)

Gould's Petrel

Fairy Prion

Wedge-tailed Shearwater

Flesh-footed Shearwater

Sooty Shearwater

Short-tailed Shearwater

Little Shearwater

Storm-Petrels *Family Hydrobatidae* pp. 46–7

White-faced Storm-Petrel breeds at 3–5 yrs. Colonial nester. **Nest** Long, narrow burrow in sand. **Eggs** 1, white, flecked reddish. **Inc.** Approx. 56 days. **Nestl.** Downy, dependent. **Fledge** 9 weeks. **Care** Both parents.

Breeding Season

J F M A M J J A S O N D

White-faced Storm-Petrel

Pelicans *Family Pelecanidae* pp. 48–9

Colonial, on islands, or inland after floods. **Nest** Lined scrape on ground, sometimes rough platform. **Eggs** 2–4, chalky white, scratched, stained. **Inc.** Both parents; 32–35 days. **Nestl.** Naked, grows down, dependent. **Fledge** Approx. 12 weeks. **Care** Need initial protection from fierce sun and inclement weather generally. Both parents feed young; chicks enter créches once they can walk.

Breeding Season (* variable)

J F M A M J J A S O N D

Australian Pelican*

Gannets, Boobies *Family Sulidae* pp. 48–51

Gannets tend to frequent southern temperate coastal waters; boobies are mostly tropical. Breed at 6–8 years. Colonial. **Nest** Mound, stick platform or shallow scrape in sand. **Eggs** 1 or 2; chalky white or pastel green, blue, when laid. **Inc.** Approx. 42 days. **Hatchl.** Downy, dependent. **Fledge** 15 weeks. **Care** One nestling is favoured, the other usually dies.

Breeding Seasons (* variable)

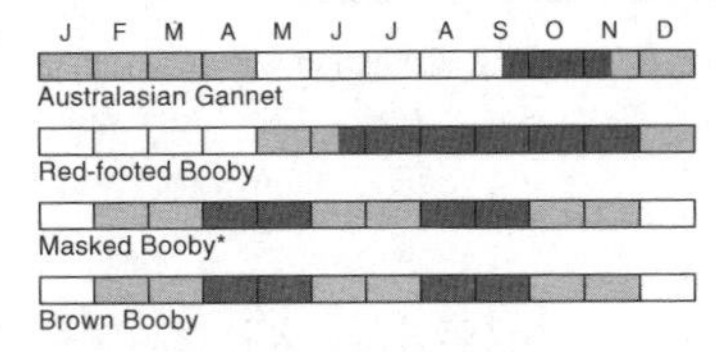

Frigatebirds *Family Fregatidae* pp. 52–3

Usually breed every 2 years. Colonial, on offshore islands. **Nest** Stick platforms on ground or on low vegetation within 2–3 m of ground. **Eggs** 1, chalky white. **Inc.** Both parents, 42–50 days. **Nestl.** Naked, becomes downy. **Fledge** 17–21 weeks approx. **Care** Dependent on parents for many months, sometimes up to a year.

Breeding Seasons

J F M A M J J A S O N D

Great Frigatebird

Lesser Frigatebird

Tropicbirds *Family Phaethontidae* pp. 52–3

Tropicbirds breed throughout year on island cliffs, often in crevices. Colonial. **Nest** Scrape. **Eggs** 1; white, variably spotted and shaped. **Inc.** Both parents, 41–50 days. **Nestl.** Naked, grows down, dependent. Fully grown after about 40 days, but does not leave nest. **Fledge** After 10–15 weeks. **Care** Both parents until fledging; juvenile then independent.

Breeding Season (* variable)

J F M A M J J A S O N D

Red-tailed Tropicbird*

Anhingas (Darters) *Family Anhingidae* pp. 54–5

Nests tend to be solitary, within loose colonies, often with cormorants, herons, etc. **Nest** Large, wide, stick structure, deep lined bowl. **Eggs** 3–5, pale blue-green. **Inc.** Both parents, 28–30 days. **Nestl.** Naked, grow down, dependent. **Fledge** 8–9 weeks approx. **Care** Both parents.

Breeding Season (* variable)

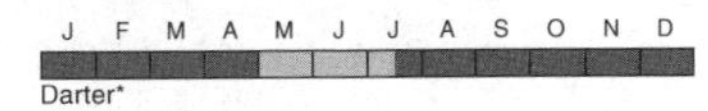

Cormorants, Shags
Family Phalacrocoracidae pp. 54–5

Colonial, often with Darters, herons, egrets, ibis. **Nest** Stick platform in trees or on ground, near water. Female builds with material male brings. Later becomes fouled with excreta. **Eggs** 2–5, chalky blue or green. **Inc.** Both parents, 27–31 days. **Nestl.** Nestlings are initially naked and look distinctly 'reptilian'. Dependent. **Fledge** Depending on size, remain in or at nest for 8–12 weeks approx. **Care** Both parents throughout period.

Breeding Seasons (* variable)

J F M A M J J A S O N D

Black-faced Cormorant*

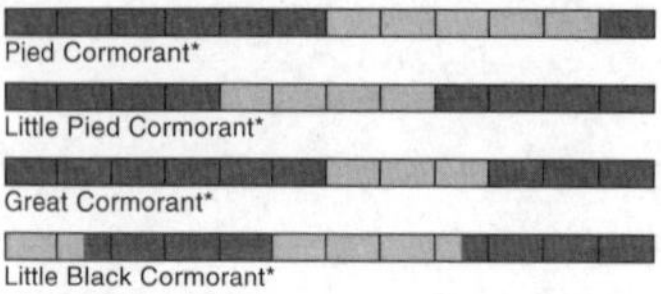

Pied Cormorant*

Little Pied Cormorant*

Great Cormorant*

Little Black Cormorant*

Grebes *Family Podicipedidae* pp. 56–7

In spectacular courtship displays, Great Crested Grebe pairs face each other in the water, shaking erect head crests and ruffs, apparently preening and offering each other nest material. Smaller grebes have vocal but less spectacular displays. **Nest** Mating occurs on the hidden, floating or anchored nest-platform, or on aquatic vegetation. **Eggs** 3–8; chalky, white or bluish, soon stained by wet leaves as adults cover eggs when leaving nest. **Inc.** Both parents, 21–30 days. **Nestl.** Precocial; downy. **Fledge** Varies with size of species: 6–7 weeks, 10–12 weeks in others. **Care** Both parents, for about 9–10 weeks. Often carried on adult's back when small. Later broods may be partly cared for by juveniles.

Breeding Seasons

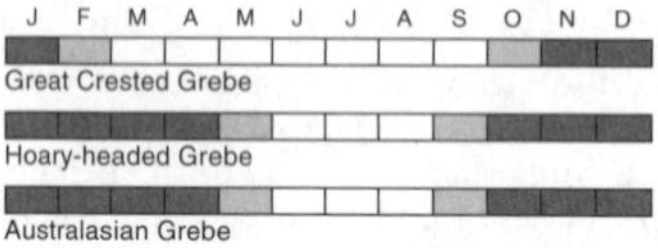

J F M A M J J A S O N D

Great Crested Grebe

Hoary-headed Grebe

Australasian Grebe

Magpie Goose *Family Anseranatidae* p. 58

Breed after wet season. Colonial. **Nest** Swamp vegetation with deep bowl, over water. **Eggs** Usually 6–8, white, stained brown. **Inc.** Both sexes; approx. 28 days. **Hatchl.** Precocial; downy; largely independent. Leave nest within a day. **Fledge** Approx. 3–4 weeks. **Care** Guarded, brooded by parents for 3 weeks or so. Sometimes two females accompany one male, sharing incubation, care of young. Fed by parents, helpers, for up to 17 weeks.

Breeding Season (* variable)

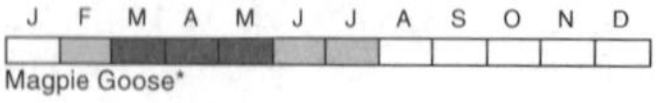

J F M A M J J A S O N D

Magpie Goose*

Geese, Swans, Ducks *Family Anatidae* pp. 58–67

Geese and swans usually mate for life; ducks believed to take a new partner every year. Swans mature at 5 years. Courtship displays vary from 'haughty' posturing in geese to animated displays by brightly coloured male dabbling ducks. **Nest** On ground or high in tree hollows; vary from scrapes lined with down (ducks) to large bulky nests of vegetation (swans). **Eggs** 5–8, lustrous white or greenish. **Inc.** 21–28 days for stiff-tailed and dabbling ducks, 35–40 days for swans. Some females incubate alone. **Hatchl.** Precocial; downy; independent. Leave nest when clutch hatched; capable of swimming immediately. **Fledge** From 5 weeks for teal, to over 14 weeks for swans. **Care** Both parents (geese, swans); both sexes or female (ducks). Young feed themselves (except Musk Duck).

Breeding Seasons (* variable)

J F M A M J J A S O N D

Black Swan*

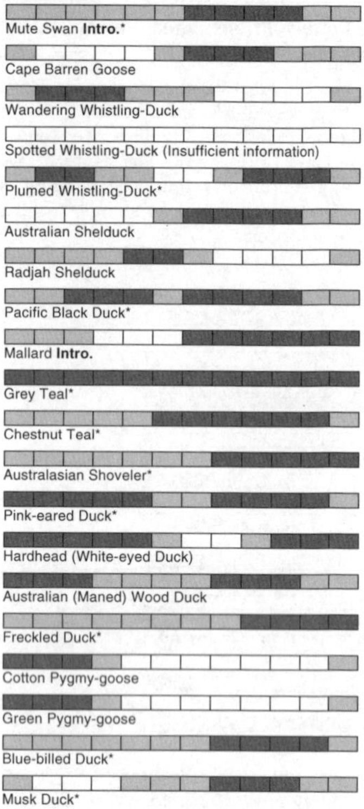

Mute Swan **Intro.***

Cape Barren Goose

Wandering Whistling-Duck

Spotted Whistling-Duck (Insufficient information)

Plumed Whistling-Duck*

Australian Shelduck

Radjah Shelduck

Pacific Black Duck*

Mallard **Intro.**

Grey Teal*

Chestnut Teal*

Australasian Shoveler*

Pink-eared Duck*

Hardhead (White-eyed Duck)

Australian (Maned) Wood Duck

Freckled Duck*

Cotton Pygmy-goose

Green Pygmy-goose

Blue-billed Duck*

Musk Duck*

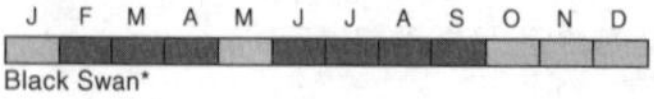

Rails, Crakes, Swamphens, Coot *Family Rallidae* pp. 68–73

Often strongly territorial when breeding. **Nest** On ground, in or near water. Bulky, cup-like, lined with fibrous material, well concealed in thick vegetation. **Eggs** 3–10, white (Red-necked Crake) to dark brown, spotted (Baillon's Crake). **Inc.** 16–28 days, usually both sexes. **Hatchl.** Precocial, downy, dependent. **Fledge** 4–6 weeks approx. **Care** Parents; also some additional family members (Purple Swamphen, Tasmanian Native-hen).

Breeding Seasons (* variable)

J F M A M J J A S O N D

Buff-banded Rail*

Lewin's Rail

Chestnut Rail

Red-necked Crake

Baillon's Crake*

Australian Spotted Crake

Spotless Crake

White-browed Crake

Bush-hen

Tasmanian Native-hen

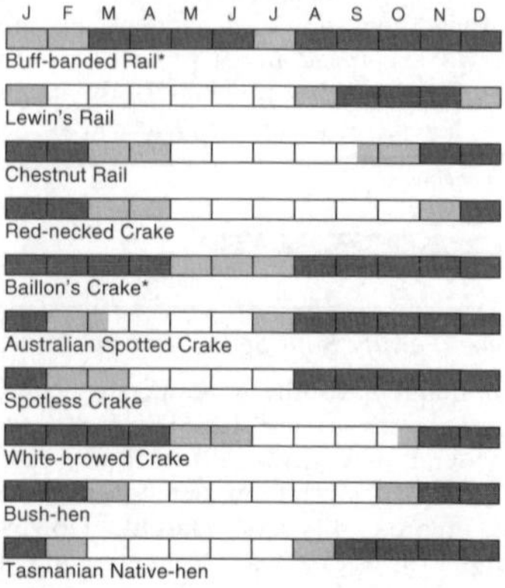

Black-tailed Native-hen*

Dusky Moorhen*

Purple Swamphen*

Eurasian Coot*

Herons, Egrets, Bitterns *Family Ardeidae* pp. 74–9

Herons and egrets are monogamous, pairing for at least the breeding season. The nest, whether solitary or within a colony, is vigorously defended. Australasian Bittern is related to the polygamous European Bittern. Several females nest in a male Australasian Bittern's territory. Egrets – including Cattle Egrets, White-necked Herons – are often in spectacular colonies; may have cormorants, Darters, in association. **Nest** Usually a large platform with central depression, of sticks, or other coarse material. Usually in a tree; often at height. **Eggs** 2–6, pale blue-green. **Inc.** Both parents, 22–30 days. Hatching is asynchronous. **Nestl.** First chick tends to get food advantage over others. Last chick to hatch may die if more than three nestlings. **Fledge** At about 8–9 weeks. May leave nest prior to fledging; may return or remain nearby to be fed. **Care** Small nestlings brooded, guarded; both parents feed young. Older young largely independent, but often fed for many months beyond fledging as well.

Breeding Seasons (* variable)

J F M A M J J A S O N D

Great-billed Heron

White-necked (Pacific) Heron

Pied Heron

White-faced Heron

Cattle Egret

Great Egret*

Little Egret*

Intermediate Egret*

Eastern Reef Egret

Striated (Mangrove) Heron

Nankeen (Rufous) Night Heron

Little Bittern

Black Bittern

Australasian Bittern

Ibis, Spoonbills *Family Threskiornithidae* pp. 80–1

Usually colonial, with herons, egrets, cormorants. **Nest** Formed nests of sticks, other vegetation, and with lining, in trees in or near water, or packed close together on reed-beds, low bushes, muddy islands. **Eggs** 2–4, white (Glossy Ibis, blue-green). **Inc.** Both sexes. 21–29 days (ibis); 26–31 days (spoonbills). Hatching asynchronous. **Nestl.** Downy, dependent. **Fledge** Ibis can fly at about 4–5 weeks; spoonbills at about 7 weeks. **Care** Ibis fledglings stay in or about nest for 4–5 weeks. Both parents feed them. Crèches may form. Later, juveniles feed with adults, roost with them. Spoonbills are less well known. Apparently fed by parents for some weeks, and away from nest site.

Breeding Seasons (* variable)

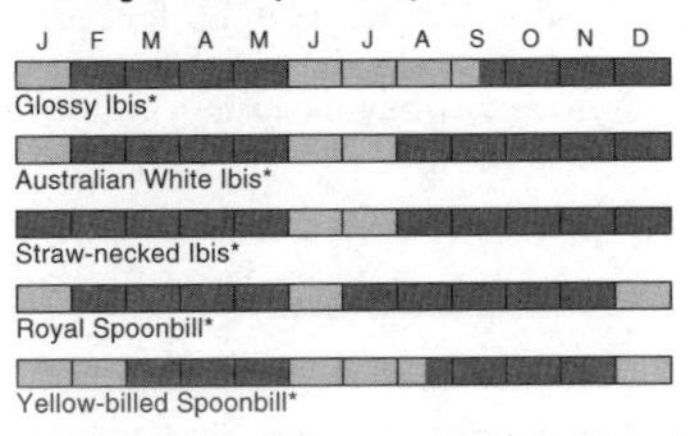

Storks *Family Ciconiidae* pp. 80–1

Black-necked Storks are sedentary, remain paired for many years. **Nest** Very large stick-and-reed platforms in tall trees, low bushes or on ground surrounded by water. **Eggs** 2–4?, white, textured surface; rapidly become stained. **Inc.** Probably both parents. **Nestl.** Downy, dependent. Possibly 14–17 weeks as nestlings; little data. **Fledge** Rarely do all nestlings survive the fledging weeks to nest departure. **Care** Both parents.

Breeding Season

J F M A M J J A S O N D

Black-necked Stork

Cranes *Family Gruidae* pp. 82–3

Brolga and Sarus Crane are monogamous, probably forming life pairs. Breed during wettest months; drought may halt breeding. **Nest** Both sexes build a bare scrape with sticks around on dry land, or a mound of coarse grass, sticks and leaves, raised above water level. **Eggs** 2–3, white (Brolga marked brown, lavender). **Inc.** Both sexes, mostly female; approx. 28–31 days. **Hatchl.** Precocial, downy, can run and swim but are fed by the parents. **Fledge** Approx. 8–11 weeks; can fly at about 14 weeks. **Care** Both parents; for 1 year and (rarely) to 2 years.

Breeding Seasons (* variable)

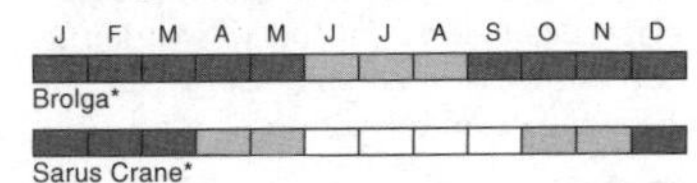

Bustards *Family Otididae* pp. 82–3

Polygamous. Males breed at 5–6 years, females at 2–3 years. **Nest** Ground scrape near bush, with open views. Not colonial. **Eggs** 2, glossy, variable: reddish to olive-green, heavily marked olive-brown. **Inc.** 21 days, by female. **Hatchl.** Precocial, downy, camouflaged. Fledge at about 4–5 weeks. **Care** By female; can be for more than 1 year.

Breeding Season (* variable)

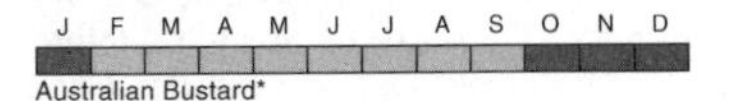

Plains-wanderer *Family Pedionomidae* pp. 82–3

The Plains-wanderer appears to lose or suppress its body- and foot-scent, as do quail, during breeding. Capable of breeding twice in a season if conditions good. **Nest** Ground scrape, lined and shielded by grass. **Eggs** 4, pyriform; pale green-buff, blotched and spotted with brown, grey and olive. **Inc.** 21 days. **Hatchl.** Precocial, downy. **Fledge** Approx. 8 weeks. **Care** Smaller, more cryptically coloured male normally incubates eggs, cares for young.

Breeding Season

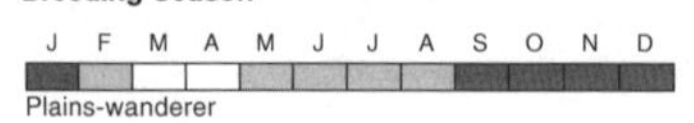

Curlews, Sandpipers, Snipes, Godwits, Phalaropes *Family Scolopacidae* pp. 84–95

Of this large wader family, not one species breeds in Australia. Those migrating to Australia tend to breed in north-eastern Siberia and Alaska rather than western Siberia or Canada, although some vagrants may come from these areas. Juveniles hatch in the northern summer and, arriving from spring to early summer in Australia, do not return to their breeding areas until they are more than a year old.

Pratincoles *Family Glareolidae* pp. 94–5

Nest Scrape amongst stones on rising ground with good views. **Eggs** 2, creamy, variably flecked brown. **Inc.** 21 days. **Nestl.** Precocial, downy. **Fledge** Approx. 3½–4 weeks, when can fly. **Care** Both parents, until young can fly.

Breeding Season (* variable)

J F M A M J J A S O N D

Australian Pratincole*

Painted Snipe *Family Rostratulidae* pp. 96–7

Female lays several clutches in good season. **Nest** Near or in water. Shallow scrape on damp ground, usually hidden in swampy vegetation. **Eggs** 4, glossy, whitish, 'marbled' black and brown. **Inc.** 3 weeks. **Nestl.** Precocial, downy, striped for camouflage, dependent. Capable of swimming. **Fledge** Period not known for certain. **Care** Smaller, duller males incubate eggs, care for young.

Breeding Season (* variable)

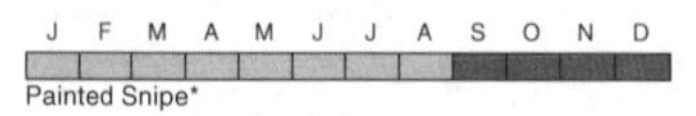

Jacanas (Lotusbirds) *Family Jacanidae* p. 96–7

Polygamous. Breed during rainy/monsoon periods. Not colonial, but several nests often together in suitable habitat. **Nest** Damp pile of floating herbage in water over 1 m deep. **Eggs** 3–4. Beautifully marked gold, red and black. **Inc.** Males only; 21–26 days. **Nestl.** Precocial, downy, strongly striped; can dive. Small downy chicks are sometimes carried under the wings of an adult. **Fledge** Approx. 6 weeks. Can fly by approx. 9 weeks. **Care** Mostly by male.

Breeding Season (* variable)

J F M A M J J A S O N D

Comb-crested Jacana*

Stone-curlews (Thick-knees) *Family Burhinidae* pp. 96–7

Both species very susceptible to human disturbance or predation by dogs, foxes, raptors.

BUSH STONE-CURLEW: **Nest** Lay in scrape on bare ground in open, lightly timbered grassland, often in same site for many years, relying on cryptic colouring for protection at all stages. Often surround nest with other material: sticks, dried dung. **Eggs** 2. Similar to Beach Stone-curlew (below); may vary regionally in colour. **Inc.** Both sexes; 25–27 days approx. **Hatchl.** Precocial, downy, striped. **Fledge** Approx. 6 weeks; can fly at 7–8 weeks, but variation in timing. **Care** Both sexes, period varies, may be up to 8–10 months.

BEACH STONE-CURLEW: Make shallow depression in sand or among mangroves. **Eggs** 1–2. Pale, no lustre, ground colours with variable markings; often denser toward larger end. **Inc.** 25–30 days. **Nestl.** Precocial, downy, strongly patterned. **Fledge** Approx. 6 weeks. **Care** Both sexes; up to 12 months.

Breeding Seasons (* variable)

J F M A M J J A S O N D

Bush Stone-curlew*

Beach Stone-curlew

Oystercatchers *Family Haematopodidae* pp. 96–7

Pair bonds may persist over a long period. **Nest** Hollow scratched in sand above high watermark amongst shells or driftwood, some lined, some not (both species) or rarely, between rocks on dry vegetation (Sooty). **Eggs** 2–4, 'plump' eggs, yellowish-buff to sandy coloured; streaked, blotched, dark brown and lavender. **Inc.** 28 days. Both parents. **Hatchl.** Precocial; dependent. **Fledge** Approx 7–8 weeks (Pied); longer, period uncertain; independent of parents by about 14 weeks (Sooty). **Care** Both parents, continues for a while after fledging.

Breeding Seasons (* variable)

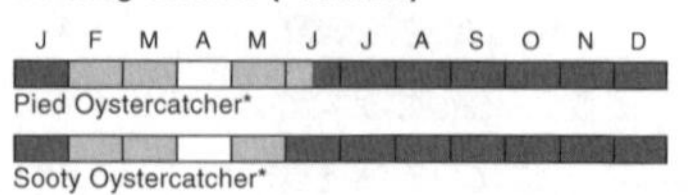

Lapwings, Plovers, Dotterels *Family Charadriidae* pp. 98–103

No Northern Hemisphere migratory plovers breed in Australia, nor does Double-banded Plover from New Zealand. **Nest** Territorial ground-nesters in scrapes in sand or among stones, usually lined with vegetation scraps, in open situation with good views. Hooded Plovers nest above tide-line of beaches, usually backed by grassy dunes; in WA they also breed around inland salt lakes. Inland Dotterels breed inland following rains. Red-kneed Dotterels may breed in colonies, in wet ground. Banded, Masked, Lapwings strongly defend nest; some pairs breed on flat factory roofs. **Eggs** 2–4; dull, smooth, pale to dark yellow- or greenish-brown, blotched brown, black, to suit habitat. **Inc.** Both parents. 24–31 days. **Hatchl.** Precocial; downy, partly dependent. **Fledge** 3–5 weeks; large species take longest. **Care** Both parents but feed themselves.

Breeding Seasons (* variable)

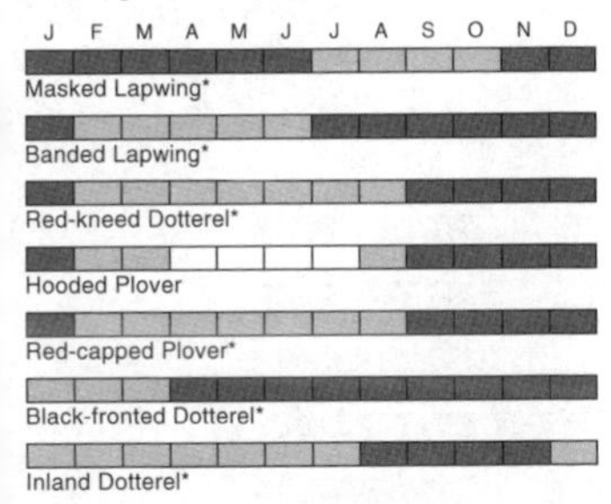

Stilts, Avocets *Family Recurvirostridae* pp. 102–3

Three genera represented, therefore differences. **Nest** Black-winged Stilt, Red-necked Avocet: Usually near water, on damp ground, or on platforms in shallow water. Nest singly or small to large loose colonies, after good rains. Scrape, often lined, or more elaborate nest. Banded Stilt: Often similar, but nest in huge, tight-packed colonies, at temporary inland saline lakes when conditions are right. Ground scrape, rarely lined, or in bare scrapes. **Eggs** Black-winged Stilt, Red-necked Avocet: 3–4, pale, creamy to dark olive, with dark spots, blotches; Avocet eggs larger. Banded Stilt's eggs white, chalky, dull, with black wavy lines. **Inc.** Approx. 22–24 days (all species; Avocet details less well known). **Nestl.** Precocial, downy, camouflaged, dependent (Black-winged Stilt, Red-necked Avocet). Banded Stilt pure white. Young leave nest within very short time, assemble with others in large créches and feed themselves. **Fledge** Approx. 4 weeks (Black-winged Stilt); (Red-necked Avocet, Banded Stilt believed similar but little data on either). **Care** Young remain in family group from weeks to months (Black-winged Stilt). Not much data (Red-necked Avocet). May be little or no parental care (Banded Stilt).

Breeding Seasons (* variable)

J F M A M J J A S O N D

Black-winged Stilt*

Banded Stilt*

Red-necked Avocet*

Skuas, Jaegers, Gulls, Terns
Family Laridae pp. 104–15

Skuas and jaegers are strongly territorial, fiercely defending nests and young, but do not breed on the Australian continent, being from polar and sub-polar regions.

GULLS: May nest alone, though most are social breeders. Larger gulls tend to breed along shores or on offshore islands; smaller species on sand banks, small islands or in marshes or swamps. **Nest** Both sexes build. Shallow scrape, sparsely or fully lined, or quite elaborate structures in bushes. **Eggs** 2–3, blue, grey or olive, variably marked brown. **Inc.** 21–28 days. **Hatchl.** Precocial, downy. **Fledge** Approx. 4–5 weeks. **Care** Both parents; longer period for larger gulls.

TERNS, NODDIES: Colonial nesters. **Nest** Scraped hollow in sand, shells, stones, sometimes lined or surrounded with local debris (Crested Tern). Bulky platforms in low shrubs (noddies). **Eggs** 1–4, dull white to brown, greenish or grey, varying blotches and spots (Crested Tern). 1, whitish, variably blotched darker (noddies). **Inc.** Both sexes; Crested Tern 14–28 days, Common Noddy 33–35 days. **Hatchl.** Precocial. Chicks of Crested Terns, also noddies, may enter large créches after some weeks. **Fledge** Crested Tern 5–6 weeks; Common Noddy approx. 7 weeks or more. **Care** Both parents.

Breeding Seasons (* variable)

J F M A M J J A S O N D

Silver Gull*

Pacific Gull

Kelp Gull

Whiskered (Marsh) Tern*

Caspian Tern*

Gull-billed Tern*

Roseate Tern*

White-fronted Tern

Black-naped Tern*

Sooty Tern*

Bridled Tern*

Little Tern*

Fairy Tern*

Crested Tern*

Lesser Crested Tern*

Common (Brown) Noddy*

Lesser Noddy

Black Noddy

Osprey [sometimes in own Family Pandionidae] Kites, Goshawks, Eagles, Harriers
Family Accipitridae pp. 116–25

Usually males of each species hunt, females look after nest building, incubation and guarding the young. Letter-winged Kites may breed frequently during rat plagues. **Nest** Stick nests, in trees. May be lined with green vegetation (Brahminy Kites, seaweed). Osprey, Wedge-tailed Eagle, White-bellied Sea-Eagle may add to massive stick nests over many years. Spotted Harriers are the only tree-nesting harriers. Swamp Harriers create a platform in tall grass, crops or rushes, sometimes in water. Black-breasted Buzzards share incubation, nest guarding and hunting almost equally. Unusually, they feed nestlings and one another at the same time. **Eggs** 2–6, most 2–3, white, variably blotched brown. **Inc.** Most species take

35–42 days. **Nestl.** White-downed; dependent. **Fledge** Probably from about 4–5 weeks in small species; largest one take longest, perhaps 10 weeks or more. **Care** Post-fledging care not well known. Most juveniles (1st year young) probably become independent quite quickly.

Breeding Seasons (* variable)

J F M A M J J A S O N D

Pacific Baza*

Black-shouldered Kite*

Letter-winged Kite*

Osprey

Square-tailed Kite*

Black-breasted Buzzard*

Black Kite*

Whistling Kite*

Brahminy Kite*

White-bellied Sea-Eagle

Wedge-tailed Eagle

Little Eagle

Brown Goshawk*

Collared Sparrowhawk*

Grey (White) Goshawk*

Red Goshawk* (not well known)

Spotted Harrier

Swamp Harrier

Falcons *Family Falconidae* pp. 124–7

No reliable published reports exist to indicate that any Australian falcons build their own nests. **Nest** On cliff ledges, in tree hollows or in disused stick nests of other species (often raptors, corvids). **Eggs** 2–4, dull pink-white, blotched reddish brown/lavender. **Inc.** 33–35 days approx., mostly by female, except Peregrine. **Nestl.** White down; dependent. **Fledge** 4–6 weeks. **Care** Both parents until independence.

Breeding Seasons

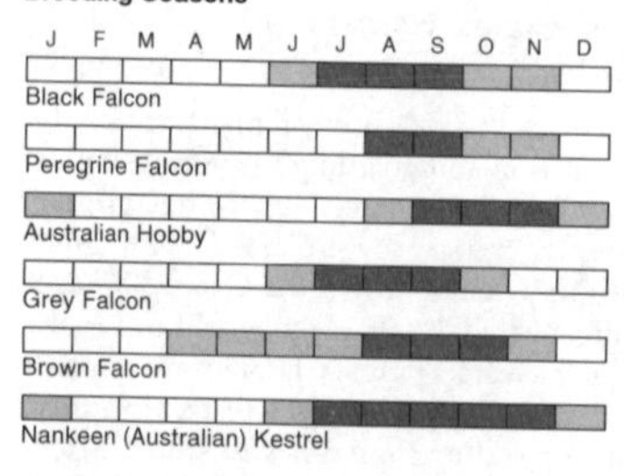

Pigeons, Doves *Family Columbidae* pp. 128–35

Breeding details of many species not well known. **Nest** Both parents build loosely structured stick nest or platform on ground or rock ledge, in tree-fork or vines. **Eggs** 1–2 glossy white to cream. **Inc.** Most 14–21 days. **Nestl.** Downy. **Care** Both parents. Young are fed on regurgitated 'milk' from gland in crop of both sexes. As they grow, other food is also regurgitated to them. **Fledge** Approx. 2–4 weeks (smaller species); approx. to 4–5 weeks (larger species); but not well known for all species. By the time they leave the nest, the young are eating normal adult food.

Breeding Seasons (* variable)

J F M A M J J A S O N D

Banded Fruit-Dove

Superb Fruit-Dove

Rose-crowned Fruit-Dove

Wompoo Fruit-Dove

Pied (Torresian) Imperial-Pigeon

Topknot Pigeon

White-headed Pigeon

Rock Dove (Feral Pigeon) **Intro.***

Spotted Turtle-Dove **Intro.**

Laughing Turtle-Dove **Intro.**

Brown Cuckoo-Dove

Peaceful Dove*

Diamond Dove*

Bar-shouldered Dove*

Emerald Dove

Common Bronzewing

Brush Bronzewing*

Flock Bronzewing*

Crested Pigeon*

Squatter Pigeon*

Partridge Pigeon*

White-quilled Rock-Pigeon

Chestnut-quilled Rock-Pigeon

Spinifex Pigeon

Wonga Pigeon

Cockatoos *Family Cacatuidae* pp. 136–9

Tend to form life-long pair bonds. **Nest** Almost all are dependent on availability of old-growth trees with suitable hollows; their floors lined with chewed wood. Pairs often use same site over many years. Galahs line nests with fresh eucalypt leaves. Corellas, Galahs occasionally nest in holes in volcanic ash (tuff); also animal burrows. **Eggs** 1–6, white. **Inc.** 19 days (Cockatiel); 24 (corellas); 28–30 (black-cockatoos). **Nestl.** Helpless. Most are naked; grow down, then pin feathers. **Fledge** Approx. 4 weeks (Cockatiel);

approx. 7 weeks (corellas); 8–9 weeks (black-cockatoos). **Care** All dependent for some weeks after fledging. Young of larger cockatoos may remain in nest for 2–4 months. Juveniles then travel with parents, often for long periods.

Breeding Seasons (* variable)

J F M A M J J A S O N D

Palm Cockatoo

Red-tailed Black-Cockatoo

Glossy Black-Cockatoo

Yellow-tailed Black-Cockatoo*

Short-billed (White-tailed) Black-Cockatoo*

Long-billed Black-Cockatoo

Gang-gang Cockatoo

Galah*

Long-billed Corella

Little Corella*

Western (Muir's) Corella

Major Mitchell's (Pink) Cockatoo*

Sulphur-crested Cockatoo*

Cockatiel*

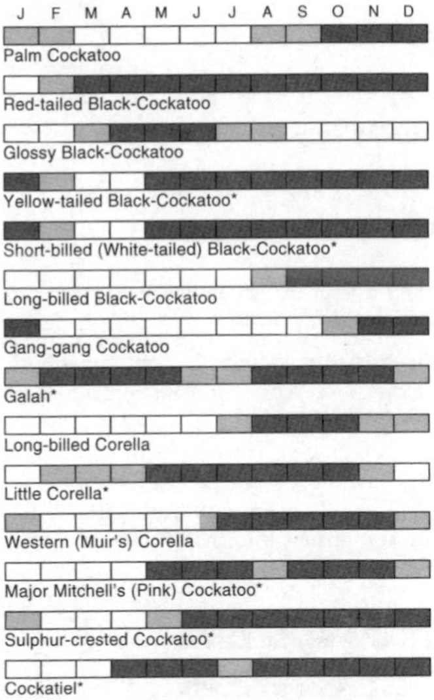

Parrots *Family Psittacidae* pp. 138–51

Like cockatoos, most parrots nest in hollows in mature trees. **Nest** Tree hollows, especially in broken limbs of eucalypts, lined with chewed wood. Hooded, Golden-shouldered, Paradise Parrots, breed only in tunnels in certain types of termite mounds. Ground, Night Parrots build nests of coarse grass in dense tussocks. Rock Parrots nest in crannies between boulders on coastal islands. **Eggs** 3–8, white, smooth, glossy. **Inc.** Mostly by female. Male feeds female at nest. Approx. 18 days (Budgerigar), 19 (rosellas), 21 (Double-eyed Fig-parrot), 20 (*Neophema*). **Nestl.** Helpless. Most are naked; grow down, then pin feathers. **Fledge** Approx. 5 weeks (Budgerigar, rosellas); 7–8 weeks (Double-eyed Fig-Parrot); 4–5 weeks (neophemas). **Care** Males later share care of young, which stay with parents for several weeks or months after fledging.

Breeding Seasons (* variable)

J F M A M J J A S O N D

Eclectus Parrot

Red-cheeked Parrot

Rainbow Lorikeet

Red-collared Lorikeet

Scaly-breasted Lorikeet

Varied Lorikeet

Musk Lorikeet

Purple-crowned Lorikeet

Little Lorikeet

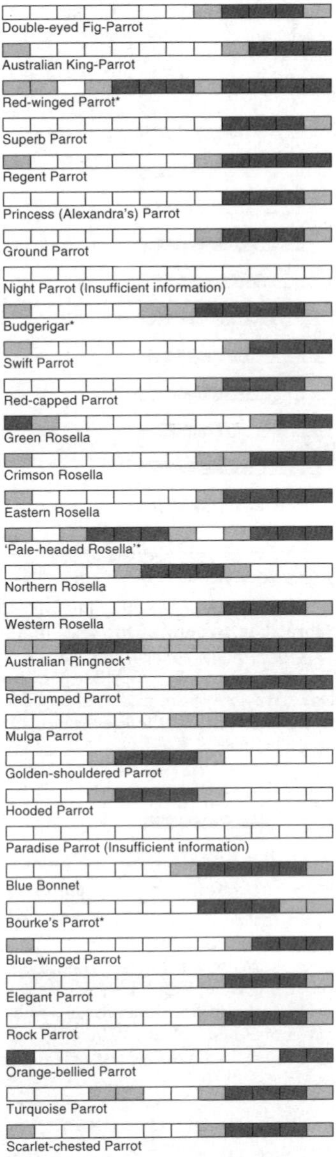

Double-eyed Fig-Parrot

Australian King-Parrot

Red-winged Parrot*

Superb Parrot

Regent Parrot

Princess (Alexandra's) Parrot

Ground Parrot

Night Parrot (Insufficient information)

Budgerigar*

Swift Parrot

Red-capped Parrot

Green Rosella

Crimson Rosella

Eastern Rosella

'Pale-headed Rosella'*

Northern Rosella

Western Rosella

Australian Ringneck*

Red-rumped Parrot

Mulga Parrot

Golden-shouldered Parrot

Hooded Parrot

Paradise Parrot (Insufficient information)

Blue Bonnet

Bourke's Parrot*

Blue-winged Parrot

Elegant Parrot

Rock Parrot

Orange-bellied Parrot

Turquoise Parrot

Scarlet-chested Parrot

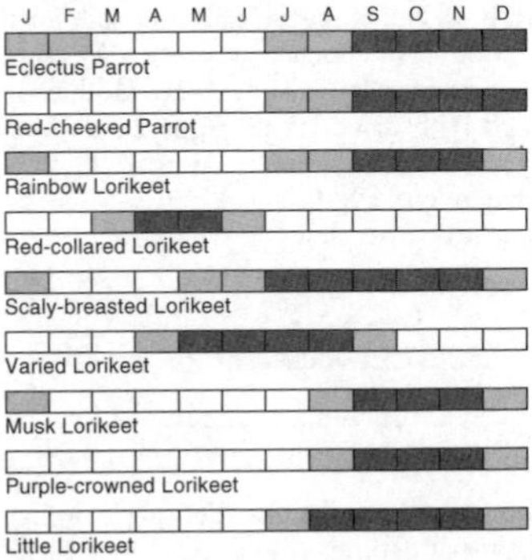

Parasitic Cuckoos *Family Cuculidae* pp. 152–5

All Australian cuckoos are parasitic on a wide variety of native birds. **Eggs** Cuckoos parasitic on small birds often lay small eggs, resembling their hosts' in size and colour. Eggs may vary regionally, e.g. Brush Cuckoo. A host's egg is removed and a cuckoo's substituted. **Inc.** By host species. **Hatchl.** The naked baby cuckoo tends to eject all other objects in the nest, including the host's eggs and nestlings. In some species, nestling mimics the plumage appearance of host's nestling. **Fledge** May be forced by increasing size to leave nest early. **Care** Begging postures and juvenile calls, well after fledging, ensure a constant food supply for the juvenile cuckoo. Adult cuckoos of some species may later meet their real parents, but this not fully established.

Breeding Seasons (* variable)

J F M A M J J A S O N D

Pallid Cuckoo

Brush Cuckoo

Chestnut-breasted Cuckoo

Fan-tailed Cuckoo

Black-eared Cuckoo

Horsfield's Bronze-Cuckoo*

Shining Bronze-Cuckoo

Little Bronze-Cuckoo

'Gould's Bronze-Cuckoo'

Common (Pacific) Koel

Channel-billed Cuckoo

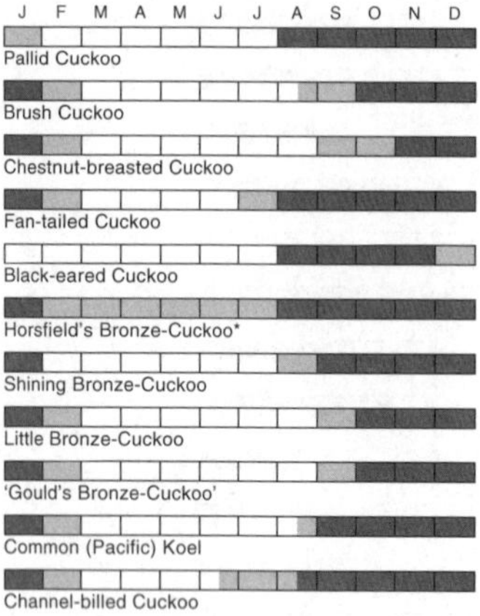

Coucals *Family Centropidae* pp. 154–5

Allied to cuckoos but not parasitic on other birds. **Nest** Large, open, cup-shaped, in swampy, coarse grass. **Eggs** 3–5, white, slight lustre, easily stained. **Inc.** Approx. 14 days. **Nestl.** Precocial, dependent; wispy down. Leave nest before feathers have grown or bird can fly; hide nearby; return to nest to be fed. **Fledge** Approx. at 2 weeks. **Care** Mostly by male.

Breeding Season

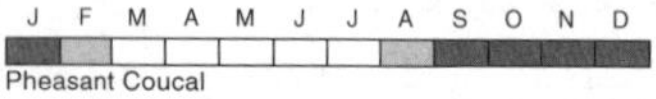

J F M A M J J A S O N D

Pheasant Coucal

Hawk Owls *Family Strigidae* pp. 156–7

Ninox owls form pairs that vigorously defend territories with monotonous 'hooting'. **Nest** In tree hollow, often prepared by male. Same hollow may be used annually, or intermittently over many years. **Eggs** 1–3, white, dull lustre. **Inc.** By female. Males feed incubating females by calling them away from nest. **Nestl.** White down, dependent. **Fledge** 5–8 weeks. **Care** Depend on parents for several months.

Breeding Seasons

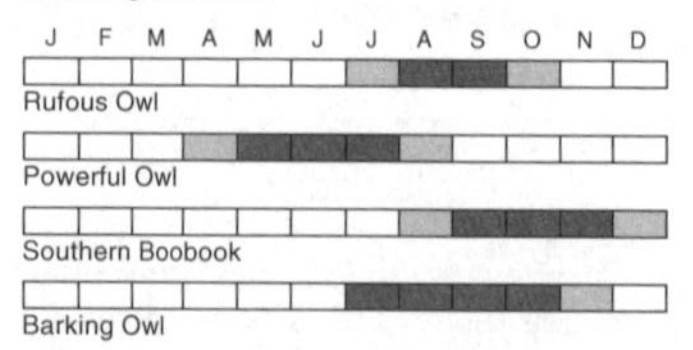

Barn Owls *Family Tytonidae* pp. 158–9

Tyto owls generally defend nest territories not with calling but with postures. Some are not regionally territorial. **Nest** In deep tree hollows, caves. Grass Owl builds nest on ground in dense vegetation; Barn Owl often in farm outbuildings. **Eggs** 1–8, white, slightly lustrous. **Inc.** Female only. Males feed females at the nest. **Nestl.** White down at hatching; denser 'true' down follows. **Fledge** Uncertain, suggested 4–10 weeks; varies with size of species. **Care** Dependent on parents for several months.

Breeding Seasons (* variable)

J F M A M J J A S O N D

Sooty Owl*

Lesser Sooty Owl

Masked Owl*

Barn Owl*

Grass Owl*

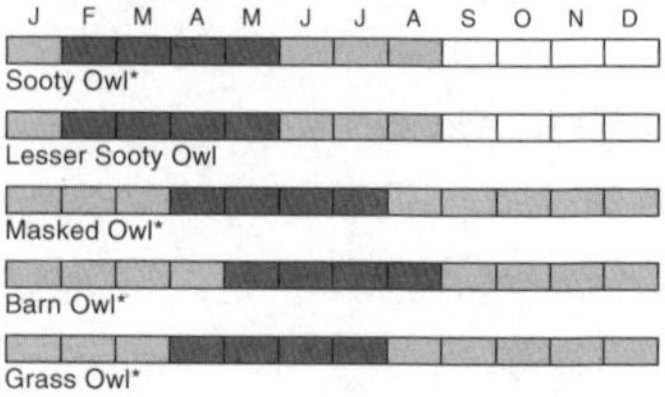

Frogmouths *Family Podargidae* pp. 160–1

Nest On top of horizontal forks, a tiny, apparently inadequate nest. **Eggs** 1–5, white, dull lustre. **Inc.** Both parents. Male in daytime, both take turns at night (Tawny). Approx. 30 days. **Nestl.** White downy; dependent. **Fledge** About 4 weeks (Tawny); about 6 weeks (Marbled). **Care** Remain with both parents after fledging for weeks, sometimes months.

Breeding Seasons

J F M A M J J A S O N D

Tawny Frogmouth

Papuan Frogmouth

Marbled Frogmouth

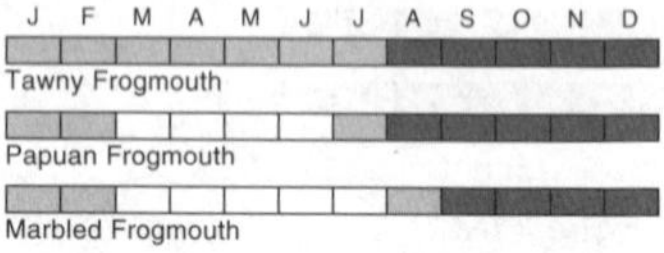

Nightjars *Family Caprimulgidae* pp. 160–1

Nest No real nest made. On the ground, amid leaf litter, stones, bark. **Eggs** Normally 1, lustrous; variable pale ground cover, lightly spotted purple-brown. **Inc.** Both parents; 18–30 days approx. **Hatchl.** Semi-precocious. **Fledge** Little data; just over 4 weeks. **Care** Both parents.

Breeding Seasons

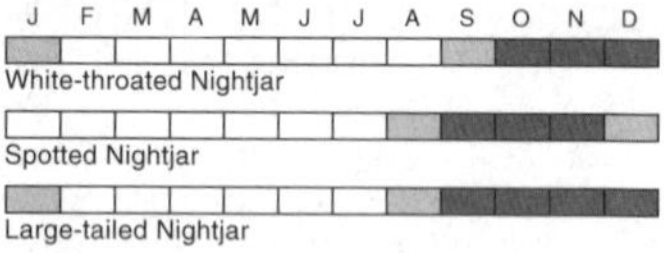

J F M A M J J A S O N D

White-throated Nightjar

Spotted Nightjar

Large-tailed Nightjar

Owlet-nightjars *Family Aegothelidae* pp. 160–1

Large eyes, striped head and churring calls resemble small glider possums, a 'mimicry' which may prevent invasion of hollow by other mammals or birds. **Nest** Hollow in tree or stump, lined with dried leaves. **Eggs** 2–4, white, dull lustre. **Inc.** Probably both parents. Approx. 28 days. **Nestl.** Downy, dependent. **Fledge** 3–4, rarely 5 weeks. **Care** Both parents; little post-fledging data.

Breeding Season (* variable)

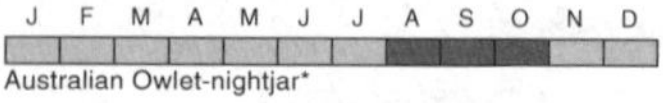

J F M A M J J A S O N D

Australian Owlet-nightjar*

Swiftlets, Swifts *Family Apodidae* pp. 162–3

No large swifts breed in Australia. Swiftlets are colonial. **Nest** In total or virtual darkness in eastern Queensland caves. Tiny, scoop-shaped pendant nests, of fine vegetation, parental feathers and partly of saliva, are glued to the walls. **Eggs** 1 per nest, white, faintly glossy. **Inc.** Both by parents; approx. 21–26 days. A second egg is often laid and then incubated by the first nestling. **Nestl.** Naked. Grows pin feathers after 12 days approx. Dependent. **Fledge** In 6–7 weeks, depending perhaps on seasonal food availability. **Care** Both parents; little post-fledging data.

Breeding Season

J F M A M J J A S O N D

White-rumped Swiftlet

River Kingfishers *Family Alcedinidae* pp. 164–5

Nest Dig straight nesting tunnels in overhanging banks, rotting stumps. No lining. **Eggs** 4–7, white, lustrous. **Inc.** Both parents. Approx. 21 days. **Nestl.** Naked, dependent. **Fledge** Approx. 5 weeks. **Care** Both parents; young independent by about 2 weeks.

Breeding Seasons

J F M A M J J A S O N D

Azure Kingfisher

Little Kingfisher

Tree Kingfishers *Family Halcyonidae* pp. 164–7

Nest Kookaburras nest in tree hollows, other tree kingfishers use these too, but some also tunnel into arboreal termite mounds, or use holes in banks. Paradise-Kingfishers excavate tunnels in terrestrial termite mounds. **Eggs** 2–6, white, variable with species, slightly to fully lustrous. **Inc.** About 21 days (small kingfishers); 28 days (Kookaburras). **Nestl.** Naked; grow pin feathers; dependent. **Fledge** 3–5 weeks. **Care** Small species independent about 4–6 weeks after fledging. Kookaburra parents and other group members may feed and protect young for many months.

Breeding Seasons

J F M A M J J A S O N D

Laughing Kookaburra

Blue-winged Kookaburra

Forest Kingfisher

Red-backed Kingfisher

Sacred Kingfisher

Collared Kingfisher

Yellow-billed Kingfisher

Buff-breasted Paradise-Kingfisher

Bee-eaters *Family Meropidae* pp. 164–5

Notes refer only to Rainbow Bee-eater. **Nest** Tunnel into flat or slightly sloping ground (occas. into sandy banks). Unlined. Female is principal excavator. **Eggs** 4–5, white, dull. **Inc.** Both parents. About 24–25 days. **Nestl.** Naked; dependent. **Fledge** 4–5 weeks approx. **Care** Up to eight adults have been seen at one nest hole acting as auxillary feeders. Remain with parents for 4–5 weeks after fledging.

Breeding Season

J F M A M J J A S O N D

Rainbow Bee-eater

Rollers *Family Coraciidae* pp. 164–5

Notes refer only to Dollarbird. **Nest** Hollows in tall trees; unlined. **Eggs** 3–4, white, glossy. **Inc.** Approx. 18–20 days. **Nestl.** Naked; dependent. **Fledge** Maybe 4 weeks. **Care** Both parents. Breeding data uncertain for this species.

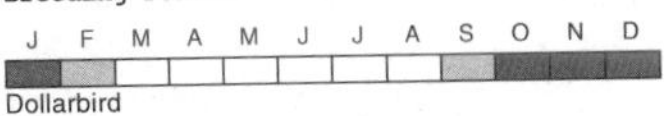

Pittas *Family Pittidae* pp. 168–9

Monogamy likely. Solitary pairs. **Nest** Built by both parents. Bulky, on or close to ground on logs, debris, between diverging or emergent tree roots, or trees to 20m. Partly or wholly domed, with large side entrance. **Eggs** 2–4, round, white, lustrous, variously patterned or marked, purple, brown, lavender. **Inc.** Both parents. About 15–17 days. **Nestl.** Naked, grow feathers. Dependent. **Fledge** Approx. 2–3 weeks (14–20 days). **Care** Both sexes assist at nest. No apparent 'helpers'.

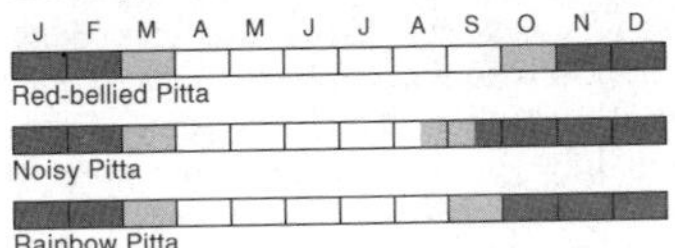

Lyrebirds *Family Menuridae* pp. 168–9

Polygamous males display autumn, winter, on dancing mounds. Females may visit more than one male before mating, but male–female association is brief; pair-bonding as such seems absent. **Nest** Large stick nest has side-entranced nest chamber lined with fibre, breast feathers and whole nest often roofed or hooded with bark. **Egg** 1, grey-brown to purplish-brown, with fine to heavy reddish-mauve marks. **Inc.** 50 days. **Nestl.** Grey down; grows feathers. Dependent. **Fledge** At almost 7 weeks (47 days). **Care** Partly fed by female for up to 8 months.

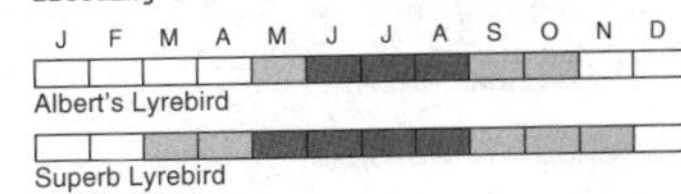

Scrub-birds *Family Atrichornithidae* pp. 168–9

Probably monogamous (male possibly opportunistically polygamous). **Nest** Females build domed nests close to the ground with small side-entrances, lined with thin, papery wood pulp. **Eggs** 1, pale pinkish-buff, speckled (Noisy Scrub-bird); 2, pale buff, blotched (Rufous Scrub-bird). **Inc.** Females incubate. Approx. 38 days. **Nestl.**

Dependent. **Fledge** Approx. 3–4 weeks. **Care** Females raise young after fledging.

Breeding Seasons

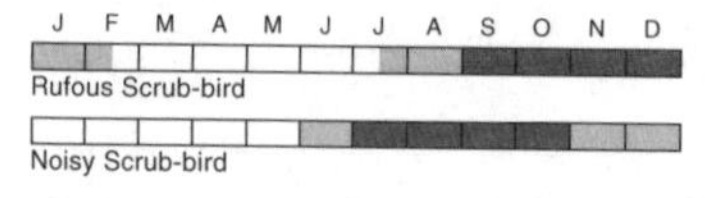

Sittellas *Family Neosittidae* pp. 170–1

Nest Built by all members of a group, that tends to consist of a mated pair, 1–2 unattached adults, and the young of the previous year's breeding. Placed above 10 m, in forks of dead branches, superbly camouflaged with cobwebs, scraps of bark to resemble broken stump. Deep cup inside. **Eggs** 2–3, slightly lustrous, greyish, blotched various browns to match lichen or other lining. **Inc.** Approx. 21 days, by dominant female only. She is fed on, or near, the nest by the other birds. **Nestl.** Naked, grow feathers. Dependent. **Fledge** At about 3 weeks. **Care** Assistance is given by young from earlier broods attending later broods in the same season. Young travel with foraging parents later, for at least 2 months, and some for perhaps much longer.

Breeding Season (* variable)

J F M A M J J A S O N D

Varied Sittella*

Treecreepers *Family Climacteridae* pp. 170–1

WHITE-THROATED TREECREEPER: Breeds in solitary pairs and may have two broods annually. **Nest** Female builds cup of soft material in hollow branch or stump. **Eggs** 2–4, white, dull, lightly spotted, blotched, purple-red. **Inc.** Female; 22–24 days; is fed by male at nest. **Nestl.** Naked, grows feathers. Dependent. **Fledge** Approx. 3–4 weeks. **Care** Both parents. Juveniles probably remain with parents for a period after fledging.

RED-BROWED, BLACK-TAILED, BROWN AND RUFOUS TREECREEPERS: **Eggs** 2–4 pale salmon-beige; thickly spotted, blotched, purple-red. **Inc.** Female. **Nestl.** Naked, grows feathers; dependent. **Fledge** 3–4 weeks. **Care** Both parents, but because these treecreepers breed cooperatively, extra birds, mostly males, help feed young. Young remain with parents for up to 12 weeks or so.

Breeding Seasons

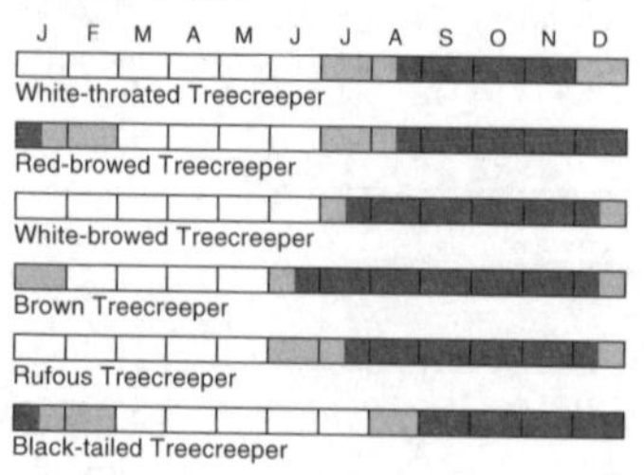

Fairy-wrens *Family Maluridae* pp. 172–9

Mating commonly occurs outside the socially bonded family group; females are usually the initiators of promiscuity.

FAIRY-WRENS: **Nest** Dominant female usually builds side-entranced, loosely structured dome, lined with feathers, fine grass. **Eggs** 2–4, dull white, spotted, flecked, red-brown speckles at larger end. **Inc.** Dominant female; approx. 13–16 days. Hatching is synchronous. **Nestl.** Naked, grow feathers. Dependent. **Fledge** Approx. 12 days; leave before wing, tail feathers fully grown. **Care** Co-operative groups, dominant male and female with subordinate non-breeding birds. Other group members help to rear young, but although there are plenty of variations in 'helper' arrangements, they do not build, incubate or brood small young.

EMU-WRENS: A poorly known group compared to fairy-wrens. **Eggs** 2–4. **Nestl.** Almost naked; some thin down. After a few days, feathers appear. Dependent. **Care** Parental. 'Helpers at the nest' seem to be the exception, not the rule.

GRASSWRENS: Only one brood per year by solitary pairs. **Eggs** 2–3. **Inc.** Mostly by females; approx. 13–14 days. **Nestl.** Naked, grow feathers. Dependent. **Fledge** Approx. 12–14 days. **Care** Parental; may receive some 'helper' assistance from any earlier brood.

Breeding Seasons (* variable)

J F M A M J J A S O N D

Purple-crowned Fairy-wren*
Superb Fairy-wren
Splendid Fairy-wren
Variegated Fairy-wren
Lovely Fairy-wren
Blue-breasted Fairy-wren
Red-winged Fairy-wren
White-winged Fairy-wren
Red-backed Fairy-wren
Southern Emu-wren
Mallee Emu-wren
Rufous-crowned Emu-wren
Black Grasswren
White-throated Grasswren
Carpentarian Grasswren
Striated Grasswren*
Short-tailed Grasswren (Provisional)
Eyrean Grasswren
Grey Grasswren
Thick-billed Grasswren*
Dusky Grasswren*
Kalkadoon Grasswren (Provisional)

Pardalotes, Bristlebirds, Scrubwrens, Gerygones, Thornbills

Family Pardalotidae (Acanthizidae) pp. 180–93

General note (see below for detail) applying to all species. **Nest** Variable. Most of this large group build domed nests with side entrances. Some use feather linings. **Eggs** 2–4 on average. **Inc.** Both parents. **Nestl.** All species hatch naked, grow feathers. Dependent. **Fledge** Varying periods. **Care** Both parents plus 'helpers' in some species.

PARDALOTES: **Nests** All build cup or domed nests in tree hollows or in burrows excavated in the ground (some in loose colonies). Both parents work at hole and nest construction. **Eggs** White. **Inc.** Both parents for about 14–16, up to 22, days. **Fledge** Periods are relatively long, and not well known for any species. About 3–4 weeks (Forty-spotted Pardalote). **Care** Other individuals may assist in feeding young. Juveniles forage with adults later.

'SCRUBWREN' GROUP: **Nests** May be in or under vegetation on or very low to the ground (Pilotbird, Fernwren, White-browed Scrubwren, Scrubtit, heathwrens, fieldwrens, Redthroat, Speckled Warbler). Nests are also suspended in a cave (Rockwarbler), or up to 10–12 m in rainforest (Yellow-throated Scrubwren, Large-billed Scrubwren). **Eggs** Bristlebirds lay 2 large, almost white eggs, but heavily marked dark-spotted brown to pinkish (Eastern); more finely marked (Rufous). Pale eggs, faintly pink or brown, with fine speckles, marks, mostly at large end (heathwrens, scrubwrens). Plain pale grey-mauve (Pilotbird). White (Fernwren, Rockwarbler (also called Origma)). A rich plain chocolate red (Speckled Warbler). **Inc.** Approx. 3 weeks (bristlebirds). Not well known (heathwrens, fieldwrens). Approx. 21–27 days after all eggs laid (Rockwarbler). **Nestl.** Naked, grow feathers. Dependent. **Fledge** Secretive nature of these species has provided little overall data. 'At least 11 days' (Eastern Bristlebird); at approx. 3 weeks (Rockwarbler). **Care** Both parents so far as is known.

GERYGONES, WEEBILL: **Nest** Fairy Gerygone often constructs its nest close to a 'wasp' or hornet nest. Gerygones have a suspended nest, the entrance protected by a spout. Weebills sometimes build in association with communal spiders, an untidy thornbill-like nest. **Eggs** 2–3, white, with fine, to stronger, red speckles and marks (various gerygones). Almost white, few speckles (Weebill). **Inc.** Both parents. Approx. 12–17 days (most gerygones); approx. 15–20 days (Weebill). **Nestl.** Naked, grow feathers. Dependent. **Fledge** Prob. 2–3 weeks (little data for some species). **Care** Both parents, so far as is known.

THORNBILLS, WHITEFACES: **Nest** All build similarly – a slightly untidy, lined, domed, side-entranced nest of grass and other fine materials. Yellow-rumped Thornbills sometimes add an extra cup on top of the main domed nesting chamber. **Eggs** Thornbills lay 2–4; whitefaces 2–5. All species' eggs are generally white, very finely speckled toward large end. **Inc.** Both parents. **Nestl.** Naked, grow feathers. Dependent. **Fledge** Prob. 2–3 weeks (some well known; little data for most species). **Care** Parents. Juveniles of all species appear to forage with adults after fledging.

Breeding Seasons (* variable)

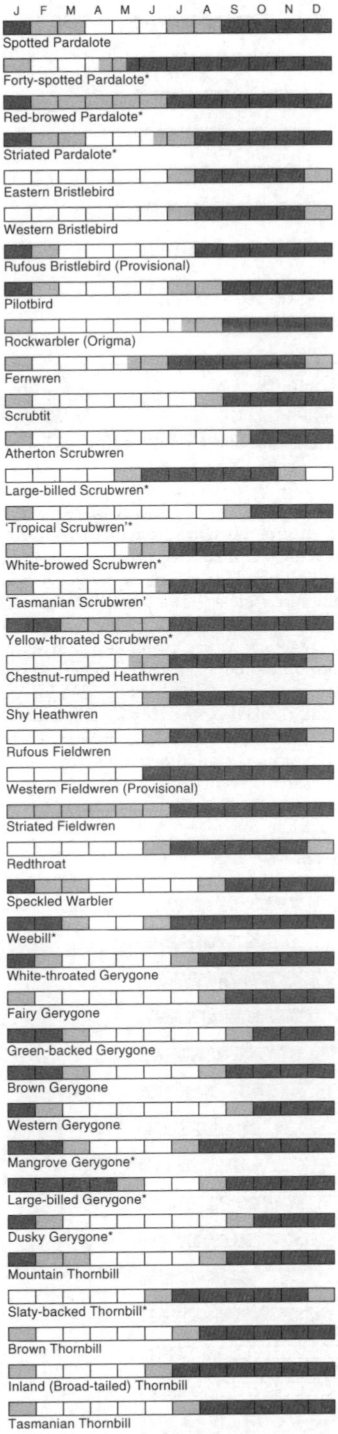

J F M A M J J A S O N D

Spotted Pardalote
Forty-spotted Pardalote*
Red-browed Pardalote*
Striated Pardalote*
Eastern Bristlebird
Western Bristlebird
Rufous Bristlebird (Provisional)
Pilotbird
Rockwarbler (Origma)
Fernwren
Scrubtit
Atherton Scrubwren
Large-billed Scrubwren*
'Tropical Scrubwren'*
White-browed Scrubwren*
'Tasmanian Scrubwren'
Yellow-throated Scrubwren*
Chestnut-rumped Heathwren
Shy Heathwren
Rufous Fieldwren
Western Fieldwren (Provisional)
Striated Fieldwren
Redthroat
Speckled Warbler
Weebill*
White-throated Gerygone
Fairy Gerygone
Green-backed Gerygone
Brown Gerygone
Western Gerygone
Mangrove Gerygone*
Large-billed Gerygone*
Dusky Gerygone*
Mountain Thornbill
Slaty-backed Thornbill*
Brown Thornbill
Inland (Broad-tailed) Thornbill
Tasmanian Thornbill

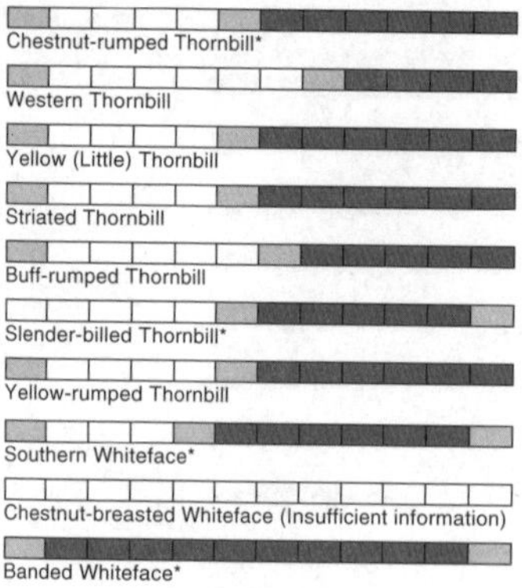

Chestnut-rumped Thornbill*

Western Thornbill

Yellow (Little) Thornbill

Striated Thornbill

Buff-rumped Thornbill

Slender-billed Thornbill*

Yellow-rumped Thornbill

Southern Whiteface*

Chestnut-breasted Whiteface (Insufficient information)

Banded Whiteface*

Honeyeaters, Australian Chats

Family Meliphagidae pp. 194–215

Cuckoos, bronze-cuckoos and Common Koel parasitise many honeyeater species. **Nest** Sizes vary with size of species. Females build nests which vary from large cup of sticks to tiny suspended woven basket of twigs and strips of bark, sometimes moss, held together by spiders' web, often lined with mammal hair, soft plant material or feathers. Chats build on low bushes, in spinifex, or on the ground. Gibberbirds line a ground scrape. **Eggs** 1–2 in many rainforest species; 2–4 in many woodland species. All have generally white to pinkish-buff eggs, with darker spots or blotches. Different genera show varying egg colour tendencies. **Inc.** About 12–17 days, by female. **Hatchl.** Naked; grow down. Dependent. **Fledge** About 11–20 days, depending on size. **Care** Both sexes feed nestlings, sometimes aided by other flock members, particularly in miners *Manorina*; to a lesser extent in *Melithreptus*. Juveniles may forage, travel, with parents for a while.

Breeding Seasons (* variable)

J F M A M J J A S O N D

Red Wattlebird*

Yellow Wattlebird

Western Wattlebird*

Little (Brush) Wattlebird*

Spiny-cheeked Honeyeater*

Striped Honeyeater*

Helmeted Friarbird*

Silver-crowned Friarbird*

Noisy Friarbird*

Little Friarbird*

Regent Honeyeater

Blue-faced Honeyeater*

Macleay's Honeyeater

Tawny-breasted Honeyeater

Bell Miner*

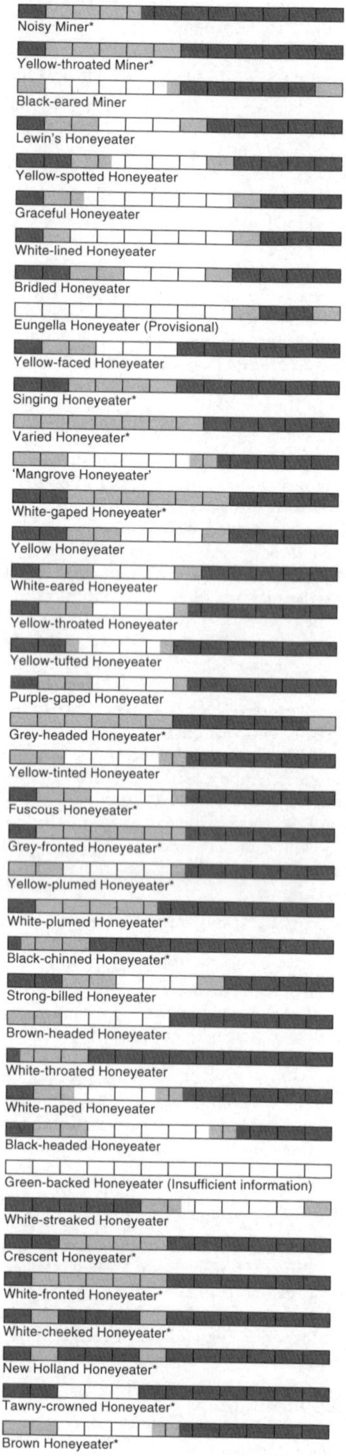

Noisy Miner*

Yellow-throated Miner*

Black-eared Miner

Lewin's Honeyeater

Yellow-spotted Honeyeater

Graceful Honeyeater

White-lined Honeyeater

Bridled Honeyeater

Eungella Honeyeater (Provisional)

Yellow-faced Honeyeater

Singing Honeyeater*

Varied Honeyeater*

'Mangrove Honeyeater'

White-gaped Honeyeater*

Yellow Honeyeater

White-eared Honeyeater

Yellow-throated Honeyeater

Yellow-tufted Honeyeater

Purple-gaped Honeyeater

Grey-headed Honeyeater*

Yellow-tinted Honeyeater

Fuscous Honeyeater*

Grey-fronted Honeyeater*

Yellow-plumed Honeyeater*

White-plumed Honeyeater*

Black-chinned Honeyeater*

Strong-billed Honeyeater

Brown-headed Honeyeater

White-throated Honeyeater

White-naped Honeyeater

Black-headed Honeyeater

Green-backed Honeyeater (Insufficient information)

White-streaked Honeyeater

Crescent Honeyeater*

White-fronted Honeyeater*

White-cheeked Honeyeater*

New Holland Honeyeater*

Tawny-crowned Honeyeater*

Brown Honeyeater*

Painted Honeyeater*
Bar-breasted Honeyeater*
Brown-backed Honeyeater
Grey Honeyeater (Provisional)
Rufous-banded Honeyeater
Rufous-throated Honeyeater
Eastern Spinebill
Western Spinebill
Dusky Honeyeater*
Red-headed Honeyeater*
Scarlet Honeyeater*
Banded Honeyeater*
Pied Honeyeater*
Black Honeyeater*
Crimson Chat*
Orange Chat*
Yellow Chat*
White-fronted Chat*
Gibberbird*

Logrunner, Chowchilla
Family Orthonychidae pp. 216–17

Nest Females build large, complex, well-camouflaged, side-entranced domed nests of moss and sticks, on the ground or close to it, and in dense vegetation. Rather resembles structure (platform, nest itself, 'roof') of Lyrebird nests, but smaller. **Eggs** Normally 2; glossy white (Logrunner); 1 white (Chowchilla). **Inc.** Female; approx. 20–25 days. **Nestl.** Has dark down at an early age. Grow feathers. Dependent. **Fledge** 16–19 days (Logrunner); 22–27 days (Chowchilla). **Care** Parental; may extend for several months.

Breeding Seasons (* variable)

J F M A M J J A S O N D

Logrunner*
Chowchilla*

Whipbirds, Wedgebills, Quail-thrushes
Family Cinclosomatidae (Eupetidae) pp. 216–19

Being largely secretive in habits, there are gaps in knowledge of some species within this Family.

WHIPBIRDS, WEDGEBILLS: **Nest** Open, cup-shaped nest of leaves and bark, built very close to, or on the ground, by both sexes (whipbirds). Wedgebills build low in shrubs. **Eggs** Usually 2; bluish-white to greenish or sky-blue, lightly spotted black. **Inc.** Approx. 17–21 days, by both sexes. **Nestl.** Naked, grow feathers. Dependent. **Fledge** From 1½ to 2½ weeks, approx. **Care** Parental (all species). Since they are communal species, there may be some 'helpers' among wedgebills (we are not certain of this) whose juvenile/immatures, once independent, enter loose flocks and fend for themselves.

QUAIL-THRUSHES: **Nest** Female builds a lined cup in a ground scrape beneath vegetation. **Eggs** 2–3; variable creamy colours – that may be related to regional soil colour – and with many brownish speckles. **Inc.** Approx. 21 days. **Nestl.** Naked, grow dark down, then feathers. Dependent. **Fledge** From 1½ to 2½ weeks, approx.; about 19 days for Spotted Quail-thrush. **Care** Parental. Young forage locally with adults for a period.

Breeding Seasons (* variable)

J F M A M J J A S O N D

Eastern Whipbird
Mallee Whipbird
Western Whipbird
Chirruping Wedgebill*
Chiming Wedgebill*
Spotted Quail-thrush*
Chestnut Quail-thrush*
Chestnut-breasted Quail-thrush*
Cinnamon Quail-thrush*

Australo-Papuan Babblers
Family Pomatostomidae pp. 220–1

Communal nesters. White-browed may have up to 4 broods if conditions are good. Two females may share one nest. **Nest** Domed, untidy stick nests, thickly lined with grass, hair, feathers; often in dead trees. Side entrance near the top. Similar constructions built for communal roosting; less lining material used. Trees in a territory may contain numerous old nests. **Eggs** 2–4, whitish, with dark wavy lines, streaks. Between species, vary somewhat in size, shape, colour. **Inc.** Approx. 17–25 days, by female – family group feeds her. **Nestl.** Naked, grow feathers. Dependent. **Fledging** Approx. 19–22 days; may vary regionally. **Care** Parental, and numerous 'helpers' from group.

Breeding Seasons (* variable)

J F M A M J J A S O N D

Grey-crowned Babbler*
White-browed Babbler
Hall's Babbler*
Chestnut-crowned Babbler*

Robins *Family Petroicidae* pp. 222–9

Robins may raise several broods in a season. *Microeca* flycatchers have the smallest nests of any Australian birds. Most genera breed as single pairs; a few genera have 'helpers' at times. **Nest** Female *Petroica* robins build nest; cup-shaped, of fine vegetation, often decorated with cobwebs and vertically placed scraps of mosses, lichens, usually in small forks or on horizontal branches. Both *Microeca* parents build the nests. Scrub-robins *Drymodes* build on ground. **Eggs** 1–4 (mostly 2–3), soft lustre, green, blue, sometimes cream, buff or white, marked brown or grey, heavier toward larger end. **Inc.** Female in *Petroica*, fed by male. Approx. 14–20 days. **Nestl.** Naked, grows down. Dependent. **Fledge** Approx. 12–22 days. Most species have cryptically plumaged juvenile plumage. **Care** Normally both parents. Sometimes there are 'helpers'.

Breeding Seasons (* variable)

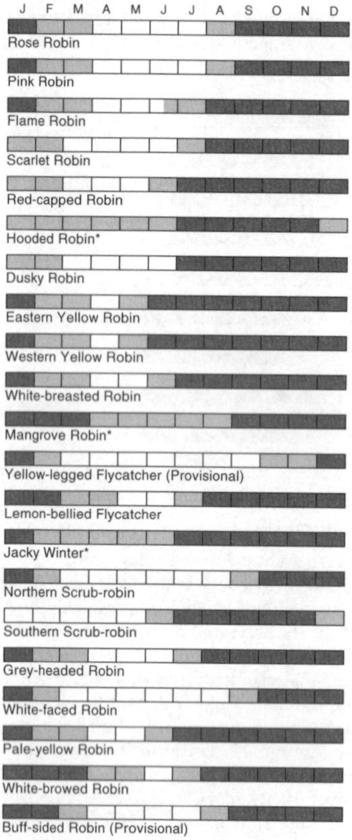

J F M A M J J A S O N D

Rose Robin
Pink Robin
Flame Robin
Scarlet Robin
Red-capped Robin
Hooded Robin*
Dusky Robin
Eastern Yellow Robin
Western Yellow Robin
White-breasted Robin
Mangrove Robin*
Yellow-legged Flycatcher (Provisional)
Lemon-bellied Flycatcher
Jacky Winter*
Northern Scrub-robin
Southern Scrub-robin
Grey-headed Robin
White-faced Robin
Pale-yellow Robin
White-browed Robin
Buff-sided Robin (Provisional)

Shrike-tits, Crested Bellbird, Shrike-thrushes, Whistlers *Family Pachycephalidae* pp. 228–35

All species in this Family are monogamous.

SHRIKE-TITS: The Crested Shrike-tit has been divided into 3 regional species: Eastern, Northern, Western. **Nest** Deep nest in fork, often high above ground, of shredded bark, with much cobweb. Neatly finished. **Eggs** 2–3, white, marked olive or brown. **Inc.** Mostly by both parents. **Nestl.** Naked, grow feathers. Dependent. **Fledge** Approx. 2 weeks. **Care** Parents, but communal 'helpers' often assist to rear young shrike-tits.

CRESTED BELLBIRD: **Nest** Similar to larger whistlers, shrike-thrushes, but unusual with frequent addition of live but immobilised hairy caterpillars around nest rim. **Eggs** 3–4; white, lightly marked with dark colours. **Inc.** Probably similar to others in Family. Naked, grow feathers. Dependent. **Fledge** Approx. 2 weeks. **Care** Parents.

SHRIKE-THRUSHES: **Nest** Large, deep cup-shaped nest of twigs, bark, roots, leaves, in tree forks, old stumps, rock crevices. **Eggs** 2–3, white, marked olive or brown. **Inc.** Approx. 16–18 days. **Nestl.** Naked, grow feathers. Dependent. **Fledge** Approx. 2–2½ weeks but some uncertainty. **Care** Parental.

WHISTLERS: **Nest** Deep, neat, cup-shaped nest of twigs, bark, roots, leaves, in tree forks, old stumps. **Eggs** 2–3, glossy, pinkish, buff-white, or 'stone' coloured, marked olive or brown. **Inc.** Approx. 12–17 days. Mostly by both parents. **Nestl.** Naked, grow feathers. Dependent. **Fledge** 1½–2½ weeks. **Care** Parental.

Breeding Seasons (* variable)

J F M A M J J A S O N D

Eastern Shrike-tit
Western Shrike-tit (Provisional)
Northern Shrike-tit (Provisional)
Crested Bellbird*
Little Shrike-thrush
Bower's Shrike-thrush
Sandstone Shrike-thrush
Grey Shrike-thrush*
Golden Whistler
Mangrove Golden Whistler
Gilbert's Whistler
Red-lored Whistler
Olive Whistler
Grey Whistler*
Rufous Whistler*
White-breasted Whistler*

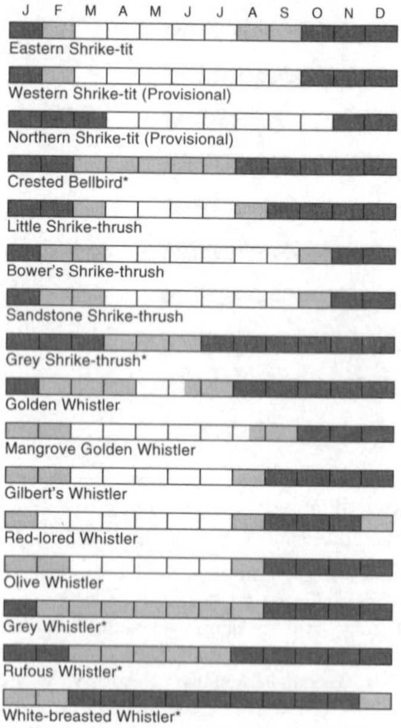

Monarchs, Magpie-lark, Flycatchers, Fantails, Drongo *Family Dicruridae* pp. 236–43

Nest Cup-shaped or variations of it (all species). Boatbill: male builds a shallow cup suspended at height. Monarchs, flycatchers: in some species, female alone builds deep cups, coated with moss, lichen, cobwebs. Fantails use fine fibrous material, often bark, to match the branch, bound with cobwebs, and with dangling 'wine-glass stems' below. Willie Wagtails build a small cylindrical cup of bark and cobweb with dense lining, on a horizontal twig. Australian Magpie-lark: both sexes contribute to a lined, bowl-shaped mud-nest, allowing it to dry for some days before use (because of this were previously considered related to Choughs and Apostlebirds, but now known not to be). Spangled Drongo's nest is a large, deep, open, cup of woven vines, fine bark; suspended from twigs, and usually placed in external foliage of a tree. Both sexes build. **Eggs** Usually 2–3; white to cream, with evenly distributed fine speckles, or with bands of slightly coarser dark spots, often around the widest part (most species, and with minor size, shape variation). 2; white, sparsely speckled (Yellow-breasted Boatbill). Pinker eggs with heavy red-brown marks, spots (White-eared Monarch). 3–5, pinkish to whitish, with sparse reddish spots (Magpie-lark). Mostly 2–3, pale cream to faintly mauve, with a medium density of reddish spots towards large end (Drongo). **Inc.** Little data for most monarchs, but both sexes probably share incubation. By both sexes but little data on duration (Boatbill). About 14–15 days (White-eared Monarch, Grey Fantail, Rufous Fantail, Leaden Flycatcher, Willie Wagtail). Both sexes; usually 17–18 days (Magpie-lark). Both parents; approx. 14–16 days (Spangled Drongo). **Nestl.** Naked, grow feathers. Dependent (all species). **Fledge** Period not known for some species. **Fledge** Little data (Boatbill). Approx. 2 weeks (White-eared Monarch, Leaden Flycatcher, Grey Fantail, Willie Wagtail). Period not well known (Drongo). **Care** Both parents (all species).

Breeding Seasons (* variable)

J F M A M J J A S O N D

Northern Fantail

Grey Fantail

Mangrove Grey Fantail

Rufous Fantail

Arafura Fantail (Provisional)

Willie Wagtail*

Broad-billed Flycatcher

Leaden Flycatcher

Satin Flycatcher

Shining Flycatcher

Restless Flycatcher*

Paperbark Flycatcher (Provisional)

Yellow-breasted Boatbill

Black-faced Monarch

Black-winged Monarch

Spectacled Monarch

Frill-necked Monarch

Pied Monarch

White-eared Monarch

Magpie-lark*

Spangled Drongo

Orioles, Figbird *Family Oriolidae* pp. 244–5

Nest Orioles build strong, deep, cup-shaped nests, suspended by the rim. Yellow Oriole's nest is often placed over a stream or pool. Figbird nest is more flimsy; birds nest in loose association, sub-colonies. **Eggs** 2–3, rarely 4, cream, lightly spotted (Orioles). 2–3, greenish, dull, red-brown marks, spots (Figbird). **Inc.** Females only, 17–18 days (Orioles). Both sexes share incubation, care of nestlings (Figbird). **Fledge** 2–2½ weeks (Orioles); 2 weeks (Figbird). **Nestl.** Naked; grow feathers. Dependent (all species). **Care** Both parents (Orioles). Both, plus some help from unrelated bird(s) at times (Figbird) whose juveniles/immatures, when independent, form flocks that are nomadic; may travel widely.

Breeding Seasons (* variable)

J F M A M J J A S O N D

Yellow Oriole

Olive-backed Oriole*

Australasian Figbird

Birds of Paradise *Family Paradisaeidae* pp. 246–7

Each adult male riflebird displays alone on conspicuous perches in the tree tops and mates with many females. Trumpet Manucode has a series of flying, chasing and bowing displays. **Nest** Females build large, sturdy, well-concealed, open-topped cup nests. Riflebirds sometimes add cast snake-skins to the rims of their nests. Manucode nest similar but shallower, and of less solid construction. **Eggs** 1, usually 2; glossy; reddish ground-colour, with longitudinal red-brown streaks (Victoria's, Paradise, Riflebirds). Duller, whiter, with reddish streaks (Magnificent Riflebird). Pale buff-pink with fine reddish-purple and grey streaks (Manucode). **Inc.** Details not well known for any species but almost certainly female only. Doubtful if any males assist. **Nestl.** Naked; grows feathers. Dependent. Female generally considered to rear the young alone. **Fledge** Little or no information on period to fledging. **Care** Female only until independence. May be with female for a year or more (all species) but information patchy.

Breeding Seasons

J F M A M J J A S O N D

Paradise Riflebird

Victoria's Riflebird

Magnificent Riflebird

Trumpet Manucode

Bowerbirds *Family Ptilonorhynchidae* pp. 246–9

Polygamous bowerbird males clear courts or build complex bowers for display. Decorated, often 'painted', 'run-through' courts are constructed by Fawn-breasted, Satin, Regent, Western, Spotted and Great Bowerbirds. Male of Golden builds so-called 'maypole' bower, twin towers between two young trees, with an elevated display perch between them. Females bowerbirds mate with males, then do all nest building, incubation and feeding of young. Male catbirds do not build bowers and are not promiscuous. They pair with one female, defend an all-purpose territory and assist in feeding their offspring. **Nest** Varies with species from flimsy to substantial cups of twigs, bark, leaves, tendrils. **Eggs** Usually 1, white (Golden). Usually 1–2, occasionally 3 eggs, pale ground colour with speckles, fine blotches, scribbly or wavy lines in Fawn-breasted, Regent, Western, Spotted and Great Bowerbirds. Satin eggs have no wavy lines, are plainer than the others. Tooth-billed Bowerbird, catbirds

2–3 eggs, plain, off-white. **Inc.** Female only. Where known, most bowerbird species incubate from just under, to just over, 3 weeks; catbirds may take an extra day or two. **Nestl.** Naked, grow feathers. Dependent. **Fledge** Most species just under, to just over, 3 weeks. Not well known in Spotted, Western and Tooth-billed Bowerbirds. **Care** Female only. Juveniles may become independent of females 2–3 months after fledging. Juvenile to immature Satin Bowerbirds often in small nomadic groups.

Breeding Seasons

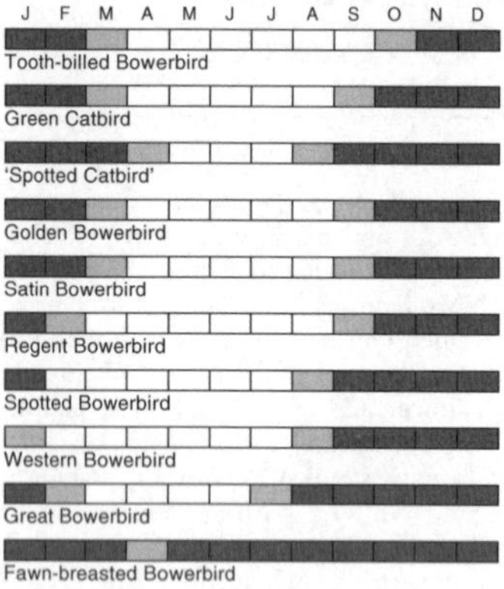

J F M A M J J A S O N D

Tooth-billed Bowerbird

Green Catbird

'Spotted Catbird'

Golden Bowerbird

Satin Bowerbird

Regent Bowerbird

Spotted Bowerbird

Western Bowerbird

Great Bowerbird

Fawn-breasted Bowerbird

Cuckoo-shrikes, Trillers

Family Campephagidae pp. 250–1

Cuckoo-shrikes and trillers build their very small nests on top of horizontal branches or forks and they are almost invisible from the ground. Nests of cuckoo-shrikes are so shallow that eggs or young may be lost in high winds. They sometimes use the empty nests of other bird species; an abandoned mud nest of the Magpie-lark is a favoured choice. Trillers sometimes breed in loose association, with several nests in same small area, and both sexes build. **Eggs** All species vary from green to olive or grey-green ground colour, variably sparsely or moderately densely marked with reddish, grey and brown speckles, blotches. Lay clutches of 2–3 (Black-faced, White-bellied, Ground); 2 (Barred); 1 (Cicadabird); 2–3 (White-winged Triller); 1 Varied Triller. **Inc.** Period not well known for some of the species. Female only, approx. 22 days (Cicadabird). Both sexes incubate (cuckoo-shrikes, trillers). **Nestl.** Naked, grow feathers. Dependent (all species). **Fledge** Period not well known for some of the species. Approx. 3½ weeks (Black-faced). Approx. 4 weeks (Cicadabird). Approx. 2 weeks (White-winged Triller). **Care** Both parents (all species). The Ground Cuckoo-shrike is a cooperative breeder, with additional 'helpers' within the group.

Breeding Seasons (* variable)

J F M A M J J A S O N D

Black-faced Cuckoo-shrike*

Barred Cuckoo-shrike

White-bellied Cuckoo-shrike

Cicadabird

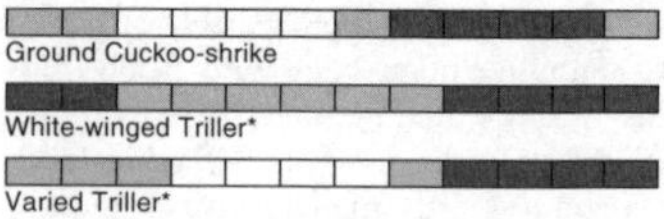

Ground Cuckoo-shrike

White-winged Triller*

Varied Triller*

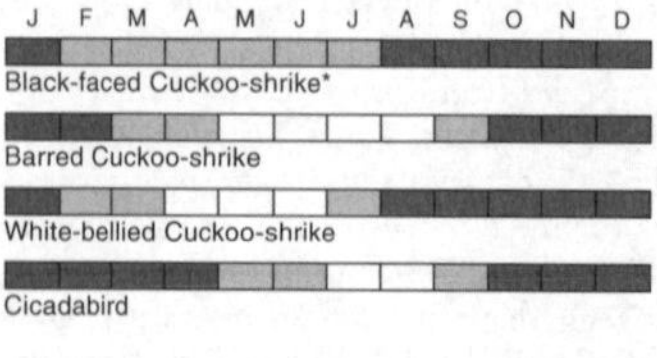

Woodswallows, Butcherbirds, Currawongs

Family Artamidae pp. 252–7

Birds seemingly different in appearance in this family are still relatively uniform in breeding behaviour.

WOODSWALLOWS: **Nest** Both sexes build flimsy nests of fine twigs in tree forks, angles of broken bark or in hollows of old stumps. **Eggs** White, dull, speckled and spotted with small dark marks; some minor variation. **Inc.** Both sexes. **Nestl.** Naked, grow feathers. Dependent. **Fledge** Not much information on time to fledging. **Care** Both parents feed, guard young, with some 'help' from older young.

BUTCHERBIRDS, MAGPIES AND CURRAWONGS: **Nest** Build more substantially of sticks and twigs, lined with dry grasses, placed in tree forks. Magpies may incorporate scraps of wire. **Eggs** Colour varies considerably. Butcherbirds' greenish-grey, and currawongs brownish. Mostly bluish- to olive-green (Magpie). All have darker streaks and spots. Lay 3–5 (butcherbirds); 2–4, and eggs are more tapered (currawongs); usually 3–5 (Magpie). **Inc.** Female only (except Black Butcherbird, where both sexes participate). 23–26 days (Grey Butcherbird). Little data on duration (currawongs). About 20–21 days (Magpie). **Nestl.** Naked, grow feathers. Dependent. **Fledge** Depending a little on species size, but approx. 4–5 weeks (all species). Not so well known for some. **Care** Both parents feed, guard young, with some 'help' from older young in Black Butcherbird, Australian Magpie.

Breeding Seasons (* variable)

J F M A M J J A S O N D

White-breasted Woodswallow*

Masked Woodswallow*

White-browed Woodswallow*

Black-faced Woodswallow

Dusky Woodswallow

Little Woodswallow

Black Butcherbird

Grey Butcherbird

Silver-backed Butcherbird

Black-backed Butcherbird

Pied Butcherbird

Australian Magpie

Pied Currawong

Black Currawong

Grey Currawong

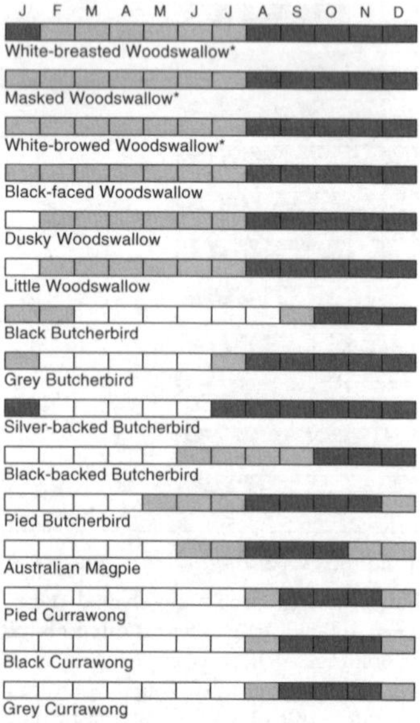

Ravens, Crows *Family Corvidae* pp. 258–9

Corvids are monogamous. Little Raven and Little Crow have a shorter breeding cycle than larger corvids. They breed semi-colonially, in habitats unsuitable for the three large, more strongly territorial species, whose nests are far more widely spaced. **Nest** Corvids build a large, untidy, bowl-shaped stick nest in trees or man-made structures (telephone poles, cable towers). The Little Crow's nest contains a layer of mud or clay under the lining. **Eggs** Normally 4–5, large, with pale greenish or bluish ground colour and often heavy markings (all species). **Inc.** Females incubate and tend chicks; males supply food. 19 days approx. **Nestl.** Naked; grows feathers. Dependent. **Fledge** From approx. 4–6 weeks (Little Raven, Little Crow); 5–7 weeks (the larger species). **Care** Both parents for 4–8 weeks or more after fledging. Independent young then form dispersive flocks of immature birds.

Breeding Seasons

J F M A M J J A S O N D

Australian Raven

Forest Raven

Little Raven

Little Crow

Torresian Crow

Australian Mud-nesters
Family Corcoracidae pp. 260–1

Breeding groups of about seven White-winged Choughs or ten Apostlebirds include a dominant male and female, other mature females, and a number of immature birds. **Nest** Construction, brooding and feeding of the young are shared more or less equally among all members. The large basin-like nest, of mud and plant fibre is built in stages on a horizontal limb. **Eggs** Normal clutch size is 2–5 (Apostlebird); 3–5 (Chough). Eggs are pale, lustrous, with a variable pattern of grey, brown and maroon spots. Larger clutches, to 10 eggs, are formed when more than one female lays in the same nest. **Inc.** Appears to be adults only. **Nestl.** Naked; grows feathers. Dependent. **Fledge** At approx. 2–3 weeks (Apostlebird); 4 weeks (Chough). Only four chicks normally reach fledgling age. A second brood may follow heavy summer rain and availability of a fresh mud supply. Second broods often fail. Two broods per season may occur more often in the Apostlebird. **Care** All members of family group assist to raise young.

Breeding Seasons

J F M A M J J A S O N D

White-winged Chough

Apostlebird

Swallows, Martins
Family Hirundinidae pp. 262–3

Monogamous for each breeding attempt. Males guard nest sites. **Nest** White-backed Swallow breeds in burrows, and often small colonies, in sandy banks. Burrow entrance 'squarer' than other burrow-breeders' holes. Welcome Swallows build a half-cup mud nest, usually under roof-eaves, bridges or culverts in southern and eastern Australia. Fairy Martins build bottle-shaped mud nests, often under bridges, culverts or cliff overhangs. Tree Martins line hollow tree limbs, cliff holes, with vegetation and often use mud to 'narrow' the entrance. All roost as well as breed in their nests. **Eggs** 4–6, usually 5; white (White-backed Swallow). From 2–6, pale in colour; often spotted reddish-brown (Welcome Swallow, martins). **Inc.** Mostly by female. Approx. 14–16 days. **Nestl.** Naked, grows feathers. Dependent. **Fledge** Probably about 2 weeks. **Care** Both parents. Juveniles then fly and feed with parents for a period. All roost and raise young in their nests.

Breeding Seasons (* variable)

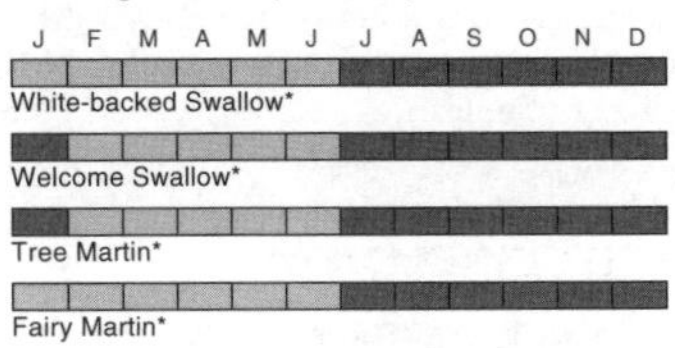

Old World Pipits, Wagtails
Family Motacillidae pp. 264–5

Australian (Richard's) Pipit is the only Australian breeding member of this Family. All others are irregular Northern Hemisphere migrants or vagrants to Australia. **Nest** A cup of grass in a depression, usually in the shelter of a stone or tussock. **Eggs** 3–4, finely freckled, off-white. **Inc.** By female; 12–13 days approx. **Nestl.** Naked, grow feathers. Dependent. **Fledge** Approx. 2 weeks. **Care** Presumably both parents.

Breeding Season (* variable)

J F M A M J J A S O N D

Australian (Richard's) Pipit*

Old World Larks *Family Alaudidae* pp. 266–7

Nest The Singing Bushlark, and introduced Skylark, both build on the ground: nests often fully-domed or almost so (Bushlark); deep open cup-shaped (Skylark). **Eggs** 2–4, white, dull, greyish-brown marks, spots (Bushlark); 3–5, white, dull, brown markings (Skylark). **Inc.** Mostly by females; males feed them and young in the nest. Approx. 11–14 days (Skylark). **Nestl.** Naked, grow feathers. Dependent. **Fledge** Not much data: probably 1½–2 weeks (both species). **Care** Both parents.

Breeding Seasons (* variable)

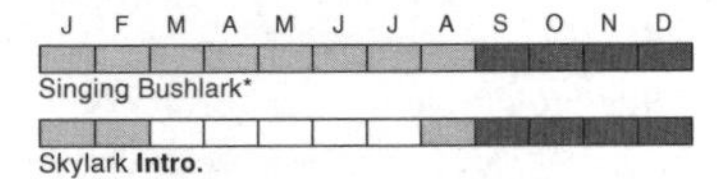

Old World Warblers *Family Sylviidae* pp. 264–5

Most building and nesting activities shared by sexes of a pair. **Nest** Australian (Clamorous) Reed-Warbler breeds in reed and bullrush beds in SE Australia, where it binds several stems together and builds a deep nest to prevent eggs being lost on windy days. Most species build open cups. Songlark males are frequently polygamous. Their females construct a fairly 'traditional' open cup-shaped grass nest, normally on the ground, in cover of a grass tussock or in light scrub. Little Grassbird builds similarly to Reed-Warbler, but nest less substantial; also frequently uses abandoned Reed-Warbler nests. Cisticolas construct deep nests with cobweb, fine grasses or fibre and a side entrance toward the top. **Eggs** Size differences with species but generally most lay 3–4 dull creamy or pinkish to reddish eggs, with fine speckles, blotches. Cisticolas' eggs, by contrast, are blue, but with the usual marks. **Inc.** Little information for most species. Approx. 13–15 days (Australian (Clamorous) Reed-Warbler). **Nestl.** Naked, grow feathers. Dependent. **Fledge** There is little published information on periods to fledging. Approx. 13–15 days (Australian (Clamorous) Reed-Warbler). **Care** Probably both parents in the smaller species. Not much male attention in Songlarks.

Breeding Seasons (* variable)

J F M A M J J A S O N D

Australian (Clamorous) Reed-Warbler*

Tawny Grassbird*

Little Grassbird*

Spinifexbird*

Rufous Songlark*

Brown Songlark*

Zitting Cisticola*

Golden-headed Cisticola*

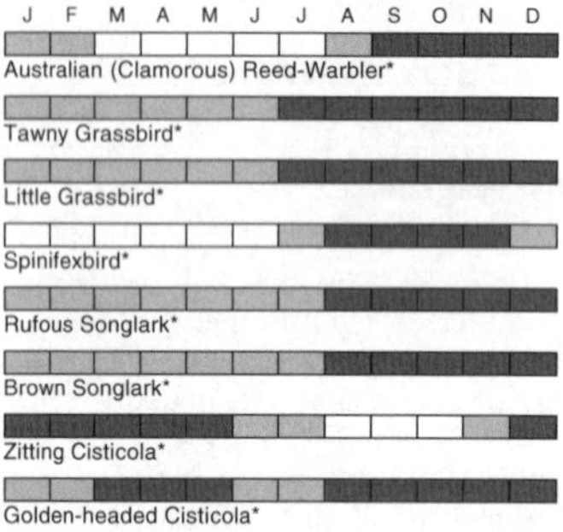

Old World Sparrows *Family Passeridae* pp. 270–1

Nest Bulky, spherical, of grass with side entrances and inner cups lined with feathers are built in dense bushes, tree hollows; gaps and crevices of buildings. **Eggs** 3–6 grey-white eggs, blotched brown (House Sparrow); 4–6 brown-white eggs with fine brown speckles (Eurasian Tree Sparrow). Both sexes feed the nestlings. Young birds fledge 14–16 days after hatching. **Inc.** Female only, 14–15 days. **Nestl.** Naked; grow feathers. Dependent. **Fledge** At approx. 2–2½ weeks. **Care** Both parents until independence.

Breeding Seasons

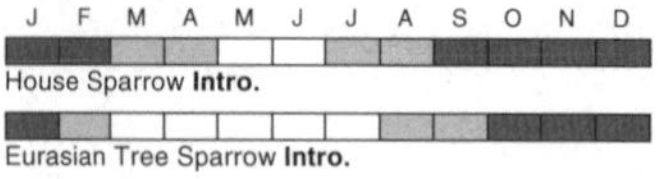

J F M A M J J A S O N D

House Sparrow **Intro.**

Eurasian Tree Sparrow **Intro.**

True Finches *Family Fringillidae* pp. 270–1

Nests Small, neat, open-topped cup nests; normally in leafy tree or shrub foliage (both species). **Eggs** 4–6 whitish eggs with brown spots (Greenfinch); 3–7 pale bluish-white eggs, spotted brown (Goldfinch). **Inc.** Females incubate for 12–14 days. **Nestl.** Naked, grow feathers. Dependent. **Fledge** About 2 weeks after hatching. **Care** Both parents.

Breeding Seasons

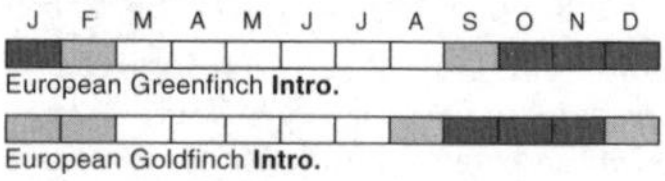

J F M A M J J A S O N D

European Greenfinch **Intro.**

European Goldfinch **Intro.**

Waxbills, Grass-Finches, Mannikins *Family Estrildidae* pp. 272–7

Nest Smaller than sparrows'; most species build a roofed, unwoven, grass nest with a side-entrance; considerable variation between species. Blue-faced Parrot-Finch uses rainforest-derived fine materials. Gouldian Finch builds inside hollow tree branches. **Eggs** Lay 4–6 pure white eggs. **Nestl.** Naked, grow feathers. Dependent. Beg uniquely with their head down to one side, and also have intricate palate and tongue patterns. **Inc.** Normally by both parents. Period variable, dependent perhaps on size, approx. 12–16 days. **Fledge** Approx. 3–3½ weeks. **Care** Both parents. Juvenile birds travel, feed with them until independent.

Breeding Seasons (* variable)

J F M A M J J A S O N D

Double-barred Finch*

Zebra Finch*

Long-tailed Finch

Masked Finch*

Black-throated Finch

Plum-headed Finch

Crimson Finch*

Red-browed Finch (Firetail)

Star Finch*

Red-eared Firetail

Beautiful Firetail

Diamond Firetail

Painted Finch (Firetail)*

Pictorella Mannikin

Nutmeg Mannikin

Yellow-rumped Mannikin

Chestnut-breasted Mannikin*

Blue-faced Parrot-Finch

Gouldian Finch

Sunbirds *Family Nectariniidae* pp. 278–9

Nest Olive-backed Sunbirds build a spectacular suspended nest of plant material, with a side entrance and a small 'porch-like' roof protruding, Sometimes placed under verandahs of buildings. **Eggs** 1–2 is usual; greenish- or bluish-grey, and with heavy markings of olive, grey and brown. **Inc.** By female and approx. 15 days. **Nestl.**

Naked; grows feathers. Dependent. **Fledge** Approx. 2 weeks (15 days). **Care** Both sexes rear juveniles.

Breeding Season (* variable)

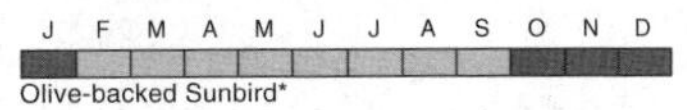

Flowerpeckers *Family Dicaeidae* pp. 278–9

Nest Female Mistletoebird builds a neat pear-shaped 'purse' nest with a slit-like side entrance, of plant down and spider web, hanging from a level twig. External surface often decorated/camouflaged with tiny dead flower fragments and possibly also with caterpillar droppings (frass) from wood-boring insect burrow entrances. **Eggs** 1 to (usually) 3. White, lustrous; usually lightly speckled. **Inc.** By female but little data – 14–18 days? **Nestl.** Naked; grow feathers. Dependent. **Fledge** About 2 weeks (15+ days). **Care** Both parents provide food and rear young.

Breeding Season (* variable)

J F M A M J J A S O N D

Mistletoebird*

White-eyes *Family Zosteropidae* pp. 278–9

Nest Parents build a small cup of fine grasses, rootlets, cobwebs, etc., suspended from twigs in dense cover. Pale White-eyes use leaves but little is known of their breeding sequences and behaviour. Following notes apply to Silvereye only: **Eggs** 2–4; pale blue, fairly glossy. **Inc.** Both parents; approx. 10 days. Frequently have 2 broods in a season. **Nestl.** Naked; grow feathers. Dependent. **Fledge** 1–2 weeks approx. **Care** Juveniles travel with parents after fledging.

Breeding Seasons (* variable)

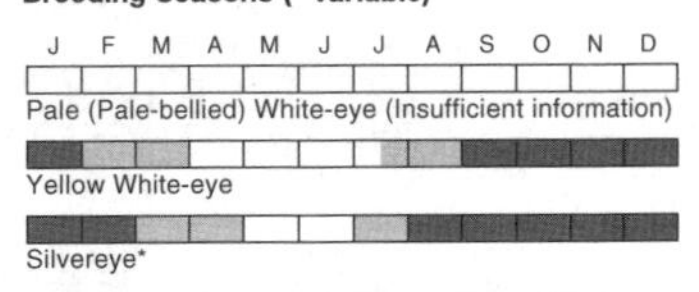

Bulbuls *Family Pycnonotidae* pp. 280–1

One introduced species, Red-whiskered, survives in small numbers about Sydney, and a few other localities in SE Australia. All nesting activities by both parents. **Nest** Finely lined open cup of bark, leaves, scraps of roots; occasionally paper shreds, in dense low tree or shrubbery. **Eggs** 2–4; whitish or buff, glossy; numerous small dark spots. **Inc.** Period in Aust. not determined; suggest 10–12 days. **Nestl.** Naked, grow feathers. Dependent. **Fledge** Time not well known. **Care** Both parents.

Breeding Season

J F M A M J J A S O N D

Red-whiskered Bulbul **Intro.**

Old World (True) Thrushes *Family Muscicapidae* pp. 280–1

INDIGENOUS BASSIAN, RUSSET-TAILED THRUSHES: **Nest** Females build bulky open bowl, of vegetation (grass, bark, rootlets), decorated (camouflaged) with moss. **Eggs** 2–3, bluish to grey, or pinkish-grey, dull, reddish heavy marks toward larger end (Bassian); 2–3 eggs, pale blue-green or greenish, lightly speckled reddish (Russet-tailed). **Inc.** Not much data but mostly by female (both species). **Nestl.** Naked, grow feathers. Dependent. **Fledge** No data; perhaps 2 weeks. **Care** Both parents.

INTRODUCED COMMON BLACKBIRD AND SONG THRUSH: **Nest** Females build open cup (bowl), using vegetation (grass, bark, rootlets) but with mud as inner nest foundation. Nest hidden in dense shrubbery where possible. **Eggs** 3–5, blue-green with small reddish, greyish speckles (Blackbird); 2–4, turquoise-blue, lightly spotted with black (Song Thrush). **Inc.** Mostly by female; 13–14 days (both species). **Nestl.** Naked, grow feathers. Dependent. **Fledge** Approx. 2 weeks. **Care** Remain with parents for several weeks or more.

Breeding Seasons (* variable)

J F M A M J J A S O N D

Bassian (Ground) Thrush*

Russet-tailed Thrush*

Common (Eurasian) Blackbird **Intro.**

Song Thrush **Intro.**

Starlings, Mynas *Family Sturnidae* pp. 280–1

Nest Metallic Starlings maintain traditional nest colonies in tall trees, often isolated or taller than surrounding forest canopy. Nests are large, untidy, crowded together, pendulous and vermin-ridden. Common Starling, Common Myna compete with native birds (especially small parrots) for nesting holes, and also breed in buildings. **Eggs** 2–3, rarely 4; glossy, pale blue or greenish with speckles (Metallic Starling). Usually 1–6, plain pale blue (Common Starling). 3–4, greenish-blue (Common Myna). **Inc.** Both sexes by day, but more by female. Female at night; 13–14 days (Common Myna). **Nestl.** Hatched naked; grow feathers (all species). Dependent. **Fledge** At about 3–4 weeks (all species). **Care** Rear young for 3–4 weeks after fledging (all species).

Breeding Seasons (* variable)

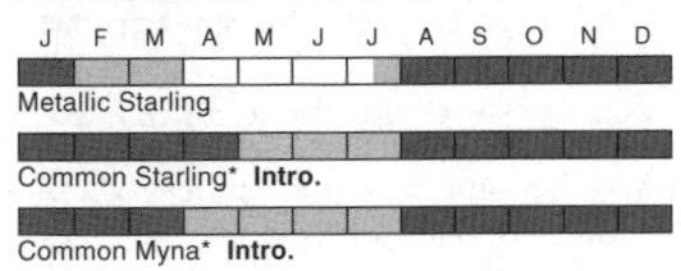

Australian Island Territories Checklists

Recent work indicates a need to study and conserve the fauna and flora of the island territories administered by the Commonwealth of Australia. The RAOU's *Handbook* series (*HANZAB*), deals with the Australia, New Zealand and Antarctic region. We feel it important for mainland Australian bird-watchers to be aware of what is on our major oceanic islands, to promote their study and protection, and to know that these birds too are part of our avifaunal region and our responsibility. Not everyone can get to every island, but all of our islands, even Heard Island, are being visited more frequently at present. Lists of birds, and an understanding of what each island contains in the way of bird populations, is thus being gathered. Lists (except that for Boigu, Saibai and Dauan Islands, which are adjacent to New Guinea) include the sea area of 200 nautical miles (i.e. the Economic Exclusion Zone) around each island. We sincerely thank **Mike Carter** for his assistance in revision and in bringing these lists up to date as of February 2003. Some further sightings, not listed here because not yet officially endorsed, will increase our knowledge of species on the islands, and also the number of rare and vagrant birds on the Australian list.

Names of birds We use only the accepted common name, unless the species is not represented on the Australian continental list, when the Latin name is also provided.

Codes used The coding has been kept as simple as possible. You are asked to see the papers and books listed as references for each island to obtain far more details of each bird species and its status at each locality. Other measures of abundance have been given in a few cases.

AM	Annual Migrant
Br.	Breeding species
IE	Island Endemic species or subspecies (race), not found anywhere else
Intro.	Introduced species – usually an indication of a real or possible pest species
IV	Irregular Visitor
R	Resident all year round
RV	Regular Visitor
SR	Summer Resident – leaves for the winter months
Vagr.	Vagrant species
WR	Winter Resident – leaves for the summer months

Birds known to have become recently extinct, whether endemic or introductions that subsequently died out, have not been entered in these lists. For recent passerine taxonomic changes see Schodde & Mason (1999). For information of the rarity, conservation status and proposed recovery plans for many species in these lists, see Garnett & Crowley (2000).

Norfolk Island (and adjacent Nepean, Phillip Islands)

Latitude 29°02' S; Longitude 167°57' E. Lies 1367 kilometres off the east coast of Australia. An oceanic island of volcanic origin. Situated 675 km S of New Caledonia, 900 km NE of Lord Howe Island, and 772 km NW of New Zealand. Norfolk Island is about 8 km long, 5 km wide and rises to two peaks, 316 and 318 m respectively. Nepean Island is 1 km E; Phillip Island is 6 km E. Both are uninhabited. There is a resident human population on Norfolk, a popular tourist destination with direct air flights.

Red Junglefowl	Intro.; Br.; R
California Quail	Intro.; Br.; R
Black Swan	Vagr.
Australian Shelduck	Vagr.
Pacific Black Duck	Br.; R?
Mallard (many hybrids between Pacific Black Duck and Mallard)	Vagr.
Hardhead	Vagr.
Australasian Grebe	Vagr.
Southern Giant-Petrel	Vagr.
Cape Petrel	Vagr.
Tahiti Petrel	Vagr.
Providence Petrel	Br.; WR
Kermadec Petrel	Br.; SR
Mottled Petrel	AM?
White-necked Petrel	Br.; SR
Black-winged Petrel	Br.; SR; AM
Gould's Petrel	Vagr.
Fairy Prion	Vagr.
Wedge-tailed Shearwater	Br.; AM; SR
Flesh-footed Shearwater	Br.; SR
Sooty Shearwater	RV?
Newell's Shearwater	Vagr.
Little Shearwater	Br.; AM?; WR
Wandering Albatross	Vagr.
Laysan Albatross	Vagr.
Black-browed Albatross	Vagr.
White-bellied Storm-Petrel	Vagr.
Red-tailed Tropicbird	Br.; R
White-tailed Tropicbird	Vagr.
Australasian Gannet	(rare) Br.; SR
Masked Booby *Sula dactylatra fullagari*	Br.; SR
Brown Booby	Vagr.
Little Pied Cormorant	Vagr.
Little Black Cormorant	Vagr.
Great Cormorant	IV
Australian Pelican	Vagr.

Species	Status
Great Frigatebird	Vagr.
Lesser Frigatebird	Vagr.
White-faced Heron	Br.; R
Little Egret	Vagr.
White-necked Heron	Vagr.
Great Egret	Vagr.
Cattle Egret	Vagr.
Australian White Ibis	Vagr.
Straw-necked Ibis	Vagr.
Royal Spoonbill	Vagr.
Yellow-billed Spoonbill	Vagr.
Swamp (Marsh) Harrier	IV
Brown Goshawk	Vagr.
Nankeen Kestrel	Br.?; R
Buff-banded Rail	Br.; R
Spotless Crake	Br.; Vagr.; R?
Purple Swamphen	Br.; R
Eurasian Coot	Vagr.
Latham's Snipe	IV
Hudsonian Godwit	Vagr.
Bar-tailed Godwit	AM; SR
Whimbrel	AM; SR
Eastern Curlew	IV
Common Greenshank	Vagr.
Terek Sandpiper	Vagr.
Common Sandpiper	Vagr.
Grey-tailed Tattler	IV
Wandering Tattler	IV
Ruddy Turnstone	AM; SR
Red Knot	IV
Red-necked Stint	IV
Pectoral Sandpiper	Vagr.
Sharp-tailed Sandpiper	IV
Curlew Sandpiper	Vagr.
Ruff	Vagr.
South Island Pied Oystercatcher *Haematopus finschi*	Vagr.
Black-winged Stilt	Vagr.
Red-necked Avocet	Vagr.
Pacific Golden Plover	AM; SR
Double-banded Plover	AM; WR
Lesser Sand Plover	IV
Greater Sand Plover	Vagr.
Masked Lapwing	IV
Oriental Pratincole	Vagr.
South Polar Skua	Vagr.
Skua (*Stercorarius* sp.)	IV
Arctic Jaeger	Vagr.
Pomarine Jaeger	Vagr.
Silver Gull	Vagr.
Crested Tern	Vagr.
White-fronted Tern	Vagr.
Sooty Tern	Br.; SR
White-winged Black Tern	Vagr.
Common Noddy	Br.; SR
Black Noddy	Br.; SR
Grey Ternlet	Br.; SR
White Tern	Br.; R
Rock Dove	Intro.; Br.; R
Emerald Dove	Self-intro.; Br.; R
Rose-crowned Fruit-Dove	Vagr.
Crimson Rosella	Intro.; Br.; R
Red-crowned Parakeet (Green Parrot) *Cyanoramphus novaezelandiae*	Br.; IE; R
Oriental Cuckoo	Vagr.
Pallid Cuckoo	Vagr.
Shining Bronze-Cuckoo (locally 'Greenback')	AM
Long-tailed Cuckoo (Long-tailed Koel) *Eudynamys taitensis*	IV
Channel-billed Cuckoo	Vagr.
Southern Boobook *Ninox novaeseelandiae undulates*	**Endangered** Br.; IE; R
Morepork *Ninox n. novaeseelandiae* (males from NZ introduced to breed with remaining 1 or 2 old Southern Boobook females)	Intro.
Barn Owl	Vagr.
White-throated Needletail	Vagr.
Fork-tailed Swift	Vagr.
Sacred Kingfisher	Br.; R
Dollarbird	IV
Norfolk Island Gerygone *Gerygone modesta*	Br.; IE; R
Pacific Robin *Petroica multicolor multicolor* (now split from Scarlet Robin *P. boodang*)	**Vulnerable** Br.; IE; R
Golden Whistler *Pachycephala pectoralis xanthoprocta*	**Vulnerable** Br.; IE; R
Grey Fantail *Rhipidura fuliginosa pelzelni*	Br.; IE; R
Masked Woodswallow	Br.; Vagr.
White-browed Woodswallow	Vagr.
Australian (Richard's) Pipit	Vagr.
House Sparrow	Intro?; Br.; R
Common Chaffinch *Fringilla coelebs*	Vagr.
European Greenfinch	Self-intro.?; Br.; R
European Goldfinch	Self-intro.?; Br.; R
Welcome Swallow	Br.?; R
Silvereye	Self-intro.; Br.; R
Slender-billed White-eye *Zosterops tenuirostris tenuirostris*	Br.; IE; R
Common Blackbird	Intro.; Br.; R
Song Thrush	Intro.; Br.; R
Common Starling	Self-intro.; Br.; R
Common Myna	Vagr.

Note Bristle-thighed Curlew, Little Tern and Fairy Martin have been reported but lack documentation. White-breasted White-eye *Zosterops albogularis* believed extinct, *circa* 1994. Island Thrush (Grey-headed Blackbird or Guava Bird) *Turdus poliocephalus poliocephalus* is extinct on Norfolk Is.

Reading

Bell, Brian D. (1990), 'The status and management of the White-breasted White-eye and other birds on Norfolk Island, A Report for the ANPWS, May 1990', RAOU, Moonee Ponds, Victoria.

Hermes, N. (editor) (1985), *An Annotated Checklist of Vascular Plants and Vertebrate Animals of Norfolk Island*, Flora and Fauna Society of Norfolk Island/Australian National Parks and Wildlife Service, Norfolk Island.

Hermes, N. (1991), *Birds of Norfolk Island*, Wonderland Publications, Norfolk Island.

Moore, J.L. (1999), 'Norfolk Island Bird Notes, 1977 to 1997', *Notornis* **46**: 354–64.

Schodde, R., Fullagar, P. & Hermes, N. (1983), 'A review of Norfolk Island birds: past and present', *Special Publication* **8**, Australian National Parks and Wildlife Service, Canberra.

Lord Howe Island (and associated Balls Pyramid)

Lat. 31° 33' S; Long. 159° 05' E. Lies 570 km off the eastern coast of New South Wales: Norfolk Island is 900 km to the NE. New Zealand is 1350 km to the SE and New Caledonia is 1250 km to the NNE. Administered by the Government of New South Wales. Permanent resident human population. Tourist destination. Direct air flights.

The island is about 11 km long, and up to 2.8 km wide; total land area is about 1455 hectares. Two mountains – Mt Lidgbird 777 m, Mt Gower 875 m – are the highest points. The island is subtropical and of submarine volcanic origin. Balls Pyramid, a volcanic stack or spire, rises to 551 m, 23 km to the SE.

Black Swan Vagr. ☐☐☐
Canada Goose *Branta canadensis* Vagr. ☐☐☐
Paradise Shelduck *Tadorna variegata* Vagr. ☐☐☐
Mallard (many hybrids between Pacific Black Duck and Mallard at the island) Vagr. ☐☐☐
Pacific Black Duck Br.; R ☐☐☐
Grey Teal Vagr. ☐☐☐
Chestnut Teal Vagr. ☐☐☐
Australasian Grebe Vagr. ☐☐☐
Hoary-headed Grebe Vagr. ☐☐☐
Little Penguin Vagr. ☐☐☐
Giant-Petrel (species not known) Vagr. ☐☐☐
Cape Petrel Vagr. ☐☐☐
Great-winged Petrel Vagr. ☐☐☐
White-headed Petrel Vagr. ☐☐☐
Providence Petrel Br.; AM; WR ☐☐☐
Kermadec Petrel (Balls Pyramid) Br. AM; SR ☐☐☐
Mottled Petrel Vagr. ☐☐☐
White-necked Petrel Vagr. ☐☐☐
Black-winged Petrel Br.; AM; SR ☐☐☐
Gould's Petrel Vagr. ☐☐☐
Antarctic (Dove) Prion Vagr. ☐☐☐
Fairy Prion Vagr. ☐☐☐
Wedge-tailed Shearwater Br.; AM; SR ☐☐☐
Buller's Shearwater Vagr. ☐☐☐
Flesh-footed Shearwater Br.; AM; SR ☐☐☐
Sooty Shearwater Vagr. ☐☐☐
Short-tailed Shearwater Vagr. ☐☐☐
Fluttering Shearwater Vagr. ☐☐☐
Hutton's Shearwater Vagr. ☐☐☐
Little Shearwater Br.; AM; WR ☐☐☐
Wandering Albatross Vagr. ☐☐☐
White-bellied Storm-Petrel Br.; AM; SR ☐☐☐
Red-tailed Tropicbird Br.; R ☐☐☐
White-tailed Tropicbird Vagr. ☐☐☐
Australasian Gannet RV ☐☐☐
Masked Booby Br.; R ☐☐☐
Red-footed Booby Vagr. ☐☐☐
Brown Booby Vagr. ☐☐☐
Little Pied Cormorant Vagr. ☐☐☐
Pied Cormorant Vagr. ☐☐☐
Little Black Cormorant Vagr. ☐☐☐
Great Cormorant Vagr. ☐☐☐
Great Frigatebird Vagr. ☐☐☐
Lesser Frigatebird Vagr. ☐☐☐
White-faced Heron Self-intro.; Br.; R ☐☐☐
Great Egret Vagr. ☐☐☐
Intermediate Egret Vagr. ☐☐☐
Cattle Egret RV ☐☐☐
Nankeen Night Heron Vagr. ☐☐☐
Little Bittern Vagr. ☐☐☐
Australasian Bittern Vagr. ☐☐☐
Glossy Ibis Vagr. ☐☐☐
Australian White Ibis Vagr. ☐☐☐
Straw-necked Ibis Vagr. ☐☐☐
Royal Spoonbill Vagr. ☐☐☐
Yellow-billed Spoonbill Vagr. ☐☐☐
Black-shouldered Kite Vagr. ☐☐☐
Swamp Harrier RV ☐☐☐
Brown Falcon Vagr. ☐☐☐
Nankeen Kestrel Self-intro.; Br.; R ☐☐☐
Buff-banded Rail Intro. ? or Self-intro.; Br.; R ☐☐☐
Lord Howe Island Woodhen *Gallirallus* (*Tricholimnas*) *sylvestris* **Vulnerable** (subject of rehabilitation programme) Br.; IE; R ☐☐☐
Baillon's Crake Vagr. ☐☐☐
Purple Swamphen Self-intro.; Br.; R ☐☐☐
Dusky Moorhen Vagr. ☐☐☐
Eurasian Coot Vagr. ☐☐☐
Latham's Snipe IV ☐☐☐
Black-tailed Godwit Vagr. ☐☐☐
Bar-tailed Godwit AM; SR ☐☐☐
Little Curlew Vagr. ☐☐☐
Whimbrel AM; SR ☐☐☐
Eastern Curlew IV ☐☐☐

Marsh Sandpiper Vagr. ☐☐☐
Common Greenshank RV ☐☐☐
Terek Sandpiper Vagr. ☐☐☐
Common Sandpiper Vagr. ☐☐☐
Grey-tailed Tattler RV? ☐☐☐
Wandering Tattler IV? ☐☐☐
Ruddy Turnstone AM; SR ☐☐☐
Red Knot Vagr. ☐☐☐
Red-necked Stint IV ☐☐☐
Pectoral Sandpiper Vagr. ☐☐☐
Sharp-tailed Sandpiper Vagr. ☐☐☐
Curlew Sandpiper Vagr. ☐☐☐
Buff-breasted Sandpiper Vagr. ☐☐☐
Painted Snipe Vagr. ☐☐☐
Pied Oystercatcher/South Island Pied Oystercatcher *Haematopus finschi* (both claimed; S.I.P.O. is species more likely) Vagr. ☐☐☐
Black-winged Stilt Vagr. ☐☐☐
Pacific Golden Plover AM; SR ☐☐☐
Grey Plover Vagr. ☐☐☐
Double-banded Plover AM; WR? ☐☐☐
Lesser Sand Plover Vagr. ☐☐☐
Greater Sand Plover Vagr. ☐☐☐
Oriental Plover Vagr. ☐☐☐
Banded Lapwing Vagr. ☐☐☐
Masked Lapwing Self-intro.; Br.; R ☐☐☐
Oriental Pratincole Vagr. ☐☐☐
Australian Pratincole Vagr. ☐☐☐
Long-tailed Jaeger Vagr. ☐☐☐
Kelp Gull Vagr. ☐☐☐
Silver Gull Vagr. ☐☐☐
Crested Tern Vagr. ☐☐☐
Black-naped Tern Vagr. ☐☐☐
Common Tern Vagr. ☐☐☐
Arctic Tern Vagr. ☐☐☐
Little Tern Vagr. ☐☐☐
Sooty Tern Br.; AM; SR ☐☐☐
White-winged Black Tern Vagr. ☐☐☐
Common Noddy Br.; AM; SR ☐☐☐
Black Noddy Br.; R ☐☐☐
Grey Ternlet Br.; R ☐☐☐
White Tern Br.; AM; SR ☐☐☐
Rock Dove Intro.; Br.; R ☐☐☐
Spotted Turtle-Dove Vagr. ☐☐☐
Pied Imperial-Pigeon Vagr. ☐☐☐
Emerald Dove Br.; R ☐☐☐
Brush Bronzewing Vagr. ☐☐☐
Peaceful Dove Vagr. ☐☐☐
Oriental Cuckoo Vagr. ☐☐☐
Pallid Cuckoo Vagr. ☐☐☐
Brush Cuckoo Vagr. ☐☐☐
Fan-tailed Cuckoo Vagr. ☐☐☐
Common Koel Vagr. ☐☐☐
Shining Bronze-Cuckoo IV ☐☐☐
Long-tailed Cuckoo (Long-tailed Koel) *Eudynamys taitensis* IV ☐☐☐
Masked Owl Introduced (subject of control programme) Br.; R ☐☐☐
White-throated Needletail Vagr. ☐☐☐
Fork-tailed Swift Vagr. ☐☐☐
Sacred Kingfisher Br.; SR ☐☐☐
Rainbow Bee-eater Vagr. ☐☐☐
Dollarbird Vagr. ☐☐☐
Noisy Friarbird Vagr. ☐☐☐
Golden Whistler *Pachycephala pectoralis contempta* Br.; IE; R ☐☐☐
Leaden Flycatcher Vagr. ☐☐☐
Magpie-Lark Intro.; Br.; R ☐☐☐
Grey Fantail Vagr. ☐☐☐
Black-faced Cuckoo-Shrike Vagr. ☐☐☐
Masked Woodswallow Vagr. ☐☐☐
Pied Currawong *Strepera graculina crissalis* **Vulnerable** Br.; IE; R ☐☐☐
Australian Raven Vagr. ☐☐☐
Australian (Richard's) Pipit Vagr. ☐☐☐
Common Chaffinch *Fringilla coelebs* Vagr. ☐☐☐
European Goldfinch Vagr. ☐☐☐
European Greenfinch Vagr. ☐☐☐
Common (Lesser) Redpoll *Carduelis flammea* Vagr. ☐☐☐
Yellowhammer *Emberiza citrinella* Vagr. ☐☐☐
Welcome Swallow Br.; R ☐☐☐
Fairy Martin Vagr. ☐☐☐
Silvereye (Lord Howe White-eye) *Zosterops lateralis tephropleura* Br.; IE; R ☐☐☐
Common Blackbird Self-intro.; Br.; R ☐☐☐
Song Thrush Self-intro.; Br.; R ☐☐☐
Common Starling Self-intro.; Br.; R ☐☐☐

Reading

Hutton, Ian (1991), *Birds of Lord Howe Island Past and Present*, The Author, Coffs Harbour Plaza, NSW.
Knight, B. (1989), 'Report on Lord Howe Island observations', *Australian Birds* **22** (1 & 2), 41–3.
Miller, B. & Muellette, K.J. (1985), 'Rehabilitation of an endangered Australian bird: the Lord Howe Woodhen *Tricholimnas sylvestris* (Sclater)', *Biological Conservation* **34**, 55–95.
Heather, B. & Robertson, H. (1996), *The Field Guide to the Birds of New Zealand*, Viking, Auckland.

Cocos (Keeling) Islands

Lat. 12° 10' S; Long. 96° 50' E. Lie 3685 kilometres due west of Darwin, 2768 km NW of Perth, in the Indian Ocean. Small resident human population. Air and sea access from Perth or Indonesia.

Red Junglefowl Intro. (declining); Br. ☐☐☐
Green Junglefowl *Gallus varius* Intro.; Br. ☐☐☐
Herald Petrel (winter visitor); Br.? ☐☐☐
Barau's Petrel Vagr.? ☐☐☐
Wedge-tailed Shearwater Br. SR ☐☐☐

Yellow-nosed Albatross Vagr.? ☐☐☐
Red-tailed Tropicbird (occasionally) Br. ☐☐☐
White-tailed Tropicbird Br.; R ☐☐☐
Masked Booby Br.; R ☐☐☐
Red-footed Booby Br.; R ☐☐☐
Brown Booby Br.; R ☐☐☐
Great Frigatebird Br.; R ☐☐☐
Lesser Frigatebird Br.; R ☐☐☐
Christmas Frigatebird Vagr. ☐☐☐
White-faced Heron Vagr. ☐☐☐
Little Egret Vagr. ☐☐☐
Eastern Reef Egret Br.; R ☐☐☐
Cattle Egret Vagr. ☐☐☐
Nankeen Night Heron Br.; R ☐☐☐
Black-crowned Night Heron *Nycticorax nycticorax* Vagr. ☐☐☐
Glossy Ibis Vagr. ☐☐☐
Greater Flamingo *Phoenicopterus ruber* Vagr. ☐☐☐
Buff-banded (Cocos) Rail *Gallirallus philippensis andrewsi* (common locally; declining on some islands) Considered **Endangered** IE; R ☐☐☐
Swamp Harrier Vagr. ☐☐☐
Nankeen Kestrel Vagr. ☐☐☐
Pin-tailed Snipe IV ☐☐☐
Little Curlew Vagr. ☐☐☐
Whimbrel RV ☐☐☐
Common Greenshank Vagr. ☐☐☐
Common Sandpiper RV ☐☐☐
Ruddy Turnstone AM ☐☐☐
Sanderling IV ☐☐☐
Sharp-tailed Sandpiper Vagr. ☐☐☐
Pacific Golden Plover AM ☐☐☐
Grey Plover Vagr. ☐☐☐
Greater Sand Plover Vagr. ☐☐☐
Oriental Plover Vagr. ☐☐☐
Oriental Pratincole Vagr. ☐☐☐
Common Tern Vagr. ☐☐☐
Bridled Tern Vagr. ☐☐☐
Sooty Tern (a few, declining?); Br.; R ☐☐☐
White-winged Black Tern Vagr. ☐☐☐
Common Noddy Br.; R ☐☐☐
White Tern Br.; R ☐☐☐
Dove (unidentified) Vagr. ☐☐☐
Nightjar (unidentified) Vagr. ☐☐☐
White-throated Needletail Vagr. ☐☐☐
Wagtail (unidentified) Vagr. ☐☐☐
Barn Swallow AM ☐☐☐
Christmas Island White-eye *Zosterops natalis* Intro. (a few; may be declining) ☐☐☐

Note Buffy Fish-Owl *Ketupa ketupa* claimed; unconfirmed.

Reading

Carter, Mike (1994), 'Birds of the Cocos-Keeling Islands', *Wingspan*, No. **15**, Sept.: 14–16, 18.
House of Representatives Standing Committee on Environment, Recreation and the Arts (1990), 'Tourism in the Indian Ocean Territories', The Parliament of the Commonwealth of Australia, Aust. Government Publishing Service, Canberra, ACT.
Stokes, Tony, Sheils, Wendy & Dunn, Kevin (1984), 'Birds of the Cocos (Keeling) Islands, Indian Ocean', *Emu* **84** (1): 23–8.

Christmas Island

Lat. 10° 25' S; Long. 105° 40' E. Lies 1400 kilometres north-west of Western Australia in the Indian Ocean, 900 km NE of the Cocos (Keeling) Islands, and 330 km SE of Java. Resident human population. Air and sea access from Perth or Indonesia. Tourist destination.

Red Junglefowl Intro. (a few present); Br.; R ☐☐☐
Garganey Vagr. ☐☐☐
Barau's Petrel Vagr.? ☐☐☐
Bulwer's Petrel Vagr. ☐☐☐
Antarctic Prion Vagr. ☐☐☐
Wedge-tailed Shearwater Vagr. ☐☐☐
White-faced Storm-Petrel Vagr. ☐☐☐
Matsudaira's Storm-Petrel Vagr. ☐☐☐
Red-tailed Tropicbird Br.; R ☐☐☐
White-tailed Tropicbird *Phaethon lepturus 'fulvus'* Br.; IE; R ☐☐☐
Abbott's Booby **Vulnerable** Br.; IE; R ☐☐☐
Red-footed Booby Br.; R ☐☐☐
Brown Booby Br.; R ☐☐☐
Little Black Cormorant IV ☐☐☐
Great Cormorant Vagr. ☐☐☐
Australian Pelican Vagr. ☐☐☐
Great Frigatebird Br.; R ☐☐☐
Lesser Frigatebird Br.; RV ☐☐☐
Christmas Frigatebird **Vulnerable** Br.; IE; R ☐☐☐
White-faced Heron Self-intro.; Br.; R ☐☐☐
Little Egret Vagr. ☐☐☐
Eastern Reef Egret (small numbers) Br.; R ☐☐☐
Great Egret Vagr. ☐☐☐
Intermediate Egret Vagr. ☐☐☐
Cattle Egret Vagr. ☐☐☐
Striated Heron Vagr. ☐☐☐
Nankeen Night Heron IV ☐☐☐
Malayan Night Heron *Gorsachius melanolophus* Vagr. ☐☐☐
Yellow Bittern Vagr. ☐☐☐
Cinnamon Bittern *Ixobrychus cinnamomeus* Vagr. ☐☐☐
Black Bittern Vagr. ☐☐☐
White-bellied Sea-Eagle Vagr. ☐☐☐
Oriental Honey-buzzard *Pernis ptilorhynchus orientalis* Vagr. ☐☐☐
Varied Goshawk *Accipiter hiogaster natalis* **Vulnerable** Br.; IE; R ☐☐☐
Peregrine Falcon Vagr. ☐☐☐
Nankeen Kestrel Self-intro.; Br.; R ☐☐☐
White-breasted Waterhen *Amaurornis phoenicurus* Self-intro. (1992 approx.); Br. ☐☐☐
Baillon's Crake Vagr. ☐☐☐

Species	Status
Ruddy-breasted Crake *Porzana fusca*	Vagr.
Watercock *Gallicrex cinerea*	Vagr.
Pin-tailed Snipe	RV
Bar-tailed Godwit	Vagr.
Little Curlew	Vagr.
Whimbrel	IV
Common Redshank	Vagr.
Marsh Sandpiper	Vagr.
Common Greenshank	IV
Wood Sandpiper	IV
Terek Sandpiper	Vagr.
Common Sandpiper	RV
Grey-tailed Tattler	IV
Ruddy Turnstone	RV
Red-necked Stint	IV
Long-toed Stint	Vagr.
Sharp-tailed Sandpiper	Vagr.
Sanderling	Vagr.
Curlew Sandpiper	Vagr.
Sooty Oystercatcher	Vagr.
Black-winged Stilt	Vagr.
Grey Plover	Vagr.
Pacific Golden Plover	RV
Little Ringed Plover	Vagr.
Lesser Sand Plover	Vagr.
Greater Sand Plover	Vagr.
Oriental Plover	IV
Masked Lapwing	Vagr.
Oriental Pratincole	IV
Australian Pratincole	Vagr.
Arctic Jaeger	Vagr.
Mew Gull *Larus canus*	Vagr.
Crested Tern	Vagr.
Common Tern	Vagr.
Sooty Tern	Vagr.
Whiskered Tern	Vagr.
Common Noddy	SR; AM?; Br.
White Tern	Vagr.
Emerald Dove *Chalcophaps indica natalis*	Br.; IE; R
Christmas Island Imperial-Pigeon *Ducula whartoni*	Br.; IE; R
Pied Imperial-Pigeon	Vagr.
Christmas Island Hawk-Owl *Ninox natalis* (rare) **Vulnerable**	Br.; IE; R
Oriental Cuckoo	Vagr.
Pallid Cuckoo	Vagr.
Horsfield's Bronze-Cuckoo	Vagr.
Savanna Nightjar *Caprimulgus affinis*	Br.?; IV
Glossy (Christmas Island) Swiftlet *Aerodramus esculenta natalis*	Br.; IE; R
Fork-tailed Swift	Vagr.
Sacred Kingfisher	Vagr.
Collared Kingfisher	Vagr.
Dollarbird	Vagr.
Blue-winged Pitta	Vagr.
Brown Shrike *Lanius cristatus*	Vagr.
Yellow Wagtail	RV
White Wagtail races *leucopsis, ocularis*	Vagr.
Grey Wagtail	RV
Eurasian Tree Sparrow	Intro.; Br.; R
Java Sparrow *Padda oryzivora*	Intro.; Br.; R
Barn Swallow	RV
Red-rumped Swallow	Vagr.
Asian House Martin *Delichon dasypus*	Vagr.
Christmas Island White-eye *Zosterops natalis*	Br.; IE; R
Wheatear *Oenanthe* sp. unidentified	Vagr.
Island Thrush *Turdus poliocephalus erythropleurus*	Br.; IE; R
Purple-backed (Daurian) Starling *Sturnus sturninus*	Vagr.

Note Rose-ringed Parakeet *Psittacula krameri* introduced as pet birds but probably now extinct. Claims of Purple Heron, Javan Pond Heron, Chinese Goshawk, Japanese Sparrowhawk, Drongo Cuckoo, Black-nest Swiftlet, Brown-backed Needletail, Dark-rumped Swift, Common Kingfisher, a Pipit sp., a Flowerpecker sp. and an Oriental Reed-Warbler remain unconfirmed.

Reading

Carter, M.J. (1994), 'Birds of Australia's Christmas Island', *Wingspan* **13** March, pp. 18–21.

Gray, H.S. (1981), *Christmas Island – Naturally*, The Author, Geraldton, WA.

Norman, J.A., *et al* (1998), 'Molecular data confirms the species status of the Christmas Island Hawk-Owl *Ninox natalis*', *Emu* **98** (3): 197–208. [Three related papers are also included in this issue.]

Stokes, T. (1988), 'A review of the birds of Christmas Island', *Occasional Paper* No. **16**, Australian National Parks and Wildlife Service, Canberra, ACT, 39 pp.

Stokes, T., Merton, D., Hicks, J. & Tranter, J. (1987), 'Additional records of birds from Christmas Island, Indian Ocean', *Australian Bird Watcher* **12** (1), 1–7 [adds 31 new species for the island; extra records of 14 species described as rare to the island].

Boigu, Saibai and Dauan Islands

Boigu Island is at Lat. 9° 17' S; Long. 142° 13' E. This is the most northerly island (7150 hectares) of Queensland and the Australian continent, in northern Torres Strait. Nearest mainland is Papua New Guinea. A resident human population lives in a small settlement. The island consists of mangrove forest and freshwater swamps. Prior arrangement for visits is essential; permission from the Island Council is required. Limited accommodation and facilities. Access is by air from Thursday (Horn) Island. Boigu Island is a place for potential 'new bird sightings' for the Australian list, hence its sudden interest to bird-watchers and 'twitchers' from Australia. However, one is reminded that evidence for acceptance of a new bird (from anywhere in Australia) is rigorous and must be thoroughly corroborated.

Saibai Island is at Lat. 09° S; Long. 143° E, approx. 50 km to the east of Boigu Island, and 3.5 km from the Papua New Guinea coast. Prior arrangement for visits is essential; permission from the Saibai Island Council is required. Limited accommodation and facilities. Access is by air from Thursday (Horn) Island.

Dauan Island is approx. 10 km immediately to the west of Saibai Island. Similar rules apply for access, which is by ferry from Saibai.

In this list, we have combined the three islands, but the data for Breeding (Br.), Status (Vagr., R, etc.), and for Seasonal Occurrence (AM; WR) APPLIES ONLY to Boigu Island. It will be noted there is great similarity between the lists for these three islands. Distribution is given in square brackets [B = Boigu; D = Dauan; S = Saibai]. A few recently recorded species have no Status attributed to them; we consider it would be wrong to do so, so soon after their initial sighting.

Species	Status
Orange-footed Scrubfowl [B, S]	Br.; R
Magpie Goose [B, S]	Br.?; AM
Wandering Whistling-Duck [B, S]	AM
Spotted Whistling-Duck [B]	Br.?; IV
Radjah Shelduck [B, S]	AM
Green Pygmy-goose [S]	
Pacific Black Duck [B, D, S]	Br.; AM
Grey Teal [B, S]	Vagr.
Australasian Grebe [S]	
Darter [B, S]	Vagr.
Little Pied Cormorant [B, S]	IV
Little Black Cormorant [B, S]	IV
Great Cormorant [B, S]	Vagr.
Australian Pelican [B, D, S]	Br.?
Lesser Frigatebird [B, D, S]	Vagr.
White-faced Heron [B, D, S]	IV
Little Egret [B, S]	IV
Eastern Reef Egret [B, S]	Br.?; AM
White-necked Heron [B, S]	Vagr.
Great-billed Heron [B]	Vagr.
Pied Heron [B, D, S]	Br.?; R
Great Egret [B, D, S]	AM
Intermediate Egret [B, S]	IV
Cattle Egret [S]	
Striated Heron [B, D, S]	Br.; R
Nankeen Night Heron [B, D, S]	R?
Black Bittern [B, S]	Vagr.
Glossy Ibis [B, S]	Vagr.
Australian White Ibis [B, S]	IV
Straw-necked Ibis [S]	Vagr.
Royal Spoonbill [B]	IV
Black-necked Stork [B, S]	IV
Osprey [B, S]	IV
Pacific Baza [B]	
Black Kite [S]	
Whistling Kite [B, D, S]	AM
Brahminy Kite [B, D, S]	AM
White-bellied Sea-Eagle [B, S]	Br.; R
Swamp Harrier [B, S]	AM
Brown Goshawk [S]	
Collared Sparrowhawk [S]	
Gurney's Eagle [B] *Aquila gurneyi*	Vagr.
Australian Hobby [B, D, S]	AM; WR
Peregrine Falcon [B]	Vagr. B
Nankeen Kestrel [B, D, S]	IV
Brolga [S]	
Buff-banded Rail [B, S]	
White-browed Crake [B, S]	Vagr.
Purple Swamphen [S]	
Australian Bustard [S]	
Red-backed Button-quail [B, D, S]	Br.?; R
Red-chested Button-quail [S]	
Latham's Snipe [B]	
Swinhoe's Snipe [B, S]	
Black-tailed Godwit [B, S]	IV
Little Curlew [B]	
Whimbrel [B, D, S]	AM; SR
Eastern Curlew [B, S]	AM
Marsh Sandpiper [B, S]	IV
Common Greenshank [B, D, S]	AM; SR
Wood Sandpiper [B]	Vagr.
Terek Sandpiper [B, S]	Vagr.
Common Sandpiper [B, D, S]	AM; R
Grey-tailed Tattler [B, D, S]	AM; SR
Wandering Tattler [D]	
Ruddy Turnstone [B, D]	AM
Great Knot [S]	
Red-necked Stint [B, D, S]	AM; R
Pectoral Sandpiper [B]	Vagr.
Sharp-tailed Sandpiper [B, S]	IV
Curlew Sandpiper [B, S]	Vagr.
Beach Stone-curlew [D]	
Black-winged Stilt [B, S]	AM
Pacific Golden Plover [B, S]	Vagr.
Grey Plover [B, D]	Vagr.
Lesser Sand Plover [B, D, S]	AM
Greater Sand Plover [B, D, S]	AM
Oriental Plover [B]	Vagr.
Red-kneed Dotterel [B, S]	Br.?; IV
Masked Lapwing [B, D, S]	R
Australian Pratincole [B, S]	AM; WR
Silver Gull [D, S]	
Gull-billed Tern [B, D, S]	R
Caspian Tern [B, S]	IV
Crested Tern [B, D, S]	R
Roseate Tern [S]	
Black-naped Tern [B]	
Common Tern [B, S]	IV
Little Tern [B, D, S]	Vagr.
Sooty Tern [D]	
Whiskered Tern [B, S]	AM

Species	Status
White-winged Black Tern [B, S]	Vagr.
Emerald Dove [B, S]	Rare R
Peaceful Dove [B, S]	Rare R
Bar-shouldered Dove [B, D, S]	Br: R
Superb Fruit-dove [S]	
Rose-crowned Fruit-dove [D, S]	
Collared Imperial-Pigeon [B, S]	R
Pied Imperial-Pigeon [B, D, S]	Br.; AM; R
Rainbow Lorikeet [B, S]	Br.?; AM R
Eclectus Parrot [B, D, S]	R
Red-cheeked Parrot [B]	
Fig-Parrot *Cyclopsitta* spp.[B, S]	IV
Oriental Cuckoo [B, D, S]	Vagr.
Brush Cuckoo [B, D, S]	Vagr.
Horsfield's Bronze-Cuckoo [B, S]	
Shining Bronze-Cuckoo [S]	
Little Bronze-Cuckoo [B, D, S]	RV
Common Koel [B, S]	Vagr.
Channel-billed Cuckoo [D, S]	AM
Pheasant Coucal [B, D, S]	R
Barking Owl [S]	
Large-tailed Nightjar [B, S]	Vagr.
White-throated Needletail [S]	
Fork-tailed Swift [B, D, S]	IV
Azure Kingfisher [B]	
Little Kingfisher [B, S]	Vagr.?; or rare R
Buff-breasted Paradise-Kingfisher [B]	AM
Forest Kingfisher [B, D, S]	Vagr.
Sacred Kingfisher [B, D, S]	AM; WR
Collared Kingfisher [B, S]	R?
Rainbow Bee-eater [B, D, S]	AM; WR?
Dollarbird [B, S]	Vagr.
Noisy Pitta [D]	
Mangrove Gerygone [D, S]	
Large-billed Gerygone [B, D, S]	Br.; R
Tawny-breasted Honeyeater [B, S]	Br.; R
Varied Honeyeater [B, S]	Br.; R
Brown Honeyeater [S]	
Brown-backed Honeyeater [B, D, S]	Br.; R?
Rufous-banded Honeyeater [B, D, S]	Br.; R
Dusky Honeyeater [B, S]	Br.; R
Red-headed Honeyeater [B, D, S]	Br.; R
Mangrove Golden Whistler [B, D]	R? R
Black-faced Monarch [B, S]	AM
Black-winged Monarch [S]	
Spectacled Monarch [B, S]	
Frilled Monarch *Arses telescopthalmus harterti* [B]	Vagr.
Broad-billed Flycatcher [B, D, S]	Br.; R
Leaden Flycatcher [B, D, S]	Br.; AM; R?
Satin Flycatcher [B]	Vagr.
Shining Flycatcher [B, D, S]	Br.; R
Restless Flycatcher [S]	
Magpie-lark [B, S]	Vagr.
Rufous Fantail [B]	
Mangrove Grey Fantail [S]	
Northern Fantail [B, S]	R?
Willie Wagtail [B, D, S]	Br.; R
Spangled Drongo [B, D, S]	Br.; AM; R?
Black-faced Cuckoo-shrike [B, D, S]	AM; WR
White-bellied Cuckoo-shrike [B, D, S]	AM; WR
Cicadabird [B, D, S]	AM
White-winged Triller [S]	
Varied Triller [B, D, S]	Br.; R
Olive-backed Oriole [D, S]	
White-breasted Woodswallow [B, S]	Br.; R
Black Butcherbird [B, D, S]	Br.; R
Trumpet Manucode [B, S]	Rare R?
Torresian Crow [B, D, S]	Br.?; R
Singing Bushlark [S]	
House Sparrow [B, D, S]	Self-intro.; Br.; R
Chestnut-breasted Mannikin [B]	IV
Olive-backed Sunbird [B, D, S]	Br.; R
Red-capped (Papuan) Flowerpecker *Dicaeum geelvinkianum* (syn. *pectorale*) [S]	Prob. Br.
Barn Swallow [B, D]	AM?
Welcome Swallow [B, S]	AM
Red-rumped Swallow [B]	Vagr.
Tree Martin [B, D, S]	AM; WR?
Fairy Martin [B, S]	
Tawny Grassbird [S]	
Zitting Cisticola [S]	
Golden-headed Cisticola [B, D, S]	Br.; R
Pale White-eye [B, D]	R?
Metallic Starling [B, D, S]	AM
Singing Starling *Aplonis cantoroides* (the only sites in Australia where this species occurs regularly) [B]	Br.; R

Note A previous report of Grey-headed Goshawk is now considered doubtful due to recent sightings of a similar but unidentified accipter. Reports of Orange-fronted Fruit Dove, Uniform Swiftlet, Rufous-bellied Kookaburra, Streak-headed Mannikin and Pacific Swallow await documentation/endorsement by BARC.

Reading

There are few published bird lists – we present principal bird literature to 1998.

Carter, M.J., O'Brien, R. & Macumber, N. (1997), 'Singing Starlings *Aplonis cantoroides* and other birds on Boigu Island, Torres Strait, Queensland', *Aust. Bird Watcher* **17** (1): 20–4.

Carter, M., *et al* (1998), 'Response to comments by B.G. Totterman on Carter, *et al* (1997)', *Aust. Bird Watcher* **17** (6): 311–13.

Draffan, R.D.W., Garnett, S.T. & Malone, G.J. (1983), 'Birds of Torres Strait: an annotated list and biogeographical analysis', *Emu* **83**: 207–34.

O'Brien, R. (1995), 'Trip report, Boigu Island, Torres Strait', *Australian Birding* **2** (3): 16–17.

Totterman, B.G. (1998), 'Birds of Boigu Island, Torres Strait: a comment on Carter, *et al* (1997)', *Aust. Bird Watcher* **17** (6): 310–11.

Heard Island (and associated Macdonald Islands)

Lat. 53° S; Long. 73° 30' E. Lies some 4450 km off the south-western Western Australian coast. Nearest significant land is French-administered Kerguelen Islands (Isles de Kerguelen), 520 km to NW. No resident human population. Intermittent scientific presence; entry restricted; permits required. Administered by Australian Federal Government through Antarctic Division, Tasmania. Research personnel are principal visitors at present; a few tourist ships call by. A source of many seabirds in Australian seas.

Species	Status
King Penguin	Br.
Emperor Penguin *Aptenodytes forsteri*	Vagr.
Gentoo Penguin	Br.; R
Adelie Penguin	Vagr.
Chinstrap Penguin	(may breed); Vagr.
Rockhopper Penguin, race *filholi*	Br.; AM; SR
Macaroni Penguin	Br.; AM; SR
Common Diving-Petrel	Br.; R
South Georgian Diving-Petrel	Br.; SR
Southern Giant-Petrel	Br.; SR
Northern Giant-Petrel	AM
Southern Fulmar	IV
Antarctic Petrel	IV
Cape Petrel	Br.; R
Snow Petrel	Vagr.
Kerguelen Petrel	AM
Great-winged Petrel	IV?
White-headed Petrel	AM
Soft-plumaged Petrel	AM
Barau's Petrel	Vagr.
Blue Petrel	IV
Antarctic Prion	Br.; SR
Slender-billed Prion	AM
Fulmar Prion	Br.; R
White-chinned Petrel	IV
Grey Petrel	AM
Sooty Shearwater	AM?
Short-tailed Shearwater	AM?
Wandering Albatross	Br. (1 pair)
Royal Albatross	Vagr.?
Black-browed Albatross	Br.; SR
Grey-headed Albatross	AM
Light-mantled Sooty Albatross	Br.; SR
Wilson's Storm-Petrel	Br.; SR
Grey-backed Storm-Petrel	AM?
Black-bellied Storm-Petrel	Vagr.
Imperial (Heard) Shag *Leucocarbo atriceps (nivalis)* **Vulnerable**	Br.; R
Common Greenshank	Vagr.
Black-faced (Heard Island) Sheathbill *Chionis minor nasicornis*	Br.; R
Great Skua	Br.; AM; SR
Kelp Gull	Br.; R
Arctic Tern (passes island on way south)	AM
Antarctic Tern	Br.; AM?; SR

Reading

Few published bird lists.

Downes, M.C., Ealey, E.H.M., Gwynn, A.M. & Young, P.S. (1959), 'The Birds of Heard Island', *ANARE Reports*, Series B, Vol. **1**, *Zoology*, Australian National Antarctic Research Expeditions, Antarctic Division, Department of External Affairs, Melbourne.

Watson, G.E. (1975), *Birds of the Antarctic and Subantarctic*, Antarctic Research Series, American Geophysical Union, Washington, DC, USA.

Woehler, E.J. (1991), 'The status and conservation of the seabirds of Heard Island and the Macdonald Islands', in *Status and Conservation of the World's Seabirds*, Croxhall, J.P., Evans, P.G.H. & Schreiber, R.W. (editors), *ICBP Technical Publication* No. **11**, International Council for Bird Preservation, Cambridge, pp. 263–77.

Macquarie Island

Now called **Macquarie Island Nature Reserve** and includes Judge and Clerk Rocks, and Bishop and Clerk Rocks.

Lat. 54° 30' S; Long. 159° E. Lies approximately 1500 km SSE of Tasmania and 1100 km SSW of New Zealand. The island is about 34 km long and 5 km wide at its widest point. Area is approximately 12785 hectares. Several peaks rise to 400 m; highest point is 433 m. The nearest islands are northward: the Auckland Islands (640 km) and Campbell Island (700 km). Administered by Tasmanian National Parks and Wildlife Service, and serviced by the Antarctic Division, Tasmania. Ship access only. Permits required. Permanent research personnel present. Tourist ships now regularly call for brief visits and limited shore-time. A source of many seabirds in Australian and New Zealand seas.

Species	Status
Mallard	Self-intro.; Br.; R; few
Pacific Black Duck	(common); Br.; R
Grey Teal	Vagr.
King Penguin	(abundant); Br.; R
Emperor Penguin	Vagr.
Gentoo Penguin	(abundant); Br.; R
Adelie Penguin	Vagr.
Chinstrap Penguin	Vagr.
Rockhopper Penguin race *filholi*	(abundant) Br.; AM; SR
Snares Penguin	Vagr.
Erect-crested Penguin	IV
Macaroni (Royal) Penguin	(abundant) Br.; AM; SR
Common Diving-Petrel	(a few; rare); Br.?
South Georgian Diving-Petrel	(a few; rare); Br.
Southern Giant-Petrel	Br.; AM; SR
Northern Giant-Petrel	Br.; AM; SR
Southern Fulmar	IV
Antarctic Petrel	Vagr.
Cape Petrel	Br,; RV

Snow Petrel Vagr. ☐☐☐
Kerguelen Petrel IV ☐☐☐
Great-winged Petrel Vagr. ☐☐☐
White-headed Petrel Br.; AM; SR ☐☐☐
Soft-plumaged Petrel Br.; AM ☐☐☐
Mottled Petrel IV ☐☐☐
Blue Petrel Br.; SR ☐☐☐
Antarctic Prion (abundant) Br.; AM; SR ☐☐☐
Slender-billed Prion (rare); Br.? ☐☐☐
Fairy Prion (a few); Br.; AM; SR ☐☐☐
White-chinned Petrel Vagr.? ☐☐☐
Grey Petrel (a few; increasing); Br.? ☐☐☐
Flesh-footed Shearwater Vagr. ☐☐☐
Sooty Shearwater Br.; AM; SR ☐☐☐
Short-tailed Shearwater AM ☐☐☐
Little Shearwater Vagr. ☐☐☐
Wandering Albatross (declining); Br.; AM; SR ☐☐☐
Royal Albatross races *epomophora, sanfordi* AM? ☐☐☐
Black-browed Albatross Br.; AM; SR ☐☐☐
Shy Albatross IV ☐☐☐
Grey-headed Albatross Br.; AM; SR ☐☐☐
Buller's Albatross Vagr.? ☐☐☐
Light-mantled Sooty Albatross Br.; AM; SR ☐☐☐
Sooty Albatross Vagr. ☐☐☐
Wilson's Storm-Petrel AM ☐☐☐
Grey-backed Storm-Petrel
(rare; poor data); Br.? ☐☐☐
Black-bellied Storm-Petrel AM ☐☐☐
Australasian Gannet Vagr. ☐☐☐
Great Cormorant Vagr. ☐☐☐
Imperial (Macquarie) Shag
Leucocarbo atriceps purpurascens
(small population) **Vulnerable** Br.; IE; R ☐☐☐
White-faced Heron Vagr. ☐☐☐
Little Egret Vagr. ☐☐☐
Great Egret Vagr. ☐☐☐
Cattle Egret Vagr. ☐☐☐
Swamp Harrier Vagr. ☐☐☐
Baillon's (Marsh) Crake Vagr. ☐☐☐
Eurasian Coot Vagr. ☐☐☐
Latham's Snipe Vagr. ☐☐☐
Bar-tailed Godwit Vagr. ☐☐☐
Common Greenshank Vagr. ☐☐☐
Ruddy Turnstone Vagr. ☐☐☐
Red Knot Vagr. ☐☐☐
Red-necked Stint Vagr. ☐☐☐
Red-necked Phalarope Vagr. ☐☐☐
Black-winged Stilt Vagr. ☐☐☐
Grey Plover Vagr. ☐☐☐
Great Skua (common); Br.; AM; SR ☐☐☐
South Polar Skua AM? ☐☐☐
Pomarine Jaeger Vagr. ☐☐☐
Kelp Gull (common); Br.; R ☐☐☐
Arctic Tern Vagr. ☐☐☐
Antarctic Tern (a few); Br.; R ☐☐☐
White-throated Needletail Vagr. ☐☐☐
Fork-tailed Swift Vagr. ☐☐☐
European Goldfinch Vagr. ☐☐☐
Common Redpoll *Carduelis flammea*
(common); Br. R ☐☐☐
Welcome Swallow Vagr. ☐☐☐
Silvereye Vagr. ☐☐☐
Common Blackbird
Self-intro.; (was rare but
breeding); now Vagr.? ☐☐☐
Song Thrush Vagr. ☐☐☐
Common Starling
Self-intro.; (common); Br.; R ☐☐☐

Note Claims of Yellowhammer, Common Chaffinch remain unconfirmed.

Reading

Department of Environment and Land Management, 1993, *One of the Wonder Spots of the World* ..., Macquarie Island Nature Reserve, Cox, R. (ed.), DELM Tasmania, 36 pp.
National Parks and Wildlife Service, Tasmania, 1987, *Macquarie Island Nature Reserve*: Visitor's Handbook, Nat. Parks & Wildlife Service, Hobart, Tasmania, 48 pp.

Appendices

Hints for birdwatchers

It is easy to imagine, looking out at the 12–64 bird species in your own garden or the 70–124 species in the surrounding neighbourhood, that there cannot possibly be any more to discover about any one of them. But this is not so. Pick one, any one, of the most common birds and then make a point of looking up as much as you can of its published literature. With very few exceptions you will find that gaps still exist in the printed knowledge of even the most common local species – no matter where you live. So, try it! Observe keenly, report correctly and without any exaggeration, and try to write fifty words for a local newspaper, school magazine, or for popular or scientific journals.

We urge you to see as many bird species as you can in Australia. You may choose to carry your hobby to other countries in due course. Start today! Tick off the species in the tick-boxes provided beside the maps on the pages facing the colour plates. No cheating – treat it like a game of golf; keep a clean scorecard.

Take thorough notes on any strange or new birds that you see – try to do one or more little sketches (see mine below) and add as many significant details as possible. Include proportions, relative size and comparisons with other bird species about you, the colours of plumage and soft parts (eyes, legs and facial skin). Record behaviour, postures, flight mannerisms and calls. Take notes on *anything* which will help you to identify the bird accurately. The first set of field notes of the recent sighting of a Black-headed Gull at Broome, for example, was not only several pages long but accompanied by about 15–20 clear sketches and several photographs! Use your noggin. Knowing the diameter of the metal pipe or the branch where a bird perched would later help give a scale for a measurement in any photograph. So, when the bird has gone, measure the pipe or branch! Use other bird species as comparisons (e.g. see drawings pp. 122, 260).

Obtain a two-post binder, a punch, and commence a scrapbook or research file on the bird species you are seeing regularly, that you have decided to study in more detail, or that you see for the first time. Keep your day-to-day bird lists safely. They may become a contribution to habitat or regional surveys, for conservation statements, environmental impact studies, or town planning. Notes kept systematically are easier to interpret later. Use a computer!

Do you live near an environmentally sensitive area? Any land likely to be logged, inadvertently burned, 'developed' or in some other way damaged? Start to record the birds (animals and plants) in this area and be meticulous with dates and times. Take habitat photographs. If inappropriate development is threatened, you will then have data of great value – anticipate such a need!

Knowing that the bird's home environment is of vital importance to its day-to-day and year-to-year survival, we have devoted eight pages to describing Australia's habitats. The summaries are brief, far too brief we know, but you can go on building your knowledge of these habitat categories, and what goes on inside each and between each. The 'bird in its habitat', the 'habitat and its birds', will provide you with a lifetime's study. Please specialise in one major habitat type and assist in its protection Australia-wide.

Examine dead birds on roads and beaches – send rare ones or juvenile/immature birds to the nearest natural history museum. Always inform a representative of the state fauna authority as quickly as possible that you have found something unusual. The laws in all parts of the land are such that, at the very least, you need to cover yourself before moving protected fauna, dead or alive. In other words, make sure you are not accused of having native fauna illegally in your possession. The paradox is that scientific institutions really do need specimens, but 'the system' can make it difficult to get them there.

1 Contact the authority, inform them you have found the bird, and ask them if they want it.
2 Ask permission to bring it to them. Find out your contact's name. Ask them to record your call.
3 Ask for any special transport instructions for the body.
4 Add a label with basic information on the body: date, locality, your name and contact number.
5 Wrap bird neatly in newspaper, roll in plastic, freeze if possible. If several birds, keep each strictly separated to avoid any contamination, particularly from blood, other fluids, parasites.
6 Follow instructions to get it to the appropriate authority. They may even collect it from you.
7 Obtain an official receipt, dated and signed.

One page from a bird observer's notebook.

Hint, Hint, Hint, Hint ...

General

- Always record the locality, date, and time of day on *all* your records, notes and specimens. If summer, also state whether daylight-saving time is in operation; most birds haven't heard of it (and there are occasions in bird study programmes where real time is important).
- Try to map the territory of several different bird species that live near you. Firstly, select common birds around your home. Choose some small, medium and very large birds.
- Now look for differing territory sizes of each of these. As a rule, larger species will occupy the most area. Fairy-wrens a few hectares; Wedge-tailed Eagles several dozen square kilometres at the very least.
- Look for overlapping territories of different species, and also of adjacent territories of the same species. Record interactions between same and different species.
- No matter where you are, always look for indirect evidence of birds – tracks, bark scratches, feathers, droppings, regurgitated pellets, damaged fruits and flowers. Play detective: what did this? You would be surprised how often the presence of a bird in a district is given away by a stray moulted feather.

Equipment

- Keep a notebook in a waterproof cover. Use a permanent black-ink pen or a 2B pencil, not felt-tipped pens, which may fade or dissolve into a complete mess if your pages become wet, or are stored long-term in a humid place. Biros should also be a second choice.
- Use binoculars and/or a suitable telescope for easier and more satisfying birdwatching. The sky's the limit when buying these. Choose to suit your need. Insure your purchase.
- Take a camera into the bush and try to photograph a bird or two – then think about buying a tripod and a telephoto lens!
- Try sound recording – a very specialised field but the results can be most rewarding.

Legal

- Report all banded (ringed) birds to the authority named on the band. Never remove a band from a living bird. Read the number, record the circumstances and hop on the phone, fax or e-mail. In Australia the address is Bird- and Bat-Banding Scheme, P.O. Box 8, Canberra, ACT., 2601; tel. (02) 6274 2407.
- Nest robbing and bird poaching are rife. Report people behaving suspiciously or irresponsibly to land-owners, park rangers or police. Do not approach possible transgressors. Observe accurately, record vehicle numbers and slip away quietly. Safeguard the bush and its inhabitants.

Safety

- Your vehicle should be equipped with hats, clothing which is quiet (in colour and non-rustling) and footwear changes, food and drink, first-aid kit, torch, maps and a travelling bird book library. Mobile phone, GPS recorder and CB radio are bonuses. In the arid interior, perhaps carry a spare vehicle battery in a cooler box – extreme heat can destroy battery efficiency. Check the local radio station for weather information. The further you plan to go, the better your preparations should be. Contact state automobile organisations for advice on long-distance touring.
- Be careful not to birdwatch too hard when driving, i.e. do not wander into another traffic lane or a tree at 80 kph whilst peering the other way. Do not make a sudden stop without due warning. Check your rear vision mirror before such a manoeuvre.
- Inform relatives, other birders or police of your plans if going off-road. Stick to the plan. Remain with your vehicle if trouble develops. Obey all normal rules of country travel – gates as you find them; ask permission to enter or camp on private or designated land, etc.
- Observe fire ban days or weather warnings. A couple of heavy woollen blankets could be very useful. Never camp in a creek or river bed (flash floods), or under any large trees (falling limbs).
- Always leave a colourful surface marker if you enter a cave, a mine or climb on cliffs, and remove it when you come out/up/down. It is best not to do any of these activities alone.

Birdcraft and bushcraft

- Keep the sun behind you when observing.
- Rather than look at the sun to see where it is, instead walk into a wide shadow of a tree on the ground, position your own head's shadow inside that of the tree's and then you can look around without destroying your vision.
- If you have a choice, begin birdwatching through a day's length 'down-sun', by travelling west in the morning, south during the middle of the day, and finally east in the mid to late afternoon and so back to your starting point.
- If stalking a bird for a better look, move slowly and walk upwind, so that no sound or aroma is carried to your quarry.
- Be systematic in your observing. Mentally 'partition' any landscape or habitat into sections and scan each for birds in turn.
- Practise throwing a 'mental clock face' over any tree, shrub, group of rocks or building, and use it to explain to your colleagues where the bird is perched in relation to the chosen object. Discussion prior to departure on a walk will enable you to bend the 'clock' to fit perfectly a round, a very tall or even a misshapen tree.

- Practise describing out loud (when you are alone, or to friends) the features of birds you have in view. It will speed up your recognition skills and ability to pass on information. It will also assist you in recording. In fact, you can do it into a cassette recorder. Also, practise explaining scenery, bird behaviour, etc., out loud. Soon you'll be giving authoritative lectures!
- Learn to read the daily weather map. Try to relate each day's weather to the activities and dispersal of birds. Examples: the direction swifts take to feed depends on the daily wind direction; seabirds may be close to shore on one wind, far to sea on another.
- On a really hot day, or during the middle of such a day, you may expect to see fewer birds than when it is cooler. Use this time to rest yourself, or to travel to a new locality.
- On cloudy–fine days, expect more avian activity when the sun is out. Gloom will quieten birds down. Birds often retire to a secure perch during heavy rain or hail.

Birdwatching in various habitats

Open forests

- In all forests, woodland or mangroves, scan the ground (floor) first for birds, then the big trunks and lower branches and finally the crowns or canopy. Treat each as a separate component of a larger system. Remember to relate the birds to each 'zone'. Trends will become noticeable as you gain experience. Recognise consistent foraging zones and behaviour for different species or groups of species, Soon, you will look for birds with ease and expectation in each observation zone.
- If you are moving through forest and need to watch high in the trees, first look on the ground ahead before walking forward. Pick a short route to avoid fallen branches, rocks, holes, other obstacles and the odd snake. Do it all again before moving the next time.
- Look for the non-breeding, autumn and winter, flocks of small birds moving as a mixed species feeding group (MSFG) through the forest. Record and analyse the species associations, their activities and interactions.
- Take a torch or red-shaded spotlight into the bush at night. Which birds are up and about? Where do the rest roost? We do not promote people crashing around in the bush at night, so keep to tracks, move quietly, and please keep away from any known owl nesting trees in the breeding season.

Rainforests: tropical or temperate

- Look at the floor of the forest, then vertical trunks, and the underside of the canopy. Any break in the canopy is an important place for viewing birds. Any opportunity to see *over* the upper surface of the canopy should be taken, along a mountain road or from a ridge; pigeons, parrots, raptors may be feeding or moving about, audible but not visible from below.
- Sound is very important in rainforest. Bird calls seem amplified, or their directions seem 'changed' by intervening vegetation. Stand quietly, listen, if possible see what is calling, and learn that call.
- Check all the party occasionally for ticks and leeches, if in habitats where these occur. Learn to avoid stinging trees, lawyer vines and green tree ants. Use mosquito repellent.

Coast

- At the beach, look in turn at the sandy, rocky or muddy areas, then scan the breaking wave zone, middle horizon and far horizon. Look from left to right each time, taking time to familiarise yourself fully with the physical appearance and content of each zone in turn. Then scan the sky, turn around and look behind you; turn again and repeat the whole process.
- Scan the very farthest horizon from any vantage point from time to time – you will be surprised at the number of birds you can see and *sometimes* identify, even though they are genuinely far, far away.
- Try not to disturb large roosting (resting) flocks of waders, terns, cormorants and gulls. Waders especially need a quiet period between tides. Watch from well back, using a telescope if possible. Explain to dog owners with free-running dogs why 'those birds' should not be disturbed.
- Go on a pelagic boat trip if the chance arises. You'll have a fascinating day with the seabirds at the edge of the continental shelf. Take sun-cream, hat, very warm clothes with long sleeves, light or dry food, water. Get a good night's sleep beforehand.
- On the beach, analyse tracks and trails in the sand. Go beach-combing for the bodies of pelagic seabirds. Report, photograph, but do not disturb moulting large penguins.
- Take an opportunity to watch the gulls at the beach or in the city–then try to interpret all their postures and calls. Take photos or do sketches. Look for gulls of differing ages, for peck order and dominance, for the range of plumages, eye, bill and leg colours.
- Burrowing seabirds may live in dunes – keep out of such colonies and advise others to do the same. Collapses smother chicks!

Alpine areas

- Be *fully* prepared for suddenly changing weather. Always carry a bag with adequate survival clothing, extra food, water, torch.
- Do not expect to see quite so many bird species in high country. Quite often the best results will be gained about alpine settlements.
- Analyse tracks and trails in the snow. Look closely at what the mountain birds are feeding on in the winter.

Wetlands

- Arriving at a swamp, small lake, dam, or stretch of river, scan the nearest margins or edges for birds first. Then systematically sweep, in turn, all open water stretches, the emergent marginal vegetation, the far banks, and trees or structures beyond. Then the whole sky. Begin again, left and right of your position, and keep working through the sequence. Sometimes look behind you.

- Analyse tracks and trails in the mud: was that made by a duck, a heron, a crab, a mudskipper, a turtle or a crocodile? Speaking of which, don't go swimming and don't linger on or close to the banks of tropical rivers and tidal estuaries.
- Be wary of holes if walking through shallow water. Do not get out of your depth. Keep an eye on rips and returning tides. Wear stout-soled shoes when wading – the possibility of cuts, bites or stings is very high.

Deserts

- Tracks and trails in the sand can be very revealing: footprints of many creatures can be found: Emu, Malleefowl, pigeons, parrots, malurid wrens or chats; also kangaroos, lizards, snakes, beetles, geckoes and mice.
- Very, very carefully investigate animal burrows in the heat of the day. Some birds may actually go underground to escape the heat. If you find any (or other creatures), do not frighten them out – observe, record, and move away quietly.
- Watch for birds (pigeons, parrots, honeyeaters, finches) flying to water in the late afternoon. Follow and watch from well back but do not disturb them. They really need that daily water.

Farmland

- Ask permission to enter private property. If need be, obtain addresses in advance, and write (phone, e-mail or fax) ahead to request entry. Always be extremely courteous – landowners are doing you a favour by allowing access. Leave all gates exactly as you find them. Keep away from stock. Don't camp under big trees or so that stock are blocked from drinking at dams, tanks or a creek access. Walk around the edges of crops. Birdwatching along rural roads and lanes can be most rewarding, especially if there is remnant or plantation vegetation and a few watering points.

Cities

- Mentally divide city and urban areas into broad observing sectors, as you would for any other habitat. Look for birds on the ground, roads, nature strips. Then try sides of buildings, eaves and rooflines. Check telephone poles, TV antennae, chimneys; look along wires and cables for perched birds. Think of buildings as 'trees'. Treat all real trees as before – main trunk, upper branches, canopy. Watch the sky above – many birds fly high over cities.
- Birds inhabiting cities exhibit many adaptations in foraging techniques, food sources, nest sites, etc. Look for these; record them. Bird lists from city parks over a period are very rewarding.

Parks and reserves

- Select one or more local parks and reserves and 'adopt' them. Perhaps join a 'Friends of ...' group. Record on a seasonal basis the birds that come to the park. Remember that your bird records, with numbers of birds seen each time, are a valuable resource.
- Treat all public parks, reserves, and recreation areas as extensions of your own garden. Look after them. A little voluntary weeding or litter collection is good PR. Report abandoned cars, vandalism, to the local authorities. Observe park regulations.

House and garden

- Feeding wild birds is controversial. If doing so, feed only in late afternoon, after birds have foraged for themselves all day. Build a small feeding table in a safe place. Or suspend a bowl (with a little drainage hole) from the eaves. Place it where you can see and supervise it. Keep bowls clean; don't overfeed birds.
- Are you always at the sink, your desk, in the lounge? Keep a chart where you spend the day and record all the birds that pass before your favourite window. What are they up to? Why are they there?
- Set up two or three reliable water bowls, bird-baths or other sources of shallow permanent water in your garden. For your enjoyment, place at least one where you can see it frequently from the house. Watering points should have overhead cover for shade and for small bird protection. Hot water attracts no birds. Set bowls high enough to discourage cats, dogs and small children. Nothing is more important than dependable water sources to birds for washing and drinking, even in winter, and they will come in droves. Water is more important than food in a garden. Keep these bowls clean, refill them daily and the results will delight you.
- Do you have a space in your garden? Plant a tree or shrub of local origin for nectar, seeds or shelter for small birds.

Reading

Balmford, R. (1990), *The Beginner's Guide to Australian Birds*, 2nd ed., Penguin Books Australia, Ringwood.

Simpson, K. & Wilson, Z. (1998), *Birdwatching in Australia and New Zealand*, Reed New Holland, Frenchs Forest, NSW. [A book for beginner birdwatchers.]

Glossary

Abrasion Wearing down of the feathers.

Adult Birds that breed or are known to have breeding capabilities. Adult plumages are those that do not change in appearance in subsequent moults (allowing for alternating eclipse plumages in some species, e.g. male ducks, waders, fairy-wrens).

Albinistic Partial lack of normal pigment in plumage, sometimes also from skin, resulting in white or patchy-white birds.

Albino Total lack of normal pigment, even to eyes, which are pink.

Allopatric The geographical range of one species does not overlap with that of another, similar, species.

Allopreening Preening of one bird by another.

Alula Four small feathers found on a bird's 'thumb'. They control airflow over the leading edge of the wing – the 'bastard wing'.

Anhedral Wings held downward, below level of the back, when gliding, e.g. Gang-gang Cockatoo (and see *Dihedral*).

Antiphonal song Two birds contribute to the same song, taking a different part each, e.g. Eastern Whipbird, Magpie-lark.

Asynchronous hatching A clutch of eggs hatching progressively, not all together (synchronous), e.g. megapodes, herons.

Auricular patch A distinct colour-patch of feathers over or about the ear, e.g. King Penguin, Musk Lorikeet, Black-eared Miner, 'Spotted Catbird'.

Axilla The area where the underwing joins the body – the 'armpit'. Feathers here are known as axillaries.

Bar A fine, transverse mark on a group of feathers e.g. Bar-tailed Godwit, or across the body of a bird, e.g. Bar-breasted Honeyeater, Red-eared Firetail.

Barbules Tiny side branches of the feather, with hooks that interlock with neighbouring ones to (collectively) form the rigid surface plane (vane) of a feather.

Brood-parasitism Egg-laying by cuckoos in other birds' nests.

Bustle The 'clump' of long wing feathers which fall loosely over the tail of cranes (Brolga, Sarus Crane) when wings are folded.

Bib Rounded breast patch from the chin (= gorget).

Carpal joint (flexure) Wrist joint between the 'arm' and the 'hand' of the wing; = 'Bend of wing', p. 1.

Casque A helmet-like structure on the skull or bill, e.g. Southern Cassowary, Helmeted Guineafowl, Helmeted Friarbird.

Cere Bare, wax-like, or fleshy structure at the base of the upper beak, containing the nostrils, e.g. Cape Barren Goose, Peregrine Falcon, Budgerigar.

Chevrons 'V'-shaped stripes, usually on breast, e.g. Powerful Owl.

Class The division of classification into which is placed the whole of a significant group of organisms, e.g. Class Aves: the birds. A higher taxonomic category.

Cline A graded series of changes in the 'character' (e.g. body- or bill-size; or colour) of a bird across a geographic area, e.g. Varied Sittella, Figbird.

Colour morph Different colouring within a single interbreeding population, unrelated to season, sex or age (previously called 'colour phase'), e.g. Southern Giant-Petrel, Eastern Reef Egret, Grey Goshawk.

Commensalism When a species benefits from an activity or aspect of a second species, but the second species derives no obvious benefit from, and is indifferent to, the actions of the first, e.g. Yellow-rumped Thornbill nesting in the base of a Whistling Kite's nest; Cattle Egrets feeding about stock.

'Commic' terns Collective name sometimes applied to the group of terns typified by Common, Arctic, Antarctic, White-fronted and Roseate. Word derivation possibly from amalgamation of 'Common' and 'Arctic'.

Conspecific Of the same species.

Coverts Small feathers over and protecting the bases of larger ones: lesser, median, greater coverts p. 1.

Crepuscular Appearing or flying at late dusk or pre-dawn, e.g. Bush Stone-curlew, frogmouths, nightjars.

Crissum The undertail coverts together with the feathers around the vent of a bird.

Cryptic Has protective colouring or camouflage, e.g. Australasian Bittern, Bush Stone-curlew, juvenile robins.

Cubital bar Term often used for dark shoulder bar (mark or smudge), of 'commic', and some other, terns.

Culmen The ridge along the whole length or top of the upper mandible. In petrels, includes *Nail*.

Dewlap Prominent bunch of feathers beneath chin e.g. Brolga.

Diagnostic Having value in a description for the purpose of classification or for positive identification.

Dihedral Wings held up in a 'V' when gliding, e.g. Black-shouldered Kite, Rock Dove (see *Anhedral*).

Dimorphism (sexual) Occurrence of two distinct types of difference between the sexes of the same species. Examples are (a) plumage colour and/or patterns, e.g. Eclectus, and many other, parrots, also Shining Flycatcher; (b) structure e.g. bills of Red-necked Avocet, riflebirds; (c) also refers to overall body shape and size, e.g. Masked Owl, Brown Songlark. There are many and varied examples.

Dorsal ('Dorsum') Pertaining to the upper surface of the body, p. 1 (see also *Upperparts*).

Down Wispy, fine insulating feathers of hatchlings; and surrounding the feather bases of almost all bird plumages.

'Downy' Term for hatchlings of geese, ducks, rails.

Ear tufts Feathers protruding near ears, e.g. Common Pheasant, Yellow-tufted Honeyeater.

Eclipse (plumage) Dull, (less conspicuous) seasonal plumage assumed by many bird species during late summer, autumn or winter, e.g. grebes, some males of ducks, waders; male malurid wrens.

Egg tooth Tiny scale-like upper-bill protrusion on many baby birds to help chip through their eggshell.

Endemic Native to, or peculiar to, a particular or defined area, and breeding only there.

Extant Species, family, etc., alive at the present day.

Extinct No individuals of a species, etc., left alive today. Prehistoric; gone forever; no longer extant.

'Eye-spot' Round, centrally placed mark in a feather, e.g. in male peafowl tail. Also white patches behind head resembling watching eyes when a bird's back is turned, e.g. Azure Kingfisher.

Facial disc A bird's face, disc-like in form, being well-defined and comparatively flat, e.g. owls, harriers.

Family The division of classification into which an Order is divided and which has one or more genera, i.e. the taxonomic rank below Order.

Feral Having returned to the wild after domestication. An introduced animal foreign to any environment.

'Fingers' Term used when a bird spreads attenuated (narrow-tipped) primary wing feathers in flight, e.g. Little Eagle, corvids.

Flank Area on the bird's side, directly below the forepart of the closed (folded) wing, e.g. plumes of whistling-ducks; strong flank colour of Tasmanian race of Silvereye (see p. 1).

Fledging The process of moult from natal down to 1st juvenile plumage.

Fledgling (Pertains to leaving the nest.) Partly or wholly feathered bird. Flightless or partly flighted, but before full flight capability has been attained.

Foreneck The whole front (ventral) neck section.

Frons Feathered front of crown, just above upper bill base. Also 'Forehead', 'Front'. Plain (in most birds); often of different colour, e.g. White-fronted Tern, Common Bronzewing, Purple-crowned Lorikeet, White-fronted Honeyeater, Red-capped Robin.

Frontal shield Distinctive, non-feathered, horny or fleshy forehead that extends down to base of the upper bill, e.g. Eurasian Coot. Does *not* include nostril.

Gape The fleshy corner (angle) of the beak, which is often yellow, cream or pinkish in young birds.

Genus (pl. *genera*) The division of classification into which a Family is divided and which has one or more species, i.e. the taxonomic rank below Family.

Gorget A 'breast plate': the iridescent 'crescent'-shaped throat and breast feather groups of the male riflebirds, also Yellow-bellied Sunbird (= 'Bib').

Gular 'Of the throat'.

Gular fluttering Quick panting movement visible at the throat of birds when they are over-heated e.g. cormorants.

Gular pouch Distensible skin in the central area of the throat, e.g. male Musk Duck, Australian Pelican, Great Cormorant.

Hackles Neck feathers that are longer than normal, e.g. Trumpet Manucode, corvids.

Hatchling 'Just out of the egg'. In this book considered as precocial downy young needing minimum parental care in the nest; move out quite quickly; from a few hours to a day or two only (cf. *Nestling*).

Hibernation Over-wintering in a reduced animation state; dormancy (see *Torpidity*).

Hood Coloured feather mass (usually black) covering the head, e.g. Hooded Robin, Australian Hobby.

Hybridisation Interbreeding of different species, any offspring of which are infertile and known as 'hybrids', e.g. offspring of Pacific Black Duck and Mallard. Hybrids between subspecies (races) of the *same* species *are* fertile, and show intermediate characteristics e.g. Masked Lapwing, Figbird, Australian Magpie (and *all* humans).

Hybrid zones Geographic areas between related subspecies where some breeding overlap (sympatry) is evident, and where birds intermediate in plumage between each full subspecies (races) may be found, e.g. Masked Lapwing, Eastern Rosella, Varied Sittella, Australian Magpie.

Immature (plumage) All plumages following the first moult after juvenile plumage. Includes all sub-adult stages, until full breeding plumage is reached. Birds are usually independent of adults by the end of two years at most.

Infraorder The taxonomic level above Parvorder and below Suborder; a higher taxonomic category.

Iridescence Play of colours (in feathers) by light on feather structure; not a pigment colour, e.g. speculum of ducks, wing sheen of Straw-necked Ibis, gorget of Magnificent Riflebird.

Irruption Sudden appearance of large numbers of a species in an area where not normally present, e.g. Black-tailed Native-hen, Letter-winged Kite, Black Honeyeater, woodswallows.

Isolating mechanisms Biological or physiographic features that split or separate populations into widely spread and eventually discrete entities; may lead to new races, then to speciation.

'Jizz' A birdwatcher's word used (especially by 'twitchers') to describe everything about a bird in one, all-embracing term; the 'essence' or 'character' of a bird in the field.

Juvenile(= Juvenal, U.S. spelling) A bird's first covering of true feathers, i.e. first feather plumage after moult of natal down. Fledging to free-flying birds, still under parental control, or recently independent.

Kleptoparasitism Piratical behaviour. Stealing food from other species; particularly practised by frigatebirds, jaegers and skuas.

Lamellae Small layers of stiff hairs (membranes) on the inner edge of the bill, used to sieve food particles from water, e.g. some ducks, prions.

Lanceolate Spear-like feather shape.

Leading edge The front edge of a wing or flipper.

Lores Area between the bill and eye, e.g. Little Tern, males of Grey Shrike-thrush, Red-lored Whistler.

Malar stripe Cheek stripe e.g. males of fairy-wrens, Carpentarian Grasswren, whipbirds, Zebra Finch.

Mandible The upper, or lower, half of a bird's bill.

Mantle Feathers forming a covering of the upper back and the base of the wings, e.g. Paradise Riflebird.

Mask Black or dark area that encloses the eyes and part of the face, e.g. Yellow-throated Scrubwren, Masked Woodswallow.

Melanistic An excess of black pigment (melanin) in the feathering.

Migratory Of regular geographical movement.

Mirror White circle (spot) in wings of some gulls, appearing when white tips of black primary feathers are seen when wings are folded e.g. Silver Gull.

Monotypic Single species. A monotypic species only has one form, and is therefore by definition a single clearly defined species. Examples are Plains-wanderer, Banded Stilt, Swift Parrot, Pilotbird, Spinifexbird, Mistletoebird.

Morph Term introduced in 1955 to replace word 'phase' (considered less precise). Refers to constant plumage colour variants within dimorphic or polymorphic species, e.g. Red-footed Booby, Grey Goshawk, Brown Falcon, White-bellied Cuckoo-shrike.

Nail The hooked central tip of the upper mandibles of albatrosses and petrels; also of ducks (*sensu stricto*).

Nape The back of a bird's neck (see *Nuchal crest*).

Nestling In the nest. Naked, or with natal down only, or as feathers develop before fledging. In this book considered as naked young needing maximum parental care in the nest; usually remain in nest from one to several weeks, or (rarely) more (see *Hatchling*).

Nictitating membrane A third 'eyelid'. Is drawn across the eye from the nasal side, for eye protection, lubrication and cleaning. Some are translucent, some have a clear central window so vision is not seriously impaired. Most birds have it.

Nomadic Of variable, often erratic movement with regard to time, season and locality. Wandering singly or in flocks to forage, or even breed, where 'conditions' are better (cf. *Irruption*).

Nominate If there is more than one race (subspecies) in a (therefore polymorphic) species, the race that takes the sub-specific name identical to the specific name of that species is known as the nominate race and, where practicable, should always be listed first. We have generally followed this practice.

Non-passerine Birds that are not suboscines or oscines. In this book all birds placed between pp. 18–167. The pittas are suboscines; the remainder are oscines (also called songbirds or passerines).

Nuchal crest 'Of the nape', e.g. lilac-pink nuchal crest of Spotted Bowerbird is positioned on the nape.

Nuptial Of or pertaining to breeding, e.g. nuptial plumage; nuptial behaviour.

Orbit Space on each side of skull containing eyeball.

Orbital ring A circular colour patch, fleshy or feathered, surrounding the eye; can be inconspicuous (Broad-billed Flycatcher) or conspicuous (female Australian Shelduck, Silvereye). May also be a partial ring, e.g. Light-mantled Sooty Albatross.

Order The division of classification into which a Class is divided and which has one or more Families, i.e. the taxonomic rank below Class.

Oscines The true songbirds. Previously often used synonymously with 'passerine birds' but now defined by Sibley & Ahlquist (1990) to include all birds in the Suborder Passeri.

Osteology The study of the skeleton and related elements of any vertebrate animal.

Palmate Three forward toes joined by webbing, e.g. petrels, ducks, gulls; the fourth toe is free, small (see *Totipalmate*).

Parasite (Parasitic behaviour) An organism obtains its living, or part thereof, by living on, in, or around another organism, or 'steals' from that organism, giving nothing in return. Invertebrates infesting vertebrates are best-known examples – fleas, lice, flat-flies, ticks, worms, protozoans, etc. Other usage of the term in Australia, e.g. robbing or stealing behaviour of frigatebirds, skuas, etc., probably better called piracy or *Kleptoparasitism*. Egg-laying by cuckoos in other birds' nests is better described as *Brood-parasitism*.

Partial migrant A term applied to a species in which only part of the population migrates annually e.g. a high proportion of Australian birds.

Parvorder The taxonomic level above Superfamily, the level below Infraorder; a higher taxonomic category.

Passerines (passeriform birds) An Order that includes all of the so-called 'songbirds', 'perching birds' or 'passerine birds' – descriptions used synonymously in Europe. Sibley & Ahlquist (1990) define passerines as all those world species in the Suborder Passeri, i.e. Parvorders Corvida and Passerida. In this book, from Albert's Lyrebird to Common Myna.

Pelagic Oceanic. Living far out at sea, generally beyond any continental shelves, except when nesting.

Pellet The regurgitated and indigestible remains of prey – usually feathers, hair, bone, scales. Produced by skuas, gulls, raptors, owls, swifts, corvids and others.

Phase An outmoded term (see *Morph*).

Plumage Entire layer of feathers and down covering a bird's body.

Plume A long, showy, display feather, e.g. egrets.

Polygamy Multiple mates. Polyandry: one female with two or more males. Polygyny: one male with two or more females.

Polytypic Complex species. A 'polytypic species' is one in which more than one form of the species exists. We call these subdivisions 'races' or 'subspecies'. A few local examples are Striated Heron, Little Corella, Variegated Fairy-wren, Varied Sittella, Grey Currawong and Australian Magpie. Sometimes another word, intended to be the equivalent, is substituted for 'polytypic species' and that is 'superspecies'. The Golden Whistler is a good example; the Grey Fantail another. Both could have been in the list above (cf. *Monotypic*).

Powder-down A fine white powder produced by feathers of some species (a) by disintegration of parts of some feathers or (b) by shedding cells that enclose a portion of a newly growing feather's barbules e.g. pigeons, parrots, woodswallows.

Precocial Young down-covered birds mobile very soon after hatching e.g. megapodes, quail, ducklings, plovers, gulls.

Primaries Main or outer flight feathers, controlling manoeuvrability of the bird – an old term is 'quill'.

Race A group sharing common characteristics that distinguish them from other members of the same species. They can inter-breed viably only within the species. Variations may have hybrid zones between their populations. Often they form a geographically isolated group. In this book the term is used instead of 'subspecies', and *only* because it is six letters shorter!

Ratite(s) A group name for flightless ground-dwelling birds that run. Sternum (keel-bone) undeveloped; loose 'shaggy' plumage. Includes moas (extinct), Ostrich, Cassowaries, Emu, Rheas, Kiwis.

Rectrix (pl. **Rectrices)** Any main feather(s) of a bird's tail.

Relict population (or species, race, morph) A word used for an isolated population, genus, species, etc., which may now represent a population with a previously much greater range or distribution, e.g. Night Parrot, Masked Owl, and the Forest ('Relict') Raven of north-east NSW.

Remex (pl. **Remiges**) Any primary or secondary feather(s) in a bird's wing.

Rictal bristles Stiff, whisker-like protrusions about the bill base, e.g. Australian Owlet-nightjar, many flycatchers.

Roost A resting or sleeping place; a perch for birds; a term applied to a group of resting waders.

Rump The squarish area between lower back and tail base, e.g. Red-rumped Parrot, Yellow-rumped Thornbill.

Scapulars Feathers that lie along the side of the back of a bird, overlapping the dorsal base of the wing (p. 1).

Secondaries Middle group of flight feathers attached to the forearm (see *Tertials* and p. 1).

Sedentary Locally living; not travelling far; not considered migratory or nomadic.

Shaft The main stem (rachis) of any feather.

Shoulder General term for the dorsal lesser and median coverts, at 'bend of wing' (p. 1; see also *Cubital bar*).

Size We define it as the total length in centimetres of a bird, from bill tip to tail tip (usually measured along the bird's midline). Extremely long-tailed birds, e.g. Red-tailed Tropicbird, sometimes have the extra length added as a second measurement (p. 52). Not considered here as a measure of bulk or mass (see p. 1).

Soft parts Non-feathered areas of the body – bill, eyes, legs, feet, and any bare skin on face, neck, such as casque, comb, wattles, etc.

Species The division of classification into which a genus is divided, the members of which can interbreed among themselves, i.e. the taxonomic rank below genus.

Speculum Iridescent, reflective dorsal patch on a duck's wing; contrasts with the rest of the wing. Usually situated on the secondaries and forms a colour bar in flight, e.g. Pacific Black Duck.

Spur Sharp, bony projection on the leg (Feral Chicken – rooster), or wing (Masked Lapwing).

Striated (Streaked) Having striations. Usually dark marks aligned on long axis of a bird's feathers e.g. Striated Fieldwren, Striated Thornbill, Little Grassbird.

Sub-adult A more precise definition than *Immature*. In this book, considered to include all plumages after all kinds of parental supervision is dropped; by the end of two years at most. May persist as sub-adult for a few months (some small passerines) or many years (some albatrosses); (see *Immature*).

Sub-oscines (or Suboscines) Passeriform birds with different, supposedly more primitive, syrinyx (voice box) anatomy, compared to the remainder of the song- or perching birds (the Oscines). In Australia, the pittas only).

Subspecies See *Race*.

Sub-terminal 'Nearly at the end' – e.g. dark tail band of Nankeen Kestrel, Pacific Gull, Scrubtit.

Sulcus Groove along the bill of albatrosses, some petrels.

Superciliary The eyebrow stripe of some birds, e.g. Fiordland Penguin, Pacific Black Duck, White-browed Robin, Hall's Babbler, Yellow-breasted Boatbill.

Superfamily A grouping of taxonomically related bird Families. The taxonomic level below Suborder.

Synchronous hatching Most songbirds hatch all eggs of the clutch within a very short period (see *Asynchronous hatching*).

Talons Sharply hooked claws used for holding and killing prey, e.g. all diurnal raptors; owls.

Tapetum A reflecting layer behind the eye's retina that permits the better utilisation of dim or low light levels; many nocturnal animals have this feature.

Tarso-metatarsus Fused tarsal and metatarsal leg elements; the 'lower leg' of birds, just above the toes. This is commonly called the 'tarsus'. May be feathered, partly so, or not at all.

Terminal 'At the very end', e.g. white tail tips: Chestnut-crowned Babbler or black: Australian Magpie.

Tertials (sing. **Tertiary**; pl. **Tertiaries**) The innermost flight feathers of a bird's wing ('upper arm'); (see p. 1).

Tertiary The third Geological Era – Palaeocene to Pleistocene.

Tibiotarsus In birds, the prominent lower leg bone (tibia) is characteristically fused with some tarsal bones at the ankle.

Tomium The cutting edge of the mandible (upper or lower). Neatly defined with black in the Royal Albatross and 'New Amsterdam Albatross'.

Tomial tooth (teeth) A notch and protrusion on the edge of the mandible for killing prey, e.g. Peregrine Falcon. This is not a true tooth.

Torpidity Lowering of body temperature to overcome adverse weather or cold and to conserve energy. May be daily, or for longer periods. Nightjars, swifts, capable of it, but may rarely need to do it in Australia. Other species reported as entering torpor, e.g. Mistletoebird (see *Hibernation*).

Totipalmate All four toes completely linked by webbing e.g. Australian Pelican, Darter, cormorants, gannets, boobies.

Trailing edge Colour pattern on the back or hind edge of a wing or flipper, e.g. Little Penguin, Hardhead, Hooded Plover.

'Twitcher' Term for a birdwatcher so keen on seeing every bird species possible that they will cross a continent at a moment's notice if a rare bird is reported. Your lazy editor is not often one of them!

Underparts ('Ventrum') Chin, throat, breast, belly, underwing, flank, vent and undertail coverts, and undertail – the ventral surface of a bird (see *Ventral*).

Undulating flight Gentle rise and fall in forward flight as a bird flaps, then glides for a short distance, e.g. rosellas, cuckoo-shrikes.

Upperparts ('Dorsum') Frons, lores, face, crown, nape, mantle, back, upperwing, rump, base of tail, uppertail – the dorsal surface of a bird.

Vagrant A bird found in an area that is not its usual habitat, having strayed there through disorientation, adverse winds, or possibly some other mistake. May be an Australian bird or an international species.

Vent Refers to patch of feathers surrounding the cloaca. Sometimes used to include cloaca as well: anus, oviduct and sperm duct openings (see *Crissum*).

Ventral The undersurface of the body (see *Underparts*).

Vermiculated Densely patterned feathers with fine winding or wavy lines on them, e.g. Wandering Albatross, Australian Wood Duck.

Wattle Paired fleshy lobes or appendages, often brightly coloured, hanging from the face, throat, or neck of certain birds, e.g. Southern Cassowary, Red Junglefowl, Masked Plover, Yellow Wattlebird.

Wing load (loading) Relates the total body weight to the wing area.

Wingspan The shortest distance between the wingtips; the greatest extent of the spread wings.

Birdwatching societies and related organisations

Australia

Australian Bird Study Association
PO Box A313
Sydney South, NSW 1235
www.absa.asn.au
Corella

Avicultural Society of Australia Inc.
52 Harris Road
Elliminyt, VIC 3249
Australian Aviculture

Bird Observers Club of Australia
PO Box 185
Nunawading, VIC 3131
www.birdobservers.org.au
BOCA has 30 branches and affiliates in eastern Australia.
The Bird Observer
Australian Field Ornithology (from 2003; previously *The Australian Bird Watcher*)

Birding NSW (NSW Field Ornithologists Club Inc.)
PO Box Q277
QVB Post Shop
Sydney, NSW 1230
Australian Birds

Birds Australia (Royal Australasian Ornithologists Union)
415 Riversdale Road
Hawthorn East, VIC 3123
www.birdsaustralia.com.au
Wingspan
Emu
Special BA interest groups:
Australasian Raptor Association
Circus (newsletter)
Boobook
Australasian Wader Studies Group (also associated Wader Studies Groups in QLD, NSW, VIC, WA)
The Tattler (newsletter)
The Stilt
Birds Australia Parrot Association
Eclectus

Birds Australia Western Australia
71 Oceanic Drive
Floreat, WA 6014
Western Australian Bird Notes (newsletter)

Birds NSW (NSW Bird Atlassers Inc.)
18 Lewis Drive
Medowie, NSW 2318

Birds Queensland (Queensland Ornithological Society)
PO Box 6097
St Lucia, QLD 4067
www.birdsqueensland.org.au
The Sunbird

Birds SA (South Australian Ornithological Association Inc.)
c/o South Australian Museum
North Terrace
Adelaide, SA 5000
www.birdssa.asn.au
The South Australian Ornithologist

Birds Tasmania (formerly Bird Observers Association of Tasmania)
GPO Box 68a
Hobart, TAS 7000
Tasmanian Bird Report

Canberra Ornithologists Group Inc.
PO Box 301
Civic Square, ACT 2608
www.canberrabirds.dynamite.com.au
Gang-gang (newsletter)
Canberra Bird Notes

Cumberland Bird Observers Club
PO Box 550
Baulkham Hills, NSW 1755
www.cboc.org.au

Northern Territory Field Naturalists
PO Box 39565
Winnellie, NT 0821
Nature Territory (newsletter)
The Northern Territory Naturalist

Victorian Ornithological Research Group Inc.
133 Graydens Road
Moorooduc, VIC 3933
http://home.vicnet.net.au/~vorg/lecvorg.htm
VORG Notes

Western Australian Naturalists Club
PO Box 8254
Perth Business Centre, WA 6849
The Western Australian Naturalist

New Zealand

Royal Forest & Bird Protection Society of NZ
PO Box 631
Wellington, New Zealand
Forest & Bird

Ornithological Society of New Zealand
PO Box 316
Drury, South Auckland, New Zealand
Southern Bird (newsletter)
Notornis

Core library

This suggested list of books will help you to develop your new interest a little further. We believe that birdwatchers should study Australasia as one unit. We urge you to branch out and study the relationships, distribution, migration, dispersal and conservation of birds. New Zealand, New Guinea and Antarctica influence our Australian fauna (the Australasian Avifaunal Region) and share many species. Extra titles have been added for these countries. You might also study the Palaearctic in the Northern Hemisphere, the home of many of our migratory birds.

Many books have been used in the preparation of this field guide. We recognise and acknowledge the varied, often incredible, achievements of our predecessors and peers. Some books select themselves. To present a selection such as this is like preparing for three years on a desert island. Remember, this is a sample only! The references in each book will create a paper-trail which will lead you on a fascinating, zig-zag course into ornithological history. Choose your essential books; create your own Core Library.

Anatomy

Proctor, N.S. & Lynch, P.J. (1993), *Manual of Ornithology: Avian Structure and Function*, Yale University Press, New Haven, Connecticut.

Art

Olsen, P. (2001), *Feather and Brush: Three Centuries of Australian Bird Art*, CSIRO Publishing, Collingwood, VIC.

Pearce, B. (1989), *Australian Artists, Australian Birds*, Angus & Robertson Publishers, North Ryde, NSW.

Atlases

International

Bull, P.C., Gaze, P.D. & Robertson, C.J.R. (1985), *The Atlas of Bird Distribution in New Zealand*, Ornithological Society of New Zealand, Wellington.

National

Barrett, G. et al (2003), *The New Atlas of Australian Birds*, RAOU, Melbourne.

Blakers, M., Davies, S. & Reilly, P. (1984), *The Atlas of Australian Birds*, Melbourne University Press, Melbourne.

Regional and state

Cooper, R.M. & McAllan, I.A.W. (1995), *The Birds of Western New South Wales: A Preliminary Atlas*, NSW Bird Atlassers Inc., Albury, NSW.

Emison, W. et al (1987), *Atlas of Victorian Birds*. Dept of Conservation, Forests and Lands, and RAOU, Melbourne.

Reid, T. et al (2002), 'Seabird Atlas of South-eastern Australian Waters', *Birds Australia Monograph* **4**, RAOU, Hawthorn East, VIC.

Saunders, D.A. & Ingram, J.A. (1995), *Birds of Southwestern Australia: An Atlas of Changes in Distribution and Abundance of the Wheatbelt Fauna*, Surrey Beatty & Sons, Chipping Norton, WA, in assoc. with CSIRO.

South Australian Ornithological Association (1994), 'A Second Bird Atlas of the Adelaide Region, Part 2: Distribution Maps 1984–1985', *South Australian Ornithologist* Vol. **31** (8), 195–265.

Taylor, McC. & Canberra Ornithologists Group (1992), *Birds of the Australian Capital Territory – An Atlas*, Canberra Ornithologists Group and National Capital Planning Authority, Canberra.

Thomas, D. (1979), *Tasmanian Bird Atlas*, Fauna of Tasmania Handbook No. **2**, University of Tasmania, Hobart.

Aviculture and bird care

Hand, S. (ed.) (1990), *Care and Handling of Australian Native Animals, Emergency Care and Captive Management*, Surrey Beatty & Sons, Chipping Norton.

Macwhirter, P. (1994), *Everybird*, 2nd edn, Inkarta Press, Melbourne.

Olsen, J. (1990), *Caring for Birds of Prey*, Author, Canberra.

Parsons, H. (1999), *Caring for Australian Native Birds*, Kangaroo Press (Simon & Schuster Australia), East Roseville, NSW.

Shephard, M. (1994), *Aviculture in Australia: Keeping and Breeding Aviary Birds*, 2nd edn, Reed Books Australia, Melbourne [also lists 11 avicultural societies throughout Australia].

Temby, I. (1992), *A Guide to Living With Wildlife: How to Prevent and Control Damage in Victoria*, Dept of Conservation & Environment, Melbourne.

Walraven, E. (1991), *Wildlife Questions and Answers, The Experts Answer Your Questions ...*, Allan & Unwin, North Sydney, NSW.

Walraven, E. (1992), *Rescue and Rehabilitation of Oiled Birds: Field Manual*, Zoological Parks Board of NSW, Sydney.

Walraven, E. (1999), *Care of Australian Wildlife*, New Holland, Sydney.

Beginning birdwatching

Balmford, R. (1990), *The Beginners Guide to Australian Birds*, 2nd edn, Penguin, Ringwood.

Simpson, K. & Wilson, Z. (1998), *Birdwatching in Australia and New Zealand*, Reed New Holland, Sydney.

Behaviour

Jones, D. (2002), *Magpie Alert: Learning to Live with a Wild Neighbour*, University of NSW Press, Sydney.

Kaplan, G. & Rogers, L.J. (2001), *Birds, Their Habits and Skills*, Allen & Unwin, Crows Nest, NSW.

Rowley, I. (1975), *Birdlife*, Collins, Sydney.

Bird banding

Baker, G.B. et al (1995), 'Report on the Australian Bird and Bat Banding Scheme, 1984–1995', Australian Nature Conservancy Agency, Canberra.

Reilly, P.N. (1988), *Private Lives: Ages, Mates and Movements of Some Australian Birds*, Kangaroo Press, Sydney.

Rogers, K. et al (1986), *Bander's Aid, A Guide to Ageing and Sexing Bush Birds*, The Authors, St Andrews, VIC.

Rogers, K. et al (1990), *Bander's Aid*, Supplement No. **1**, RAOU Report No. **67**, Moonee Ponds, VIC.

[See also articles in the journal *Corella*].

Biography

Datta, A. (1997), *John Gould in Australia: Letters and Drawings*, The Miegunyah Press at Melbourne University Press, Melbourne.

Sauer, G.C. (1982), *John Gould, The Bird Man: A Chronology and Bibliography*, Lansdowne Editions, Melbourne.

Bird reports

These are published in several states of Australia, often (but not always) as supplements to existing journals. See **Birdwatching societies and related organisations**, p. 350.

Birdwatching experiences in the field

Rogers, A. (1992), *Addicted to Birds*, The Author, St Andrews, VIC.

Taylor, S. (2001), *How Many Birds is That? From the Forty-spotted Pardalote on Bruny Island to the White-tailed Tropicbird on Cape York*, Hyland House Publishing, Flemington, VIC.

Checklists

World – Popular

Clements, J.F. (2000), *Birds of the World: A Checklist*, 5th edn, Ibis Publishing Co., Vista, California.

Dickinson, E.C. (ed.) (2003), *The Howard & Moore' Complete Checklist of the Birds of the World*, 3rd edn, Academic Press, London [incl. all subsp.].

Gruson, E.S. (1976), *A Checklist of the Birds of the World*, Collins, London.

Monroe, B.L. Jr. & Sibley, C.G. (1993), *A World Checklist of Birds*, Yale University Press, New Haven and London.

Walters, M. (1980), *The Complete Birds of the World*, Reed, Sydney.

World – Scientific

Sibley, C.G. & Ahlquist, J.E. (1990), *Phylogeny and Classification of Birds: A Study of Molecular Biology*, Yale University Press, New Haven and London.

Sibley, C.G. & Monroe B.L. Jr. (1990), *Distribution and Taxonomy of Birds of the World,* Yale University Press. New Haven, Connecticut.

National: Australasia & Oceania

Beehler, B. & Finch, B. (1985), 'Species Checklist of the Birds of New Guinea', *Monograph* **1**, RAOU, Moonee Ponds, VIC.

Checklist Committee OSNZ (1990), *Checklist of the Birds of New Zealand*, 3rd edn, Random Century & Ornithological Society of NZ, Auckland.

Christidis, L. & Boles, W. (1994), 'The taxonomy and species of birds of Australia and its territories', *Monograph* **2**, RAOU, Hawthorn East, VIC.

Condon, H. T. (1975), *Checklist of the Birds of Australia*, Part I, *Non-Passerines*, RAOU, Melbourne.

Schodde, R. (1975), *Interim List of Australian Songbirds, Passerines*, RAOU, Melbourne.

States

Cooper, R.M., McAllan, I.A.W. & Curtis, B.R. (1999), *The New South Wales Bird Atlassers List of the Birds of New South Wales (including Lord Howe Island) and the Australian Capital Territory*, New South Wales Bird Atlassers Inc., Medowie, NSW.

McAllan, I.A.W. & Bruce, M.D. (1988), *The Birds of New South Wales, A Working List*, Biocon Research Group/NSW Bird Atlassers, Turramurra, NSW.

Smith, S.J. (1990), *Checklist of the Vertebrate Animals of Tasmania*, St David's Park Publishing, Hobart.

Storr, G.M. (1984), 'Revised List of Queensland Birds', *Records of the W.A. Museum Supplement* No. **19**, Perth.

Conservation

World

Bird Life International 2000 (2000), *Threatened Birds of the World, The Official Source for Birds on the IUCN Red List*, Lynx Edicions & Bird Life International, Barcelona and Cambridge, UK.

Australia

Bryant, S. & Jackson, J. (1999), *Tasmania's Threatened Fauna Handbook, What, Where and How to Protect Tasmania's Threatened Animals*, Threatened Species Unit, Parks and Wildlife Service, Hobart.

Garnett, S. (ed.) (1993), 'Threatened and Extinct Birds of Australia', 2nd edn, *RAOU Report* No. **82**, Hawthorn East, VIC.

Garnett, S.T. & Crowley, G.M. (2000), *The Action Plan for Australian Birds 2000*, Environment Australia, Canberra.

Gibbons, P. & Lindenmayer, D. (2002), *Tree Hollows and Wildlife: Conservation in Australia*, CSIRO Publishing, Collingwood, VIC.

Stanger, M. et al (1998), *CSIRO List of Australian Vertebrates, A Reference with Conservation Status*, CSIRO Publishing, Collingwood, VIC.

Dictionaries

Campbell, B. & Lack, E. (1985), *A Dictionary of Birds*, T. & A.D. Poyser, Calton, UK.

Macdonald, J.D. (1987), *The Illustrated Dictionary of Australian Birds by Common Name*, Reed Books, Frenchs Forest, NSW.

Electronic

Audio tapes

Numerous audio cassette tapes have now been published – here are some examples:

Aves, K. (1991), *Songs & Calls of 64 Tasmanian Birds*, Spectangle Productions, Tasmania.

Buckingham, R. & Jackson, L. (compilers/eds) (1983–1999), *A Field Guide to Australian Birdsong*, a 20-page booklet accompanies each cassette, Bird Observers Club of Australia, Nunawading, VIC:

1. Emu to Striated Heron
2. Rufous Night Heron to Chestnut Rail
3. Red-necked Crake to Black-naped Tern
4. Sooty Tern to Superb Parrot
5. Regent Parrot to Masked Owl
6. Eastern Grass Owl to Ground Cuckoo-Shrike
7. White-winged Triller to White-breasted Whistler
8. Little Shrike-thrush to Hall's Babbler
9. Chestnut-crowned Babbler to Redthroat
10. Calamanthus to Noisy Friarbird
11. Little Friarbird to Scarlet Honeyeater
12. Crimson Chat to Torresian Crow and Supplementary Calls

Lindsey, T.R. (1987), *What Bird Call Is That?,* Angus & Robertson Publishers, North Ryde, NSW [2 x 60-minute audio tapes and descriptive book].

McNabb, E. (1995), *Nightlife of the Dandenongs: Weird & Wonderful Sounds of Night Creatures*, Ninox Pursuits, Emerald, VIC [incl. 9 owl and nightjar spp.].

Smith, L.H. (2002), *The Song of the Lyrebird*, Bird Observers Club of Australia, Nunawading, VIC [development of song from chick to adult male].

CDs

The BOCA tapes listed above (# 1–12) are being re-worked, clarified and with additional material, being released as a series of 10 CDs. Each disc also has a booklet.

1. Ostrich to Brown Booby
2. Darter to Red Knot
3. Red-necked Stint to Cockatiel
4. Rainbow Lorikeet to Grass Owl
5. Tawny Frogmouth to Kalkadoon Grasswren

6–10. [in preparation].

CD-ROM

Lindsey, T. (c. 1996), *Encyclopaedia of Australian Birds*, Webster Publishing, Frenchs Forest, NSW.

Simpson, K. & Day, N. (1999), *Simpson & Day's CD Birds of Australia*, Version 5.1, Natural Learning, Sydney.

Videos

Numerous videotapes have now been published. Here are just five examples:

Erdos, L. & Erdos, J. (1996), 'When Birds Don't Know You're There', D. Corke (ed.), No. **5** in a series, L. & J. Erdos, Melbourne. [50 min.].

Young, G. (producer/director) (c. 1991), 'Land of Parrots: Grass Parrots', No. **7** in a series about Australian Parrots, Turramurra, NSW. [52 min.].

Young, G. (producer/director) (c. 1995), 'Pigeons of Australia: The Bronzewings', writer/director T. Lindsey, Geo Wildlife Documentaries, Sydney.

Young, G. (producer/director) (c. 1996), 'Reader's Digest Guide to 101 Australian Birds', Writer T. Lindsey, Geo Wildlife Documentaries, Sydney. [110 min.].

Young, J. (1998), 'Wings of Silence: Owls', Ray Smith Productions, Maleny, QLD [55 min.].

Encyclopaedias

Forshaw, J.M. (ed.) (1998), *Encyclopaedia of Birds*, 2nd edn, University of NSW Press, NSW.

Lindsey, T. R. (1992), *Encyclopaedia of Australian Animals: Birds*, National Photographic Index of Australian Wildlife; Australian Museum, Angus & Robertson, Pymble, NSW.

Field guides

Conventional: Australia

Morcombe, M. (2002), *Field Guide to Australian Birds*, Steve Parish Publishing, Archerfield, QLD.

Simpson, K. & Day, N. with Trusler, P. (2004), *Field Guide to the Birds of Australia.* 7th edn, Viking (Penguin), Camberwell, VIC. [**This book!**]

Slater, P., Slater, P. & Slater, R. (1989), *The Slater Field Guide to Australian Birds*, 2nd edn, Reed New Holland, Sydney.

Pizzey, G. & Knight, F. (2003), *A Field Guide to the Birds of Australia.* 5th edn, Angus & Robertson (HarperCollins), Sydney.

Conventional: Australasia and Oceania

Beehler, B., Pratt, T. & Zimmermann (1986), *Birds of New Guinea.* Handbook No. **9** of Wau Ecology Institute, Princeton University Press, Princeton, New Jersey.

Bregulla, H.L. (1992), *Birds of Vanuatu.* Anthony Nelson, Oswestry, UK.

Coates, B.J. & Bishop, K.D. (1997), *A Guide to the Birds of Wallacea: Sulawesi, the Moluccas and Lesser Sunda Islands, Indonesia*, Dove Publications, Alderley, QLD.

Doughty, C, Day, N. & Plant, A. (1999), *Birds of The Solomons, Vanuatu & New Caledonia*, Christopher Helm (A. & C. Black), London.

Heather, B.D. & Robertson, H.A. (1996), *The Field Guide to the Birds of New Zealand*, Viking, Auckland, NZ.

Pratt, D.H., Brunner, P.L. & Berrett, D.G. (1987), *A Field Guide to the Birds of Hawaii and the Tropical Pacific*, Princeton University Press, Princeton, New Jersey.

Robertson, H.A. & Heather, B.D. (1999), *The Hand Guide to the Birds of New Zealand*, Penguin Books (NZ), Auckland.

Watling, D. (2001), *A Guide to the Birds of Fiji & Western Polynesia*, Environmental Consultants (Fiji) Ltd, Suva.

Photographic

Coates, B.J. & Peckover, W.S. (2001), *Birds of New Guinea and the Bismarck Archipelago*: A Photographic Guide, Alderley, QLD.

Flegg, J. (2002), *Photographic Field Guide: Birds of Australia.* 2nd edn, Reed New Holland, Sydney.

Moon, G. (1992), *A Field Guide to New Zealand Birds*, Reed (Octopus), Auckland.

Rowland, P. (1995), *A Photographic Guide to Birds of Australia*, New Holland, Sydney, for The Australian Museum.

Trounson, A.D. & Trounson, M. (1998), *Australian Birds Simply Classified*, 4th edn, Murray David Publishing, Frenchs Forest.

Trounson, A.D. & Trounson, M. (2002), *Australian Birds, A Concise Photographic Guide*, Cameron House (Bookwise International P/L), Wingfield, SA.

States

Green, R.H. (1995), *The Fauna of Tasmania – Birds*, Potoroo Publishing, Launceston, TAS.

Storr, G.M. & Johnstone, R.E. (1985), *A Field Guide to the Birds of Western Australia,* 2nd edn, Western Australian Museum, Perth, WA.

Taylor, McC. & Day, N. (1993), *Field Guide to Birds of the A.C.T*, National Parks of the ACT Inc., Canberra.

Watts, D. (2002), *Field Guide to Tasmanian Birds*, 2nd edn, New Holland, Sydney.

Food of birds

Barker, R.D. & Vestjens, W.J.M. [1989], *The Food of Australian Birds* **1**, Non-Passerines, 1st edn & [1991], *The Food of Australian Birds* **2**, Passerines, 1st edn, Division of Wildlife and Ecology, CSIRO, East Melbourne.

Gardens for birds

Adams, G.M. (1980), *Birdscaping Your Garden*, Rigby, Adelaide.

Canberra Ornithologists Group & Urban Services, ACT (2000), *Birds of Canberra Gardens*, Canberra Ornithologists Group & Urban Services, ACT Government, Canberra.

Elliot, R. (1994), *Attracting Wildlife to Your Garden*, Lothian Aust. Garden Series, Thomas C. Lothian, Port Melbourne, VIC.

Grant, J. (1997), *The Nestbox Book*, Gould League of Victoria, Moorabbin, VIC.

Kloot, T. & McCulloch, E.M. (1980), *Birds of Australian Gardens*, Paintings by Peter Trusler, Rigby, Adelaide.

McCulloch, E.M. (2000), *Birds in Your Garden*, 2nd edn (retitled), Hyland House, Melbourne.

Pizzey, G. (1991), *A Garden of Birds*, 2nd edn, CollinsAngus&Robertson Publishers, North Ryde, NSW.

Pizzey, G. (2000), *The Australian Bird-Garden: Creating Havens for Native Birds*, Angus & Robertson, HarperCollinsPublishers, Sydney.

Veerman, P.A. (2002), *Canberra Birds: A Report on the First 18 years of the Garden Bird Survey*, Author, Kambah, ACT.

Habitat and Ecology

AUSLIG (1990), *Atlas of Australian Resources*, Third Series, Vol. **6**, *Vegetation*, Australian Surveying and Land Information Group, Dept. of Administrative Services, Canberra.

Bennett, P.M. & Owens, I.P.F. (2002), *Evolutionary Ecology of Birds: Life Histories, Mating Systems and Extinction*, Oxford University Press, Oxford, UK.

Brothers, N. et al (2001), *Tasmania's Offshore Islands: Seabirds and Other Natural Features*, Tasmanian Museum and Art Gallery, Hobart.

Cooper, R.M. and McAllan, I.A.W. (1999), *A Guide to Bird Habitats in NSW*, New South Wales Bird Atlassers Inc., Medowie, NSW.

Ford, H.A. (1989), *Ecology of Birds, An Australian Perspective*, Surrey Beatty & Sons, Chipping Norton, NSW.

Ford, H.A. & Paton, D.C. (1986), *The Dynamic Partnership, Birds and Plants in Southern Australia*, Handbook of the Flora and Fauna of South Australia [series], issued by the Handbooks Committee on behalf of the SA Government, D.J. Woolman, Govt Printer, Adelaide.

Keast, A. (ed.) (1990), *Biogeography and Ecology of Forest Bird Communities*, SPB Academic Publishing, The Hague, The Netherlands.

Keast A. et al (eds) (1985), *Birds of Eucalypt Forests and Woodlands; Ecology, Conservation, Management*, Surrey Beatty & Sons Ltd, Chipping Norton, NSW, in association with RAOU, Moonee Ponds, VIC.

Mayr, E. & Diamond, J. (2001), *The Birds of Northern Melanesia: Speciation, Ecology, and Biogeography*, Oxford University Press, New York.

History of birdwatching

Collier, R. et al (eds) (2000), *Birds, Birders & Birdwatching 1899–1999: Celebrating One Hundred Years of the South Australian Ornithologists Association*, SAOA Inc., Adelaide.

Heather, B.D. & Sheehan, P.M. (1990), *Fifty Years of Bird Study in New Zealand: An Index to* Notornis *1939–1989*, Ornithological Society of New Zealand Inc., Lower Hutt, New Zealand.

Robin, L. (2001), *The Flight of the Emu: A Hundred Years of Australian Ornithology 1901–2001*, Melbourne University Press, Carlton South, VIC.

Introduced birds

Druett, J. (1983), *Exotic Intruders: The Introduction of Plants and Animals into New Zealand*, Heinemann, Auckland.

Long, J. (1981), *Introduced Birds of the World: The Worldwide History, Distribution and Influence of Birds Introduced to New Environments*, A.H. & A.W. Reed, Sydney.

Journals with ornithological interests

See **Birdwatching societies and related organisations**, p. **350**.

Magazines

Australian Aviculture
The Bird Observer
Wingspan

Nests and eggs

Beruldsen, G. (1980), *A Field Guide to Nests and Eggs of Australian Birds*, Rigby, Adelaide.

Campbell, A.J. (1900), *Nests and Eggs of Australian Birds*, Vol. **1**, (1974 – facsimile edn), Wren, Melbourne.

Reference texts to orders, families, genera and species of birds

The very large number of books devoted to various taxonomic subdivisions of the avifauna are also extremely important to a birdwatcher's library. New books constantly appear, from within Australia and from overseas. All should be considered. This is a selection only.

Beruldsen, G. (1995), *Raptor Identification*, The Author, Kenmore Hills, QLD.

Chantler, P. & Driessens, G. (2000), *Swifts: A Guide to the Swifts and Treeswifts of the World*, 2nd edn, Pica Press, Sussex, UK.

Cleer, N. & Nurney, D. (1998), *Nightjars: A Guide to Nightjars and Related Nightbirds*, Pica Press, Sussex, UK.

Clement, P. (1993), *Finches and Sparrows: An Identification Guide*, Christopher Helm, London.

Coates, B. (1985), *The Birds of New Guinea, Including the Bismarck Archipelago and Bougainville*, Vol. **1**. *Non-Passerines*, Dove Publications, Alderley, QLD.

Coates, B. (1990), *The Birds of New Guinea* ...Vol. **2**. *Passerines*, Dove Publications, Alderley, QLD.

Cooper, W.T. & Forshaw, J.M. (1977), *The Birds of Paradise and Bowerbirds*, Collins, Sydney.

Davies, S.J.J.F. (2000), *Ratites and Tinamous: Tinamidae, Rheidae, Dromaiidae, Casuariidae, Apterygidae, Struthionidae*, Bird Families of the World [series] Oxford University Press, Melbourne.

Debus, S.J.S. (1998), *The Birds of Prey of Australia – A Field Guide*, Oxford University Press, Melbourne.

Del Hoyo, J. *et al* (eds), *Handbook of the Birds of the World*, Lynx Edicions, Barcelona, Spain [to be completed in 16 volumes - those published are listed below]:
(1992), Vol. **1**, *Ostrich to Ducks*
(1994), Vol. **2**, *New World Vultures to Guineafowl*
(1996), Vol. **3**, *Hoatzin to Auks*
(1997), Vol. **4**, *Sandgrouse to Cuckoos*
(1999), Vol. **5**, *Barn Owls to Hummingbirds*

Enticott, J. & Tipling, D. (1997), *Photographic Handbook of the Seabirds of the World*, New Holland, Sydney.

Erritzoe, J. & Erritzoe, H. (1998), *A Monograph of the Pitta Family*, The Lutterworth Press, Cambridge, UK.

Ferguson-Kees, J. & Christie, D.A. (2001), *Raptors of the World*, Helm Identification Guides, Christopher Helm, London.

Forshaw, J.M. & Cooper, W.T. (2002), *Australian Parrots*, 3rd edition, Alexander Editions, Robina, QLD.

Frith, C.B. & Beehler, B. (1998), *Birds of Paradise: Paradisaeidae*, Oxford University Press, Oxford, UK.

Fry, C.H., Fry, K. & Harris, A. (2000), *Kingfishers, Bee-eaters & Rollers*, Helm Identification Guides, Christopher Helm, London.

Gibbs, D., Barnes, E. & Cox, J. (2001), *Pigeons and Doves, A Guide to the Pigeons and Doves of the World*, Helm Identification Guides, Christopher Helm, London.

Goodwin, D. (1982), *Estrildid Finches of the World*, Oxford University Press, Oxford, UK.

Hancock, J. (1999), *Herons and Egrets of the World*, A Photographic Journey, Princeton University Press, Princeton, New Jersey.

Hancock, J., Kushlan, J.A. & Kahl, M.P. (1992), *Storks, Ibises and Spoonbills of the World*, Academic Press, London.

Handbook of Australian New Zealand and Antarctic Birds [abbreviated to *HANZAB* throughout this book], Oxford University Press, Melbourne.
[Note: We place volumes in order of publication, *not* of name of Editors, in this short list].

Marchant, S. & Higgins, P. (eds) (1990), Vol. **1A**; *Ratites to Petrels*; Vol. **1B**, *Pelican to Ducks*.
Marchant, S. & Davies, S.J.J.F. (eds) (1993), Vol. **2** *Raptors to Lapwings*.
Higgins, P. & Davies, S.J.J.F. (eds) (1996), Vol. **3** *Snipe to Pigeons*.
Higgins, P. (ed.) (1999), Vol. **4**, *Parrots to Dollarbird*.
Higgins, P. (ed.) (2001), Vol. **5**, *Tyrant Flycatchers to Chats*.
Higgins, P. & Peter, J.M. (eds) (2002), Vol. **6**, *Pardalotes to Shrike-thrushes*.

Harrison, P. (1987), *Seabirds of the World, A Photographic Guide*, Christopher Helm Ltd, Bromley, UK.

Hayman, P., Marchant, J. & Prater , T. (1991), *Shorebirds. An identification guide to waders of the world*, Christopher Helm, London.

Hollands, D. (1984), *Eagles, Hawks and Falcons of Australia*, Nelson, Melbourne.

Hollands, D. (1991), *Birds of the Night: Owls, Frogmouths and Nightjars of Australia*, Reed Books, Balgowlah, NSW.

Hollands, D. (1999), *Kingfishers and Kookaburras: Jewels of the Australian Bush*, Reed New Holland, Sydney.

Holyoak, D & Woodcock, M. (2001), *The Nightjars (Caprimulgiformes) and Their Allies*, Bird Families of the World [series], Oxford University Press, Oxford, UK.

Johnsgard, P.A. (1996), *Cormorants, Darters and Pelicans of the World*, Smithsonian Institution Press, Washington, DC.

Johnstone, R.E. & Storr, G.M. (1999), *Handbook of Western Australian Birds*, Vol. **1** *Non-Passerines (Emu to Dollarbird)*; Vol. **2** *Passerines* (2003), Western Australian Museum, Perth.

Juniper, T. & Parr, M. (1998), *Parrots: A Guide to the Parrots of the World*, Pica Press, Sussex., UK.

Kingsford, R. (1991), *Australian Waterbirds, A Field Guide*, Kangaroo Press, Kenthurst, NSW.

Konig, C., Weick, F. & Becking, J-H. (1999), *Owls*, Helm Identification Guides, Christopher Helm, London.

Konter, A. (2001), *Grebes of Our World*, Lynx Edicions, Barcelona, Spain.

Lane, B.A. (1987), *Shorebirds in Australia*, Nelson, Melbourne.

Madge, S. & Burn, H. (1994), *Crows and Jays: A Guide to the Crows, Jays and Magpies of the World*, Christopher Helm (A. & C. Black), London.

Madge, S. & Burn, H. (1988), *Wildfowl, An Identification Guide to the Ducks, Geese and Swans of the World*, Helm Bird Identification Guides, Christopher Helm, London.

Madge, S. & McGowan, P. (2001), *Pheasants, Partridges and Grouse: A Guide to the Pheasants, Partridges, Quails, Grouse, Guineafowl, Button-quails and Sandgrouse of the World*, Helm Bird Identification Guides, Christopher Helm, London.

National Photographic Index of Australian Wildlife & Australian Museum, Sydney, NSW. [A series of 10 volumes. Serventy, V.N. (series ed.): 1982, 1985; Strahan, R. (series ed.): all remaining volumes]
Pringle, J.D. (1982), *The Wrens and Warblers of Australia*
Pringle, J.D. (1985), *The Waterbirds ...*
Lindsey, T.R. (1986), *The Seabirds ...*
Pringle, J.D. (1987), *The Shorebirds ...*
Boles, W.E. (1988), *The Robins and Flycatchers ...*
Longmore, W. (1991), *Honeyeater and Their Allies ...*
Crome, F. & Shields, J. (1992), *Parrots and Pigeons ...*
Olsen, P., Crome, F. & Olsen, J. (1993), *Birds of Prey & Ground Birds ...*
Strahan, R. (1994), *Cuckoos, Nightbirds & Kingfishers ...*
Strahan, R. (1996), *Finches, Bowerbirds and Other Passerines ...*

Ogilvie, M. & Young, S. (1998), *Photographic Handbook of the Waterfowl of the World*, New Holland, Cape Town, South Africa.

Olsen, K.M. & Larsson, H., (1997), *Skuas and Jaegers: A Guide to the Skuas and Jaegers of the World*, Pica Press, Sussex, UK.

Olsen, P. (1995), *Australian Birds of Prey: The Biology and Ecology of Raptors*, University of NSW Press, Sydney.

Poole, A.F. (1989), *Ospreys*, Cambridge University Press, Cambridge, UK.

Reilly, P.N. (1994), *Penguins of the World*, Oxford University Press Australia, Melbourne.

Restall (1996), *Munias and Mannikins*, Pica Press (Helm Information Ltd), East Sussex, UK.

Robertson, C.J.R. (ed.) (1985), *The Reader's Digest Complete Book of New Zealand Birds*, Reader's Digest Services, Sydney.

Rowley, I.C.R. & Russell, E. (1997), *Fairy-wrens and Grasswrens – Maluridae*, Oxford University Press, Oxford, UK.

Schodde, R. (1982), *The Fairy-Wrens – A Monograph of the Maluridae*, Lansdowne Editions, Melbourne.

Schodde, R. & Mason, I.J. (1980), *Nocturnal Birds of Australia*, Lansdowne Editions, Melbourne.

Schodde, R. & Tidemann, S. (eds) (1997), *The Reader's Digest Complete Book of Australian Birds*, (1st revision of 1986 2nd edn). Reader's Digest Services, Sydney.

Taylor, B. (1998), *A Guide to the Rails, Crakes, Gallinules and Coots of the World*, Yale University Press, New Haven, Connecticut & London.

Tickell, W.L.N. (2000), *Albatrosses*, Pica Press, London.

Turner, A. & Rose C. (1989), *A Handbook to the Swallows and Martins of the World*, Helm Identification Guides, Christopher Helm, London.

Warham, J. (1990), *The Petrels, Their Ecology and Breeding Systems*, Academic Press, London & San Diego, California.

Williams, T. *et al* (1995), *The Penguins, Spheniscidae*, Oxford University Press, Oxford, UK.

Zann, R. (1996), *The Zebra Finch – A Synthesis of Field and Laboratory Studies*, Oxford University Press, Oxford, UK.

Palaeontology (fossil birds)

Archer, M. et al (1991), *Riversleigh, The Story of Animals in Ancient Rainforests of Inland Australia*, Reed Books, Balgowlah, NSW.

Feduccia, A. (1999), *The Origin and Evolution of Birds*, 2nd ed, Yale University Press, New Haven, Connecticut and London.

Gill, B. & Martinson, P. (1991), *New Zealand's Extinct Birds*, Random Century New Zealand Ltd, Auckland.

Rich, P.V. et al (1985), *Kadimakara, Extinct Vertebrates of Australia*, Pioneer Design Studio, Lilydale, VIC.

Vickers-Rich, P. et al (eds.) (1990), *Vertebrate Palaeontology of Australasia*, Pioneer Design Studios (with) Monash University Publication Committee, Clayton, VIC.

Vickers-Rich, P. & Rich, T.H. (1999), *Wildlife of Gondwana*, 2nd edn, Reed (Heinemann Australia), Chatswood, NSW.

Regional and local annotated bird lists

Australian Capital Territory

Canberra Ornithologists Group (1993), *Birds of Canberra Region Field List*, 4th edn, Canberra Ornithologists Group, Canberra.

Wilson, S. (1999), *Birds of the ACT: Two Centuries of Change*, Canberra Ornithologists Group, Canberra.

New South Wales

Disher, P. (2000), *Birds of the Barham District*, [NSW and VIC, Historical Summary 1930–1999], Barham Land Care Group, Barham, in assoc. with BOCA, Nunawading, VIC.

Northern Territory

Goodfellow, D. (1996), *Birds of Darwin: Mangroves & Mudflats*, The Author, Winnellie, NT.

Goodfellow, D.L. (2001), *Birds of Australia's Top End,* Scrubfowl Press, Darwin.

Noske, R. & Brennan, G. (2002), *The Birds of Groote Eylandt,* Northern Territory University, Darwin.

Queensland

Durrant, B. & MacRae, I. (1994), *Birds of Bribie Island, Pumicestone Passage and Environs,* Bribie Is. Environmental Protection Assoc. Inc., Bribie Island, QLD.

Fearnley, C. (1998), *Common Birds of Noosa, Cooloola and the Sunshine Coast,* Author, Doonan, QLD.

Garnett, S. (1988), *Birds of the Townsville Common,* 2nd edn, Queensland NPWS, Townsville, QLD.

Nielson, L. (1991), *Birds of Lamington National Park and Environs, A Guide's Guide,* Author, Canungra, QLD.

Nielsen, L. (1996), *Birds of Queensland's Wet Tropics and Great Barrier Reef,* Gerard Industries P/L, Bowden, SA.

Noyce, J. (ed.) (1997), *A Bird Watcher's Guide to Redcliffe, Pine Rivers and Caboolture,* The Wildlife Preservation Society of Caboolture Shire Inc., Caboolture, QLD.

Wieneke, J. (1996), *Birds of Magnetic Island,* The Author, Townsville, QLD.

South Australia

Baxter, C. & Berris, M. (1995), *An Annotated List of the Birds of Kangaroo Island.* 2nd edn, NPWS (SA), Kingscote, Kangaroo Is., SA.

Thompson, H. (1997), *Adelaide's Birds,* Shag on a Rock, Blackwood, SA.

Tasmania

Green, R.H. (1989), *Birds of Tasmania, An Annotated Checklist with Illustrations,* 3rd edn, Potoroo Publishing, Launceston, TAS.

White, G. (1980), *Islands of South-west Tasmania,* Author, Sydney.

Victoria

Bridley, A. (compiler) (1991), *Birds of the Bendigo District.* Bendigo Field Naturalists Club Inc., Bendigo, VIC.

Garnett, S. et al (1986), *Birds of Port Phillip Bay,* Ministry for Planning & Environment, Melbourne.

Kloot, T. (2000), *Birds of Box Hill,* Victorian Ornithological Research Group Inc., Melbourne.

Norris, M. (ed.) et al (1995), *Local Birds of Bayside,* Bayside City Council, Sandringham, VIC.

Quinn, D. & Lacey, G. (1999), *Birds of French Island Wetlands,* Spectrum Publications, Richmond, VIC.

Western Australia

Barrett, G. et al (1995), *Common Birds of Kalgoorlie-Boulder,* Goldfields Naturalists Club Inc., Kalgoorlie, WA.

Clay, P. & Clay, B. (1996), *Field Guide: Birds of Cape Naturaliste,* The Authors, Dunsborough., WA.

Collins, P. (1995), *The Birds of Broome,* Broome Bird Observatory, Broome, WA.

Reports

Scientific reports, from federal and state institutions (museums, universities, zoos, other research organisations), professional consultants and some ornithological societies, are legion. Your core library should contain a selection relating to your special interest. Lists of titles are sometimes published by government departments; payment may be required.

Where to find birds

International

Chambers, S. (1989), *Birds of New Zealand: Locality Guide,* Arun, Hamilton, New Zealand.

Wheatley, N. (1998), *Where to Watch Birds in Australasia and Oceania,* A. & C. Black, UK.

National

Bransbury, J. (1992), *Where to Find Birds in Australia,* Waymark Publishing, Fullarton, SA.

Morcombe, M. (1990), *The Great Australian Bird Finder.* Lansdowne, Melbourne.

Thomas, R. & Thomas, S. (1996), *The Complete Guide to Finding the Birds of Australia,* Frogmouth Publications, Cottenham, UK.

Regional

Donato, D. *et al* (1997), *Finding Birds in Australia's Northern Territory,* CSIRO Publishing, Collingwood, VIC.

Roberts, P. (1993), *Birdwatcher's Guide to the Sydney Region,* Kangaroo Press, Kenthurst, NSW.

Saunders, D.A. & Rebeira, P. de (1993), *The Birdlife of Rottnest Island,* 2nd edn, Surrey Beatty & Sons, Chipping Norton, NSW, for the Authors.

Van Delft, R. (1997), *Birding Sites Around Perth,* 2nd edn, Birds Australia – WA Group, Perth.

Wieneke, J. (2000), *Where to Find Birds in North-East Queensland,* 3rd edn, The Author, Belgian Gardens, Townsville, QLD.

Wildlife including birds (urban and country)

There are scores of books which include birds together with other animals; here are a few examples.

Clyne, D. (1990), *Wildlife in the Suburbs,* Oxford University Press, Melbourne.

Frith, D.W. & Frith, C.B. (1995), *Cape York Peninsula: A Natural History,* Reed Books Australia, Chatswood, NSW.

MMBW (1987), *The Yarra Book on Urban Wildlife,* Melbourne & Metropolitan Board of Works, Melbourne.

Ryan, M. (ed.) (1995), *Wildlife of Greater Brisbane,* The Queensland Museum, South Brisbane, QLD.

Wilson, J. (1991), *Victorian Urban Wildlife,* Collins Angus&Robertson Publishers, North Ryde, NSW.

Index of Latin Names

Bold number indicates the colour plate, with illustrated species or subspecies highlighted. Entries in the Vagrant Bird Bulletin, where description and colour images are on the same page, are given as example shown here: VBB **301** if illustrated; VBB 301 if mentioned or otherwise referred to.

Index of Common Names

Bold number indicates the colour plate. Common names on the main colour plates are not indexed if they relate to text on the opposite (facing) page, but names of comparative species are. Blue Bonnet, Jacky Winter and 'Scissors Grinder' are entered as written here. Common names listed or used as examples in the Fast Find Index, Key to Species, Habitats, Handy Hints, Glossary, are not indexed. Entries in the Vagrant Bird Bulletin where description and colour images are on the same page are given as example shown here: VBB **301**.

Writers, artists and their contributions to the first, second and third editions

All alterations to the text of fourth to seventh editions (*Field Guide* version) have been made by Ken Simpson, who also accepts responsibility for any errors of commission or omission. Species numbers have been removed from the seventh edition; researchers may use editions one to six to find the Families or species each writer contributed. We thank everybody for their fine contributions.

Tom Aumann, BSc, BEd: Species in Families (Fam.) Pandionidae, Accipitridae, Falconidae.

Australasian Wader Study Group *Principal contributors*: Angela Jessop, BSc (Hons), Brett Lane, BA, Clive Minton, PhD, Mick Murliss. *Contributing members*: John Bransbury, Peter Curry, Peter Dann, Berrice Forest, Stephen Garnett, David Henderson, Marilyn Hewish, Roger Jaensch, Tom Lowe, Alan McBride, Jim McNamara, Mike Newman, Danny Rogers.

David Baker-Gabb, BAg, DipSc, MSc, PhD: Species in Fam. Pandionidae, Accipitridae, Falconidae.

Kevin Bartram: Species in Fam. Procellariidae, Oceanitidae, Pelecanoididae, Pelecanidae, Sulidae, Anhingidae, Phalacrocoracidae, Fregatidae, Phaethontidae, Phasianidae, Pedionomidae, Rallidae, Stercorariidae, Laridae, Cuculidae, Muscicapidae

Simon Bennett, BAppl.Sc: Fam. Turnicidae.

Ron Brown (deceased): Species in Fam. Anatidae.

Margaret Cameron, BA: Oceanitidae, Pelecanoididae.

Mike Carter, CEng: Species in Fam. Diomedeidae.

Andrew Corrick, BSc (Hons).: Fam. Ardeidae, Ciconiidae, Plataleidae.

Stephen Debus, BA, Dip.Nat.Resources, Dip.Ed, MSc: Fam. Pandionidae, Accipitridae, Falconidae, Corvidae.

Denise Deerson: Fam. Anatidae.

Xenia Dennett, BSc, PhD: Species in Fam. Muscicapidae.

Peter Fell, BSc: Species in Fam. Meliphagidae.

Kate Fitzherbert, BSc (Hons), PhD: Fam. Gruidae, Otididae.

Cliff Frith: Fam. Ptilonorhynchidae, Paradiseidae.

Geoff Gayner: Species in Fam. Maluridae.

Belinda Gillies, BA, Dip.Ed: Fam. Grallinidae, Cracticidae.

Marc Gottsch (deceased): Fam. Megapodiidae, Strigidae, Podargidae, Aegothelidae, Caprimulgidae.

Murray Grant: Fam. Orthonychidae, Timaliidae.

John Hatch, BA, PhD: Species in Fam. Procellariidae.

Victor Hurley, BSc: Species in Fam. Dromaiidae, Casuariidae, Struthionidae, Megapodiidae, Orthonychidae, Maluridae, Ephthianuridae, Dicaeidae.

Jack Hyett, TPTC (deceased): Fam. Pedionomidae.

Andrew Isles, BSc: Fam. Psittacidae.

Jaroslav Klapste, and also Peter Klapste (deceased): Fam. Podicepedidae, Alcedinidae, Meropidae, Coraciidae, Alaudidae, Motacillidae, Hirundinidae, Sylviidae.

Tess Kloot: Fam. Dicruridae, Oriolidae, Pycnonotidae, Sturnidae.

Alan Lill, BSc, PhD: Fam. Menuridae, Corcoracidae.

Gordon McCarthy: Fam. Acanthizidae.

Ellen McCulloch: Fam. Dicruridae, Oriolidae, Campephagidae, Sturnidae.

Peter Mason, BEd, Dip.T: Fam. Struthionidae, Dromaiidae, Casuariidae, Campephagidae.

Peter Menkhorst, BSc: Fam. Psittacidae.

Richard Noske, PhD: Fam. Neosittidae, Climacteridae.

Ian Norman, PhD: Family Anatidae.

David Paton, BSc (Hons), PhD: Family Meliphagidae.

Paul Peake, BSc: Fam. Strigidae, Tytonidae, Podargidae Artamidae.

Trevor Pescott, Dip.Civ.Eng, MSc *(Honoris causa)*: Family Columbidae.

Des Quinn: Fam. Megapodiidae, Strigidae, Podargidae, Aegothelidae, Caprimulgidae, Acanthizidae, Ephthianuridae.

Pat Vickers-Rich, PhD: Modern avifaunal regions, Prehistoric birds.

Bruce Robertson, BSc, BVSc: Fam. Laridae.

Len Robinson: Families Cuculidae, Pittidae.

Tony Robinson, BSc (Hons), PhD: Where the birds live: vegetation and landform habitats of Australia.

Ken Simpson, MSc *(Honoris causa)*: Fam. Podicipedidae, Spheniscidae, Diomedeidae, Phasianidae, Cuculidae, Aegothelidae, Caprimulgidae, Apodidae, Atrichornithidae, Muscicapidae, Necatariniidae.

Lance Williams, BSc: Fam. Muscicapidae, Zosteropidae, Corcoracidae.

John Woinarski, BSc (Hons): Fam. Pardalotidae.

Richard Zann, BSc, Dip.Ed, PhD: Fam. Fringillidae, Passeridae, Ploceidae.

Contributing illustrator to coloured 'Key to Families':
Jeremy Boot.

Contributing illustrators of black and white line drawings:
Kevin Bartram, Alistair Coutts, Nicolas Day, Annette Dowd, Graham Milledge, Peter Trusler.

Quick Index

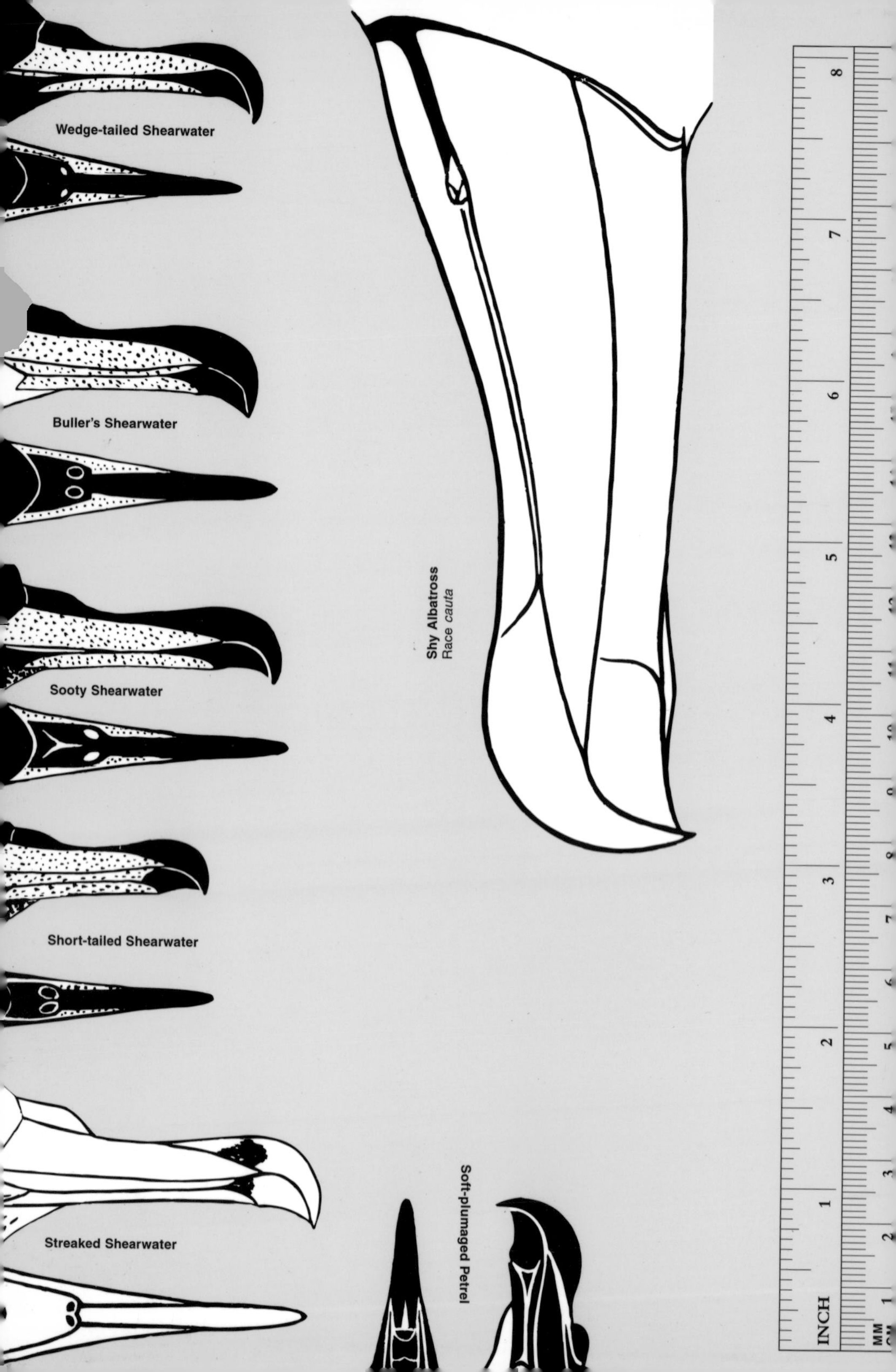

Wedge-tailed Shearwater
Buller's Shearwater
Sooty Shearwater
Short-tailed Shearwater
Streaked Shearwater
Shy Albatross
Race cauta
Soft-plumaged Petrel
INCH
MM
1
2
3
4
5
6
7
8